Table of Contents

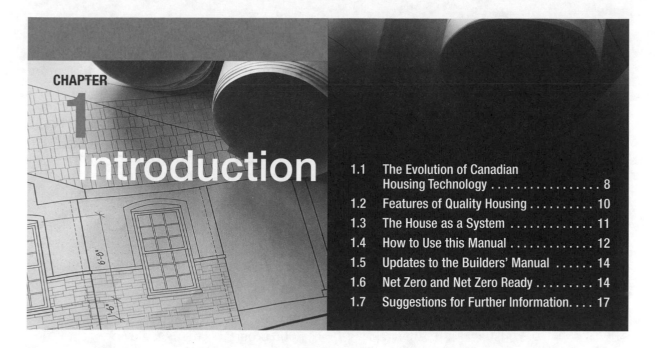

CHAPTER

1

Introduction

Canadians are recognized for building some of the best, most innovative and resource-efficient housing in the world. For more than 75 years, the Canadian Home Builders' Association (CHBA), in cooperation with the federal government, has worked with manufacturers, suppliers and researchers to provide builders with information about state-of-the-art housing technologies, systems and processes. This edition of the Builders' Manual is a recent initiative of CHBA to inform Canadian builders and other building trades of advanced construction techniques; techniques that will result in better-built housing that is more comfortable, more energy efficient, healthier and more environmentally responsible than ever before.

The CHBA Builders' Manual has drawn upon the knowledge and first-hand experience of leading Canadian builders, researchers and manufacturers in identifying practical and proven home building techniques. Many of the housing innovations introduced in recent years are the result of partnerships between CHBA and government, including the R-2000 Program, the Advanced Houses Program and the Healthy Housing Program. The Canadian Centre for Housing Technology and the EQuilibrium Housing initiative continue this tradition. The federal government's technical and financial support of these leading-edge initiatives has helped to advance Canadian housing design and construction.

Quality building requires care, attention to detail, and the application of the most efficient and up-to-date construction techniques and technologies. As every good builder knows, ensuring quality is essential, especially in Canada's demanding climate.

This Builders' Manual is intended to help a wide range of people – from building trade students, suppliers and manufacturers, professional builders, designers and code officials, to learn and understand leading-edge house construction principles and techniques. It is neither an exhaustive treatment of building science nor a building code summary. It outlines fundamental principles for building high-quality, energy- and resource-efficient housing.

1.1 The Evolution of Canadian Housing Technology

Over the past 60 years there have been many changes to the way houses are built in Canada (Table 1.1). Adjustments and innovations have resulted in a better housing product, consisting of higher quality materials and systems. Changes have also resulted in increased productivity on the construction site, allowing a quality product to be built in a shorter period of time. Homes today are far superior in terms of energy efficiency, environmental responsibility and occupant satisfaction, with high levels of comfort, convenience and peace-of-mind.

Energy efficiency increased in importance for builders and their customers after the oil price shocks of the mid and late 1970s. As energy prices increased, Canadian builders began to look for ways to improve energy efficiency. In Saskatoon, researchers and builders developed "super energy-efficient" homes that could be heated for only a few hundred dollars a year.

In 1980, the federal government decided to stimulate the rate of construction of more energy-efficient homes by establishing the Super Energy Efficient Home (SEEH) Program. Under this program, Natural Resources Canada (NRCan) provided builders with training and incentives to construct what are now called R-2000 homes. In 1982, the Canadian Home Builders' Association (CHBA) assumed responsibility for the delivery of the R-2000 Program. Although delivery shifted to a provincial model in the 1990s, CHBA retains a strong role in supporting R-2000 and beyond. CHBA is working to assist builders in constructing and labeling Net Zero Homes, Renovations, Communities and MURBs. The R-2000 program's main achievements include providing technical training to builders across the country, and serving as a catalyst for the research and development of technologies that enhance the energy efficiency of all homes built in Canada. Net Zero Housing is possible because of the foundation laid by R-2000.

Table 1.1 The evolution of house construction

Area	Practice	Advancement or trend
Basement	1940s	Concrete block and site-mixed concrete; forming lumber reused as wall and roof sheathing
	1960s	Ready-mixed concrete and prefabricated formwork
	1980s	Some use of preserved wood foundations
	1980s, 1990s	Insulated concrete forms
	1980s, 1990s	Free draining membranes and insulations
	2000s	Interior foam insulation systems
Framing	1940s	Platform framing
	1960s	Pre-cut studs
	1980s	New framing options; some use of prefabricated panels; introduction of pneumatic nailing and cordless power tools, 'House-as-a-system' concept
	1980s, 1990s	Increased use of trusses and composite materials
	2000s	Increased use of engineered wood products and advanced framing details

Area	Practice	Advancement or trend
Roof	1940s	Laid out and constructed by skilled trades
	1960s	Engineered, prefabricated trusses in general use
	1980s	New truss designs available, little change in process
	1980s, 1990s	Increased use of clay or composite tiles
	2000s	Increased availability of longer warranties and materials with recycled content
	2010s	Introduction of fibreglass shingles
Sheathing	1940s	Boards
	1960s	Fibreboard and plywood sheets
	1980s	Waferboard sheets, insulative sheathings, use of pneumatic nailing tools
	1980s, 1990s	Common acceptance of insulative sheathings, OSB sheathing
	1980s, 1990s	Common use of house wrap air barrier materials
	2000s	Development of materials with variable vapour permenace
	2010s	Increased use of exterior insulation to reduce thermal bridging
Siding	1940s	Wood clapboard, brick, stucco
	1960s	Pre-coated aluminum, steel and hardboard
	1980s	Vinyl siding
	2000s	Fibre-cement siding, advanced weather details (rainscreens), improved flashing details
Plumbing, Heating and Ventilation	1940s	Site-fitted and installed
	1960s	Prefabricated chimneys, some ductwork sub-assemblies
	1980s	Plastic plumbing, prefabricated chimneys and flues, energy-efficient equipment, mechanical ventilation systems, electronic air cleaners and power humidifiers
	1980s, 1990s	Broader acceptance of balanced mechanical ventilation systems Integration of components of mechanical systems (HRV/ERV)
	1980s, 1990s	Broader use of ground source heat pumps
	1980s, 1990s	Increased awareness and use of water-saving fixtures
	2000s	Increased use of radiant floor heating
	2010s	Concept of net-zero energy use. Updates to Standard for sizing mechanical systems to better address low-load housing
		Net Zero Homes built, cold-climate air source heat pumps in use
Interiors	1940s	Wet-finished with plaster, cured, brush-painted
	1960s	Dry-finished with drywall, roller-painted
	1980s	Little change, some use of spray-paint equipment
	1990s, 2000s	Low-emissions finish materials (paints, flooring and cabinetry)
Windows, Doors and Cabinetry	1940s	Fabricated on-site
	1960s	Prefabricated windows, cabinetry, and countertops
	1980s	Sealed thermal windows, insulated metal doors, pre-hung doors, prefabricated stairs, modular cabinets
	1980s, 1990s	Super windows comprising low-E, gas fill; insulated spacer, low conductivity frames
	1990s, 2000s	Lower-emissions materials and finishes

In 1993, ten Advanced Houses were built across Canada. Each was designed to be twice as energy-efficient as the R-2000 requirements at the time. The houses also met strict environmental and indoor air quality criteria. The Advanced Houses were built as part of a joint government and industry initiative to provide a showcase for research and development of innovative housing products and technologies. Extensive monitoring was part of the program. Some of the successful technologies became part of mainstream housing construction.

Building on the success of the Advanced Houses, new criteria were added to the R-2000 Technical Requirements in 2000 for indoor air quality, environmentally responsible materials selection and construction practices. These changes once again placed R-2000 at the forefront of Canadian home building.

New homes are increasingly incorporating healthy house features for improved indoor air quality and enhanced occupant comfort. These features build on the research, development and demonstration initiatives of Canada Mortgage and Housing Corporation (CMHC).

The Canadian Centre for Housing Technology (CCHT) research facility was established in 1998 at the National Research Council's Ottawa campus to advance the development and market acceptance of technologies and materials to improve the safety, comfort and energy efficiency of housing. CCHT is a joint venture of NRC's Institute for Research in Construction, Canada Mortgage and Housing Corporation, and Natural Resources Canada. In 2015 construction began on an expansion of the CCHT to include 2 Net Zero Ready, semi- detached, smart homes to evaluate low energy solutions and technologies for the multi-unit market.

In 2012 CMHC coordinated the development of 12 EQuilibrium Housing projects (net-zero housing). This was a national program that brought the private and public sectors together to develop healthy homes that produce as much energy as they consume on an annual basis. The EQuilibrium homes focused on the core principles of occupant health and comfort, energy efficiency, renewable energy production, resource conservation, reduced environmental impact and affordability.

Within the past decade, a number of environmental labels for houses have entered the Canadian market. All of them include energy efficiency as a key element based on the building practices pioneered by R-2000 and described in this manual. In 2012, the R-2000 standard was updated, making 2012 R-2000 homes twice as energy-efficient as before. The EnerGuide for New Houses labeling is being encouraged for all new houses and EnerGuide ratings for existing housing is also being supported by the CHBA.

At the time of updating this manual, CHBA had formed a Net Zero Energy Housing Council, developed Net Zero Technical Requirements based on the R-2000 Technical Requirements and the EnerGuide Rating System. Hundreds of houses have been labeled as Net Zero and Net Zero Ready.

1.2 Features of Quality Housing

Houses built using the construction techniques described in this Manual share several characteristics:

- Cost-effective insulation levels;

- Airtight building envelopes;

- High-efficiency heating and cooling systems that are appropriately sized;

- Appropriately sized, user-controlled, balanced mechanical ventilation systems; Efficient use of energy, water and resources;

- High-performance windows;

- Healthy and resource-efficient building materials;

- Environmentally responsible building practices; and

- Use of appropriate on-site renewable energy.

These characteristics result in value-added performance attributes:

Greater Comfort

An airtight building envelope reduces air leakage, thus eliminating uncomfortable drafts and reducing dust, insects and outside noise. At the same time, enhanced control of ventilation air and indoor humidity levels allows improved occupant comfort.

Healthier Indoor Environment

Appropriately sized, user-controlled, balanced mechanical ventilation systems exhaust stale air and replace it with fresh outdoor air. The fresh incoming outdoor air is preconditioned by the outgoing stale air. It is then mixed with indoor air, heated or cooled to a comfortable temperature, filtered when necessary, and distributed throughout the house. The selection and use of materials with reduced toxicity and mechanical equipment that minimizes the potential for spillage of combustion gases are additional means to ensure a healthier indoor environment.

Better Energy Efficiency

Higher insulation levels and lower air leakage rates keep heat loss to a minimum and enhance comfort. Efficient mechanical systems reduce the energy required for space conditioning and water heating. In addition, efficient lighting systems and appliances further reduce energy needs.

More Durable Construction

Proper construction details reduce moisture- and weather-related problems that can cause premature deterioration of structural components and interior finishes. A well-built home requires less maintenance and repair, and retains its value better. Less waste material is generated due to repair and replacement.

Improved Resource Efficiency

Fixtures that reduce the use of water, electricity and construction processes based on the "3 Rs" (reduce, reuse and recycle) of waste management, in conjunction with energy efficiency, all lessen the effect of construction on the environment.

1.3 The House as a System

At one time, designers and builders often considered each part of a building including; foundation, floors, walls, roofs, windows and doors, plumbing and electrical systems, heating, cooling and ventilation systems-individually. Today, builders recognize that the various parts of a house work together as a system to create a comfortable, durable and energy-efficient building. The house system itself interacts with both its surrounding environment and with its occupants.

The climate and environment of where the house is located plays an important role. As well, there are a number of components within a house that have an effect on the performance of the overall system:

- The external environment such as temperature, wind, rain, air quality, dust, and noise;

- The occupants, including pets;

- The building envelope, including the foundation and above-grade walls, windows, roof, and floors;

- Interior fixed components such as partitions, floors, and finishes;

- Appliances, equipment and furniture; and,

- The mechanical/electrical system including heating, ventilating, air conditioning, plumbing and electrical components.

The individual characteristics of these components and the way they interact affect the performance of the house as a whole, in terms of the:

- Protection provided from the external environment;

- Service connections to municipal or on-site water and sewer;

- Usability of spaces and components within the home;

- Quality of the interior environment including the balance of natural and electric light, noise levels, air quality, temperature, humidity, dust levels, etc.;

- Durability/longevity of the house and its sub-systems;

- Energy performance;

- Capital and operating costs; and,

- Character and ambiance.

The concept of a house as a system is best illustrated with two examples.

1. Supplying fresh air was once considered to be simply a matter of opening windows. Air only moves when there is a pressure difference so wind was needed to drive the process. However, it was highly inefficient because fresh air entering the window did not mix well with the rest of the air in the house.

2. When mechanical exhaust systems were introduced into houses with naturally-aspirating, fuel-fired furnaces and water heaters they were regarded as totally separate components, independent of any other element or appliance in the house. This perception led to intermittent problems in some houses, as the action of exhaust fans caused back-drafting of the furnaces and/or water heaters, resulting in combustion gases to be drawn into living spaces.

Today, there is an understanding that the interaction of the sub-systems in a house affects indoor air quality. The tightness of the envelope determines the degree to which air infiltrates or exfiltrates. The cooking, laundry and washing habits of the occupants affect the production of moisture and the need for air exchange.

Environmental factors such as location, exposure, wind speed and direction, can affect heating, cooling and ventilation needs. All these factors influence the design and operation of mechanical sub-systems. The best way to provide comfortable, safe indoor air conditions for the occupants is by constructing a well-insulated, tight building envelope, provide energy efficient mechanical systems and using controlled, balanced ventilation.

1.4 How to Use this Manual

A house is a complex interaction of many design considerations. Each is important, and needs to mesh with the others. The theme of the house-as-a-system underlies the organization of this Manual as shown graphically in Figure 1.1.

Part 1—House Design (Chapters 2 to 5) covers the basic principles of building science and design which underpin the solutions described in later chapters.

Part 2—Building Envelope (Chapters 6 to 14) deals with the foundation, floors, walls, ceilings and roof, windows and doors, and describes various ways to ensure that the building envelope is airtight and has optimum insulation levels. This section also addresses the selection and proper installation of windows and doors.

Part 3—Mechanical Systems (Chapters 15 to 23) covers mechanical and home automation systems, with information to help builders determine the most appropriate type of equipment, and to provide a level of understanding to allow builders to discuss mechanical system issues with specialized subcontractors. Manufacturers and distributors can provide more detailed information on specific products or particular installations. Chapter 24 provides predictions into the future of housing and house construction.

This edition of the Manual makes reference to both printed and online information. Website links provided are solely for reference; the Canadian Home Builders' Association does not control or necessarily endorse the content on these websites, and recognizes that the information available may change or be removed.This Manual also contains an index and several appendices. These include tables indicating the permeability and insulating values of building materials, common conversion factors, and a glossary.

New to this edition of the Manual are additional appendices which are available online. In some cases, these appendices represent information which we expect will be of interest to a subset of builders and designers specializing in specific areas of housing technology such as zoning of heating systems. In other cases the decision to put an appendix online was to allow users to have the most up-to-date information on topics such as the Net Zero Technical Requirements. For all appendices available on line CHBA will be updating these if changes are made by their respective authors.

Figure 1.1 Builders' Manual contents

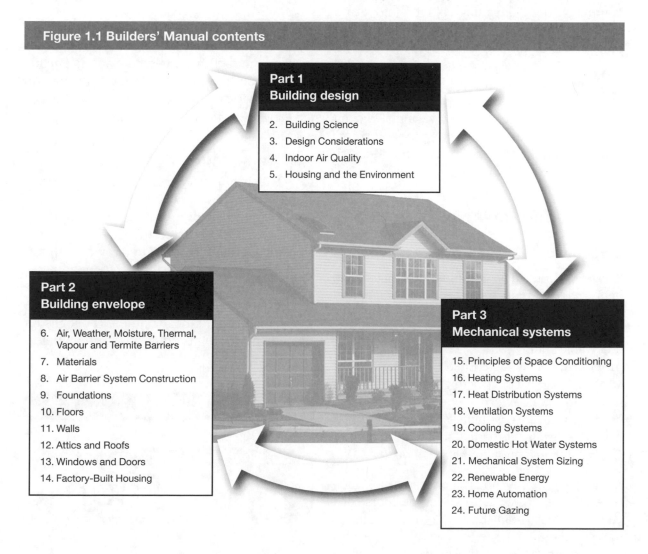

Part 1
Building design

2. Building Science
3. Design Considerations
4. Indoor Air Quality
5. Housing and the Environment

Part 2
Building envelope

6. Air, Weather, Moisture, Thermal, Vapour and Termite Barriers
7. Materials
8. Air Barrier System Construction
9. Foundations
10. Floors
11. Walls
12. Attics and Roofs
13. Windows and Doors
14. Factory-Built Housing

Part 3
Mechanical systems

15. Principles of Space Conditioning
16. Heating Systems
17. Heat Distribution Systems
18. Ventilation Systems
19. Cooling Systems
20. Domestic Hot Water Systems
21. Mechanical System Sizing
22. Renewable Energy
23. Home Automation
24. Future Gazing

1.5 Updates to the Builders' Manual

This Manual has been reviewed by selected technical advisors and builders to incorporate the latest materials, best practices and code requirements. Figures and text have been revised and updated to reflect changes to the 2015 National Building Code of Canada. Chapters have been edited to include aspects of Net Zero Energy Housing. New Chapters have been added on Sizing Mechanical Systems and Future Gazing. In addition, the Builders' Manual is taking advantage of technology and selected Appendices are only available on-line. This allows us to keep the Appendices up-to-date, and it allows users to contribute and to comment. Also, for the first time, CHBA will making architectural details available for download with the intended result of having architects and builders use them in their plans. Drawings are in 3D – a direction the industry is expected to be moving.

1.6 Net Zero and Net Zero Ready

Introduction

For several decades, continual advances have been made to reduce the heating, cooling and energy used by housing to minimize expenses for home owners and to conserve non-renewable energy sources. This Manual presents the concept of Net-Zero Energy Housing (NZEH) and the goal of constructing housing that has no net annual external energy demands. It describes features, benefits and lessons learned from the design, construction and operation of Canadian low-energy and NZEH houses.

A net-zero energy house generates as much renewable energy as it uses over the course of a year. A net-zero ready house has all the building envelope and energy efficiency measures as a net-zero energy house, but does not include a renewable energy system. House orientation, sufficient roof area and ideally, pre-wiring for easy installation of a future renewable energy system are part of a net-zero ready house.

Net Zero Energy Housing Projects In Canada

In 2005, Canada Mortgage and Housing Corporation (CMHC) initiated the EQuilibrium™ Sustainable Housing Demonstration Initiative to provide a national showcase of market ready, near- and net-zero energy housing solutions in regional markets and climatic conditions across Canada. The goal was to demonstrate that the knowledge and technology was available to create cold-climate, high-performance housing solutions, and to start a continuous learning environment for improving the process and cost of achieving NZEH performance.

By the end of 2011, eleven demonstration houses (new and retrofit) had been built across Canada ranging from the mild climate of Vancouver to the cold climates of Winnipeg and Edmonton, targeting near- and net- zero energy consumption.

Interest in Net Zero grew among Canadian builders and CHBA recognized that these forward-thinking entrepreneurs needed a place where they could meet and discuss the issues around building and selling these types of houses. CHBA created the Net Zero Energy Housing Council in 2014 to provide support for members wanting to work together on this. CHBA now runs a labeling program through the Net Zero Energy Housing Council to recognize these builders and these homes. The logos for these two housing products are shown below (Figure 1.2).

Figure 1.2 Net Zero Logos

Net Zero Ready and Net Zero Energy Housing offers the following advantages:

Consumer benefits
- Low energy bills;

- Improved comfort;

- Healthy indoor environment;

- Quality design and construction; and

- Energy security

Societal benefits
- Reduced pollution and CO2 emissions;

- Reduced demand on urban infrastructure (energy, water and wastewater); and

- Energy security.

Features of Net Zero Energy Housing

The Housing demonstration projects and the pioneering work done by CHBA members is showing that net zero ready and net-zero energy housing can be built in a range of housing styles and forms (new and retrofit; single- detached, semi-detached, and multiple unit) on urban, suburban, and rural sites and in a range of climate zones. These houses share many common features (all of which will be reviewed in detail in this Manual) as follows:

Building systems
- Site- and climate-specific integrated design solution;

- Highly advanced building envelope comprising high levels of insulation, careful selection of windows based on thermal resistance and solar heat gain characteristics and air sealing that results in a low air exchange rate (1.50 AC/hr or better);

- Passive solar design strategies;

- Reduced domestic hot water usage;

- Reduced mechanical, lighting and appliance loads;

- Properly sized, high-efficiency mechanical systems;

- Heat recovery (from exhaust ventilation and waste water); and,

- Utility grid connection to exchange (buy and sell) energy.

The airtightness of projects done ranges from 0.4 to 1.4 AC/hr. Careful design and construction is required to achieve low air leakage rates. Blower door testing (see Figure 2.4) is used to measure the air leakage rate.

Renewable energy components
- Passive solar heating and cooling;

- Solar domestic hot water system;

- Earth energy or active solar space heating system; and,

- Solar photovoltaic or wind turbine electricity generating systems.

Iterative design process features
- Energy performance modeled and tested (repeatedly); and

- Continual validation of the cost/benefit of additional envelope improvement versus the cost of providing alternative energy capacity.

- Optimization of house design to account for window placement/performance, location of solar panels

The basic principles for Net Zero Ready and Net Zero Energy Housing are:

- Minimize heat losses through the building envelope with appropriate amounts of insulation, a high degree of airtightness and the use of windows with high thermal resistance and a low solar heat gain coefficient. The low solar heat gain is to reduce cooling loads in the summer in those areas of the country that typically need cooling.

- Use energy efficient lighting, appliances and minimize exterior energy use thereby reducing the base loads as much as possible.

- Use the most efficient types of space heating, water heating and ventilation systems available. This may include such measures as a drainwater heat recovery system for the DHW system.

- Provide the house's supplemental energy using a renewable energy source.

Lessons Learned So Far

Lessons learned in overall design

Keep the design of the house as close a possible to conventional house design. This reduces the cost and delivery time of components such as windows.

The objectives of the overall design should be stated and written out in advance to help avoid "design creep"; adding elements to the design which are tangent to its overall purpose.

Elements in the house should be off-the-shelf, or at least commercially available. While orientation of the house to take full advantage of solar photovoltaic energy generation is always an objective, it is often not possible. The house should be designed with adjacent architecture in mind.

Cost is always an issue. While there are extra costs associated with innovation, cost/benefit should always be an issue in deciding any feature in the house. Sometimes, choices are constrained by the homeowner himself ("I can get a deal").

Reducing air leakage is critical in Net Zero Energy Housing or Net Zero Ready design and construction. Therefore, avoid or plan around known problem areas such as attached garages, 1-1/2 storey kneewall intersections, irregular-shaped protrusions or cantilevers; be wary of three-sided intersections and suspended basement floors. Also, recessed lighting, fireplace chases and duct penetrations, especially for solar systems, need particular attention to air tightness details.

For air tightness, focus on the big leaks and the top of the building. Air leakage increases with building height. Complicated details should be drawn out in the house plans, and an air tightness test should always be done. Depending on the air barrier approach chosen, it may be possible to test during construction to allow any air leaks to be corrected before the house is finished.

Lessons learned in energy modeling

Overheating can become a concern in very well-insulated buildings, and modeling cooling loads is a vital step in assuring occupant comfort. Overheating is usually localized, and there is no reliable modeling tool to predict over heating. Thermal mass is sometimes a component in Net Zero Energy Housing design, but it has limitations. Thermal mass is all about cycling a large mass through a (usually very small) temperature range. Big mass can be expensive (concrete costs up to $200 per cubic meter), so ensure modeling takes into account the cost of adding mass against the energy savings, which often are not significant.

Lessons learned in window selection

With the increased levels of insulation and excellent air tightness being used in Net Zero Energy Houses, passive solar can be a critical design element. Over-heating in the summer is the issue, which adds to the cooling load. As a result, the lesson learned is to select a window which has a high insulation value to reduce heat loss in winter, and a low solar heat gain coefficient to reduce heat gain in summer. If the window is selected to limit solar heat gain in summer, then it also limits the heat gain in winter. However, it appears that more energy is saved by reducing the cooling load than is collected in winter. The decision of allowing heat gain vs limiting heat gain is very dependent on the location of the house. If the house is in an area where summertime cooling is common, the low solar heat gain is likely better. If the house is in a location where summertime cooling is not used, a higher solar heat gain coefficient will be a benefit by allowing more passive solar heat gain in winter.

Lessons learned in energy and mechanical systems

Solar (PV) energy production may be less than first calculated due to snow cover on solar panels or, worse, the sun being blocked by surrounding trees. Also, a significant part of the solar system may be facing the wrong way because some of the roof may not have the proper orientation. Available total roof space is a limiting factor in Net Zero Energy Housing energy production.

It's very easy for the mechanical system to become too complex. Control your ambitions when it comes to trying to seize every thermodynamic opportunity. In demonstration houses, dehumidistats failed to provide adequate control over indoor relative humidity. Control systems overall are a huge challenge. Controls can easily become too complicated, and control systems from different manufacturers may not interface and cause later problems with maintenance and warranties.

The mechanical equipment itself may not behave as predicted or one element may interfere with the operation of another. For example, does pre-heating service water using a solar system prevent the water heater from firing because incoming water is warm enough that it never hits the set-point? HRVs and ERVs do not come standard with highly efficient motors. And just how much space is required by the mechanical system?

1.7 Suggestions for Further Information

The references listed here are general in nature and apply, to varying extents, to most or all of the chapters.

Canadian Home Builders' Association
141 Laurier Avenue West, Suite 500
Ottawa, ON K1P 5J3
Phone: (613) 230-3060
Website: http://www.chba.ca
General Email: chba@chba.ca

Books and Articles

1. Canadian Building Digest and Construction Technology Updates, National Research Council of Canada, 1960-1988

2. Canadian Wood-Frame House Construction, Canada Mortgage and Housing Corporation.

3. Keeping the Heat In, Natural Resources Canada

Technical Support & Useful Information

1. Canada Mortgage and Housing Corporation (CMHC), www.cmhc-schl.gc.ca/

2. Canadian Wood Council, www.cwc.ca

3. Canadian Sheet Steel Building Institute, www.cssbi.ca/

4. Cement Association of Canada, www.cement.ca/

5. Heating, Refrigeration and Air Conditioning Institute of Canada, www.hrai.ca

6. National Building Envelope Council, www.nbec.net/

7. National Research Council, www.nrc-cnrc.gc.ca

8. Natural Resources Canada Office of Energy Efficiency, http://oee.nrcan.gc.ca/

9. Fenestration Canada, www.fenestrationcanada.ca

10. NAIMA Canada, www.naimacanada.ca

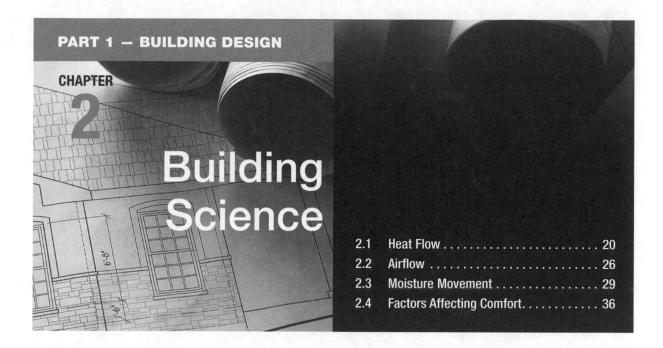

PART 1 — BUILDING DESIGN

CHAPTER

2

Building Science

Building science deals with the construction, maintenance, safety, durability and energy efficiency of buildings. Building a house is a complex process; it requires the understanding and application of many scientific principles, which are the main focus of Part 1 of this Builders' Manual. This chapter summarizes the key principles of building science that affect the durability, comfort and energy efficiency of houses.

The principles discussed in this chapter form the foundation for the construction techniques discussed in later chapters. Understanding these key concepts is the first step towards eliminating common construction problems and building better houses.

Notes Regarding Units of Measure

Canada began its conversion from Imperial units to metric (SI) in 1970. Although the conversion took the better part of that decade, Canada officially uses the metric system. Because of this, where practical, this book will convert all units to metric.

Like the construction industry itself, however, the Imperial system was developed through traditions accumulated and passed down through generations over hundreds of years. The most basic Imperial unit, the inch, wasn't even defined until the metric system was invented (it is today defined as 2.54 cm). All base units in the metric system have a definition which is derived from constants in nature.

Only the older professionals currently in the construction industry were raised on the Imperial System. A majority, however, started the profession during the transition period and continue to be comfortable with Imperial units. This has perpetuated their use.

A complicating factor is that the United States remains firmly committed to (its own version of) the Imperial System. The United States continues to supply and set the standards for the majority of manufactured materials used in construction. This is especially true for insulation products and mechanical systems. Insulation materials are still rated for their "R-value" first, which is converted for Canadian use to RSI. Domestic water tanks are manufactured with capacities in U.S. Gallons.

Further complicating the issue are derived units. An R-Value is a derived unit (square-foot x Degree Fahrenheit x hour/British Thermal Unit). To describe the capacity of an instantaneous water heater, a defined temperature rise in Fahrenheit degrees is calculated using the unit's capacity in U.S. Gallons per minute. An Imperial perm (a measure of vapour permeability) is one grain (a measure of mass) of water vapour per hour per square foot (area) per inch of mercury (pressure). In some cases, conversion to metric is fairly straightforward, in some cases, it is not.

Furthermore, virtually every wood frame house today's builder will encounter will be based upon the old measurement system. Wood studs will be described in this book by their Imperial dimensions, using the defined standards that set the "two-by" system. A two-by-four has, therefore, dimensions of 38mm x 89mm (1.5 inches by 3.5 inches).

Why is it called a 2 x 4 if it measures 1.5 x 3.5? The "rough cut" lumber does in fact measure a full 2" x 4" but after it is "dressed" at the mill and kiln-dried, it measures 1.5" x 3.5". This is true of all lumber in the "two by" system. Houses can still be found in Canada where the lumber used was "rough cut" and air-dried, meaning that the studs are a full 2" x 4".

2.1 Heat Flow

2.1.1 Energy flows in houses

Houses are in a state of energy equilibrium-the energy that enters a house is equal to the energy that leaves, usually in a different form than when it entered.

The following are ways energy can enter a building:

- **Purchased energy** is in the form of electricity, oil, natural gas, propane, or wood. This energy is used to heat and cool the house, to provide heating for domestic hot water, and to operate lights and appliances.

- **Passive solar energy** enters the house through glazed portions of windows and doors and by transmission of heat through wall and roof assemblies exposed to the sun. The contribution of solar energy to heating needs can vary considerably due to local weather conditions, the heating requirements of the building, and the size, orientation, shading and type of window glazing units. Typically, 15% of an average home's heating is attained from solar heat, but can be significantly higher when homes are designed and built to maximize solar gains. On the other side of the discussion, passive solar energy can add to the cooling load in summer, thereby requiring the use of purchased energy to operate air conditioning. Careful consideration and planning is needed to use passive solar energy to the best advantage.

- **Renewable energy** (photovoltaic, active solar thermal, wind and earth) can be used for space heating and cooling, as well as water heating and for generating electricity.

- **Internal heat gains** are derived from the occupants, lights and appliances, and can be an important heat source, especially as we build buildings approaching or reaching net zero energy requirements. These indirect heat gains reduce the need for space heating but in climatic zones that require space cooling, this contribution can become a factor contributing to higher cooling costs.

Houses use energy for the following purposes:

- **Space conditioning** is the heating, cooling and ventilation required to maintain comfortable conditions in a building. It is usually the largest use of energy in a single-family dwelling. It is also the energy use most easily reduced by improving insulation and air tightness and using efficient and correctly sized mechanical equipment. For example, the energy used to circulate heat in a forced-air system can be reduced by using an electronically commutated motor (ECM) for the furnace blower fan. As buildings approach Net Zero Energy levels, the space conditioning energy is reducing and occupant life-style is playing a more important role in total energy consumption. Electric cars for example, can be significant load as part of the total energy consumption. A typical Net Zero house may use 40 GJ (Giga-Joules) of energy annually (with no electric car). An electric car with a typcial 20,000 km per year of useage will require approximately 15 GJ per year.

- **Water heating** consumes about one-third of purchased energy in conventional housing. Water heating energy savings can be obtained by reducing hot-water use, controlling water temperature, increasing insulation levels on the domestic hot-water tank and pipes, installing higher efficiency equipment and using drain-water heat recovery.

- **Lighting** generally accounts for a small amount of purchased energy-as little as 2%, or 1,000 kWh/yr (3.6 GJ), of a typical home's purchased energy requirements. However, as heating, cooling and water heating requirements are reduced through energy savings, lighting can assume a greater significance-as much as 10%. This demand can be minimized by making use of natural light wherever possible and by installing more efficient LED lighting.

- **Operating appliances**, including stoves, refrigerators, washers, dryers, dishwashers and freezers as well as home electronic equipment for entertainment and work, uses energy. Typical use will result in consumption of 7,000 kWh/yr (approximately 25.2 GJ). The energy consumption of an appliance will depend on the model selected and the frequency of use. Many electronic appliances use electricity even when they are turned off (phantom electricity). Some new appliances consume 50% less energy than older models, with a few providing

even more substantial savings. The ENERGY STAR® symbol is a simple way to identify products that are among the most energy-efficient on the market. In Canada you will also see the EnerGuide Label (Figure 2.1) for major appliances which shows the estimated annual energy consumption in kWh (based on a standard set of operating conditions).

Figure 2.1 The EnerGuide Logo

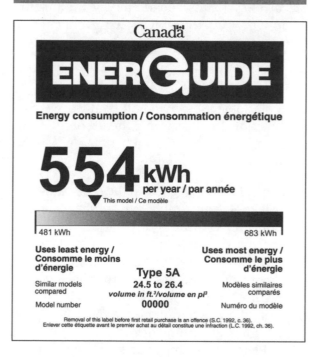

2.1.2 Mechanisms of heat transfer

Heat naturally flows from a warm area to a relatively cooler area, for example, from the house interior to the exterior in winter, or from a warm room to a cool area within the house. Heat flow cannot be stopped, but it can be slowed down through the use of materials that have a higher resistance to heat flow-a higher R-value (RSI- value). Heat flow occurs when there is a temperature differential between two surfaces or objects. The greater the differential, the faster the rate of heat transfer. Heat is transferred by three different mechanisms (Figure 2.2):

- Heat transfer by **conduction** occurs when heat moves through a material or assembly. Providing insulation in the building envelope reduces heat loss due to conduction (see Section 6.4 Thermal Barriers).

- Heat transfer by **convection** occurs in fluids such as water or air. As air or water is warmed, it becomes less dense and is displaced or pushed up by the surrounding cooler fluid. Placing insulation in empty stud cavities creates "dead" air by minimizing convection, thereby slowing convective heat transfer.

- Heat transfer by **radiation** occurs when heat transfers from a warm object to a relatively cooler object by giving off heat waves in all directions. For example, heat energy from the sun, wood stove or a heat lamp is in the form of radiant energy.

- **Putting it all together**, In the case of the sun on a roof for example, the sun heats up the roof. (radiant) the roof deck becomes hot, and the heat is transferred by conduction to the inside of the attic space. At night, radiant heat loss from the roof deck occurs (Figure 2.3). The attic space is heated by the heat conducted through the roof and by the radiant heat coming from the hot roof deck. Builders insulate the attic floor (the ceiling) to prevent heat transfer by conduction into the conditioned space. Buiders seal the ceiling to prevent hot air from the house moving into the attic (convection). During the night, the the radiant heat flows in the opposite direction and tries to heat the night sky. This is known as radiant cooling and it can also happen through windows. For radiant heat or radiant cooling there must be a path between the bodies. If there are clouds the radiant flow will be interrupted. The same is true of the radiant heat from a wood stove, in that it will not pass through a wall or a ceiling. It may warm the wall or ceiling and then the heat can transfer by conduction.

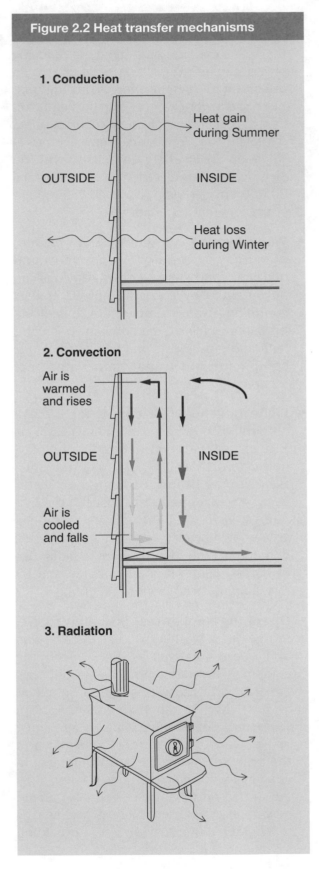

Figure 2.2 Heat transfer mechanisms

1. Conduction

OUTSIDE   INSIDE

Heat gain during Summer

Heat loss during Winter

2. Convection

Air is warmed and rises

OUTSIDE   INSIDE

Air is cooled and falls

3. Radiation

Figure 2.3 Radiant heating and cooling

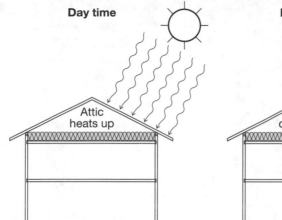

All three heat flow mechanisms are at work in a house at any given time. Most heat is lost through the building envelope, primarily by conduction and through the leakage of heated air; therefore, the following two sections focus on these heat loss mechanisms.

2.1.3 Calculating heat loss due to conduction

Heat transfer by conduction through the elements of a building envelope can be calculated. Heat flow (Q), is equal to the area of a surface (A) times the temperature differential (ΔT ("delta T")) from one side to the other, divided by the thermal resistance (RSI)

or: $Q = \dfrac{A \times \Delta T}{RSI}$

where:

Q = the rate of heat flow, in watts (W)

A = the area of the surface under consideration, in m²

ΔT = the difference in temperature between inside and outside, in °C; and

RSI = the resistance to heat flow in m² °C/W

For example, if we consider a wall, a ceiling and a window, each of 10 m² (107 ft²), typical of a conventional Code built house and the same product, but upgraded for a typical Net Zero house, the importance of the insulation becomes evident. Assuming an indoor temperature of 20°C (68°F), and an outdoor temperature of –10°C (14°F), the rate of heat flow through these sections can be calculated as follows (Table 2.1):

Table 2.1 Conventional vs Net Zero Housing	
Conventional (Code Built)	**Net Zero**
R-20 Wall (RSI-3.52)	**R-40 Wall (RSI-7.0)**
Q = A x ΔT /RSI = 10 m² x 30 C / 3.52 m² C/W = 85.23 W	Q = A x ΔT /RSI = 10 x 30 / 7.0 = 42.86 W
R-40 Ceiling (RSI-7.0)	**R-65 Ceiling (RSI-11.45)**
Q = A x ΔT /RSI = 10 x 30 / 7.0 = 42.86 W	Q = A x ΔT /RSI = 10 x 30 / 11.45 = 26.2 0 W
Double Glazed Window (R-2) (RSI-0.35)	**Triple Glazed Window (R-4) (RSI- 0.70)**
Q = A x ΔT /RSI = 10 x 30 / 0.35 = 857.14 W	Q = A x ΔT /RSI = 10 x 30 / 0.70 = 428.57 W

This table does not take into account the "effective" insulation values, only the nominal insulation values in order to simplify the discussion and to illustrate the importance of improving the insulation level. The effect of the studs reducing the effective insulation levels through thermal bridging is discussed in Appendix 1 – Calculating the Thermal Resistance of Building Assemblies.

A comprehensive table of thermal resistance values for a wide range of materials is provided in Appendix 1.

2.1.4 Heat loss due to air leakage

- The National Building Code of Canada (NBC) requires a continuous air barrier to reduce air leakage, to decrease energy loss and to reduce the likelihood of moisture problems within the envelope.

- A blower door can be used to measure the air tightness of a building's envelope. This device consists of a fan, a calibrated opening used to measure airflow, an adjustable door, and metering equipment (Figure 2.2). The blower door is installed in an exterior door opening of the building that is to be tested. The fan is turned on with the windows, exterior doors, and other intentional openings closed, to blow air out of the building and depressurize the home. Operation of the fan causes an equal amount of air to leak in through cracks and holes in the house envelope. A low-pressure blower door test can be used to locate air barrier leakage prior to completion of a house.

A blower door is capable of measuring two things: the rate of air flow, usually expressed in litres or cubic metres, over a period of time (minutes or hours), and the pressure difference between the inside and outside of the building, usually expressed in Pascals of pressure. The blower door can be adjusted to change the pressure difference, and the measured rate of air flow is usually taken at several different pressures.

The rate of air flow tells you nothing about the leakiness of the building unless the surface area of the building is taken into account. Dividing the air flow at specific pressure differences by the surface area of the building envelope allows you to compare the "leakiness" of buildings of different sizes. A blower door test can't be done without consideration to outdoor conditions. Natural wind pressure can make precise readings of airflow difficult. The larger the building, the more of a problem this becomes. Therefore, the air flow is measured at several different pressure differences. From here, the computer operating with the blower door takes over.

Several different formulae have been devised to use the surface area information and manipulate the data from measuring air flow at different pressure differences. The outcome of all these calculations is a single number that allows simple comparisons.

Figure 2.4 Fan depressurization (blower door) test

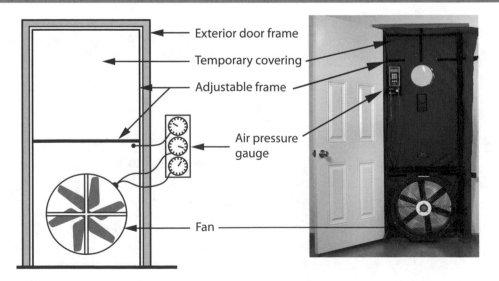

Exterior door frame

Temporary covering

Adjustable frame

Air pressure gauge

Fan

Unfortunately, the number itself isn't simple and is calculated in a number of ways, depending on the preference of local codes and regulations. One such measure is Effective Leakage Area (ELA). Confusingly, there is another measurement called Equivalent Leakage Area (EqLA). The two are not the same, but both are intended to describe the size of hole required to allow an equal air flow to what the blower door has measured. There is also Normalized Leakage Area (NLA).

ELA imagines a theoretical hole, with rounded edges, that would be required to allow the air flow across a pressure difference of 4 Pa.

EqLA imagines a theoretical hole, with sharp edges, that would be required to allow the air flow across a pressure difference of 10 Pa.

Both 4 and 10 Pa. are such small pressure differences (4 Pa. is the equivalent of a 9 km/h wind) that they are difficult to measure accurately in the field, so in each case, the actual measurements are extrapolated by the computer attached to the blower door.

ELA and EqLA were used in the early days of air tight construction, because it is easy for a builder to picture how well he did on air sealing if the effectiveness of the air barrier is described as one hole in the wall (ELA is presented in cm² or in²).

NLA is the EqLA (or the ELA – depending on the standard being used) divided by the surface area of the building envelope that surrounds the heated space. NLA is also presented as cm²/m². This parameter "normalizes" the equivalent hole and presents it as the size of the hole in each square meter of building envelope if the the hole was evenly distributed in all parts of the envelope.

The most common way to express air leakage in residential housing today is Air Changes per Hour. Instead of dividing the air flow by surface area, it divides by the heated volume of the building. This gives you a number that expresses how much air escapes the house relative to its volume. Two air changes per hour means the house is leaking (air flow) air twice the total volume of the house every hour, at a pressure difference of 50 Pa. (Roughly the equivalent of a 33 km/h wind blowing on all surfaces of the house simultaneously.)

The 50 Pa. pressure difference is almost always used for residential construction, mainly because of historic reasons. It is a large enough number that it is fairly easy to measure, and is large enough to discount the impact of variable light winds hitting the house during the test. For large and commercial buildings, a larger test pressure, 75 Pa. is ore commonly used.

Fortunately, all these measurements, and several others, can be calculated by the blower door simply by pressing a button.

The R-2000 Program, the first Canadian building standard to set a target for air tightness, chose 1.5 ACH at 50 Pa. Reasons for this exact number were demonstrated by field testing done after the initial R-2000 training programs. Suffice to say, the 1.5 ACH50 target is readily achievable by careful builders who have been trained in air tightness techniques. The 1.5 ACH50 target has also been shown to be sufficient to construct very energy-efficient houses, including Net-Zero Energy Houses however, many builders are striving to meet targets less than 1.0 ACH. Programs introduced after R-2000 have set tighter air tightness targets, but even after several revisions, R-2000's target remains 1.5 ACH50.

2.1.5 Designing to manage heat loss

By using the R-values of the various building components, the air leakage rate, the efficiency of mechanical equipment, the averaged local climatic information, and estimates of internal and solar heat gains, the annual energy requirement for a given house is determined.

The annual energy requirement is used to size heating/cooling equipment. It also allows design adjustments to meet a certain energy performance objective. These calculations can be done manually, or with the aid of one of the many computer programs currently on

CANADIAN HOME BUILDERS' ASSOCIATION

the market, such as HOT2000, available from Natural Resources Canada. In addition, the CSA Standard F280-12 (R2017) Determining the Required Capacity of Residential Space Heating and Cooling Appliances, should be used. This Standard provides room-by-room heating and cooling requirements, which become very important when designing and sizing duct work.

2.2 Airflow

2.2.1 Factors causing airflow

Just as heat always flows from hot to cold, air flows from a high (positive) pressure area to a low (negative) pressure area. The amount of airflow depends on the size of the openings and the pressure difference across the envelope.

Several factors cause a pressure difference between inside to outside, across the building envelope:

- Wind;

- Temperature differences that cause convection, known as the stack effect;

- Operation of chimneys, ventilation equipment, and heating/cooling distribution systems; and,

- Operation of exhaust appliances such as dryers and central vacuum systems.

Air leakage into or out of a building is reduced as the total area of cracks or holes through the envelope is decreased.

The wind effect

Wind blowing over and around a building is a major contributor to the pressure difference across the building envelope. Wind creates a positive pressure on the windward side of the house, which forces air in through any cracks and holes. At the same time, wind creates a negative pressure on the leeward side, which draws air out through any openings (Figure 2.5).

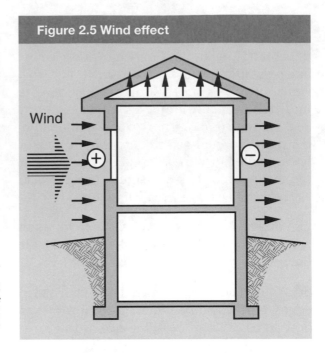

Figure 2.5 Wind effect

Windows are often opened for ventilation. A window opened on the windward side of the home provides ventilation air and pressurizes the house. Conversely, a window opened on the leeward side can depressurize the house. This is why cross-ventilation is important in rooms when windows are used for cooling during warm weather.

The stack effect

Stack effect is caused by the difference in density between warm air and cold air. As air is heated, it becomes less dense and rises, thus increasing pressures at the top of a building relative to pressures in the lower portion of the building. These pressure differences result in warm air leaking out through openings at the top of the building and cool air leaking in at the lower levels of the building (Figure 2.6).

A tall building will have a bigger stack effect than a lower one. The extent of the stack effect is also a function of how much cold air leaks into a house, and the temperature difference between inside and outside air. Air sealing will reduce the size of the openings, reducing air leakage.

Figure 2.6 Stack effect during winter

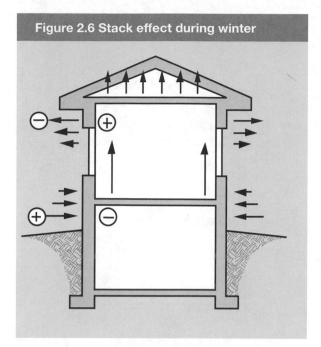

Figure 2.7 Flue and ventilation effect

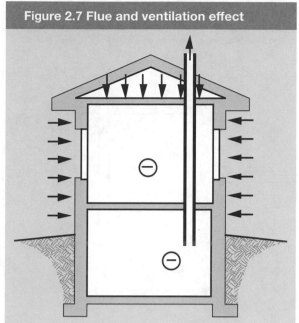

Flue and mechanical effects

Chimneys and flues serving furnaces, boilers, water heaters, wood stoves and fireplaces also cause a pressure difference that results in air leakage. When some heating equipment is operating (naturally aspirated or power-vented), air is actively drawn out of a house through the chimney to vent the products of combustion. Even when the equipment is not operating, improperly functioning dampers can permit warm air to escape up the chimney. Chimneys, whether active or passive, create a negative pressure within the house, which in turn causes outdoor air to be drawn through holes in the envelope (Figure 2.7).

Mechanical equipment used for ventilation causes an effect similar to the flue effect. Many houses contain mechanical equipment such as range hoods, bathroom fans, clothes dryers, central vacuums, and power- vented hot-water heaters and furnaces that exhaust air to the outside. When these devices are operating, they blow air out of a house, creating a negative pressure in the house. This change of pressure results in outdoor air leaking in through any

cracks or holes in the envelope. Mechanical equipment may blow more air out of the home than the envelope can admit through leakage. The resulting negative pressure can lead to backdrafting (spillage) of combustion products from fuel-fired appliances.

For this reason, combustion appliances must always have their own air supply capable of providing the required quantity of air. Sealed combustion appliances, when properly installed, do not affect house pressures.

Research has provided information on air leakage caused by ductwork that passes in and out of the house envelope or through unheated spaces. The leakage of conditioned air to the exterior through unsealed ductwork can create a significant negative pressure inside a building. The resulting infiltration of exterior air can affect energy performance, comfort, and the structural integrity of the envelope as moisture in the air can condense on colder surfaces, which can lead to mould growth and rot. For this reason, the routing of ductwork through the building envelope air

Figure 2.8 Combined effect/neutral pressure plane

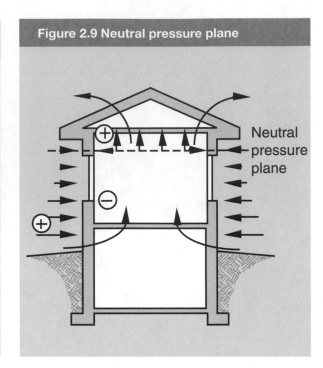

Figure 2.9 Neutral pressure plane

barrier should be avoided. If passage through the envelope is unavoidable, the duct must be properly insulated and sealed at the joints and at the points where the ductwork penetrates the air barrier.

Figure 2.8 illustrates the effect of these forces acting simultaneously on a house, and the impact on the location of the neutral pressure plane.

The neutral pressure plane

The neutral pressure plane (NPP) is a concept that can help explain how air flows in and out of houses. The plane is an imaginary line where the pressure difference between inside and outside is zero. At the neutral pressure plane, air neither leaks in nor out of the building. Below the NPP, air enters the building, while above the NPP, air leaks out of the building (Figure 2.8). The location of the neutral pressure plane will vary constantly depending on the wind effect, stack effect and the effects of flues and mechanical equipment.

If there are holes and cracks in the building envelope below the neutral pressure plane (negative pressure area), cold outdoor air will be drawn into the living space (Figure 2.9).

This is often the cause of uncomfortable drafts and dust infiltration. If the holes or cracks are above the neutral pressure plane (positive pressure area), indoor air will leak out. The best way to ensure good performance is to minimize the number of air leakage points in the building envelope by means of a continuous air barrier.

2.2.2 Role of airflow in heat loss and moisture transfer

Airflow plays a critical role in both heat and moisture flows out of a building. The stack effect can cause warm, moisture-laden air to exit from the higher levels of the house. As the moist air cools, it can condense in walls and attics, leading to deterioration of structural components. Air leakage can also account for 25 to 40 % of the total heat loss of a house.

The way to avoid heat loss and moisture transfer due to airflow is to eliminate uncontrolled air exchange by sealing potential air leakage points during construction, and to substitute the required amount of controlled air exchange using mechanical ventilation.

2.3 Moisture Movement

2.3.1 The three phases of water

Water has three phases:

- Solid (ice or frost);

- Liquid (water or condensation); and

- Gas (vapour).

Ice, water and water vapour may all be found in a building, and there is always some amount of water vapour in the air. Moisture as water vapour is not usually a problem, but water vapour, when cooled, condenses and can result in moisture damage problems such as mould, rot, corrosion, and staining.

2.3.2 Mechanisms of moisture movement

Water can move from one place to another in many ways. The four most common are:

- Gravity;

- Capillary action;

- Airflow; and

- Diffusion.

See Section 11.2 Minimizing Moisture Movement for additional information.

Gravity

Gravity causes bulk or liquid water to seek its lowest point, travelling the path of least resistance. For example, if improper drainage directs surface run-off towards a basement wall, it may enter the building through a crack in the wall and cause a basement leak.

Capillary action

Capillary action causes liquid water to move upwards, downwards or sideways through porous materials or across small gaps. A common example is how water is absorbed by a paper towel when one corner is immersed in a liquid.

Capillary action affects foundations made of concrete or other porous materials. The pores in the concrete or mortar are, in effect, long, fine tubes. Water will rise via capillary action up the foundation wall or through the slab until it is released into an area with a low water vapour pressure, usually inside the basement or crawl space. This is often why the bottom few inches of a basement or crawl space wall appears damp. Building a basement in sand may eliminate bulk water entry but provides little protection against the capillary rise of water. If moisture rises to the top of the foundation wall, it can result in rot to wood members in direct contact with the concrete. Capillary action is very strong and if a basement concrete wall is wet at the bottom, it is reasonable to assume that the wall is also wet at the top.

Capillary action is also a factor to consider for above-grade walls. Surface water absorbed into the cladding can move into other materials in the wall if there is no capillary break to stop the water transfer. An air space between the exterior cladding and the sheathing membrane eliminates that capillary action.

There are three ways to minimize capillary action:

- Seal the pores in materials by means of coatings or membranes to prevent the entry of water.

- Make the pores large enough to discourage water entry. For example, use a layer of coarse material such as crushed stone, not sand or pit run, under concrete floor slabs.

- Provide a capillary break.

Dampproofing foundation walls does not prevent water from rising through the footing. Therefore, a water- impermeable membrane or foundation coating should be installed over footings, before the foundation walls are poured, to create a capillary break (Figure 2.10).

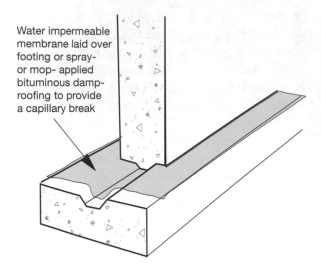

Figure 2.10 Footing detail to prevent moisture migration

Water impermeable membrane laid over footing or spray- or mop- applied bituminous damp-roofing to provide a capillary break

Airflow

Moisture enters attics and wall cavities through airflow. Figure 2.11 illustrates potential air leakage sites where warm, indoor air can move water vapour into a building envelope or attic space. All of these potential leakage sites must be sealed to prevent warm moist air exfiltrating into the building envelope where condensation can occur.

Diffusion

Diffusion is a process whereby water vapour passes through a seemingly solid material. Just as heat flows from a warm to a cool area, water vapour will flow from an area of high vapour pressure to one of low vapour pressure. For example, if water is prevented from moving through the basement walls and slabs by capillary action, it will still seek a path toward vapour pressure equalization by diffusion through the wall.

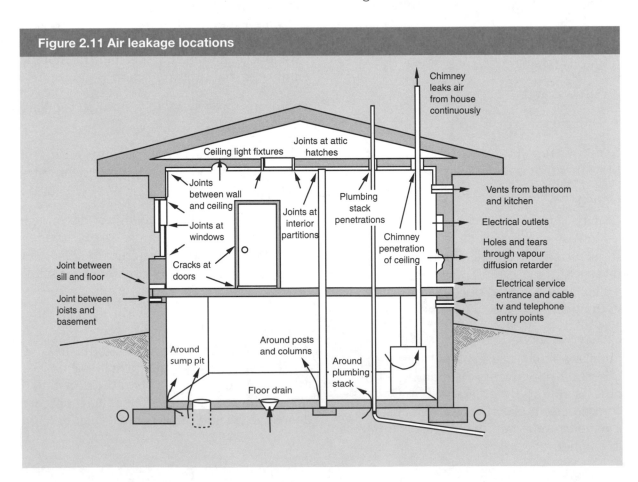

Figure 2.11 Air leakage locations

Chimney leaks air from house continuously

Joints at attic hatches

Ceiling light fixtures

Joints between wall and ceiling

Joints at interior partitions

Plumbing stack penetrations

Vents from bathroom and kitchen

Joints at windows

Electrical outlets

Chimney penetration of ceiling

Holes and tears through vapour diffusion retarder

Cracks at doors

Joint between sill and floor

Joint between joists and basement

Electrical service entrance and cable tv and telephone entry points

Around posts and columns

Around sump pit

Around plumbing stack

Floor drain

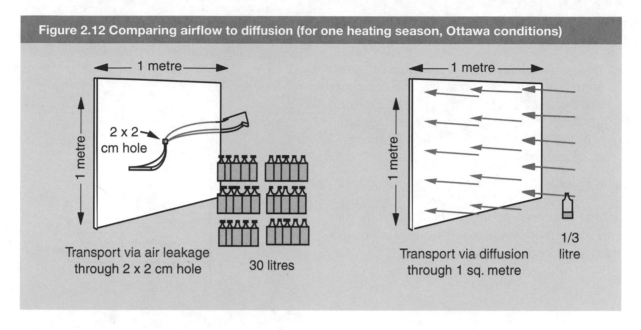

Figure 2.12 Comparing airflow to diffusion (for one heating season, Ottawa conditions)

1 metre

1 metre

2 x 2 cm hole

Transport via air leakage through 2 x 2 cm hole

30 litres

1 metre

1 metre

Transport via diffusion through 1 sq. metre

1/3 litre

Vapour diffusion is never stopped, merely retarded. However, the common term used in Canada for this retarder is vapour barrier (whereas in the United States it is called a vapour retarder). To ensure water vapour does not reach a temperature where it will condense, the vapour barrier must be placed on the warm side of the wall. This will be inside in a heating climate, and outside in a cooling climate. Since some materials slow the diffusion of moisture better than others, the National Building Code of Canada (NBC) has established certain performance requirements for vapour barriers. A list of the water vapour transmission coefficients of various materials is included in Appendix 2.

Comparing airflow to diffusion

Studies have shown that approximately 100 times more moisture enters a building structure by airflow than by diffusion under moderate pressure differentials between the exterior and interior. (Figure 2.12) This is why so much emphasis is placed on the achievement of an appropriate level of airtightness. The NBC requires that house air barriers be continuous. The R-2000 Program (and CHBA's Net Zero Energy Housing Program) requires that the effectiveness of the air barrier be verified by means of a blower door test.

2.3.3 Sources of moisture in houses

Since warm air can hold more water vapour than cold air, moisture levels are considerably higher inside a heated house than outside under normal winter conditions. In a well-built house, indoor humidity levels are controlled by a combination of better building practices and the use of a properly designed and operated mechanical ventilation system.

There are several sources of moisture in homes:

- Day-to-day activities such as breathing, cooking, bathing, washing and drying clothes generate moisture.

- Furniture, drywall and framing materials inside the house absorb moisture from humid air during the summer. This is called "seasonal storage." Once the heating season begins, this moisture is released back into the house air. This can mean seasonal fluctuations in the moisture content of certain (hydroscopic) building materials (Figure 2.13).

- Concrete footings, foundation walls and floor slab can allow moisture entry. A crawl space or basement in an older house with an earthen floor can be a significant source of moisture.

- Unseasoned firewood stored in the house will also give off considerable moisture.

- New construction has significant moisture stored in the materials used to construct the home. Concrete, drywall and framing lumber, for example, emit a considerable amount of moisture in the first year or two after installation.

- Indoor plants can be a source of moisture.

Table 2.2 shows the amounts of moisture that various activities can contribute to a house's moisture content.

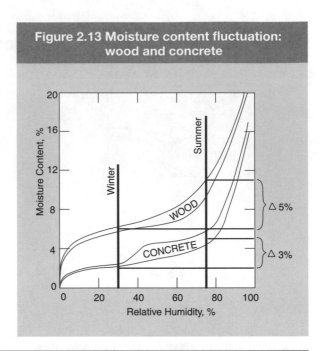

Figure 2.13 Moisture content fluctuation: wood and concrete

Table 2.2 Sources of moisture in houses

Typical moisture sources (per day)

Occupant-related		Building-related	
4 occupants	5 L (1.3 gal)	exposed, uncovered earth crawl space	40-50 L (10.5-13.2 gal)
clothes drying indoors	1.2 L (0.32 gal)	drying and burning of firewood	5 L (1.3 gal)
floor washing/10 m² (107 sq. ft.)	1 L (0.26 gal)	new construction— drying of framing and concrete over the first 18 months	4-5 L (1-1.3 gal)
cooking (3 meals/day)	1 L (0.26 gal)		
dishwashing (3 meals/day)	0.5 L (0.13 gal)		

2.3.4 Damage potential

Knowing the thermal resistance of all the elements of an assembly, the thermal gradient can be calculated for various locations in the assembly. Figure 2.14 shows the calculation and plot of the thermal gradient for a typical wood-frame wall assembly with a rigid foam exterior sheathing.

Using the psychrometric chart (Figure 2.15) and the thermal gradient, it is possible to determine the location of the dew point – the point at which condensation occurs in a building assembly. This calculation allows the designer to ensure that the vapour barrier is always on the warm side of the dew point.

Water vapour alone is not a problem, but it can cause problems when it reaches the dew point temperature and condenses. When water condenses on surfaces, it can support mould growth (see Section 4.1.4) and break down protective coatings of paint or caulking. If it condenses within the envelope, it will reduce the performance of the insulation. If condensate is allowed to accumulate within the envelope, it can lead to more serious problems. If the moisture content of wood rises and stays above 25 to 30 % and the temperature stays between 18° and 35° C (64° and 95° F), wood rot can become established. Serious structural damage can result.

Figure 2.14 Temperature gradient through an exterior wall

	Wall Component	RSI	$\triangle T$ across component ($RSI/RSI_t \times \triangle T_t$)
1	Exterior air film	0.0053	0.039
2	Metal siding	0.0211	0.157
3	Air space with strapping	0.0300	0.224
4	50 mm (2") extruded polystyrene	1.761 (R10)	13.125
5	38 x 89 mm (2 x 4") studs with batt insulation	2.113 (R12)	15.749
6	38 x 64 mm (2 x 3") horizontal strapping with batt insulation	1.409 (R8)	10.502
7	Gypsum wall board	0.0062	0.046
8	Interior air film	0.0211	0.1572
	Totals	RSI_t 5.3667	$\triangle T_t$ 40°C

Winter conditions

Inside temperature	+20°C
Outside temperature	-20°C
$\triangle T_t$ across wall assembly	40°C

Theoretical temperature gradient

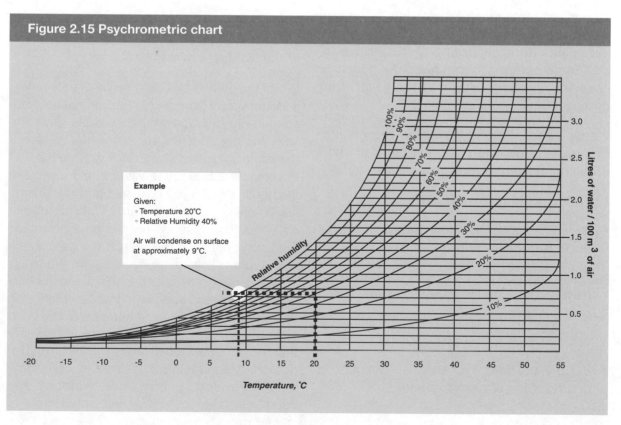

Figure 2.15 Psychrometric chart

Example

Given:
° Temperature 20°C
° Relative Humidity 40%

Air will condense on surface at approximately 9°C.

Relative humidity

Litres of water / 100 m³ of air

Temperature, °C

Using Figures 2.14 and 2.15, as an example, the 20C, 40% RH air in the home will condense at a temperature of 9C. The thermal gradient in Figure 2.14 shows that under the conditions of -20C outside and +20C inside, a temperature of 9C occurs approximatley at a point where the two pieces of batt insulation meet (pieces 5 & 6, Figure 2.14). This means that the water vapour in the air flowing through the wall has reached the dew point. In order to condense, the vapour needs a condensing surface to form on. Recall that an insulation batt functions by trapping air so there are a lot of air spaces in the batt. The fibres in the batt insulation may may act as a condensing surface and see some condensation, however it is more likely that the condensation will form on the interior side of the rigid foam (piece 4, Fig 2.14). Note that the interior side of the rigid foam is below freezing, which will result in the moisture condensing and freezing on the surface of the foam. It will remain in that state until the temperature conditions change, and the temperature of the rigid foam goes above zero.

To prevent moisture accumulation in the wall in this case, the interior should be vapour permeable (to allow drying to the inside), or, additional exterior foam should be added to keep the interior surface of the foam from dropping in temperature below the dew point.

Water, in its various forms, is responsible for most homeowner complaints. Common problems related to moisture include:

- Condensation on windows;

- Deterioration of window frames and wall finishes under windows;

- Leaks in the ceiling caused by the melting of frost accumulated in unheated attics during cold weather;

- Paint peeling from exterior wood sidings;

- Efflorescence, spalling of brick and deterioration of mortar joints;

- Dusting or staining of the interior side of exterior ceilings and walls in corners and along joists and studs or on nail or screw heads;

- Mould and mildew in these same locations;

- Mould and mildew on rafters, trusses or roof sheathing;

- Sagging of roof sheathing;

- Deterioration of the structural framework of the building due to rot;

- Ice damming and the formation of icicles;

- Water leakage from fans caused by condensation in uninsulated ducting that runs through unheated space;

- Basement leaks due to poor surface grading, inadequate drainage around the foundation, or condensation off the foundation wall behind the insulation; and

- Cracks in foundation walls or poor dampproofing.

Most of these problems can be eliminated by adequate ventilation and air and vapour sealing of the building envelope.

When building to Net Zero performance levels, it is important to ensure that air barriers are adequately detailed and that walls have the ability to dry. Much of the older housing stock has survived because water that got into the wall system was able to dry. It was able to dry because the house was poorly insulated and the energy lost through the walls assisted with drying the wall. Net Zero walls will not see anywhere near this level of heat loss and as such any water in the wall is more likely to dry by diffusion. While it is impossible to keep water out, we can do our best to try. This means adequate drainage planes on the exterior (covered in Chapters 6 & 11), good air barriers, properly installed and tested to verify that the air barrier is delivering the performance desired. It also means that detailing of flashing around envelope penetrations, windows and doors will take on heightened importance to ensure water does not get in.

Figure 2.16 A Practical Example

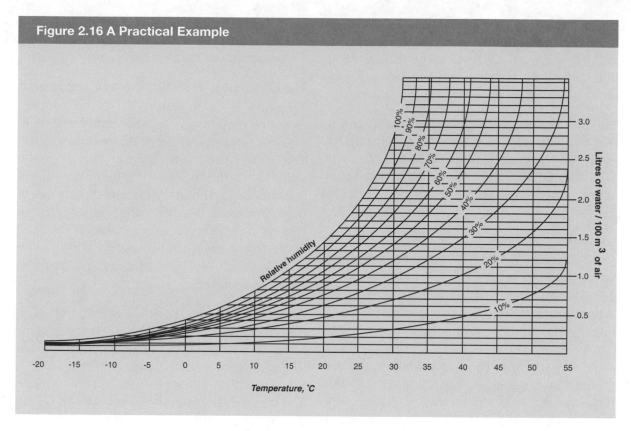

The psychrometric chart looks intimidating but it is an important tool for avoiding or for diagnosing moisture problems. Despite the complicated look, the chart is easy to use once you try it. Here is a an example.

You have been asked to construct a high performance house. The simulations showed that you can meet your energy target with new vinyl frame, double glazed, low-e, argon windows that were equipped with insulating spacers. You have enough experience that you have seen situations in new houses where the bathroom windows have condensation during showers in winter, especially on the lower part of the glass. This is not a situation you want to see again and you know that the client has teenage children so long showers are likely.

Write down what you know.

1. The problem is in the winter. What is winter? Cold outside. Low RH inside.

2. The problem is in the bathrooms. What is special about the bathrooms? Localized high RH when the shower is on.

3. House temperature is likely about 22 C.

4. In other cases you have not seen other windows in the houses condensing.

Form and test a theory.

1. Lets say the RH in the bathroom is 80% during the shower. (room will be foggy, at 100% it is raining). Also the temperature may be higher because the hot water is heating up the air. Let's assume the air is at 25 C.

2. Winter, so outdoor temperature is say -15 C.

Using the psychrometric chart, enter at 25 C and go up to the 80% RH line. Then move directly to the left until it hits the 100% line. What is the temperature where your line intersects the 100% line? About 22 C. Is there a chance that the inner glazing of the window will be below 22 C? Absolutely, if it is -15 C outside and the window is R-3 at the centre of glass so it is even lower where the spacer is.

But what if we guessed the RH wrong and it was actually 60%? Back to the psychometric chart. Go in at 25C and go up to the 60% RH line, then straight left to the 100% RH line. What is the temperature? 16 C or 17 C. Could the window be below 17 C? Of course it could.

We also know from past experience that the other windows in the house are not condensing. Why? What do we have? House temperature at 22 C. Winter so the RH is likely 40% or lower. What temperature would the windows need to be at before condensation will form? Enter the psychrometric chart at 22 C. Go straight up to the RH = 40% line. Then go straight to the left until it reaches the 100% RH line. What s the temperature? Approximately 8 C. That's why there is no condensation. The inner surface of the windows is above 8 C.

What can be done?

1. Add adequate task ventilation in the bathrooms to ensure that the RH in the bathroom stays low during the showers. Go back to the psychrometric chart and notice how, even at 25 C how the temperature of the surface of the window at which condensation will form changes as the RH goes down. Notice that as the RH drops, so does the temperature at which condensation will form on the window. Source ventilation is a potential answer.

2. You could choose triple-glazed windows for the bathrooms. What would that have done? It would have resulted in a higher surface temperature on the inner surface of the glass – the inner surface of the window glass will not get as cold. This will mean that the window will be more resistant to condensation at high humidity levels. While this, combined with source

ventilation may not stop all of the condensation, it will certainly reduce the possibility of condensation forming.

The Concept of R per Inch and $ per R-inch

Referring again to Figure 2.14, the concept of R/inch may be an important way to look at insulation types. Different types of insulation have different R-values/inch. In this case, the rigid foam is R-5/inch and the batt insulation is R-3.4/inch. For the same total insulation value, more inches of batt insulation is required to achieve the same insulation value of the rigid foam. To achieve R-10, two inches of rigid foam is required while of batt insulation nearly three inches is required.

Another important concept is $/R-inch. The cost of insulation varies by type. If the goal for a Net Zero House is to construct an R-40 wall, this can be done in a variety of ways. A 2" x 8" stud with 3" of rigid foam on the outside and batt insulation in the cavity will be (7.5"x 3.4 R/inch) + (3" x 5 R/inch) = R-25.5 + R-15 = R-40.5. Alternatively, a double stud wall 10" thick and 1.5" of rigid foam on the exterior will create (10" x 3.4 R/in) + (1.5" x 5 R/in) = R-34 + R-7.5 = R-41.5. The cost of materials, the willingness of the framing crew to venture outside of their comfort zone, the decision to use more floor space to allow for a thicker wall, all are inputs to deciding on how to meet the design goal of an R-40 wall. (Note: this example is only dealing with nominal insulation levels, not effective insulation levels. That discussion will follow later in this Manual.)

2.4 Factors Affecting Comfort

2.4.1 Sound

Noise, or unwanted sound, can be a major concern for occupants since it affects their ability to enjoy their home. It can originate inside the home from furnace blowers, dryers, and refrigerators, for example, or from people moving around, playing or working with tools. It can also originate outside, from cars, trucks, trains, neighbours, etc. A well-built home is designed and constructed to minimize the transmission of sound and to reduce the likelihood that noise becomes a problem for the occupants.

Some considerations of sound transmission are:

- **Siting**—housing should be situated so that natural terrain, trees and other structures provide shelter from noise generated elsewhere (for example, neighbouring air conditioners, roads or near airport aircraft corridors). At very noisy locations, wall and window construction with suitable noise reduction ratings is required.

- **Layout**—the house floor plan should be designed to separate noisy areas from quiet ones. Closets and hallways should be used to buffer bedrooms from areas where noise will be generated, such as family and laundry rooms.

- **Mechanical equipment**—some mechanical equipment installed in houses can be noisy. Furnace fans, clothes dryers and ventilation systems should be isolated from the structure, have quiet motors, and be located away from bedrooms. Proper ductwork design can reduce noise from forced-air furnaces.

- **Plumbing**—most noise from plumbing can be controlled by avoiding contact between pipes and wall surfaces, using extra drywall for walls or ceilings near pipes, and using resilient lining such as foam pipe insulation to separate pipes from the building structure. Heavy-wall pipes can be used in critical areas to reduce plumbing drain noise within the house.

- **Building materials and assemblies**—sound-absorbing assemblies can be used to keep outside noise from penetrating a building, and to keep sound waves from travelling from one room or area of the house to another.

Sound is vibration that travels through the air or through a solid. The control of sound is important for occupant comfort, especially in multi-unit residential construction where occupants in one unit cannot directly control the generation of noise in an adjacent unit.

There are several ways to measure sound. The decibel (dB) is commonly used to measure noise generated by appliances. The minimum sound level a person can hear in a controlled laboratory experiment is 0 dB. People whispering is approximately 20 dB. Background noise usually ranges from 10 to 50 dB, normal conversation measures about 70 dB, and conversation at a party might rise to 85 dB or more. Small-motor sound is commonly measured in units called sones. Bathroom fans should have a rating not exceeding 2.5 sones, and very quiet fans would have a rating of 0.5 sones. Although the sones and dB are not proportional, 2.5 sones is approximately 40 dB and 0.5 sones is approximatley 14 dB. Choose quiet fans (2.5 sones or less) because noisy fans won't get used. Experience shows that as houses reach Net Zero levels of insulation and air tightness, less of the exterior noise gets into the house. As a result, noise generated inside the house becomes even more obvious to occupants so quiet refrigerators, dishwashers and other appliances improve comfort for the occupants.

Sound Transmission Class (STC) is a rating for evaluating the effectiveness of construction in isolating airborne sound transmission. Higher numbers indicate more effectiveness. Figures 2.18 and 2.19 show examples of rated wall and floor assemblies used for multi-unit buildings. STC ratings for insulating concrete form (ICF) construction are available from manufacturers.

Figure 2.20 shows the range of STC ratings for windows and doors. Windows are the biggest challenge in terms of sound transmission, followed closely by doors.

Airborne sound is reduced by selecting and constructing wall and floor assemblies that have tested STC ratings. The ratings are affected by the types and application of materials. Heavy or layered materials reduce the transfer of vibration. Using insulation in cavities also reduces sound transmission. Higher-density insulations are better isolators than light-weight, low-density products. Multi-unit residential buildings have particular requirements for sound control. See Section 3.7.1.

Providing a separation between assembly layers also reduces sound transmission. Resilient channels (metal framing) are commonly used to separate drywall from wood or steel studs or floor joists (Figure 2.17). This channel helps to minimize the transmission of vibrations through the members. Resilient channels in ceilings can be very effective in reducing sound transmission from one level to the next, especially in multi-level structures. Staggering framing is another way of reducing sound transmission.

Figure 2.17 Resilient Channel

Acoustical caulking was developed specifically to seal the paths by which air leaks in or through a building. Although airtight homes are quieter, because there are fewer paths for external airborne noise to enter the home, good building practices can also lessen internal noise. Weatherstripping interior doors and using airtight electrical boxes can

reduce airborne noise travelling from one room to another. The construction techniques described in later sections of this Manual are designed to minimize air leakage through all components of the building envelope and thus reduce airborne sound. Similar techniques used within the building can reduce noise transmission inside the house.

Figure 2.18 Examples of wall assemblies with high STC ratings

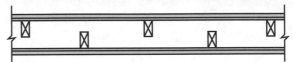

Adapted from NBC Wall W9a – STC 56
- Two rows 38 mm x 89 mm (2x4 in.) studs each spaced 400 or 600 (16 or 20 in.) mm o.c. staggered on common 38 mm x 140 mm (2x6 in.) plate
- Two layers of 15.9 mm (5/8 in.) Type X gypsum board both sides

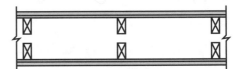

Adapted from NBCC Wall W15a – STC 66
- Two rows 38 mm x 89 mm (2x4 in.) studs, each spaced 400 mm or 600 mm (20 in.) o.c. on separate 38 mm x 89 mm (2 x 4 in.) plates set 25 mm (1 in.) apart
- 89 mm (3-1/2 in.) thick absorptive material on each side
- Two layers of 15.9 mm (5/8 in.) Type X gypsum board both sides

Figure 2.19 Examples of floor assemblies with high STC ratings

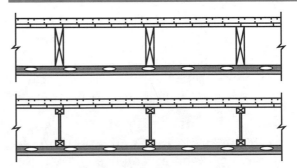

Adapted from NBCC Floor F14d – STC 58, IIC 26
- 25 mm (1 in.) gypsum-concrete topping (at least 44 kg/m^2) on wood joists spaced not more than 600 mm (20 in.) o.c.
- absorptive material in cavity
- resilient metal channels spaced 600 mm (20 in.) o.c.
- one layer 15.9 mm (5/8 in.) Type X gypsum board on ceiling side

Figure 2.20 Typical window and door STC ratings

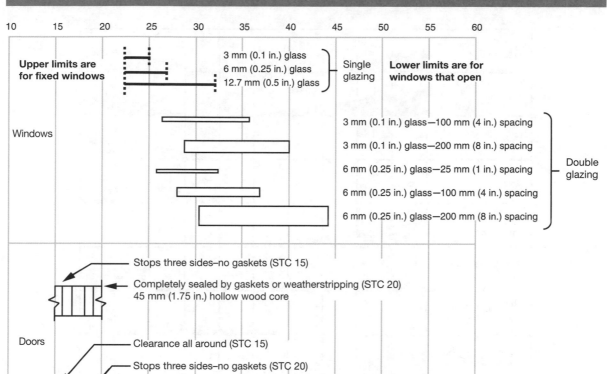

In addition to airborne sound moving by striking and passing through an assembly, another source of noise is impact from sources such as footsteps or dropped objects. The use of soft floor coverings such as carpet will help reduce sound transmission from one level in a building to the next. Both airborne and impact sound will seek paths of least resistance and may find routes to bypass sound control assemblies. This is called flanking. Additional information about impact sound and flanking can be found in Chapter 3.

2.4.2 Relative humidity

Expressed as a percentage, relative humidity refers to the quantity of water vapour in the air relative to the maximum amount of water vapour it can hold at a given temperature. Relative humidity can range from 0 to 100%. Above 100%, the air mass can hold no more water vapour-it has reached its dew point and condensation occurs in the form of dew, frost, rain, ice or snow.

Human beings are comfortable in the 20 to 85% relative humidity range, but studies show the optimum range for comfort is between 30 and 55%. However, in cold climates where window condensation is prevalent, the upper range should be lowered until the amount of condensation is at an acceptable level.

Figure 2.21 Relative humidity and air quality

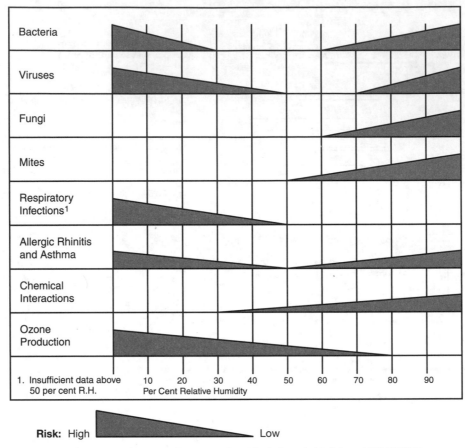

1. Insufficient data above 50 per cent R.H.

Per Cent Relative Humidity

Risk: High — Low

Source: E.M. Sterling, Criteria for Human Exposure to Humidity in Occupied Buildings, 1985 ASHRAE.

Figure 2.21 shows the humidity levels at which various air quality problems occur. Low humidity can cause static electricity, dry, scratchy throats for occupants, and excessive dust problems. High humidity can lead to mould growth and condensation on cool surfaces such as windows. In cold climates, there is very little moisture in outdoor air in winter, so indoor air will also be very dry. Though consumers may wish to humidify up to the 30 % humidity level or higher, it is best to accept a somewhat lower indoor humidity in winter and avoid damage from condensation and frost that can result from excessive humidification. Both conditions can lead to discomfort. The psychometric chart (see Figure 2.15) can be used to determine when condensation will occur on windows or on other cold surfaces.

2.4.3 Air temperature

The human comfort zone in air temperature ranges from 20 to 27° C (68 to 81°F). The core temperature of the human body is 37°C (98.6°F). The difference between the air temperature in a house and the core temperature of the occupants creates a continual heat exchange, but is also affected by radiant conditions, humidity and air movement.

The rate at which this exchange occurs is critical to the sensation of comfort. If the temperature difference is too high, occupants feel chilled. Conversely, if it is too low, they feel overheated. Individuals at rest or doing desk work will require higher air temperatures to feel comfortable than those who are more active or performing physical work.

2.4.4 Radiant exchange

Occupants will radiate heat to cooler surrounding surfaces such as uninsulated walls or windows. Surfaces that are warmer than their bodies, such as a heated ceiling or floor, will transfer heat to them by radiation. The rate of this heat transfer depends on the difference in temperature between the surface and the occupant, and on the rate at which each emits radiant heat (emissivity). The slower the rate of heat transfer, the more comfortable the environment will feel.

For example, occupants will be warmed by sunlight radiating through windows, but will lose heat to walls and windows that are cooler than body temperature. High levels of insulation in the walls and ceilings of a house will keep these surfaces warmer in winter and cooler in summer and make the occupants feel more comfortable.

Radiant heat requires a line-of-sight for it to be effective. A masonry heater in the middle of a room will radiate energy in all directions and those in the room will feel it. Move to another room and the wall between you and the masonry heater will block the radiated heat.

The sun is a common source of radiant energy. Every day it radiates energy to the earth over a distance of 93 million miles through the vacuum of space. Radiation does not need a medium in order to travel. Heat is transferred from warm objects to cooler objects. The sun is 5500 C. You are 37 C. You must be in the line of sight to feel the radiation. Step into the shade and you no longer feel the radiant energy but you will still feel the conductive and convective heat from the objects warmed by the sun.

Also of interest is the process of radiant cooling. The clear night sky is colder than you are and is approximated by the temperature of space (-80 C to -270 C). If there are clouds however, the clouds are significantly lower and at about 18 C in the summer. Radiant cooling therefore is much more apparent when the night sky is clear and your body is in a line of site with the sky. Your body radiates energy to the sky and you feel cold. The house also radiates heat to the sky, particularly through the roof. A warm roof will radiate more energy than a cold roof so ceiling insulation will help keep the radiating roof from cooling down the house. As an experiment, on a clear summer night, park a car in a carport with 1/2 the car hidden from the sky by the carport and 1/2 the car able to see the sky. Radiant cooling will cause the car seeing the sky to cool more than the part in the carport that can't see the sky. In fact, even if the outdoor temperature is 5 C, the car can cool enough to have frost on the 1/2 that can see the sky. Weather forecasters will often predict a frost warning for plants when a clear night is expected, even though the temperature is not predicted to go to 0 C at night. This is because of radiant cooling.

2.4.5 Air movement

The movement of air makes occupants feel cool. The drier the air, the cooler they feel.

The design of heating, ventilation and air conditioning (HVAC) systems must take this air movement into account and consider the following:

- Air provided by the ventilation system will be relatively cool, even with heat recovery. Such air should not enter conditioned spaces before it has been mixed or heated to room temperature.

- Even heated air seems like a cool draft if it is below body temperature. This sensation is increased just after a bath or shower, for example, when moisture is evaporating from the surface of the skin. The location of warm air ducts should be carefully planned to provide the most comfort to occupants, usually by avoiding delivering air directly to where people will be sitting or sleeping.

- Heated air will be cooled as it comes into contact with cool surfaces such as window glass. As it cools, the air becomes more dense and falls, creating drafts at the floor level. To avoid drafts, cold-air returns should be placed on interior walls in areas where furniture will not likely be placed. However, Net Zero homes have lower heating requirements, reducing furnace airflows and the likelihood of drafts.

- Net Zero homes have highly insulated walls and high performance windows. The result of this is that there is very little heat loss. Historically, warm air was introduced under the windows because the windows were cold. Introducing the air under the windows helped to warm the window and reduce condensation or frost on the glass. With high performance windows this is no longer the case and heated air can now be introduced into the room in other places such as high on the wall or from the ceiling. In addition, since less heat is required, less air needs to be moved and therefore smaller ducts can be used.

- Air stratification can also create drafts at the floor level. A strategy that provides continuous air circulation, such as the use of variable-speed furnace fans, will help to prevent these floor-level drafts.

More detailed information about the design and installation of HVAC systems is provided in Chapters 15 to 21.

2.4.6 Indoor air quality

Indoor air quality is important for comfort and health. It is a function of several factors:

- Chemical contaminants (VOCs);

- Combustion gases; Mould;

- Relative humidity; Particulate matter; and

- Soil gas (see Section 4.1.6).

See Chapter 4 for more detailed information.

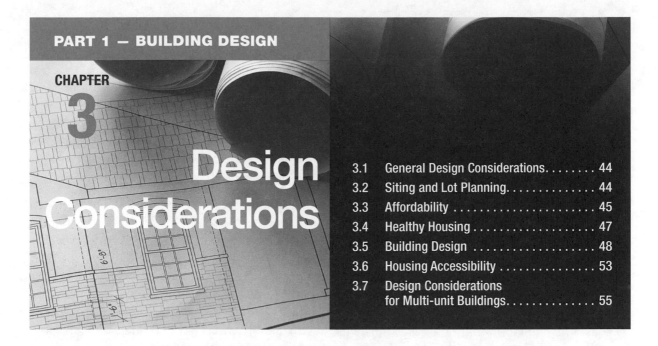

Over the next decade, there are likely to be more changes in the housing industry than ever before; the face of Canadian housing will be altered by both technological and societal change. Successful builders will be those who employ design and construction practices that enhance affordability, improve quality, and increase market share by offering more choices. Key challenges will include:

- Continuing to pursue increased energy efficiency in new and existing buildings;

- Using materials and building techniques that optimize indoor air quality;

- Reducing environmental impact by decreasing construction waste and using durable construction materials;

- Accommodating an aging population;

- Housing people with disabilities;

- Stressing the importance of quality rather than size;

- Adapting to changing availability of skilled trades people;

- Providing housing that is affordable to a broader segment of the Canadian public; and,

- Increasing the use of technology both in construction and for automation within the home.

The previous chapter reviewed the fundamental building science principles that underlie the construction techniques described in this Manual. This chapter looks at factors to consider during the design process. It reviews how various design decisions arising from the application of these principles can affect the durability, comfort, energy efficiency, and overall marketability of houses.

3.1 General Design Considerations

The design process is a series of decisions, all of which affect performance, marketability, and comfort of the occupants.

Heating and ventilation systems should be considered early in the design process, and proper sizing of equipment should take into account the type of household, the type and location of windows and vents, the availability and cost of fuels, the noise generated by equipment, and the ease of maintaining the equipment. By considering all these factors early in the design process, designers can increase the likelihood that house systems will function properly. Other considerations include:

- North-facing windows may be installed to provide views, but need to provide higher insulating levels than south-facing windows. Additional envelope insulation may also be needed.

- An open plan may facilitate air circulation, especially in homes with wood stoves or those incorporating passive solar design, but the increased noise and reduced privacy need to be considered.

- Deliberate design that takes advantage of passive solar gains can lower heating costs and provide pleasant, sunny rooms, but care must be taken to ensure the solar energy does not increase summer cooling loads.

- High levels of insulation and a well-sealed building envelope will reduce the size and cost of heating and cooling equipment required as well as the volumes of air that need to be moved to maintain temperatures.

- An efficient heat recovery ventilator (HRV) in a tightly sealed house will result in long-term energy savings and, more importantly, will improve indoor air quality.

It is important to ensure that design intent is not compromised during construction. This can be done by ensuring trades people understand the design intent and how to achieve it. Key considerations include scheduling, the presence of the right skills at the right time, availability of materials and equipment, and favourable weather conditions during critical periods.

Scheduling problems can be severe in remote and northern areas where the construction season is very short and skilled local workers may not be readily available. The fact that materials must often be shipped via winter road, barge or air adds to costs and affects timing. Ensuring that the required materials are available when needed takes considerable preplanning and pre-ordering, close supervision of shipping, careful storage, and tight control on the site.

3.2 Siting and Lot Planning

The selection of building sites should consider:

- Orientation;

- Passive solar potential;

- Renewable energy

- Topography, drainage and soil type;

- Views;

- Streetscape (the relationship of the house to its neighbours);

- Micro-climate (thermal inversion, heat-island effect, lake effect);

- Zoning, easements and other local jurisdiction regulations and ordinances;

- Location of service access for urban sites; and

- Water well and wastewater disposal prospects for rural sites.

To optimize energy efficiency, building sites should have good solar exposure. Individual lots in subdivisions should be laid out carefully so that each is provided with the maximum available solar exposure (Figure 3.1). This is optimized by orienting the majority of streets on an east-west axis. Other considerations include:

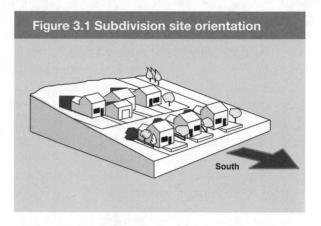

Figure 3.1 Subdivision site orientation

- Locating trees and shrubs to provide summer shade to east, west, and south-facing glazing;

- Providing good solar control during the summer by using deciduous trees, which let sunlight through during the winter (Figure 3.2);

- Orienting the home on the site to allow sunlight into the house in the spring;

- Reducing air leakage, in windy areas good windbreaks can decrease air leakage from a house by 30 to 40 % by reducing wind pressures;

- Locating doors and driveways to minimize the effects of drifting snow and driving rain;

- Designing and locating buildings so that they do not have projections or recesses that will catch snow from prevailing winter winds; and,

- Landscaping with coniferous trees to provide shelter from prevailing winds, especially on the north and west sides. Large conifers should be avoided on the south face, as they block winter sun.

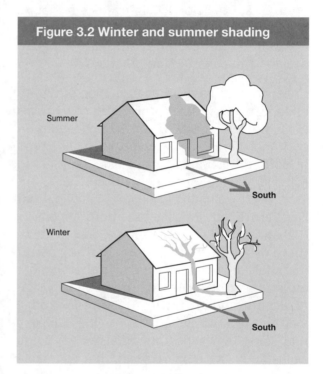

Figure 3.2 Winter and summer shading

It should be noted that trees or building additions on neighbouring properties can affect passive solar energy as well as active solar collectors.

Northern locations present special challenges. Soil bearing capacity can be a major problem where conditions include frost-susceptible soils, muskeg and permafrost, and where deep frost levels make it difficult to install services.

3.3 Affordability

Canadians enjoy a high standard of housing. Although home ownership is considered a good investment, it remains beyond the grasp of many.

The costs of construction, land, taxes and fees have increased in many parts of the country, and housing costs, as a percentage of income, continue to increase. In the 1950s it took 25 % of one family member's annual income to support a house. Today, it may take

40 to 50% of two incomes to meet present consumer expectations. Housing expectations affect affordability. Over the past half-century, the average size of Canadian houses and the amount of features in each have grown substantially. Increasing the size and number of features found in a home adds to the cost and complexity of construction. Canadian home builders are actively working to support innovation in the industry that allows better houses to be built at lower cost.

Housing affordability can be improved through optimal subdivision design and alternative development standards, conversion of under-utilized buildings, and innovative house designs and construction practices.

Governments have indicated that by 2030, building codes will be requiring all new houses to be Net Zero Ready. This has implications on cost and thereby affordability. As of the time of writing this Manual, there are 10 years to achieve the goal of all new houses being Net Zero Ready. Our experience is showing that Net Zero Ready houses are more expensive than houses built to today's Code because there is more material (insulation) better materials (higher performing windows), more attention to detail (airtightness, roof design to accommodate future PV arrays) and a looming lack of skilled trades. It is unlikely that some new super- materials will become available in the next 10 years that will make these houses less expensive to produce. That means as builders, we are going to have to build with the same materials we have now. If we want to make housing more affordable we will need to look at ourselves and figure out how to bring the cost of housing down by improving our productivity on site. Chapter 24 is dedicated to Future Gazing and reviewing technological advances which are expected to improve productivity. Some the immediate design solutions to reduce costs include:

- smaller homes on smaller lots

- multi-unit buildings instead of single-detached

- eliminate basements but build higher (a storey in the ground is more expensive than a storey in the air)

- use less expensive cladding (siding instead of brick)

- use less expensive interior finishes

- incorporate secondary suites so part of the home can be rented out to support the monthly payments

- less on-site construction, more factory building with on-site assembly

- simplifying the design (more "boxy" look is easier to insulate, air seal, and it performs better thermally because less wood is needed to create the irregular shapes).

3.3.1 Smaller lots and higher densities

One of the keys to affordability is the evolution of by-laws, regulations, and procedures to suit modern requirements. Many Canadian municipalities are re-evaluating existing standards and identifying where changes could result in cost savings without compromising safety, servicing or traffic flows. Changes being considered include:

- Reducing road allowance width;

- Allowing smaller lots, reduced frontage and setbacks;

- Eliminating double trenching for services; and

- Eliminating curbs and sidewalks.

3.3.2 Flexible design

Many young families buy a starter home with the idea of selling it and upgrading to a larger one later. Today, however, some designs are based on accommodating future needs in the same house. Demonstration projects offer new ways of looking at housing within cost and space limitations and enable one house to satisfy more owner expectations.

For example, the demonstration home at the reception centre of the Canadian Centre for Housing Technology's on the Ottawa campus of the National Research Council has features that allow it to be easily modified as occupants' needs change. A large room can be divided into bedrooms as needed, and vice versa.

Other elements of flexible design may include:

- Pre-planned flexibility to allow for easy, inexpensive conversion by providing future plumbing and electrical requirements, solar-ready capability, fire and sound separations between floors, and heating systems;

- Carefully planned interior layout to maximize the use of available floor space, strategic placement of doorways to allow good traffic flow within the unit, and cathedral ceilings on the second floor to provide volume and create a feeling of an enlarged space;

- Space-saving techniques such as ceiling-mounted heating and air conditioning systems, stackable washers and dryers, closet organizers, and small yet efficient kitchens;

- Space-enhancing decor, such as bright colours, mirrors and window coverings, as well as attractively sized and placed furniture;

- Full-span floor and roof systems to allow movement of any interior wall; and

- Energy-efficient construction to keep the home's overall operating costs to a minimum.

3.3.3 Converting underused space

Successful conversions of underused, vacant, or mothballed facilities to dwelling units have been made. Schools, for example, are often

well located within a city and community. The building design lends itself to the integration of contemporary dwelling units within the given envelope. And because they were designed for public occupancy, they usually conform to the most demanding building and fire code requirements. Even office buildings are sometimes converted into residential units.

3.4 Healthy Housing

Healthy housing provides the best quality indoor environment for its occupants that can be delivered through reasonable and affordable means that include sustainable housing principles. This may include:

- Selection of indoor materials to reduce indoor air pollution from volatile chemicals;

- Selection of floor, ceiling and wall coverings that do not trap dust and are easily cleaned;

- Installation of weather sealing, drainage, basement insulation, dampproofing and exhaust ventilation to prevent indoor moisture problems;

- Installation of an appropriate ventilation system to ensure good indoor air quality when the house is closed;

- Installation of an appropriate air filtration system to capture fine dust;

- Installation of a low-temperature heating system such as a hot-water fan-coil;

- Design for good daylight, winter sunlight and solar control in summer;

- Installation of high quality, colour-balanced and energy-efficient lighting; and,

- Placement of noise-resistant windows and landscaping in noisy locations.

About 20% of the population has some form of allergy or respiratory illness that can be avoided or improved by preventing indoor air pollution. Many more people are interested in the comfort and preventative health benefits of good indoor air quality. The merits of decent daylight, lighting and noise control are apparent. More detailed information about indoor air quality is provided in Chapter 4.

3.5 Building Design

3.5.1 Configuration

The first step in building design is to consider the house configuration, location, and orientation on the building lot. The following factors should be considered:

- Site and climatic conditions;

- Neighbourhood;

- Client needs and requirements;

- Functional usability of spaces and components;

- Capital and operating costs;

- Resale; and,

- Overall character/ambience of the home.

Site topography influences the type of building selected. A sloping site may permit taking advantage of the slope to design a two- or three-storey configuration on the lower end of a lot and a reduced profile at the other end. A two-storey house has less exposed surface area relative to its usable floor area than a single-storey design, and this can reduce construction and heating costs. Better views from the second floor may also be a factor. A measure of a building's efficiency is its usable floor area relative to its exposed surface area. However, multi-storey homes are usually not appropriate for people with physical disabilities.

In the north, the shape of the building can have a major impact on its performance because of the severe climate. Therefore, building design should attempt to:

- Minimize exposed surface area;

- Reduce the number of windows facing north;

- Place entries away from snowdrift locations; and,

- Locate unheated entry vestibules so they project out from the building.

Deciding whether or not to have a basement is an early design decision. Most houses in southern Canada have basements. Basements provide a solid foundation against frost movement, a location for heating appliances and increasingly, usable living space. Chapter 9 provides detailed information on making basements suitable for living space.

Basements or ground floor work areas are especially useful in remote and northern areas where there is often a greater need for storage, work areas and repair activities. However, crawl spaces may be more practical because of the deeper frost penetration in northern regions, and high water tables in some areas. In permafrost areas, basements are possible only in unusual circumstances, and open crawl spaces are common. In southern areas, bi-level designs or units with basements are usually cost-effective since they add considerable space at a marginal cost, provided there are no unusual soil conditions. Basements should not be used in areas with high water tables or extensive bedrock under shallow soils.

The type of roof is another important design consideration. The conventional approach is to construct a pitched roof with prefabricated raised-heel or drop-chord trusses, but there are other alternatives that allow for increased insulation and reduce lumber use. Scissor trusses or truss rafters can be used to build cathedral ceilings with full insulation and roof ventilation space. Cathedral ceilings require careful consideration of the relationship of interior partitions to the ceiling, the effect of an open plan on the occupants' lifestyle and the layout and operation of mechanical systems.

Passive solar energy through windows-which typically accounts for 15% of an average home's heating-can provide up to 40% of a home's heat in a well-designed house without compromising lifestyle or causing overheating or glare.

Design considerations include: good orientation; proper window selection (particularly important with the new glazings); suitable floor plans; appropriate shading; an increase in house mass; and a distribution system to circulate heat.

Window selection requires special attention to size, air leakage and glazing type. New glazings can control both heat loss and gain. Window selection should be based on the requirements of Canadian Standards Association (CSA) Standard A-440 and ENERGY STAR® recommendations. For detailed information about window performance and selection, see Chapter 13. Quality windows that are installed properly will lessen the potential for discomfort from overheating, drafts, or radiation of heat from an occupant's body to the cold window surface. To obtain maximum benefits from solar energy, about 50 to 60% of the total window area should face within 30 degrees of due south (Figure 3.3). Requirements for ventilation or views should also be taken into account. In addition:

- The area of non-south-facing windows should be reduced, and high performance windows should be used.

- Fixed windows are available with better seasonal performance than that of an R-20 wall, providing a net heat gain over the heating season.

- Sloped glass and skylights should be triple-glazed and equipped with low-E (low-emissivity) coatings and inert gas fill. Insulating spacers are also recommended.

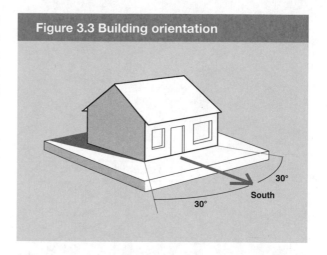

Figure 3.3 Building orientation

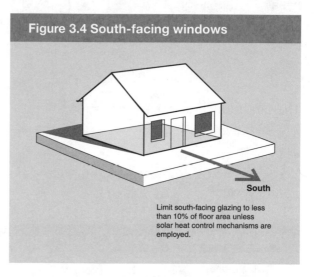

Figure 3.4 South-facing windows

South

Limit south-facing glazing to less than 10% of floor area unless solar heat control mechanisms are employed.

The orientation, window area, and the ability of the glass to transfer heat (the solar heat gain coefficient) determine how much solar heat enters the home. Thermal mass is provided by materials able to absorb and store solar heat during the day and release it overnight. A standard wood-frame house has enough thermal mass so that the south facing glazing area can be 6 to 9% of the total floor area without risk of overheating.

This amount of south-facing glazing will represent significant solar heating (Figure 3.4). If larger glass areas are used, increased mass is needed to absorb the solar heat. Proper window selection will reduce overheating (too much heat can be as much of a problem as too little heat) and reduce heat loss at night.

CANADIAN HOME BUILDERS' ASSOCIATION

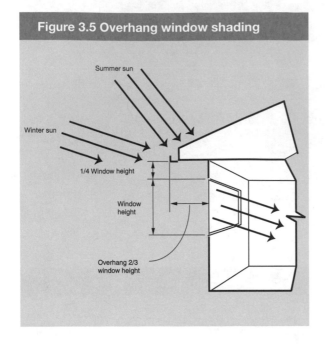

Figure 3.5 Overhang window shading

Summer sun

Winter sun

1/4 Window height

Window height

Overhang 2/3 window height

The admittance of solar energy into a house can be regulated by:

- Selecting window glass that meets design requirements for visible light, solar gain and R-value.

- Complementing the window selection by designing overhangs above the windows to shade the glass when solar heat is not desired. Figure 3.5 shows how overhangs can be used to shade windows from summer sun and admit winter sun for solar heat gain. South-facing windows are relatively easy to protect with overhangs. East and west-facing windows are more difficult to shade because of the lower sun angle during the mornings and late afternoons, which makes horizontal overhangs ineffective.

- Orienting the building to regulate heat gain and maximize natural lighting for both summer and winter (Figure 3.6).

- Using exterior louvers, screens, latticework, awnings and deciduous trees.

Internal window shading devices work to some extent, but are less effective than exterior shading devices because the solar radiation enters the building before it is blocked.

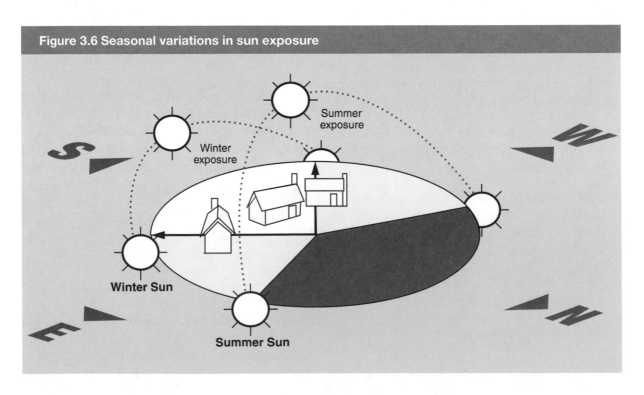

Figure 3.6 Seasonal variations in sun exposure

S

W

Summer exposure

Winter exposure

Winter Sun

Summer Sun

E

N

3.5.2 Layout and floor planning

A functional floor plan has several basic features:

- The efficient use of space in each room (use scale drawings of furniture to assess the proposed layout);

- A minimum number of circulation paths;

- A progression from common to private areas;

- A noise management plan;

- The location of hallways, utility rooms, bathrooms, etc. on the north side of the home; and,

- The appropriate use of passive solar gains and daylighting.

For custom-built homes, builders can query customers about their existing house or apartment to determine whether room size and layout is appropriate. The new design should improve on the areas they feel are too large or too small in their current home.

Beyond the purely functional requirements, aesthetic and comfort factors should be considered. The layout should exploit the best views. Rooms such as the living and family areas should be located on the south side of the building to get the most benefit from passive solar gains and daylighting (Figure 3.7). The layout of rooms and spaces is especially important in northern locations where winters are long.

CMHC studies have revealed consumers' willingness to trade overall house size for more compact, better-designed and better-appointed spaces.

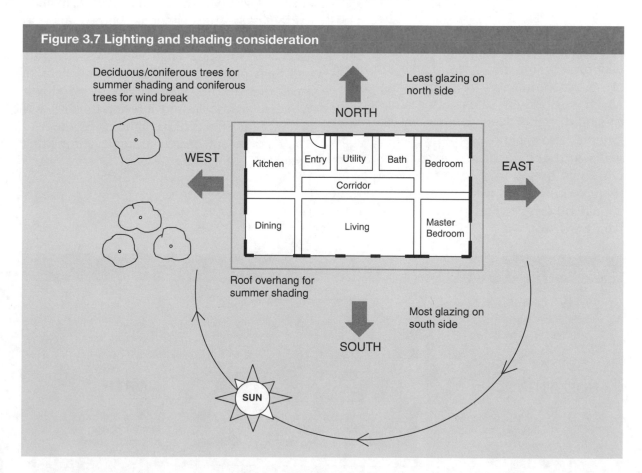

Figure 3.7 Lighting and shading consideration

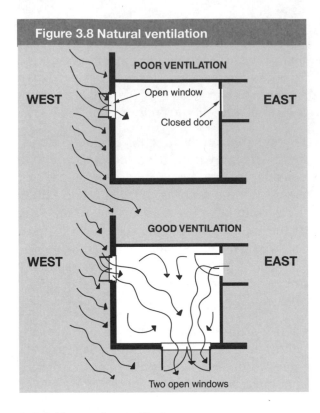

Figure 3.8 Natural ventilation

POOR VENTILATION

WEST — Open window — EAST

Closed door

GOOD VENTILATION

WEST — EAST

Two open windows

3.5.3 Natural ventilation

Where possible, a house should be oriented and windows located and sized to take advantage of natural ventilation from prevailing winds, which is especially valuable for summertime cooling. The effectiveness of natural ventilation schemes also depends on the layout of partition walls and the location of corresponding windows and doors for cross-ventilation (Figure 3.8). Windows on the leeward side should be larger than the windows on the windward side.

A solar chimney Figure 3.9 is another way of improving natural ventilation by using the natural stack effect of heating air. The air is heated using passive solar energy and the air flows upwards in a vertical shaft, drawing the warm air out of the building. The solar chimney has been used for centuries in Europe and the Middle East.

However, natural ventilation does have limited applications because it is unconditioned fresh air, and also due to the severe climate conditions experienced in most areas for the bulk of the year. This is why mechanical ventilation is a very important part of the design. Detailed information about ventilation is provided in Chapter 18.

3.5.4 Lighting

Good house design allows for high levels of natural lighting, particularly in areas that are normally occupied during the daytime. In high-use areas such as kitchens, bathrooms and central hallways, energy-efficient lighting such as LED technology. High windows, skylights and light pipes can provide natural light to areas that are not well served by windows. White or light-coloured interior finishes will enhance the effects of daylighting. Figure 3.10 illustrates several design strategies for making use of natural lighting.

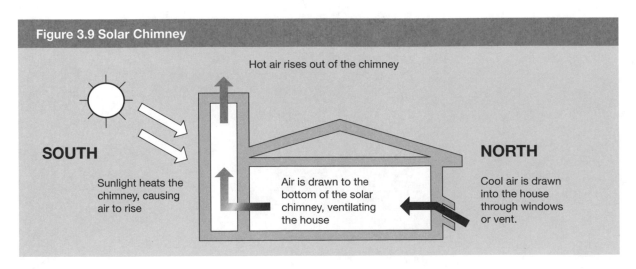

Figure 3.9 Solar Chimney

Hot air rises out of the chimney

SOUTH

Sunlight heats the chimney, causing air to rise

Air is drawn to the bottom of the solar chimney, ventilating the house

NORTH

Cool air is drawn into the house through windows or vent.

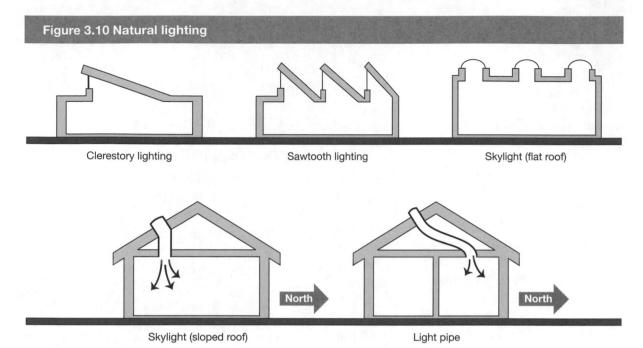

Figure 3.10 Natural lighting

Clerestory lighting   Sawtooth lighting   Skylight (flat roof)

North

North

Skylight (sloped roof)   Light pipe

3.5.5 Privacy and security

Privacy and security are two other factors that should be taken into consideration when designing a house. Privacy can be maximized by orienting the house on the lot to shield yards and decks from the street and other houses as much as possible, and through the judicious use of trees, shrubs, hedges and fences.

Security has become an increasingly important issue in recent years. Home automation can play a role in increasing safety and security (Chapter 23). Exterior doors and windows accessible from the ground are required to have hardware that cannot be forced open. Patio doors should be equipped with a bar that prevents the door from being opened when the bar is in place. Basement windows can be protected with grills (that do not interfere with egress where there are basement bedrooms). Some insurance companies require such measures in urban areas. Exterior doors should be located in a manner that makes them visible to the street or to adjacent homes. Doors should be fitted with glazed panels or viewing holes to permit occupants to determine who is at the door before it is opened.

Solid-core exterior doors should be used and be equipped with deadbolts with 25 mm (1 in.) minimum throw. Many wood panel doors do not provide acceptable security. Door hinges should have screws at least 25 mm (1 in.) long in the door, and 31 mm (1-1/4 in.) in the frame. The framing around door openings should include solid blocking at lock height on both sides of the opening. Walls around doors should be covered with plywood or OSB sheathing to prevent jamb spreading whereby pry bars are pressed against the door to increase the opening and render the lock ineffective.

Exterior lighting can also be used to help make the house more secure. Fixtures with switches and motion sensors rather than the dusk-to-dawn variety reduce electricity consumption. It may be appropriate to also provide an alarm system. For best results, a security expert should be consulted.

3.6 Housing Accessibility

The Canadian population is aging – by the year 2030, an estimated one in four Canadians will be over age 65. More than 12% of the population has some form of activity limitation, and the incidence of disabilities increases with age. Because much of the Canadian housing stock has not been designed to accommodate the needs of people with disabilities, even basic activities such as entering a home, moving from one floor to another, preparing meals, using the bathroom or operating kitchen appliances may be difficult.

Homes constructed today are those that many Canadians will be living in as they age. Stairs, kitchens, bathrooms, bedrooms, storage space, windows, and entrances will all require modifications for an aging population. Many of these modifications-grab bars in bathrooms, accessible bathtubs and showers, continuous hand railings on stairs, ramps or stair lifts, main-floor bedrooms, accessible kitchen cupboards and counters- are much less

expensive when planned during the design stage than when required in a retrofit.

CMHC has developed design aids and information on housing that is adaptable over time. This approach is often referred to as Flex Housing or aging-in-place design.

3.6.1 Design principles

Building for the aging or disabled often requires only minor modification to current designs. The ground floor of a two-storey building should contain a living room, a kitchen, at least one bedroom, and a complete bathroom that is fully accessible to a person using a manually operated wheelchair. Occupants must also be able to access the main entrance of the house from a parking or drop-off area.

Figure 3.11 Accessible kitchen

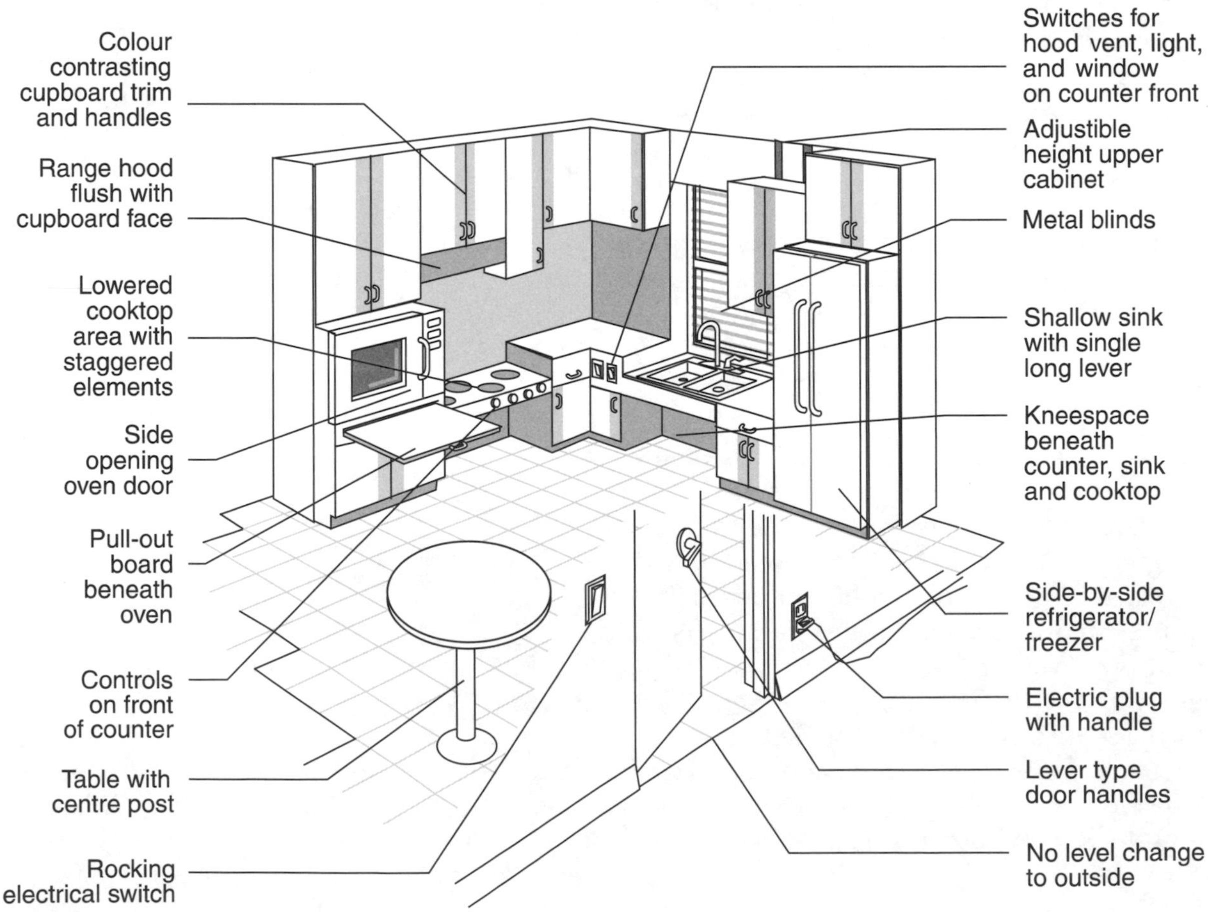

Colour contrasting cupboard trim and handles

Range hood flush with cupboard face

Lowered cooktop area with staggered elements

Side opening oven door

Pull-out board beneath oven

Controls on front of counter

Table with centre post

Rocking electrical switch

Switches for hood vent, light, and window on counter front

Adjustable height upper cabinet

Metal blinds

Shallow sink with single long lever

Kneespace beneath counter, sink and cooktop

Side-by-side refrigerator/ freezer

Electric plug with handle

Lever type door handles

No level change to outside

Safety and independence through accessibility are key points. Garages can be modified to allow for wheelchair unloading and to provide a sheltered entrance to the house. Wheelchair-accessible ramps can be integrated into conventional house design. Entrance doors can be upgraded to include wireless entry systems, flush thresholds and lowered door viewers. Security systems can be installed with built-in speakers and a siren in case of fire, break-in or other emergency. A wheelchair lift in the staircase can provide access to other floors, and a continuous smooth handrail can provide support and guidance.

Windows should be adequately sized and located low enough to view the outside from both seated and standing positions. Motorized window controls and casement windows with large handles can facilitate operation. Swing doors with a low threshold or sliding patio doors with recessed thresholds can provide easy access to the exterior. Skylights may be equipped with a special pole or motorized controls enabling them to be opened easily.

Slightly wider hallways and doorways and a well-thought-out, open floor plan will allow access to all rooms. Levered door handles, rocker light switches and electrical outlets at locations and heights accessible to everyone are simple design modifications. Installing cabinets with full-extension drawers and shelves, lower upper cabinets, and adjustable rod and shelf heights in closets, as well as providing knee space under sinks and lowered counters and workspaces will better accommodate the needs of individuals in wheelchairs. Some features, such as wider doors and hallways, can be built into any home at moderate cost and can increase future saleability.

A good accessible kitchen floor plan (Figure 3.11) will avoid through-traffic in the work area. Countertops and the cook-top area should provide a choice of work surface height to allow both seated and standing access to work areas. Cabinet doors can be side-hinged or sliding with "D" handles. Cabinets may incorporate valence

lighting. As well, a number of options are available in appliances such as front- or side-mounted controls, or side-opening wall ovens.

The entire bathroom should be designed as a wet area. The floor of the shower area should be continuous with the rest of the bathroom floor.

Various technological options are becoming available for people with disabilities. These include high-intensity task lighting and lever-handle or touchless faucets. Also available are "right-height" toilets which are higher and easier to mount and dismount, bidet seats and decorative grab bars that double as towel bars.

Stairs should have solid risers and treads, which should be painted or carpeted in contrasting colours. Visually or tactile contrasting finishes on nosings and landings make stairs more visible and easier to navigate. Non-glare flooring and contrasting colours throughout a home make it more accessible for the visually impaired.

Home security systems are easily converted to incorporate options for occupants with hearing limitations. Smoke detectors can activate a large strobe light with 'wake and warn' efficiency virtually identical to normal siren-type alarms, and doorbell chimes can incorporate a light.

3.7 Design Considerations for Multi-unit Buildings

The construction of multi-unit housing is specialized and requires enhanced knowledge about provisions for fire and sound control. Multi-unit buildings tend to lose considerable heat through thermal bridges. Many of these thermal bridges can be avoided, or their effects minimized, if they are recognized at the design stage.

- Masonry, steel and concrete conduct heat readily. Design vertical fire separations as firewalls only if required by code. Firewalls expose more surface area to the outdoor environment (Figure 3.12). Also, some insulation materials cannot be used in firewalls because of combustibility.

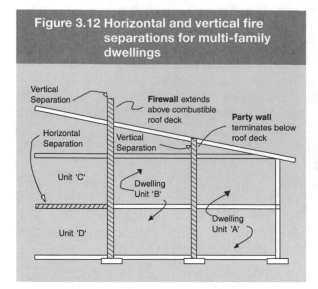

Figure 3.12 Horizontal and vertical fire separations for multi-family dwellings

- Thermal bridges such as cantilevered slabs that extend beyond the exterior walls to form balconies should be avoided.

- Design party walls to minimize heat loss, noise transmission, odour and air leakage.

Many designers use computer simulation software to assess options. These programs can help identify the best energy design options for the building envelope and the heating, cooling, and ventilation system sizing and selection.

3.7.1 Sound transmission

Sound control in multi-unit residential construction is a critical design factor-it has a significant bearing on occupant privacy and satisfaction. Design for sound privacy includes careful consideration of floor plan layouts including the locations of windows and doors, the provision of buffer zones between active, noisy areas such as living rooms and quiet zones such as bedrooms, and the location of windows and exhaust vents to prevent noise flanking (Figure 3.13) from one unit to another. In multi-unit buildings, noisy areas in one unit should be located away from quiet areas in the unit beside, above or below.

All construction assemblies separating one unit from another should have a minimum sound transmission classification (STC) rating of 50 dB (see Section 2.4.1) and 55 dB where a dwelling unit is located next to an elevator shaft or refuse chute.

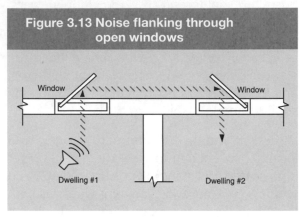

Figure 3.13 Noise flanking through open windows

3.7.2 Sound control

In 2015 changes were made to the National Building Code of Canada (NBC) in relation to sound transmission. Previous editions of the NBC focused the sound transmission requirements on laboratory rating of the separating assembly, rather than the performance of the system. This encouraged an over-simplified design approach and resulted in investment in the wrong elements. This design approach failed to provide a minimum level of performance necessary to protect occupants from noise. These provisions relied on the Sound Transmission Class (STC) ratings which account for sound transmitted directly through the assemblies. However sound transferred by other, indirect paths are known as flanking paths.

A new metric of Apparent Sound Transmission Class (ASTC) was introduced in 2015 to address this. The ASTC is the sum of all flanking sound transmission paths (indirect paths) and the direct sound transmission path. The ASTC ratings better relate to what is heard by occupants and address the performance of the complete assembly. One of the key features of the ASTC compliance paths is a provision that allows for field testing of the assemblies to demonstrate that the Code was met. This makes it easier for builders to resolve disputes related to this. To support ASTC ratings uptake, NRC developed a web application called SoundPATHS which models the direct and flanking sound transmission and calculates the ASTC. At the time of updating this Manual it is available only for wood-frame construction with the intent that other types of construction will be added later.

Adoption of the NBC by the provinces occurs sometimes several years after its publication. As such many builders many not be in a position to use the ASTC rating at this time. For that reason, the "old" approach to meeting the sound transmission requirements is also presented in this edition of the Manual. If the Building Code in your province now uses ASTC ratings, consider what follows in this section to be a history lesson.

Pre-2015 Code Requirements

Two noise transmission indicators, sound transmission class (STC) and impact insulation class (IIC), help designers select appropriate assemblies. The National Building Code of Canada (NBC) includes requirements for airborne sound transmission for the wall and floor assemblies that separate suites in multi-family construction. It does not include requirements for impact sounds between suites, nor does it address airborne sound

from the street outside. Recent testing has provided combined sound and fire resistance ratings for many common wood assemblies. (See Appendix A of the NBC.) Figures 2.18 and 2.19 (Chapter 2) show the ratings for some wall and floor assemblies typically used for multi-unit construction.

Airborne sound is produced by sources like voices and music. The STC is a measure of the average noise reduction in decibels for speech-like sounds that pass through an assembly. An assembly with a high STC rating has good sound attenuation characteristics. The most common situations requiring STC ratings are:

- Party walls between residential suites;

- Walls between public corridors and residential suites;

- Floor assemblies between residential suites; and

- Walls between residential suites and elevators, garbage chutes and service rooms.

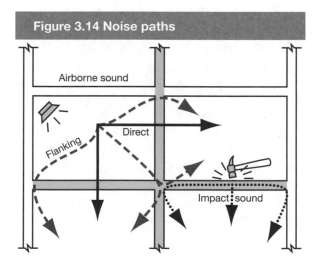

Figure 3.14 Noise paths

Table 3.1 Minimum recommended STC and IIC ratings

Assemblies	NBC Required STC	Best Practice Recommended STC	Best Practice Recommended IIC
Party walls or corridor walls	50	55	–
Bare party floors	50	55	55
Carpeted party floors	50	55	65
Elevator shafts	55	60	–

High STC ratings do not necessarily provide satisfaction for building occupants for two reasons. First, the *flanking* of airborne sound around an assembly can reduce the effectiveness of an STC rating so that an occupant in an adjoining unit experiences an *apparent* STC that can be significantly lower than the STC rating of the separating assembly. Second, impacts such as foot traffic or dropped objects can also cause sound to migrate through construction materials. Although the code does not specify levels for impact ratings, it is nevertheless important to reduce impact noise because it can be a serious source of disturbance for residents of multi-unit buildings. Figure 3.14 shows direct and flanking paths for both airborne and impact noise between adjoining units.

Because of flanking, performance can be poorer than the ratings of assemblies alone would indicate. For this reason, it is important to reduce flanking and to specify assemblies with STC and IIC ratings higher than the minimum requirements, as added protection. Table 3.1 summarizes the minimum and recommended STC and IIC ratings listed in CMHC's *Fire and Sound Control in Wood-Frame Multi-Family Buildings*.

The use of absorptive materials, additional gypsum board and resilient channels (see Figure 2.18) are typical methods for increasing the STC ratings of walls and floors for airborne sound. For floors, the addition of mass in the form of concrete topping increases the STC rating and can also reduce flanking, provided the topping is isolated from the framing. However, if flanking is the problem, increasing the STC rating of an assembly may only provide minimal improvement and may not be cost-effective. The impact rating of floors is typically improved by using an isolation pad to separate hard floor surfaces from the floor structure.

Flanking paths have much more serious consequences for impact sound than for airborne sound because impact transmits more vibration energy to the structure. For airborne sound insulation, the most important factor is the mass of an applied topping. For impact sound insulation, there are two important factors – the mass and the hardness of the exposed topping surface.

Providing sound privacy in multi-unit construction requires careful attention to detail during the design stage. It also requires careful construction to ensure that the integrity of the design is not compromised. For more information, refer to *Fire and Sound Control in Wood-Frame Multi-Frame Buildings*, Canada Mortgage and Housing Corporation. For both new construction and retrofitting, engaging an acoustical consultant can be a cost-saving investment in the long term.

Units of Sound

Measuring sound is quite complicated, and the units used to measure sound are confusing. To determine how loud a sound is requires consideration of several factors.

The first factor is the intensity of sound, by which is meant the Sound Pressure Level (SPL). This is the force exerted on the air by the sound wave. The force required for us to perceive a sound is very small, and is measured in microPascals (μPa.) of pressure.

The second factor is the sound's frequency. A young, healthy human ear can perceive sounds in frequency ranges from about 20 Hz (vibrations per second) to 20,000 Hz. Our ears are especially sensitive to frequencies in the 3,000 to 4,000 Hz. range, and we often perceive sounds in this range as being louder than their intensity would normally justify.

A third factor depends on the individual. As we age and our hearing apparatus deteriorates, we become less sensitive to higher frequencies, and perceive them as less loud.

The transmission of sound is measured in decibels (dB), which is a measure of intensity. The dB unit is not exclusive to sound, it is also widely used in electronics, signaling and communications. Decibels are actually a ratio between the intensity of different sounds, and, because of the huge range of sounds we can hear, are recorded on a logarithmic scale. The difference between a sound we can barely perceive and one which hurts our ears, is in the millions of magnitudes, so the logarithmic scale is used (i.e. using a base 10 log, 10 = 1, 101 100 = 2, 102, 1,000 = 3, 103, etc.).

Since dB measure the intensity of sound, these are the units used to measure sound transmission. The intensity of the sound will diminish as it moves through building materials.

When selecting fans, we are concerned about loudness, so a different measure, sones, is used. One sone is defined as the loudness of a tone of 1,000 Hz at an intensity of 40 dB. At frequencies other than 1,000 Hz, sones are calibrated to account for how we hear. Therefore, a sone rating takes into account all three factors. Generally, an increase in intensity of 10dB at 1,000 Hz doubles the loudness, so 2 sones is twice as loud as 1 sone.

Sone ratings are increasingly important as our houses become more air tight. Air is the medium through which sound travels. If air flow is reduced, so is sound transmission. This means houses are quieter, so a noisy fan can be heard better against a quieter background. The sone rating will give you a measure of the loudness of the fan motor. It does not take into account how the fan is mounted. Pay careful attention to mounting fans to ensure the vibration from the fan motor doesn't increase the loudness.

3.7.3 Airtightness

In addition to the air leakage paths found in detached houses, the following leakage paths have been noted in multi-unit buildings:

- Lack of or ineffective firestopping;

- Furring chases;

- Unblocked cavities in hollow masonry walls;

- Electrical penetrations and other service penetrations through party walls;

- Stairs adjacent to party walls;

- Doorways into common areas;

- Pocket doors in partitions that connect to party walls; and

- Adjoining pipe chases.

Air leakage greatly affects energy performance, structural durability, occupant comfort, controlling cooking and odours from adjoining units, and noise infiltration. Therefore, designs should be used that will reduce air leakage from these areas as much as possible.

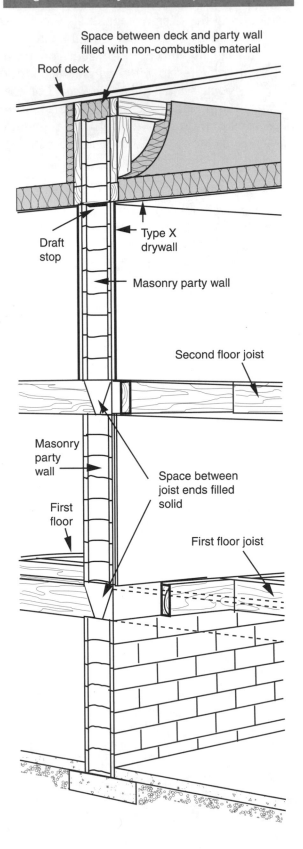

Figure 3.15 Party wall fire separation

3.7.4 Fire separation

In a residential building where no dwelling unit is located above another, for example, a townhouse, a party wall on a property line need only be a fire separation with a one-hour fire-resistance rating. It does not have to be a firewall. Continuous protection must be provided from the top of the footings to the underside of the roof sheathing. If a gap is left between the top of the party wall and the roof sheathing, it must be tightly sealed with non-combustible material (Figure 3.15).

The assemblies described in Table 3.2 have a fire resistance rating of about one hour. Actual ratings for typical assemblies can be determined from the National Building Code of Canada (Appendix A) or tests conducted by a recognized testing agency according to CAN4-5101, Standard Methods of Fire Endurance Tests of Building Construction and Materials.

Table 3.2 Examples of assemblies with at least a one-hour fire resistance rating and an STC of 50 or more

	No.	Assembly	Finishes[1,2,3]
Walls	1)	150 mm (6 in.) poured concrete wall	Both sides sealed with two coats of paint
	2)	140 mm (5.5 in.) hollow concrete block wall, 25 mm (1 in.) mineral fibre insulation	12.7 mm (1/2 in.) gypsum wallboard, resilient channels on at least one side
	3)	Single row wood stud wall, 38 x 89 mm (2 x 4 in.) studs @ 400 mm (16 in.) o.c., 75 mm (3 in.) mineral fibre insulation	Double layer of 12.7 mm (1/2 in.) gypsum wallboard each side, resilient channels each side
	4)	Staggered wood stud wall, 38 x 89 mm (2 x 4 in.) studs @ 400 mm (16 in.) or 600 mm (24 in.) o.c. on common 38 x 140 mm (2 x 6 in.) bottom plate, 75 mm (3 in.) mineral fibre insulation	Double layer of 12.7 mm (1/2 in.) Type X gypsum wallboard each side, resilient channels each side
	5)	Double row wood stud wall, 38 x 89 mm (2 x 4 in.) studs @ 400 mm (16 in.) o.c. on separate bottom plates spaced 25 mm (l in.) apart, 75 mm (3 in.) mineral fibre insulation	15.9 mm (5/8 in.) Type X gypsum wallboard, resilient channels each side
	6)	Single row metal stud wall, 90 mm (3-1/2 in.) studs @ 400 mm (16 in.) o.c., 75 mm (3 in.) mineral fibre insulation	Double layer of 12.7 mm (1/2 in.) gypsum wallboard each side, resilient channels each side
Floors	7)	130 mm (5 in.) reinforced concrete floor	None
	8)	Open web steel floor joists, 50 mm (2 in.) thick concrete deck	15.9 mm (5/8 in.) Type X gypsum wallboard ceiling, furring channels @ 600 mm (24 in.) o.c.
	9)	Wood floor joists @ 400 mm (16 in.) o.c., 15.9 mm (5/8 in.) plywood or OSB subfloor, 50 mm (2 in.) lightweight concrete topping, 75 mm (3 in.) mineral fibre insulation	Double layer of 12.7 mm (1/2 in.) Type X gypsum wallboard ceiling, resilient channels

Notes:
1. The designated finishes are required for fire ratings of one hour. If a lesser fire-resistance rating is desired, changes in finishes are possible.
2. Sound resistance of wall assemblies can be improved by increasing the thickness of the wallboard finishes indicated. However, four (4) layers of wallboard appear to be the optimal limit.
3. As indicated, floor finishes have not been included. To assist in reducing impact noise, carpets and floating floors can be considered.
4. For more details, see NBC Table A-9.10.3.1.

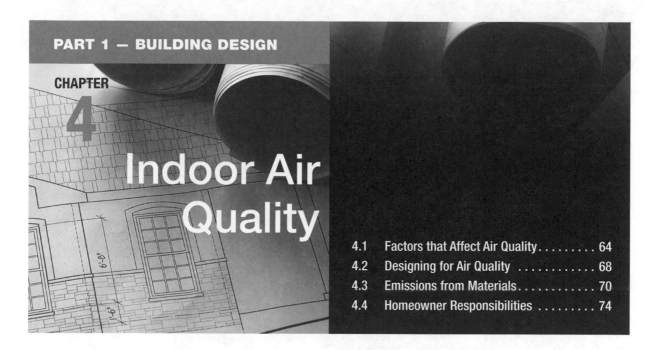

Most people spend up to 60% of their time at home, so it is essential that housing provide a healthy living environment. Although there have been significant advances in the science of indoor air quality, it remains a complex subject, even more complicated by the fact that different people are susceptible to varying concentration levels of volatile compounds and particles. For a few contaminants, the link between contaminant levels and health has become obvious, and health-related guidelines have been provided by recognized authorities. For many others, it remains difficult to predict which concentrations and exposures might lead to adverse health effects.

People encounter hundreds of contaminants in indoor environments, but generally in low concentrations; by themselves, these contaminants are mostly considered harmless, especially at short exposure times. The big question is how these different compounds and particles together affect human health in the long term. Some contaminants in indoor air can be perceived as odour-for example, the musty smell emitted by mould-but others give off no odour at all. In general, minimizing the sources of air quality problems is essential to provide a healthy indoor environment. This is especially true for people who are hypersensitive, and those who have allergies and asthma. Lower concentrations may also reduce the onset of asthma and allergies.

Indoor air quality is an important design consideration. Using the R-2000 program requirements as a base, CHBA's Net Zero Technical Requirements intend to improve air quality by means of ventilation, air filtration and material selection. The National Building Code of Canada (NBC) stipulates ventilation requirements so that harmful components are flushed to the outside. This chapter provides information on issues relating to indoor air quality (IAQ) and outlines practical steps that can be taken to improve it.

4.1 Factors that Affect Air Quality

4.1.1 Relative humidity

Relative humidity (RH) was discussed in Chapter 2 as a factor affecting comfort. It also deserves mention in this chapter as a factor that affects health. Air that is too dry can result in chapped skin, bleeding noses and respiratory problems for some people. Air that is too humid can cause mould growth, especially if condensation or conditions close to it occur.

Building design needs to allow for a means to remove excessive moisture, especially from point locations (such as bathrooms) and generally allow the indoor environment to have a relative humidity in the 30 to 50 % range. (The RH demands may have to be lowered in cold climates to a level where window condensation is not a problem.) The homeowner needs to be aware of the relative humidity level, and take steps to correct it through humidification or dehumidification. Wet rooms, such as the kitchen, bathrooms and laundry should have dedicated exhaust systems either by means of an exhaust fan or a direct connection to the HRV (heat recovery ventilator) or ERV (energy recovery ventilator).

4.1.2 Airborne particulate matter

Airborne particulates cover a wide range of diameters, from visible dust (> 5 µm or 1/200 mm) to "inhalable" particles (< 100 µm or 1/10 mm) to nanoparticles (0.001 to 0.1 µm)

(Figure 4.1). "Respirable" particles (< ~3.5 µm) can penetrate deep into the lungs. Health concerns now focus on the "fine" fraction of particulate matter (≤ 2.5 µm or "PM2.5").

Figure 4.1 Terminology and properties for particulates

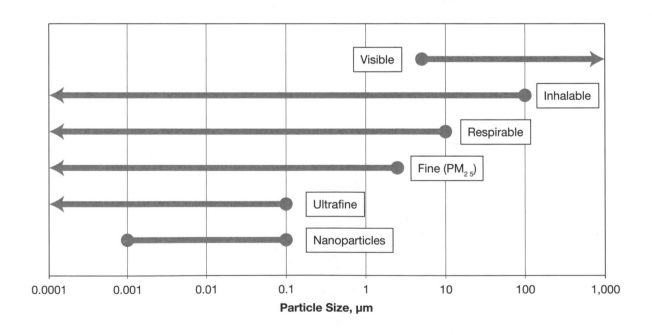

Particles larger than about 100 μm will settle rapidly and deposit on surfaces like carpets, flooring and furniture. However, larger airborne particles can be re-suspended by human activities, and broken down again to inhalable particulate matter. Small particles tend to agglomerate to larger particles, increasing their settling rates and reducing their respirability. Particles are also excellent sorbents and thus carriers for organic compounds, especially the less volatile ones (semi-volatile organic compounds, SVOCs). Thus, the inhalation of fine particles can lead to deposition of SVOCs in the lungs.

There are three critical approaches for reducing dust in indoor environments. First, the house needs to be tightly constructed to reduce air infiltration. Infiltration is unintentional air intake through defects (holes) in the building envelope. In a poorly sealed house, undesired airborne particles from the outdoor air can be introduced. Outdoor dust is typically comprised of pollen, other plant material, airborne mould spores and bacteria, fine particles of soil and stone dust, and combustion products from vehicles, industrial emissions, etc. The composition, concentration and size range, and therefore also the health effects, vary with the location, season and weather conditions, and proximity to local sources. This is one reason why it is so important to build and maintain the house to be as airtight as practical. Keeping the contaminants outside is better than trying to clean the contaminants once they are inside.

Second, incoming fresh air should come from a single source so that filtration can take place before it is distributed throughout the house. Section 15.5 provides information about the need to design and install a system for controlling, trapping and removing dust by means of filtration. Proper design, operation and maintenance of the air filtration system are essential for reducing dust, especially for the PM2.5 fraction. Under certain circumstances, especially in order to protect allergic or hypersensitive children and adults, filtration of

supply (and return) air will be more favourable for the reduction of adverse health effects.

Third, the homeowner needs to choose or optimize activities that minimize the generation of dust. Dust can be generated inside the house by activities like cooking, hobbies, smoking, burning candles, and from other sources such as pets, fibres from clothing, drapes and furniture fabrics. In the case of an unfinished basement, concrete can be a source of dust.

Removing dust makes good sense and can be done by vacuuming or wet mopping. Sweeping and vacuuming can cause dust that was resting on a surface to become airborne. To effectively remove and capture particles, a vacuum cleaner must be equipped with a high-efficiency particulate air (HEPA) filter capable of retaining breathable particles or, in the case of central vacuum cleaners, they should be discharged directly outdoors at a location away from fresh air intakes.

Heating and ventilation systems tend to accumulate dust, both on heating coils and in the ductwork. As such, heating systems should be designed to minimize unfavourable duct runs so that dust does not accumulate. Sharp edges and bends, where dust will agglomerate, should be avoided. Relevant parts of the heating and ventilation system should be accessible for monitoring and cleaning purposes. Low temperature heating such as hot-water radiant or fan coil heating has substantial air quality benefits compared to high-temperature electric, fuel-fired, or forced-warm-air heating systems.

4.1.3 Chemical contaminants

Emissions from materials, cleaning and consumer products have a major effect on air quality. Most building materials emit a range of organic compounds. These compounds can be classified into two groups based on their volatility. Volatile organic compounds (VOC's) appear in gaseous form at room

CANADIAN HOME BUILDERS' ASSOCIATION

temperatures while semi- volatile organic compounds (SVOCs) attach to airborne and settled dust particles or surfaces. Decreased air exchange resulting from increased house air- tightness and increased use of synthetic building materials and finishes over the last 20 years means that more attention needs to be paid to reducing these emissions. The presence of some volatiles can be clearly detected by their odours while others are non-odorous at 'normal' indoor concentrations. This means that the absence of odours does necessarily mean the absence of potentially harmful contaminants. See Section 4.3 for additional information.

Formaldehyde is a volatile compound that is emitted by many different sources in indoor environments. The most relevant sources are building materials (for example, engineered wood products such as particle board and medium-density fibreboard (MDF)), consumer products, clothing, but also combustion sources like open fireplaces and tobacco smoke. Health Canada has released a guideline that sets the maximum concentration for formaldehyde at 50 ?g/m3 as an average over 8 hours.

4.1.4 Mould

Moulds are microscopic fungi. They grow on organic material and can proliferate by forming spores. Many spores have a diameter of 2-3 micrometers, so they can become and stay airborne for longer periods. Airborne mould spores enter a house through open door ways and windows, as well as via heating, ventilation and air conditioning systems. Spores in the air outside also attach themselves to other airborne particles as well as to people, pets, and clothing.

When mould grows on building materials, the resulting spores may become airborne and trigger allergic reactions in susceptible people. The inhalation of mould spores causes various adverse health effects. Any type of mould growing in indoor environments is undesirable.

Health Canada has a residential guideline (www.hc-sc.gc.ca/ewh-semt/pubs/air/mould-moisissure-eng.php) recommending:

- Thoroughly cleaning any visible or concealed mould growing in residential buildings; and,

- Controlling humidity and diligently repairing any water damage to prevent mould growth.

Mould needs oxygen, water, organic nutrients (food) and a suitable temperature range to grow, typically between 0 and 38°C (32 and 100°F). Mould-growth factors that can be controlled practically in a heated building are the availability of water and nutrients. Another factor is time; mould growth is very slow and takes several days to become established. If condensation or droplets are quickly removed (for example, after showers), the chance of proliferation will be diminished. As soon as mould spores come in contact with sufficient available moisture over sufficiently long time periods, mould growth can be triggered. Mould growth can occur in building cavities that are not visible.

Mould can grow on nearly all organic materials, including paper and paper products, cardboard, ceiling tiles, wood, and wood products. Other materials such as paint, wallpaper, some insulation materials, drywall, carpet, fabric, and upholstery, even dust, may also support mould growth. It can even grow on glass or aluminium, which are non-organic materials, if a thin (often invisible) layer of organic matter (e.g., from kitchen vapours) is present.

Basements are often constructed of concrete, a material that gives off excess moisture as it cures. In addition, concrete has the ability to wick moisture, and to absorb and release it again. Chapter 9 deals extensively with keeping basements dry by preventing leakage, and moisture deposition in the building envelope via air leakage and diffusion. Indeed, all the chapters in Part 2 – Building Envelope deal extensively with reducing the movement of water and water vapour into and out of the building envelope.

Bathrooms are a high source of moisture. Often mould growth can be found on bathroom window frames, even if the frames are made of non-organic materials. The "food" in these cases is coming from the organics in common house dust which has accumulated on the window frame. In these "wet" locations, using triple-glazed windows will improve the insulating value of the window, thereby reduce condensation, which helps reduce the incidence of mould. It is important to use sealants especially formulated for interior surfaces exposed to high moisture and tested for being resistant to mould.

4.1.5 Combustion gases

Whenever there is negative pressure inside a house, there is a risk that combustion gases from naturally vented appliances can be drawn into the living space rather than out the chimney or exhaust (see Chapter 15).

Several types of by-products are of major concern: carbon monoxide, nitrogen dioxide, and organic pyrolysis products from incomplete combustion. Carbon monoxide is the product of incomplete combustion and is addressed by following standard safety procedures in installing and operating combustion appliances. Nitrogen dioxide is a product of normal combustion and can be introduced into the indoor air stream through unvented gas stoves and heaters. Significant amounts can be released into the air simply through the operation of pilot lights on gas appliances. The first step towards improvement is to use appliances with electronic ignition and to ensure that the appliance is properly vented to the outdoors.

Gas-fired kitchen stoves are unvented appliances; spillage from these stoves can be reduced but not be completely eliminated. The very design of gas stoves ensures that products of combustion will be introduced into the house every time the devices are used. Proper operation means using the exhaust fan whenever the stove is operating and even then,

the capture ratio of any range hood will never be 100%. As houses approach the air tightness levels of Net Zero Energy Housing, the need for continuous, balanced, mechanical ventilation becomes a key element of design for healthy indoor environments.

Houses that are energy-efficient minimize the effects of combustion gases because smaller heating appliances can be used, and further improvements can be made by combining functions such as space and water heating (see Chapter 16).

Unvented gas fireplaces are used in the United States but are not permitted in Canada because of spillage of combustion gases into the living spa.

4.1.6 Soil gas (radon)

Radon is a colourless, odourless, radioactive gas that occurs naturally in the environment. It comes from the natural breakdown of uranium in soils and rocks. In the open air, the amount of radon gas is usually very small and docs not pose a health risk. However, in some confined spaces like basements where air exchange is poor, radon can accumulate to relatively high levels and become a health hazard. An increase in exposure to radon has been associated with an increased risk of lung cancer, depending on concentration and exposure time.

Radon is measured in becquerels (a measure of the release of radioactivity) per cubic metre (Bq/m3). Health agencies have established the naturally occurring level of radon in outdoor air to be about 10 Bq/m3. However, levels can occasionally reach several times this amount, sometimes only for short periods of time. Indoor radon levels typically range from about 30 to 100 Bq/m3 with an average concentration of 45 Bq/m3. However, in some locations, radon can readily exceed 200 Bq/m3, and in a few cases levels have been found as high as 3,000 Bq/m3. Health Canada has developed a guideline (Canadian Radon Guideline) that recommends remedial measures wherever the average annual radon concentration is likely to exceed 200 Bq/m3 in the normal occupancy area.

CANADIAN HOME BUILDERS' ASSOCIATION

Radon gas can move through small spaces in the soil and rock under a house and seep in through earth floors, cracks in concrete, sumps, joints and basement drains. Concrete-block walls are particularly porous to radon, and radon trapped in water from wells can be released into the air when the water is used. The basement tends to be the area of highest radon accumulation, due primarily to the operation of the furnace, which tends to depressurize the basement. Radon entry into the home through the water supply is not believed to be a primary source, and builders are encouraged to control radon through good sealing of the envelope and proper ventilation techniques.

For several reasons, all houses are required to have measures to reduce radon concentration, should this become necessary after construction has been completed. First, a reliable and comprehensive radon map for Canada does not exist. Second, it is possible for high radon concentrations to be present in one building while neighbouring buildings might not have elevated concentrations. Last, it is very difficult to detect problematic radon concentrations during construction. Because mitigating high radon concentrations after construction is complete could be expensive, providing provisional measures at the time of construction can increase safety and reduce overall cost.

Protection is achieved by providing a continuous air/soil gas barrier, a gas-permeable layer between the ground and the air barrier that allows for depressurization of the space below the soil gas barrier, and a sealed outlet pipe that can be connected to a power-vented exhaust should radon prove to be a problem after construction has been completed. The outlet should be clearly labelled to indicate that it is intended for the removal of radon from below the floor-on-ground.

The only way to know if radon is present is to test the house after occupancy. Testing for radon after building occupancy is the responsibility of the building owner. If the results of the test indicate an annual average concentration exceeding 200 Bq/m3, the completion of the subfloor (sub-slab) depressurization system may be necessary to reduce the radon concentration. Although not covered by code provisions, this requires that the rough-in pipe be uncapped and connected to a ventilation system exhausting to the outside.

4.2 Designing for Air Quality

Good indoor air quality can be positively affected by good design and construction. It is also influenced by choices occupants make in terms of cleaning, the selection and use of consumer products, and activities and hobbies.

The design strategies for good indoor air quality and energy efficiency are complementary; both require a well- sealed building envelope and controlled ventilation. Ventilation strategies related to indoor air quality are dealt with in Chapter 18.

The common ways to provide good air quality in homes are to:

- Select low-emitting building materials, assemblies and systems;

- Ventilate sufficiently and appropriately remove contaminants; and

- Construct a continuous air barrier to prevent the infiltration of outdoor contaminants.

Although mechanical ventilation is helpful to reduce the level of chemical contaminants, source control is the most effective and energy-efficient way to reduce contaminants, especially those with potentially adverse health effects. This is even more important for people who are sensitive to chemical contaminants.

Here are several points for consideration:

- The building site determines the ambient air quality and whether radon and other soil gases will potentially enter a building.

Typically, the builder has no control over the site, but knowing the site conditions enables the builder to take appropriate measures during the design and construction process to eliminate potential problems. Such problems include not only soil gas issues, but also site drainage, high water table, northern/southern exposure, etc.

- Careful design of heating, ventilating and air filtration systems is necessary to minimize problems related to relative humidity, particulate matter, proliferation of mould spores and combustion gases. Source ventilation is typically provided for high-humidity rooms. Additional venting may also be recommended to remove contaminants from specialized rooms such as smoking rooms, hobby rooms or home offices.

- Constructing an envelope that is airtight and provides vapour-diffusion resistance will maintain insulation values, prevent deterioration from moisture deposition, significantly reduce the possibility of mould growth, and greatly improve the durability of the building.

- Attention to basement drainage, damp-proofing and insulating will significantly reduce the possibility of mould growth.

- The separation and/or sealing of garages from living spaces will limit the ingress of automobile emissions and chemical contaminants often stored in garages, such as fuel canisters.

- Selecting materials that have the lowest or the least toxic (Volatile Organic Compounds) VOC emissions will minimize the concentration of chemical contaminants in both the short and long term:

  ◇ Use low-formaldehyde or sealed composite wood products for cabinetry

  ◇ Limit the use of area carpeting and select low-emitting carpets

  ◇ Minimize the use of materials with a high proportion of synthetics such as vinyl wall coverings, plastic baseboard and mouldings

  ◇ Use flooring adhesives with low emission characteristics

  ◇ Use low-emission duct sealants and/or tapes

  ◇ Use low VOC paints

  ◇ Use pre-finished hardwood flooring

  ◇ Use ceramic tiles

- Provide increased house ventilation during and after the installation of high-emitting materials such as caulking, coatings and carpet.

- VOC emissions from building materials, finishes and furnishings diminish over time. If rapid construction is followed quickly by occupancy, the homeowner should ventilate aggressively for an extended period to remove contaminants. Emissions from some building materials decline very slowly, sometimes only over months and years. Therefore the selection of low-emitting materials is very important.

- The builder can use improved indoor air quality as a selling feature by including information about construction features; therefore the demonstrating of usage of low-emitting building materials can be advantageous.

- Select furnaces and heat recovery ventilators that are easy to maintain and clean. Maintenance of air- handling equipment and filters will affect ultimate air quality, no matter how well-built a house is.

4.3 Emissions from Materials

Chemical emissions from building materials, finishes and furnishings can have a significant effect on air quality, particularly in the first months after construction ends. The unmistakable "new house" smell is likely attributable to volatile organic compounds (VOCs). In general, VOCs tend to decay comparatively quickly (e.g., the time for reducing the emission rate to 50% is within weeks or months), but some materials may emit VOCs for extended periods. Semi-volatile organic compounds (SVOCs) emissions, due to their low volatility, are likely to dissipate much slower, taking months or even years.

Both the type and the concentration of VOCs and SVOCs can affect health. However, direct links between health and the levels of chemicals are difficult to establish scientifically. The chemical-tolerance variability from one person to the next and the number of different compounds typically present in indoor air also plays an important role. Therefore, it is good practice to select materials that have lower chemical emissions within any category of products, and to have a ventilation strategy to reduce the level of chemical contaminants as much as possible before a house is occupied. If a house is being custom-built for clients with extreme sensitivities, special knowledge and care is required in selecting materials, and extensive pre-testing of materials may be required to ensure a suitable air quality environment.

While some materials are emitters of VOCs and SVOCs, other materials, such as drywall, can act as "sinks" – absorbing and storing emissions. However, absorbed volatiles can also be re-emitted, depending on the concentrations in the house, the RH and temperature fluctuations, etc. These materials may at least level out peak concentrations, but may extend the period during which the compounds exist indoors. This explains why it is so difficult to rid a home of odours from cigarettes or fire damage. The sink effects are more pronounced with SVOCs due to their low volatility and high adsorptivity to indoor surface materials and dust.

Chemical emissions from building materials have been the subject of extensive research. The National Research Council, in cooperation with several partners, has developed standard test methods for quantifying chemical emissions from all kinds of building materials and consumer products, and many products have been tested.

One outcome of this research is new software that designers can use to predict or influence the concentrations of VOCs in indoor air, depending on the choices and combinations in building materials, and ventilation rates and strategies. This software, called IA-QUEST, also contains a database with test emission data ("off-gassing") for 90 "target" VOCs, "abundant" VOCs and TVOCs (total VOCs) for 69 building materials commonly used in Canada. Unfortunately proprietary products cannot be named. It also provides information about specimen details and test conditions. Both the software and the user manual can be downloaded. Frequently asked questions related to the software can be found at the website below.

https://nrc.canada.ca/en/research-development/products-services/software-applications/ia-quest-indoor-air-quality-emission-simulation-tool-frequently-asked-questions

In general, selecting products that are certified as having low VOC content (for example those that carry the Environmental Choice label) or have been tested for VOC emission rates will contribute to lowered emissions and better indoor air quality.

4.3.1 Material selection

This section provides information about the VOC emission characteristics for certain groups of materials. Materials can be separated into two groups: wet and dry. Products applied wet, such as paints and sealants, typically have very high initial VOC emissions, but the rate of emission falls sharply in the first few days after application. Dry products such as carpet may have lower emission rates, but can emit for a long period of time and can also act as sinks. Careful selection is especially important for materials such as flooring and wall coverings that cover large areas.

Paint and varnish coatings

VOC emissions from liquid coatings such as paint tend to be short-term, and decline to a very small fraction of the wet emission rate within a few days or weeks. However, interior floors, walls and ceilings absorb VOCs during painting and then release them. For this reason, it is very important to use low VOC paints, ventilate well during and immediately following application, and remove "fleecy" materials from the area that will act as sinks for the emitted chemicals from the freshly painted surfaces.

VOCs are released by both solvent-based paints and water-based formulations, but water-based (acrylic-latex) paints can be produced with very little VOC content. The safest of these products are listed as "zero VOC", according to California and New Jersey standards. Most people will notice little or no smell from these within a few hours of painting. "Low VOC"-rated paints may have very limited amounts of VOCs, and are verified by programs such as the Environmental Choice label. Be cautious, however, of the definition of "VOC" used by any product that claims "zero VOC" emission.

Products with factory finishes such as pre-finished hardwood flooring tend to be low in VOC emissions, since factory curing, storage and transportation have allowed time for the emission rate to diminish.

Solid wood products

The smell of wood, especially of softwood, which contains VOCs (terpenes) is for most people pleasant, but can cause allergic reactions for others. Wood framing located behind the air/vapour barrier has little opportunity to emit VOCs into the living space, at least if the air/vapour barrier is intact. Wood framing located in floors and partition walls can emit VOCs into the liveable space, especially while lumber is adjusting to the building moisture content. Painting or varnishing wood tends to seal the wood and slow the movement of VOCs, but the coatings themselves are high emitters initially. Pressure-treated wood should be sealed when used inside the air barrier.

Engineered wood products (structural)

Engineered wood products (glulam, wood I-joists, engineered rim framing, laminated veneer lumber (LVL), cross-laminated lumber (CLT) parallel strand lumber (PSL), plywood, and oriented strand board (OSB) need to be made with water-resistant glue to ensure their structural performance in case the members or panels become wet during construction or service. These products are usually made with phenol resorcinol adhesives. These adhesives contain formaldehyde, which is held in a chemical bond and not released. Therefore, engineered wood products rated for exterior use tend to be much lower emitters than glued wood products made with adhesives suited only for dry, interior applications. Where possible, select low formaldehyde (and other VOCs) emission products that meet required structural properties.

Composite wood products (non-structural and decorative)

Many products made for interior uses such as appearance plywood, particleboard and medium density fibreboard (MDF) are usually made with urea formaldehyde (UF) adhesives. UF glues are much more economical than phenol resorcinol adhesives, but they do not have good resistance to wetting and formaldehyde will be released in much higher rates in this situation. Particleboard and MDF are often used as substrates for cabinetry components and are faced with melamine or plastic laminates, which tend to seal the board and retard the emission of formaldehyde.

Some particleboard and MDF products are manufactured that do not contain UF adhesives. Often using phenol-formaldehyde based resins, their formaldehyde emissions are much lower, but they tend to be more expensive. They include particleboard that meets the E-1 European standard or the HUD Standard, 24 CFR Part 3280.308, or panels that have all exposed surfaces sealed with an Environmental Choice-approved sealer or other low-toxicity sealer.

Wood flooring

Solid wood floors are low VOC emitters (if treated with low-emission stains or finishes) and they reduce the dust problems associated with carpets. The sanding and finishing stages affect the air quality for installers who have to protect themselves appropriately. The area to be sanded must be carefully isolated from the HVAC system, and temporary exhaust fans must be used. Good final clean-up is required to ensure these dust particles do not remain in the living space. Floor finishes should be water-dispersed urethanes. Technically they are urethane/acrylic blends. Hardening oils, solvent varnishes and acid cured oils emit VOCs for prolonged periods and are not the best choice.

Modern low-VOC urethane coatings have much improved durability compared to early formulations.

Pre-finished flooring reduces possible air quality problems in the home, because no sanding or finishing is done on site. After installation, final cleanup with a high performance HEPA (high-efficiency particulate air) filter vacuum is recommended.

Ceramic tile and terrazzo

Ceramic tile and terrazzo are low chemical emitters. However, adhesives and sealers should be chosen carefully. Cement mortars and grouts, usually modified with acrylic additives, are the safest to handle and generate the lowest pollution. If a porous tile that needs to be sealed is used, the lowest-emitting sealers are the acrylic or water-dispersed silicone types.

Carpet and carpet cushion

Carpets and carpet cushion require careful selection to reduce chemical emissions and also avoid odour perceptions later-on. Due to the pile and loops in the carpet, the surface area of the carpet is actually many times greater than the area it is covering. Carpets with synthetic fibre pile that is heat-bonded to the backing contain no latex and have lower emissions. Fibres that do not contain special stain-resistance treatments are lower in emissions as well. Some manufacturers of all-wool carpet have specifically designed product to have minimum emissions and high durability, but these are relatively expensive. Loop pile or "berber" type carpets of any fibre type wear much longer and require less maintenance than cut pile. Carpet pads made with spun synthetic or natural fibre have lower pollutant emissions than foam plastic or rubber products.

Unrolling and airing new carpet for several days before installation will reduce emissions moderately, but many carpet emissions are "semi-volatile" and are released for many months, or even years.

Fibrous carpeting readily traps dust particles, biological materials such as pet dander, and moisture. If the carpet cannot be lifted, as in wall-to-wall installations, there might be a permanent build-up in the carpet that cannot be completely removed, even by regular vacuuming and shampooing. Carpet should not be installed in areas susceptible to moisture, such as bathrooms, kitchens and basements. Carpet and carpet cushion should carry the Canadian Carpet Institute's Green Label (www.canadiancarpet.org)

Carpet cleaning and treatment products can also be a significant source of chemical emissions. Both cleaning methods and products should be selected and applied carefully.

Resilient flooring

Vinyl, tiles, linoleum and cork are flooring materials that are low-emitting alternatives to carpet. Linoleum, made with linseed oil and cork, has low VOC emissions. Flooring with sealed "low- maintenance" surfaces is preferred for reducing the need for cleaners and waxes. Vinyl flooring should be either linoleum or synthetic vinyl tile without self-adhesive back. Sheet vinyl flooring produces higher emissions. Hard materials are usually lower in VOC emissions than soft materials. The softening agent in sheet vinyl, for example, results in higher emissions of SVOCs than vinyl tiles, which do not contain the softening agent.

Plastics

Soft plastics such as vinyl wall covering and sheet flooring are sources of air pollution. In particular, plastics based on poly vinyl chloride (PVC) are the sources of phthalates, a type of SVOC. Hard plastics such as for countertop laminates are low emitters. Water soluble contact adhesives are lower VOC emitters than solvent- based contact adhesives.

Concrete

Air pollution emissions from concrete are very low. Possible sources of high emissions related to concrete are form-release agents used to facilitate removal of formwork. As such, diesel oil or other petroleum-based release agents should not be used. Wax or vegetable oil-based form release products are available and have lower VOC emission characteristics. Sealing exposed concrete basement floors with latex paint will reduce dust and facilitate clean-up.

Thermal insulation

All common thermal insulations must be applied in such a way that they can be completely contained or isolated and cannot enter the building or air handling system. They pose a greater air quality risk to installers than to residents. Careful clean up after installation is required to remove insulation particles from the living space.

Rigid and spray-on insulation installed indoors are sources of emissions. Emissions can be reduced by the installation of an interior air barrier such as sealed polyethylene or drywall.

Fibrous insulation products can be selected that have low formaldehyde emission properties due to the choice of binding agent used during manufacture.

Sealants

Sealants are "wet", which means they are potentially high VOC emitters during the curing stage. Only sealants labeled for interior use should be used inside the building envelope. Acrylic, silicone, and siliconized acrylic sealants are typically the safest to handle and have the lowest VOC content. Initial emissions may still be high, and adequate ventilation should be provided during application.

Drywall

Drywall (gypsum board) is not a source of VOC emissions, but it is a "sink" material, meaning it absorbs airborne pollutants and then releases them over time. Priming and painting dulls the ability of chemical emissions to move in and out of drywall. As stated in the beginning of this section, paint coating can be a source of VOCs. Hypersensitive people may not be able to tolerate even low-VOC paint, in which case a thin plaster coating can be used to seal drywall.

Adhesives

Plastic adhesives with solvent bases such as standard construction adhesive and ceramic tile cements should be avoided as much as possible. Acrylic latex products listed as "Low VOC" are better choices. All plastic adhesives contain some solvents and will contribute to indoor air contaminants. Where adhesives must be used, such as for parquet flooring, cove bases and wall tile, select low-VOC products.

4.4 Homeowner Responsibilities

This chapter has dealt with several factors that affect indoor air quality. Some of these are the responsibility of the builder, while others are the responsibility of the homeowner.

The incidence of asthma and allergies has remained fairly constant since 2001. Environmental factors are considered to play a large role in asthma. The substantial amount of time spent indoors makes indoor air quality an important health determinant. For this reason, the public is much more aware of health and air quality; builders who take steps to consider air quality can use this as a selling feature. However, the best intentions of builders will be for naught unless homeowners understand the principles of indoor air quality and take steps to promote it long-term.

Occupant activities such as smoking, poor housekeeping, hobbies, use of high-VOC cleaners and solvents, and failure to maintain the ventilation system can seriously affect indoor air quality. To ensure the success of provisions that have been made to provide good air quality, homeowner manuals should cover the following:

- Relative humidity: maintain a comfortable level of relative humidity and add moisture if the air is too dry and feels uncomfortable. Remove moisture as required to avoid dampness and condensation, at least over longer period of times.

- Particulate matter: keep ventilation fans, supply air inlets and air ducts clean. Use appropriate filters to reduce particulate matter and debris in air ducts. Vent central vacuum systems to the exterior. Use HEPA filters in vacuum cleaners.

- Chemical contaminants (VOCs): select water-soluble cleaners, glues and solvents and look for Environmental Choice products. Find a temporary place to live during major repairs and renovations such as hardwood floor refinishing. Ventilate buildings thoroughly after construction or renovations. Select furnishing and contents that are not high VOC emitters.

- Mould: take steps to prevent vapour condensation, dampness and free water over extended time periods (anything over a few hours). Dry building materials, carpets, etc. that have become wet as a result of leakage or spillage immediately.

- Combustion gases: maintain heating appliances on a yearly basis. Limit automobile idling in the garage and keep the door between the house and the garage closed when doing so. Operate kitchen fans when using gas stoves.

- Soil gas: in the first or second winter after construction, test the basement area for radon gas concentration and engage a qualified radon contractor if remedial work is required.

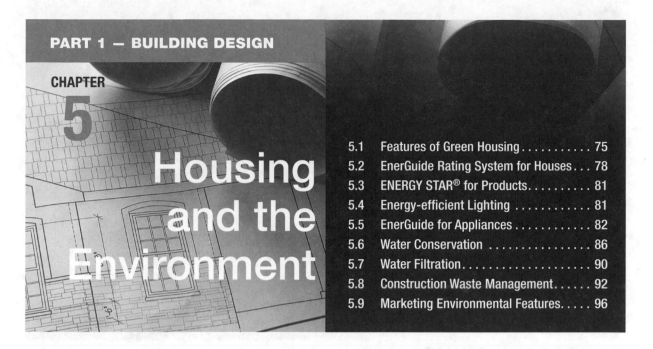

5.1 Features of Green Housing

Green housing uses less land and fewer resources to build, less energy and water to operate, and holds its value through greater durability and reduced maintenance, all while providing a healthy, comfortable living space. Some of the many features associated with green home design and construction are:

- Energy-efficient envelope and equipment;

- Compact land use and site planning;

- Modest-sized units with multi-use spaces;

- Intelligent design for future adaptability (technology) and for persons with disabilities (access);

- Passive solar design and active solar energy equipment, solar-ready construction;

- Resource-efficient materials such as engineered wood and recycled-content materials;

- Certified, sustainably harvested wood;

- Advanced framing techniques and construction waste recycling;

- Highly weather-resistant roofing, cladding and exterior door and window systems;

- Highly durable and low-maintenance interior finishes and details that release fewer chemicals to the air;

- Water-conserving fixtures, rainwater harvesting and water recycling; and,

- Drought- and pest-resistant landscaping.

There is growing market interest in green housing, particularly in those features that reduce the cost of ownership and maintenance needs and foster occupant health. Though some features will cost more initially, many buyers are increasingly willing to consider investing in the added value and reduced ownership costs that green features offer.

The move toward energy efficiency has resulted in the development of systems to help designers, builders and home buyers select building practices, materials, furnishings and appliances that provide enhanced environmental performance, usually in the form of lower energy use. These fall into two main categories: those that address the entire building and those that address components and appliances. This section is not intended to endorse particular evaluation systems, but rather to make builders aware of emerging systems and trends.

Net Zero

Green Housing has always been about the energy. You cannot design and build truly "green" without your primary attention being on the energy side. Net Zero housing focuses on this specifically. While there are a number of definitions about what Net Zero Housing is, CHBA has chosen the following definitions to support our efforts in this area.

Net Zero Energy Home

A Net Zero Energy Home is one that is designed, modeled and constructed to produce as much energy (from on-site renewable energy sources) as it consumes, on an annual basis.

Net Zero Energy Ready Home

A Net Zero Energy Ready Home is a Net Zero Home that has a renewable energy system designed for it that will allow it to achieve Net Zero Energy Home performance, but the renewable energy system is not yet installed.

For the remainder of this Manual, the above definitions will be used unless otherwise noted. In addition, it should be noted that the energy units to be used will be GJ.

There are two factors at play that are outside of the control of Canadian builders but very important to this discussion. First is the Paris Agreement and second, is the Pan-Canadian Framework on Clean Growth and Climate Change. The Paris Agreement, also known as the Paris Climate Accord, is an agreement negotiated by representatives of 196 parties and adopted by consensus on 12 December 2015. As of June 2018, 195 members have signed the agreement, including Canada. The agreement deals with greenhouse gas emissions mitigation, adaptation and finance, starting in 2020. Each country determines, plans and regularly reports on its activities. The Pan-Canadian Framework is Canada's

specific plan for what we will do to meet our commitments made under the Paris Agreement. Of interest to builders is a plan to use the Building Codes to ensure that all new housing is constructed to Net Zero Energy Ready performance by 2030.

While each building site is unique, the following is general information that will be used throughout this Manual to guide the discussion.

In 2020 Canadian homes built to meet the Building Code have energy use that is roughly as follows:

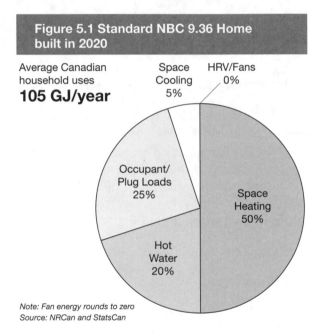

Figure 5.1 Standard NBC 9.36 Home built in 2020

Average Canadian household uses
105 GJ/year

Note: Fan energy rounds to zero
Source: NRCan and StatsCan

Energy Use	% of Total	Annual GJ
Space Heating	50	52.50
Space Cooling	5	5.25
Hot Water	20	21.00
Occupant/Plug Loads	25	26.25
HRV/Fans	0	0.00
Total	–	105.00

Air tightness is approximately 3-4 ACH50.

Figure 5.2 Net Zero Ready Home

Average Net Zero
Ready Home uses
36 GJ/year

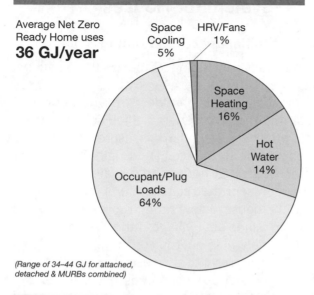

(Range of 34–44 GJ for attached, detached & MURBs combined)

Energy Use	% of Total	Annual GJ
Space Heating	16	5.8
Space Cooling	5	1.8
Hot Water	14	5.0
Occupant/Plug Loads	64	23.0
HRV/Fans	1	0.4
Total	–	36.0

Air tightness is less than 1.0 ACH50.

Of interest in these two scenarios is the significant reduction in space conditioning and water heating in the Net Zero Energy Ready house. These load reductions are all within the control of the builder. At the time of writing, builders are constructing and labeling Net Zero and Net Zero Energy Ready homes under the CHBA program. They are doing this using conventional technologies. For example, a typical building envelope thermal insulation levels to achieve Net Zero is:

- Attic R-60 +
- Walls R-35 +
- Below Grade Walls R-24 +

- Sub-Slab Insulation R-10 +
- Windows R-5 (Triple-glazed, low e, argon, insulating spacers)
- Robust air barrier (ACH 1.0 or less at 50 Pa)

The above insulation levels, window technologies and air tightness levels are achievable by most builders today. The limiting factor is cost, which drives housing affordability. Without a significant breakthrough in insulation or window technology, as the Code mandates new levels of performance, builders will need to find ways to make their houses more affordable. Some of this may come by way of improved job-site efficiencies, and some by changes to finishes or physical house sizes. (See Chapter 24 – Future Gazing)

The plug load is not in the control of the builder, it is completely dependent on the occupants. The plug load is lifestyle dependent:

- Lighting
- Television
- Home automation/security
- Gaming
- Appliances
- Hot tub
- Electric vehicle (20,000 km/year requires approximately an additional 15 GJ/year).

5.1.1 Building rating systems

Building rating systems can combine many factors such as water conservation, energy requirements to manufacture materials (embodied energy), and energy conservation. Rating factors vary from system to system. Generally, building rating systems use categories to indicate the level of environmental performance attained by a given site and building design.

5.1.2 Life Cycle Analysis

Life cycle analysis (LCA) provides builders with a method for comparing the environmental impacts of various building materials and techniques. LCA is not an overall environmental or green rating system, but it does give builders insight into the environmental consequences of their building material and construction technique choices. Typically, LCA considers all of the environmental impacts associated with the extraction, manufacturing, transportation, construction and disposal of common building materials, products and assemblies. The North American authority in this area is the Athena Institute (www.athenasmi.org).

While LCA is a useful tool for comparing the environmental profile of alternative material and construction choices, builders should bear in mind that the environmental impacts from home operation and occupant transportation over the life of a dwelling have, by far, the most significant impact on the environment. Reflecting this, LCA analysis should be used in conjunction with proper consideration of a home's overall energy and water use efficiency, as well as the community's design and services.

5.2 EnerGuide Rating System for Houses

5.2.1 Initial EnerGuide Rating System

The EnerGuide Rating System (ERS) is a national system developed by Natural Resources Canada to assist builders and homeowners in improving the energy efficiency of houses. It provides a standard measure of a home's energy performance. The original version of the ERS rated homes on a scale of 0 to 100 to represent the relative energy performance of the house. A low rating represents a home with major air leakage, little insulation and extremely high energy consumption. A rating of 100 represents a house that produces as much energy as it consumes in a year (i.e., Net Zero) (Table 5.1).

While many houses across Canada were evaluated and rated using this scale, it did have its shortcomings and it was changed. It is discussed in this book because many may encounter these labels in existing houses.

There is not a process to convert an EnerGuide Rating from the old scale to the current scale. Below is a sample EnerGuide label (Figure 5.3) that would be attached to a rated home. If the home was rated, this label can be found on

Table 5.1 Typical ERS ratings based on the initial (pre-2014) ERS rating system	
House Characteristics	**Typical ERS Rating**
Older house, not upgraded	0 to 50
Older house, upgraded	51 to 65
Energy-efficient upgraded older house	66 to 74
New house built to building code standards prior to the code having energy requirements	70 to 76
New house built to meet building code standards containing energy requirements	77 to 80
Energy-efficient new house	81 to 85
High-performance, energy-efficient new house (2005 R-2000 is ERS 80 or higher; 2012 R-2000 is approximately ERS 86 or higher)	86 to 99
Net-zero house	100

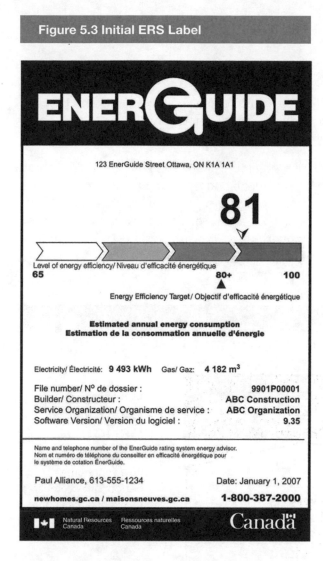

Figure 5.3 Initial ERS Label

4. The energy advisor inputs this information into NRCan's energy simulation software (HOT2000) to determine the estimated annual energy usage and EnerGuide Rating for the house, based on the design.

5. Where appropriate, the energy advisor provides variations of the simulation that include energy-efficient upgrades that will improve energy performance. The energy advisor ensures that good building science principles are maintained.

6. The provisional rating based on the building plans and the optional energy efficient upgrades are provided to the builder for costing analysis.

7. The builder meets with the homeowner to agree on the house specifications and energy-efficient components that the house will have. The plans are updated accordingly based on the decisions made and the energy simulation of the home is completed with the updated details to verify compliance.

8. When construction is complete, the energy advisor returns to the house to verify the energy efficient upgrades and performs a blower door test.

9. After the data has been collected, the homeowner is provided with the evaluation report and official label that shows the EnerGuide rating of the home. This label should then be affixed to the electrical panel.

5.2.2 Current EnerGuide Rating System

Ratings are calculated by licensed EnerGuide Rating System (ERS) evaluators based on the following process:

1. The builder contacts an EnerGuide Rating System Service Organization to get a list of local certified energy advisors.

2. The builder works with an energy advisor to enroll and label houses in the program.

3. The energy advisor undertakes an analysis of the new house plans, noting components that will affect the energy efficiency of the house (i.e., mechanical equipment, windows, building envelope, insulation levels, etc.)

ERS is used by a number of other voluntary, new home labelling initiatives including Built Green™ and EnergyStar™. CHBA has chosen to use the ERS for the Net Zero Energy Home labelling program. Houses must meet the CHBA Net Zero Technical Requirements and have an ERS Rating of 0.

The EnerGuide Rating System (ERS), developed by Natural Resources Canada in consultation with stakeholders from across Canada, will:

- Help homeowners, industry and other stakeholders, become "energy literate" regarding homes and the decisions related to them.

- Provide specific, readily accessible energy performance information to support decision making in designing, constructing, purchasing, operating or renovating a home.

The most significant change for builders and other users is the scale located in the top portion of the label (Figure 5.4). The rating scale is consumption-based, with energy use expressed in gigajoules (GJ) per year. In general, the scale will range from 0, representing a Net Zero Energy Home, to as high as is required for the home being rated.

Houses that produce more energy than they consume in a year (i.e., a net-positive energy house) would receive a 0★ rating and text will indicate that the house produces more energy than it uses on an annual basis.

The gigajoule scale is used because it can represent all energy sources and the rating will be a reasonable, whole number. The gigajoule is simply a unit of energy and can easily be converted to kilowatt hours (kWh) or calories if a homeowner is more comfortable with these units.

Figure 5.4 Current ERS Label

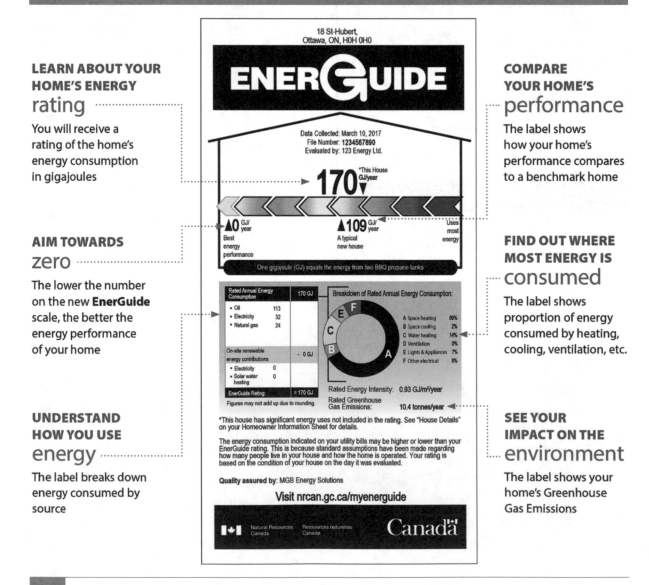

The scale allows for the comparison of all houses regardless of type or location. Good design will be reflected in the rating. For example, a house oriented and/or designed to take into account passive solar gain will have a lower rating (energy consumption) than a similar house that does not have ideal orientation (all other house parameters being the same).

The scale positions a house against a reference point. The reference point is a house built to the construction standards of a typical new house in the region where it is being constructed. The typical new house reflects the requirements of the current energy code in its region as determined by the ERS software. If there is no energy code in that region, the National Building Code is used. As codes have numerous ways of determining compliance, including non-energy requirements, the home's rating gives no indication of whether or not the house meets code. The ERS is not an indication of Code compliance and it is not intended to be.

The EnerGuide for Houses scale harmonizes with the EnerGuide scale for appliances. It allows energy improvements to be expressed as straight percentages and makes it relatively easy to demonstrate the effects of real or proposed energy improvements to a house. A sample label from the current ERS is shown on previous page.

5.3 ENERGY STAR® for Products

To be able to display the ENERGY STAR® symbol, products must meet or exceed technical specifications designed to ensure that they are among the most energy-efficient in the marketplace. Requirements vary from one product category to another, but typically an ENERGY STAR®-labelled product must be from 10 to 50% more efficient than a conventional model.

In Canada, the ENERGY STAR® designation can be given to products in a number of categories: heating, cooling, and ventilation (HVAC) products; lighting; residential and commercial appliances; fenestration products; home and commercial office equipment; and a variety of consumer electronic products.

5.4 Energy-efficient Lighting

As we move toward Net Zero Energy housing, lighting is one area where there is an excellent opportunity to save energy and improve occupant comfort. Occupant lifestyle is not something the builder can control but installing energy efficient and correct lighting is.

The most important characteristic of lighting is its ability to convert electrical energy into light energy. The luminous efficacy of a light source is defined as the ratio of the light

Table 5.2 Energy-Efficient Lighting Comparison		
Category	**Efficacy (lm/W)**	**Rated Average Life (Hours)**
Incandescent	10 to 35	1,000 to 4,000
Mercury Vapour	30 to 80	24,000 +
Light Emitting Diode (LED)	40 to 150	10,000 to 100,000
Fluorescent	40 to 100	6,000 to 30,000
Metal Halide (HID)	50 to 115	6,000 to 20,000
High Pressure Sodium (HID)	85 to 150	24,000 to 80,000
Low Pressure Sodium	100 to 200	18,000
Induction	50 to 100	60,000 to 100,000
Plasma	70 to 150	3,000 to 50,000

output (lumens) to the energy input (watts). It is expressed in units of lm/W. The higher the efficacy the better it is at converting electrical energy to light.

Different light sources vary significantly. Life expectancy of the light is also provided. Longevity of a light may be important if it is being installed in a location that is difficult to get to for changing.

The units of lighting level is the lux (lx), where 1 lx = 1 lm/m2. Lighting levels for housing should be in the 100 lux range.

It is clear from the table above that incandescent lighting is not efficient at converting electricity to light. In addition, they have short life spans. These were the first type of electric light developed and were the most common. In 2014, the Government of Canada brought in a new standard which set a minimum performance level for bulbs. This move is intended to phase-out incandescent bulbs for home use (bulb sizes ranging from 40 to 100 watts). Incandescent lighting is not a good choice for energy efficient Net Zero Energy Homes.

By changing to energy-efficient lighting, savings of 800 to 1,000 kWh per year can be achieved. Although slightly more expensive to purchase than conventional incandescent fixtures, energy-efficient lighting will pay for itself through energy savings.

The adoption of ENERGY STAR® for residential light fixtures supports the use of energy-efficient fixtures in Canada, as many consumers look for the ENERGY STAR® symbol when purchasing household products and equipment. ENERGY STAR®-qualified fixtures can reduce electricity consumption and costs for lighting by up to 90% compared to incandescent fixtures. To qualify for ENERGY STAR®, fixtures must:

- Consume at least two-thirds less energy than a conventional fixture

- Use bulbs that last at least 10,000 hours (about seven years, assuming normal usage of four hours per day)

- Carry a two-year warranty (double the industry standard)

An alternative lighting product available is the LED lamp or light bulb, which uses a solid-state, light emitting diode as the source of light. The efficiency of LED devices has improved over recent years with some chips able to emit more than 100 lumens per watt. Since LEDs do not emit light in all directions, their directional characteristics affect the design of lamps. The LED converts electric power to light with higher efficiency than incandescent lamps. The light output of light-emitting diodes is small compared to incandescent and compact fluorescent lamps, and as a result, most applications assemble multiple diodes. Although the cost of LED bulbs has dropped significantly over recent years, they are still more expensive than fluorescent lamps.

The diodes use direct current (DC) electrical power. Therefore, standard AC power must be converted using an internal or external rectifier circuit that provides a regulated current output at low voltage. LEDs are degraded or damaged by operating at high temperatures, so LED lamps typically include heat dissipation elements such as heat sinks and cooling fins. Because the LEDs use DC power, they may be a better choice for houses that incorporate photovoltaic solar collectors since that power is produced in DC. Table 5.2 and Table 5.3 show comparative information for several types of light bulbs.

5.5 EnerGuide for Appliances

Energy efficiency in appliances should be considered where the builder supplies or offers appliances as part of a new home package. Over 250,000 appliances are purchased by the housing industry every year-appliances which could, over the course of their lifetime, cost $300 million to operate.

Table 5.3 Comparative information for light bulbs

	Incandescent	Halogen	Fluorescent	LED (generic)
Purchase price (approx.)	$0.41	$4	$4	$16
Electricity usage	60 W	42 W	13 W	9 W
Lumens	860	570	660	900
Lumens/Watt	14.3	13.6	50.8	100
Lifespan (hours)	2,000	3,500	8,000	25,000

Six major appliances-the refrigerator, freezer, dishwasher, range, clothes washer and dryer-account for more than 14% of total energy use in the average home. By installing energy-efficient appliances, electrical use can be halved. The electricity saved by buying energy-efficient appliances can add up to thousands of dollars over the appliance's lifetime.

The energy consumption of an appliance will depend on the model selected and the frequency of use, but savings to the homeowner can approach 20 to 60% of the energy average that appliances would use.

The EnerGuide Directory lists the major appliances sold in Canada and includes their EnerGuide ratings (Figure 5.1). The lower the number, the more efficient the appliance is. EnerGuide allows buyers to compare the energy efficiency of many different models of household appliances or heating and cooling products sold in Canada. For some of these products, ENERGY STAR® goes one step further and identifies specific models that meet or exceed premium levels of energy efficiency.

5.5.1 Selecting appliances

Where appliances are to be supplied with the house, energy efficiency should be considered. For most appliances, washers, dryers, freezers, and refrigerators, an Energy Star label is the simplest indicator of energy efficiency. Appliances carrying an Energy Star rating have been tested to be among the best efficiencies of that appliance class.

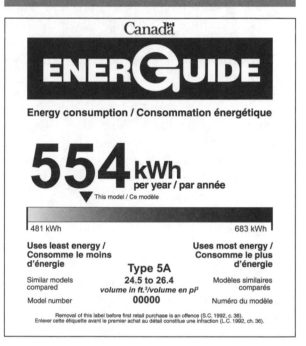

Figure 5.5 The EnerGuide logo (for appliances)

Energy Star does not rate cooking appliances – electric and gas ranges, cooktops and microwaves are not eligible to receive an Energy Star ranking. This is because they are as efficient as current technology allows. Efficiency improvements are made by better oven insulation and tighter-fitting oven doors. Most units are so close in efficiency that Energy Star does not rate them.

For traditional electric cooking appliances, Canada's EnerGuide rating system will provide an efficiency rating.

Heating elements in ranges are powered by the burning of gas, electric resistance in electric range cooking elements and by magnetic induction in the case of induction cookers.

Cooking appliances
(ranges, ovens and cooktops)

The kitchen range, combining an oven with a four-burner cooktop, is standard equipment in most Canadian homes. Self-cleaning ovens are slightly more expensive but are usually better insulated than standard ovens and use less energy as a result. The EnerGuide rating for self-cleaning electric ranges with 30-inch conventional tops ranges from: most efficient — 127 kWh per year; least efficient — 718 kWh per year (0.46 GJ — 2.58 GJ).

Convection ovens contain fans that keep heat moving throughout the cooking space. Not only do these ovens cook more evenly, but they also cook more quickly, thereby using less energy. A microwave oven is the most energy-efficient way to cook, unless it is used to thaw frozen foods in which case it uses more energy than a regular oven.

Induction cookers

Electricity is run through a coil of copper, under the cooking surface, to create an oscillating magnetic field. This wirelessly induces an electric current in the pot. The resistance of the pot creates a resistance to the current flow, and that creates heat in the pot. In essence, the pot gets hot, but not the cooktop. For this reason the pot must be made from a magnetic-based material such as, cast iron, magnetic stainless steel, and any steel based pot. Copper and aluminum pots, while good conductors of heat are not magnetic and therefore will not be affected by the oscillating magnetic field.

From an efficiency standpoint, an induction cooker, like a traditional electric range, is converting electricity to heat. In an electric range, it is the resistance in the heating element which creates the heat. There are slight efficiency losses because in traditional electric, you must heat the element, then heat the pot. Induction does not heat the element, and is therefore much quicker. Both systems are more or less equally efficient.

The main efficiencies of induction cooking come from reducing waste heat. In a traditional range, the cooktop is hot, and remains hot when the cookware is removed. This increases the cooling load in the house.

When the US Department of Energy was challenged to compare the differences of efficiencies between traditional electric, gas and induction, it based its calculation on energy transfer efficiencies – that is, how much energy is converted into useful heat (that actually cooks the food, rather than residual heat wasted once the food is finished cooking). By this test, DOE determined induction cooking has efficiencies in the mid-70 percent range, traditional electric in the low-70 percent range and gas about 40 percent.

The residual heat lost by gas cooking is significant, and may even require more ventilation to dissipate the heat. This is why gas efficiency has been rated so low

Refrigerators

Units with side-by-side doors generally use the most energy, while one-door, manual defrost models use the least. However, some of the best two-door, frost-free units use no more energy than a manual-defrost refrigerator. In addition, a two- or three-door model with large freezer compartment may eliminate the need for a separate freezer.

Most refrigerators have heating coils just under the "skin." These are intended to warm the outer surface of the unit near the door opening to prevent condensation from forming. Some refrigerators have an "energy-saver" switch that allows consumer to adjust how much energy a refrigerator uses to keep food fresh. As well, a unit with wheels will facilitate moving the refrigerator away from the wall to clean the coils-a practice that will reduce electrical use over the life of the appliance.

The ENERGY STAR® rating for frost-free, two-door refrigerators with top-mounted freezer in the 20.5 to 22.4 ft³ size ranges from: most efficient — 386 kWh per year; least efficient — 483 kWh per year (1.39 GJ — 1.74 GJ). ENERGY STAR-qualified refrigerators and freezers incorporate many advanced features, including:

- Better insulation;

- High-efficiency compressors;

- Improved heat-transfer surfaces; and

- More precise temperature and defrost mechanisms

Standard and compact refrigerators must be at least 20% more efficient than the minimum federal energy performance standard in Canada's Energy Efficiency Regulations to qualify for the ENERGY STAR® mark.

Freezers

The energy efficiency of freezers has improved steadily over the past 20 years. Chest freezers are much more efficient than upright models. They are available with up to 7.5 cm (3 in.) of foam insulation in the walls. The ENERGY STAR® rating for chest freezers with manual defrost in the 21.5-23.4 ft3 size ranges from: most efficient — 460 kWh per year; least efficient — 732 kWh per year (1.66 GJ — 2.64 GJ). ENERGY STAR-qualified standard-size freezers must exceed minimum Government of Canada energy efficiency standards by at least 10%. Compact freezer models must exceed minimum Government of Canada energy efficiency standards by at least 20%.

Dishwashers

ENERGY STAR®-qualified dishwashers save energy by using improved technology and less hot water. These appliances feature sensors that calculate the required length of washing cycles and the appropriate water temperatures needed to clean each load. Some models feature built-in heating elements that save water- heating costs.

ENERGY STAR qualified dishwashers use 20 to 50% less energy and 35 to 50% less water than standard models. To qualify for ENERGY STAR, standard dishwashers must achieve energy efficiency levels that are at least 9% higher than Canada's minimum regulated standard. Compact dishwashers must be at least 10% more efficient. The ENERGY STAR® ratings for dishwashers range from: most efficient — 130 kWh per year; least efficient — 270 kWh per year (0.47 GJ — 0.97 GJ).

Many ENERGY STAR dishwashers use "smart" sensors that match the wash cycle and the amount of water to each load. They may also have an internal heater to boost the temperature of incoming water.

Clothes washers

To be ENERGY STAR® qualified, clothes washers must be standard size, with a minimum tub capacity of 45 L (1.6 ft.3) and at least 59% more efficient than Canada's minimum energy performance standard. There is no ENERGY STAR specification for compact clothes washers.

To be ENERGY STAR qualified, a clothes washer must have advanced design features that use less energy and 35 to 50% less water than ENERGY STAR qualified washers made before January 1, 2007. They have sensors that prevent energy waste by matching water needs to the size of each load, and advanced high-speed motors that reduce the length of spin cycles and remove more water from clothes, so less time and energy are needed for drying.

Front-loading washers are usually 35% more energy-efficient than top-loading units, and they also use less water. The latest developments include a higher spin speed in the clothes washer: up to 1,600 revolutions per minute. This extracts more water from the clothes before they are put into a dryer. The mechanical energy used to remove water in the spin cycle is seventy times more effective than the heat used to evaporate moisture in tumble dryers. Other desirable features include washers that heat their own water, wash at a lower temperature, use weight and fabric recognition systems, and offer even more energy savings.

The ENERGY STAR rating for clothes washers in the 60-80 litre size ranges from: most efficient-80 kWh per year; least efficient — 200 kWh per year, (0.29 GJ — 0.72 GJ) and includes the energy required to heat the water.

Dryers

Many dryers come with sensors that automatically shut off the dryer when its contents are dry. This saves energy and wear and tear on clothes. The EnerGuide rating for standard clothes dryers ranges from most efficient — 379 kWh per year to least efficient — 965 kWh per year (1.36 GJ — 3.47 GJ). Heat pump dryers are is the range of 87 kWh per year.

Condensing dryers are electric dryers that do not have or require an exhaust vent. There are no condensing gas dryers, since the combustion products of gas dryers must be exhausted for safety reasons. Unlike vented dryers condensing dryers use a heat pump technology to dehumidify the air in the drum and condense the water out of the clothes. The condensate water discarded down the drain.

5.6 Water Conservation

Canadians are some of the highest per capita users of water in the world. While Canada possesses a considerable portion of the world's fresh water resources, much of this water is located in remote northern areas. In fact, many communities across the country will face water supply constraints in the coming decade, reinforcing the importance of using water wisely. Simple changes to water-use habits and household equipment can reduce water consumption in the home by up to 40%. Water use depletes supply from aquifers and reservoirs, and requires energy to treat, pump, distribute and treat the water again after use. For these reasons, it makes good environmental and economic sense to build housing that minimizes the use of water.

Products and systems that can dramatically reduce water consumption are available and water conservation is increasingly becoming a requirement for development approvals. Beyond the requirements, legislation and housing market demands, water conservation makes good environmental sense. Incorporating water-saving features into homes can be an important marketing edge, especially for increasingly environment-minded buyers.

Household water consumption can be minimized by making design changes outside and inside the home. Improving conservation within a house often requires little more than specifying more efficient plumbing fixtures. The major indoor water users, in order of the relative savings possible, are low-flush and ultra-low-flush toilets, low-flow showers, faucets, and clothes washers. While a conventional showerhead uses 15 to 19 L (3 to 4 gal.) or more per minute, the low-flow type uses approximately 8 to 9 L (about 2 gal.) per minute, with some models using 6 L (about 1.3 gal) per minute.

Outdoor water use can be minimized by using rainwater for irrigation, and by employing appropriate landscaping practices, including the use of permeable surfaces and drought-resistant grasses and plants.

5.6.1 Designing homes for indoor water conservation

At least 50% of a typical household's water bill comes from interior uses, and 95% of that amount is used in bathrooms and laundry rooms. The total figure can be substantially reduced for relatively little cost.

Water-saving fixtures now cost about the same as regular fixtures and work just as well. Fixtures with consumption rates similar to European models are becoming increasingly available in Canada. The R-2000 Program incorporates requirements for water-conserving fixtures.

Incorporating water-saving fixtures in houses makes sense. Each person in a Canadian household uses an average of 329 L (72.5 gal.) of water every day. Efficient fixtures can save households hundreds of dollars each year at current water and sewer rates; as these rates escalate, the savings will be even greater. In some jurisdictions, water-conserving fixtures are now required by legislation.

The water useage is broken down to the following areas:

- Toilet – 30%

- Baths and Showers – 35%

- Laundry – 20%

- Kitchen & Drinking – 10%

- Cleaning – 5%

A shower is typically 9.5 L/min x 8 minutes = 76 L of water. A full bath could use 150 L or more.

A tap that drips 6 drops per minute will waste 1200 L/year. This is water that is processed by both the water treatment plant on the way in, and by the sewage treatment plant on the way out. If the property is rural, this is a draw on the well but it also needs to be processed by the septic system.

5.6.2 Grey water treatment

Grey water is the drainage from sinks, bathing fixtures and laundry – but does not include toilets. Grey water once was the smaller volume component of sewage, but due to the increased use of low-flow toilets, grey water is now estimated at 65% of total residential water use. Grey water is only lightly contaminated with soap residue, food waste and soil, so it can potentially be easily recycled for some uses on site. It generally does not carry significant quantities of bacteria or parasites that may communicate disease. It may, however, contain hair and grease that must be removed before reusing.

In dry climates, and where the building site has a large garden area, a potential use for grey water is irrigation. This will not only offset some potable water costs, but will also reduce loads on sewer or septic tank systems. Grey water typically contains some nutrients that are good for plants; however, because grey water systems are new to health authorities, it is generally necessary to use grey water only in buried (subsoil) irrigation systems. In any case, grey water systems must be installed so that a hose cannot be connected to them. Check with health authorities – local rules for grey water systems are changing. Initiatives are underway to examine the possibility of reclaiming grey water.

While not technically grey water treatment, drain water heat recovery uses the warm water from the shower drain to pre-heat the incoming water from the mains. Research at the Canadian Centre for Housing Technology has successfully tested drain-water heat recovery devices, and these products are now common in new houses being certified to an energy efficiency standard.

It is important to check with local plumbing and health authorities before planning a grey water system. Certain jurisdictions may have little experience with grey water systems, or may prohibit them entirely. There is now a good deal of practical literature and examples of code-accepted systems being provided by companies that specialize in grey water systems.

5.6.3 Water-efficient toilets

Approximately 30% of average household water consumption is used to flush the toilets. Moderately efficient, water-saving toilets can have a substantial impact on annual water costs. Over the past decade, the performance of water-efficient toilets has improved substantially. Although costs may vary considerably from fixture to fixture, there is little correlation between price and performance. Most high-priced fixtures are simply designer models or premium colours.

Low-flow models using 4.8 L (1.1 gal.) or less per flush are available from major manufacturers at competitive prices, and are now mandatory in some jurisdictions. Some low-flush toilets are sophisticated, using compressed air or water pressure on special diaphragm chambers to provide a forceful flush with little water. Others use a more conical bowl and redesigned water channels to enhance performance.

A dual-flush toilet uses two buttons or handles to flush different levels of water and can reduce toilet water use by up to 20%.

Since a toilet should last for decades, parts availability is crucial. The fewer specialized mechanisms and moving parts, the better. Installing a warranted unit from a known, reliable manufacturer should reduce future call-back problems.

There is virtually no "consumer cost" associated with installing water-saving models. Many look and perform so much like regular toilets that users cannot perceive a difference, except in their utility bills. Maximum Performance (MaP) (www.map-testing.com/index.html) testing is a voluntary program that some manufacturers use to verify their toilets are low water consumers and are effective.

With "baby boomers" now entering their 70's there is an interest in aging-in-place. Many manufacturers are picking up on this and designing "right-height" toilets that are slightly higher, making them easier to mount and dismount. Users are finding these to be more comfortable for all ages of clients – not just elderly ones and the popularity of these is expected to grow. In addition, new features are being incorporated such as self-closing (and opening) lids and self-cleaning models.

5.6.4 Pump toilets

When it is necessary to install a flush toilet below the point where it has enough drop to drain to the sewer, a sewage pumping system is required. These systems collect the waste from the toilet and then lift it into the sewer with a pump.

The most reliable system has a gravity storage tank located below the toilet and a submersible sewage pump with a float switch. This tank must be sealed and vented so that odours do not enter the home. Packaged tank units containing the pump and controls are available, or the tank can be cast from concrete on-site.

The smallest packaged unit is a shallow, plastic tank that acts as a pedestal for, or a step up, to the toilet. These have a small capacity, and cannot be used if electricity is interrupted, but can be located on top of the floor. They can be easily retrofitted and are inexpensive. Larger packaged units must be located in a recess below floor level. These have the advantage of enough storage capacity for limited use, even when the power is off. Sewage pump units can also accept sink and shower waste and generally are designed to lift about 3 m (10 ft.). These toilets make it easy to finish a basement, even if the plumbing to the sewer is above the toilet outlet.

There are also "pump up toilets" available that have pumps built into the toilet or that use water pressure to lift sewage.

5.6.5 Water-efficient shower heads

Approximately 35% of indoor water is used for bathing. Low-flow shower heads can reduce both water and water heating costs by at least 50% when compared with standard fixtures. To use less water, some shower heads restrict the water flow by pulsing it. Others mix the water with air. Both systems perform well and give the user the impression of a more powerful flow.

There is no general correlation between price and reported performance; some more expensive shower heads receive no better reviews than inexpensive models. Constructed of plastic, metal, or combinations of materials, these fixtures are available at most plumbing supply outlets in a range of styles and colours.

Low-flow shower heads have met with widely varying reactions from homeowners. However, independent testing has shown no relationship between flow rates and perceived performance. Some low-flow units are deemed to deliver a better shower than their high-flow counterparts.

5.6.6 Low-flow faucets

Typical older bathroom and kitchen faucets have flow rates that average 13.5 L (3 gal.) of water per minute. That is far in excess of what is usually needed or can be used. Aerating faucets give the illusion of more water flowing from the faucet than is actually the case. For washing hands and brushing teeth, a flow rate of 2 L per minute is quite acceptable. In kitchen sinks and laundry tubs, flow rates of 6 to 9 L per minute are often sufficient.

Some faucets are spring-loaded, and turn themselves off either immediately or after a brief delay. These have been marketed mostly for commercial applications, but are inexpensive and may be a practical way to minimize water waste in households as well.

Higher-tech options, such as infrared sensor mechanisms built into taps, have been employed to automatically cut the water flow when hands are removed from beneath the tap. Users are finding these to be very convenient in the kitchen when preparing food. In addition, these can be very helpful for those with loss of hand strength or control.

5.6.7 Water saving appliances

Dish and clothes washers are being designed to function with less water. Conventional washers can average more than 1,200 L (266 gal.) per month, depending on household size and frequency of use.

Front-loading washing machines, which tumble the clothes through the water rather than immersing them entirely, use up to one-third less water than the commonly used top-loading machines.

5.6.8 Outdoor water use

Irrigation water for lawns and gardens can account for up to 80% of overall domestic demand in the spring and summer, depending on lot size, garden type and climate. So much water is used that municipal supplies can be strained in peak demand periods. As peak demand is the determining factor in planning for new developments and housing, outdoor water use can have far-reaching impacts.

There is a real opportunity for improvement in outdoor water use. Between one-third to one-half of this water is wasted-never reaching the plants for which it was intended, but rather being misdirected or evaporated in warmer weather.

To overcome these problems, a drip irrigation system can be installed prior to sodding or seeding. Some of these systems are perforated hoses laid under the turf and supply water directly to the root zone of plants. Others are small-diameter tubes laid above the surface and directed at plant roots.

Automatic watering systems further increase the efficiency of all irrigation. Hose couplings can be equipped with timers to ensure that watering is done at night, when demand on the municipal water system and evaporation losses will be lowest, or whole automated systems with programmable zone valves can be installed.

Moisture sensors can make the system even "smarter" by watering the lawn only when required and shutting off programmed watering during periods of rain.

Together, these measures can cut total household water consumption during the summer months by up to 50%.

5.6.9 Landscaping for water conservation

Traditional turf grass requires a great deal of irrigation. A typical suburban lawn of about 350 square metres needs as much as 200,000 L (42,400 gal.) of water through each growing season.

Lawn areas are increasingly being seen as long-term liabilities. Many homeowners are not interested in spending a great deal of time on the lawn upkeep. Alternative landscapes provide opportunities for significant and permanent reductions in household outdoor water use.

Reducing the size of turf grass areas, concentrating them in backyards, and surrounding them with native plants (which have greater resistance to insects and diseases), means far less water is used for irrigation. It also means reduced demand for fertilizers, pesticides and herbicides.

Wooden decks, gazebos, interlocking stone areas, walkways and boxed-in planting areas or gardens can preserve the earthy, rustic character of landscapes while saving the homeowner substantial maintenance time.

Top soil stripped from construction sites should always be replaced. A deep layer of top soil creates an absorbent base to retain water where plants and trees need it most.

5.6.10 Cisterns

As simple as a barrel, but more commonly an in-ground or basement tank, cisterns capture rainfall from rooftops and other hard surfaces. Often in abundant supply, this soft water lacks the mineral salts common to groundwater and is ideal for irrigation. Cisterns can provide a substantial proportion of monthly water requirements, especially in remote areas.

As much as 90% of the annual rainfall falling on the roof can be collected, depending on the gutter and downpipe system. Every 2.5 cm (1 in.) of rainfall provides approximately 20 L (4 gal.) of water per square metre (10 ft2).

Cisterns have historically been constructed of high density concrete, vibrated as it is cast in place, and allowed to wet cure before being put to use. A crystallizing, cementitious sealer applied on the inside after curing is used to minimize leakage. A tight, opaque cover can avoid problems with mosquitoes or algae. Today, manufactured polyethylene tanks are readily available, some made with potable-water grade plastic and these may be suitable for use as cisterns and water storage tanks. Polyethylene tanks have the advantage of being light-weight and therefore are easily moved and placed on a construction site without the use of heavy lifting equipment.

Water storage in a cistern also reduces the flooding impact of storms, lowering urban runoff. Cistern water storage can be an integral part of a storm water management plan. However, it does require a system of screens and sand filters to stop leaves and debris from entering the cistern.

5.6.11 Conclusion

Water-efficient design saves far more than it costs. Low-flow shower heads and toilets, for example, cost the builder no more than standard fixtures that waste water. Water-efficient homes also cost less to operate.

Building for the future shows foresight. Homes that offer less expensive long-term operations and which do not compromise the quality of living that homeowners have come to expect are both environmentally sensible and easier to sell.

5.7 Water Filtration

Many people are concerned about the quality and taste of municipal water and are buying bottled water for drinking and even cooking uses. Municipal water may be very hard, or it may contain objectionable chlorine odours and residue from treatment. Some water may also contain soil sediments and rust picked up from the distribution system. Rural well water may have any number of contaminants in it, including naturally occurring sulfur and iron, as well organic matter, bacteria and parasites from surface runoff.

The installation of in-home water treatment, or the provision of plumbing connections for adding it later, can be a very important amenity to homebuyers who are health and budget conscious. Treating water in the home instead of buying bottled water can rapidly pay for the system and is far more convenient. Water treatment can remove suspended solids (cloudiness), salts, chlorine residues, objectionable odours and taste (such as sulfur and iron compounds), organic compounds such as agricultural and industrial chemicals, and bacteria and parasites. Specialized water treatment can also remove dissolved metals and metal compounds and other pollutants. Water softening, the removal of excess hardness (dissolved limestone and other minerals), is another water treatment process that is common in areas with hard water.

It is very important that the treatment method be well matched to the contaminants that need to be removed from the water. To determine the required process for rural water, samples should be taken for analysis. If water comes from a public water system, records of recent water analysis can be obtained from the water district offices. In either case, some expert knowledge may be required to choose the best treatment method, though a packaged treatment system that treats for the most common concerns such as chlorine odours and sediment can be safely chosen for city water.

5.7.1 Typical system packages

There are two types of equipment to consider: *whole house treatment* and *point-of-use treatment*. The whole house system treats water to the kitchen and baths, but usually not to the outdoor taps or to toilets. The advantage is that chlorine residues and other odours are removed before they reach the water heater, bath and shower. Exposure to some water contaminants in the shower can be a concern, as they are absorbed through the lungs and skin when vaporized. Whole house systems are usually preferred for those who have special health problems and must avoid exposure to these contaminants as much as possible. A whole house system requires that supply plumbing to toilets and outdoor taps be separated from other supplies. These systems need access to a drain and an electrical outlet, and are about the same size as a water softener. Most systems use a pre-filter and a large tank filled with sand and carbon. The sand and carbon must be changed every one or two years.

A packaged *point-of-use system* is about the size of a small suitcase and can be mounted on a utility room wall or under a cabinet and piped to a separate tap at the sink. The water generally is used only for cooking and drinking. The most complete systems contain a sediment filter, a reverse osmosis filter, a storage tank and a carbon filter. A sterilizer can also be added. The full packaged unit requires a wall space, water supply and drain. If a sterilizer or electric control is used, an electrical outlet is also needed. Much simpler point-of-use units are also available that contain only a sediment and carbon filter. They are piped to a separate tap, but do not require a drain or electricity. The most common treatment methods are described in the following sections.

Particle filters

All water treatment systems must have a particle filter installed ahead of any other filters to trap silt and other suspended debris. These are available as small cartridge units that can handle only the flow to a kitchen drinking water system, or larger units that can handle whole house flow. Filters are inexpensive and easy to change when plugged. A "20-micron" filter is a common type for sediment removal.

Reverse osmosis

Reverse osmosis uses a dense polyester fabric membrane to filter water under pressure. The membrane blocks passage of salts, dissolved minerals, most organic chemicals and bacteria and parasites. The membrane is continuously "washed" during use by water bypassing the filter. This type sends about 20% of the water passing through to a storage tank and 80% to the drain. To save water, it can be automatically shut off when the tank is full. It requires a control valve and drain connection. The filter element is expensive to replace but generally lasts a few years.

Activated carbon

Activated carbon traps chemicals in the complex, microscopic pores of its surfaces while allowing water to pass through. It can effectively remove chlorine residue and odours such as sulfur. It must be replaced when its porosity deteriorates, but is modestly priced and lasts from several weeks to about a year, depending on size and use. The carbon element must always be protected from clogging by a particle filter upstream.

Sterilization

If a rural water source is used that may contain bacteria or parasites, or if city water is treated to remove chlorine and then stored for use, contact with a sterilizer is recommended before use. The most common sterilizer has a ultra-violet lamp inside a tube that the water passes through as it flows to the tap. The light destroys bacteria and parasites. These devices require access to an outlet for the power supply, and should always be the last stage in the filtration system. They use very little electricity and last for many years.

Special treatment

There are other types of treatment used for special water problems such as those that occur in rural areas. A water treatment specialist should design this type of system using water test results.

In-home water treatment is not a substitute for a safe drinking water supply. It is only a method to make potable water taste better and to replace bottled water. Water to the home must be provided from a safe potable supply.

5.8 Construction Waste Management

Waste produced during site clearance and construction of new homes and residential renovations accounts for a substantial volume of solid wastes currently taken to landfill sites in Canada.

Bans and restrictions on a number of construction wastes and hazardous and recyclable materials are already in place in many parts of Canada, and more are being considered all the time. Many municipalities now have programs to divert solid waste from landfills. Some of these are specifically targeted at the construction industry. Many municipalities require source separation of different waste materials. Some refuse mixed loads or charge a substantially higher tipping fee for them. Consult local waste management authorities for specific details.

Cutting back on the amount of wastes slated for landfill can help builders:

- Reduce the cost of materials purchased;

- Reduce haulage and tipping fees;

- Improve efficiency through altered construction practices; and

- Improve a company's public image by demonstrating a responsibility towards the environment.

5.8.1 The three Rs audit

Basic waste management begins with the three Rs:

- Reducing waste at source

- Reusing what would normally be land-filled

- Recycling materials for which there is no immediate reuse

Construction wastes vary across the country, depending on local practices and materials used.

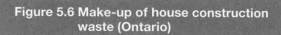

Figure 5.6 Make-up of house construction waste (Ontario)

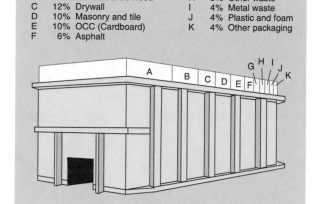

A	25% Dimension lumber	G	5%	Fibreglass
B	15% Manufactured wood	H	5%	Other waste
C	12% Drywall	I	4%	Metal waste
D	10% Masonry and tile	J	4%	Plastic and foam
E	10% OCC (Cardboard)	K	4%	Other packaging
F	6% Asphalt			

Figure 5.6 illustrates typical waste generated in Ontario projects.

Waste will vary according to design, construction techniques, site management procedures and materials. An audit will determine what wastes are being produced and what they are costing to dispose. Identifying conventional waste volumes, determining where wastage can be reduced, and distinguishing what materials can be reused and recycled is the foundation of an effective waste management plan.

A small-volume builder may only need to examine waste resulting from one or two houses, while a large builder may need to track waste for a period of months to obtain a complete picture. A comprehensive audit system should include:

- Tracking the waste contents of each bin over a specified amount of time.

- Using a new audit sheet each time a bin is emptied.

- Using a chart to track source-separated materials.

- Keeping track of the different construction phases by starting a new chart as a new phase begins. This will help identify operations that produce the most waste.

Checklists will vary according to the type of work each company performs.

5.8.2 Reduce

Reducing waste at source is the most efficient and effective activity of the three Rs. Less waste means decreases in materials purchased and disposed of, with direct savings to the company.

Waste can be reduced by using materials more efficiently and through smart purchasing and handling practices, including:

- Altering floor plans at the design stage to eliminate redundant materials and off-cuts.

- Leaving trees standing where possible or chipping roots and branches on-site at the site-clearing stage.

- Improving materials storage procedures during construction to minimize weather damage.

- Reducing the amount of packaging left at the site by suppliers by requiring recycling of cardboard, plastic and pallets.

- Purchasing materials such as fasteners, paint, caulking and drywall mud in bulk containers.

- Buying more durable materials such as kiln-dried wood to reduce the amount of material rejected due to warping and shrinkage.

- Using factory-made wall panels, engineered wood products and advanced framing techniques (see Advanced Framing Techniques).

- Buying materials made either entirely or partially of recycled materials (using recycled materials reduces the amount of virgin material harvested and consequently reduces the amount of virgin material that ends up as landfill).

- Making sub-trades responsible for dealing with their own waste, or at least requiring sub-trades to place their wastes in separated bins.

- Developing a centralized cutting and storage area on a multi-unit job to keep all wood waste in one spot. This promotes reuse of off-cuts, allows for better collection of waste wood, and makes for faster clean-up.

Manufacturers are already offering less wasteful products and products with decreased packaging. The number of construction materials with recycled content is also growing. Builders can expedite this process by asking suppliers for resource-conserving products (Figure 5.7).

5.8.3 Reuse

Reusing what would normally be landfilled is the second most important element of the three Rs. All too often, perfectly useful materials are thrown into the disposal bin for convenience. The following are a few of the ways that builders and renovators can save money and increase quality by reusing waste materials.

- Off-cuts from framing lumber can be reused as bridging, blocking or forming stakes.

- Excess insulation from exterior walls can be reused as sound barrier material in interior walls that carry plumbing pipes; using this excess is cheaper than paying for its haulage.

- Drywall pails can be used as tool caddies, dust bins, etc.

- Plastic packaging can be reused as garbage bags or as protective covers for materials.

Builders can also pool waste resources, storing them at a common location, from where they can be diverted to different jobs, sold for profit or donated to non-profit societies who can use them. A number of centres already divert construction wastes in reusable form.

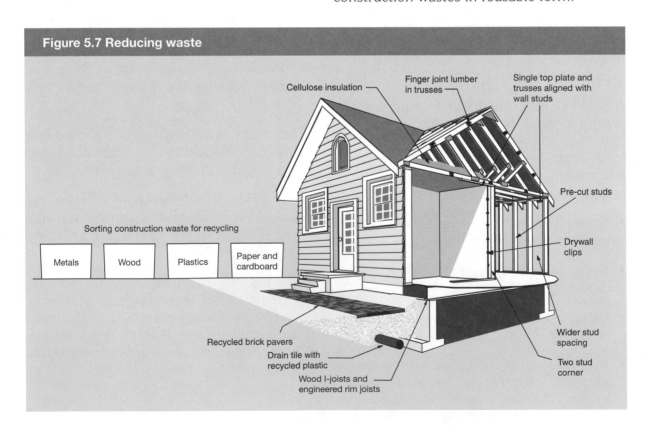

Figure 5.7 Reducing waste

Cellulose insulation

Finger joint lumber in trusses

Single top plate and trusses aligned with wall studs

Pre-cut studs

Drywall clips

Wider stud spacing

Two stud corner

Sorting construction waste for recycling

| Metals | Wood | Plastics | Paper and cardboard |

Recycled brick pavers

Drain tile with recycled plastic

Wood I-joists and engineered rim joists

5.8.4 Recycle

The recycling logo (Figure 5.8) is a familiar symbol, but recycling is the last option that builders should consider. Any production process that makes new materials out of old ones creates new by-products that in turn become waste. But recycling is nevertheless superior to throwing usable material away-anything left in the dumpster should be considered for recycling.

Figure 5.8 The recycling label

Materials already being recycled in various parts of the country include asphalt, concrete, wood, drywall, cardboard, masonry, metals, glass, plastics and paints. Plastics, for example, are being recycled into numerous products like drainage tiles, sump liners and wood substitutes.

Some waste can be sold to recyclers. If recyclers charge to remove waste, the fees are generally less than landfill site tipping fees. In some cases, if amounts warrant, the recycler will provide bins and haul the waste free of charge. However, most builders will set up their own bins for source separation. Wastes such as wood, drywall, cardboard, etc. must be separated and stored independently.

The economics of recycling are much more attractive when the material is clean and not contaminated with other wastes. Where there is a market, clean waste always brings a higher price.

Bins for each kind of waste will have to be clearly labelled, identifying what materials go where. On smaller jobs, a single bin with a series of dividers can be used to keep wastes separate from each other. To keep waste clean, consider locking containers – someone else's garbage bag inside an otherwise clean load can spoil the entire load. Larger companies might consider setting up a blue box system for residents who move in early and do not have garbage pick-up.

The list of potential sources and uses of recycled materials grows daily. More specialized equipment for recycling, and more specialized recycled materials, will begin to appear. Find out what materials can be recycled locally, and be aware of new developments as new uses for old materials become more practical and widespread.

5.8.5 Materials Selection to Reduce Environmental Impact

As the energy required to operate houses is reduced, the importance of the energy required to manufacture, transport, recycle or dispose of building materials increases. The most environmentally responsible builders should consider this when selecting construction materials.

Recycled and renewable materials are preferable, but as environmental responsibility increases in importance, many materials once thought of as environmentally irresponsible, are reducing their impact on the environment through the use of recycled materials or lower-impact manufacturing processes.

Blown cellulose insulation, for example, has always generated high marks for environmental responsibility because it is often made from recycled paper. But rock wool is also made of recycled waste. Fibreglass insulation can have a very high recycled content. Check labels and manufacturers' claims to ensure you are choosing the most sustainable materials.

Wood from sustainably-managed forests is always a good choice – it is re-usable, recyclable, renewable and sequesters carbon from the atmosphere. Selection of finger-jointed finishes and engineered wood reduces the impact on old-growth forests. But wood is certainly not the only environmentally-responsible choice. Almost all steel is recycled, for example. Bamboo has an increasing range of useful products. No industry has made greater strides in reducing the impact of their products than the concrete industry. Paint and finishing manufacturers have also been very diligent.

Research is always required to ensure you are making the best environmental choices.

Summary

The common practice of leaving mixed garbage in random piles around the construction site must be discontinued if waste reduction is to succeed.

The introduction of new practices may require some planning. However, once these changes have been properly implemented, they will become a regular component of site management procedures. Often, it is simply a matter of substituting one routine for another.

5.9 Marketing Environmental Features

There is no doubt that public concern about the environment is increasing, and more and more, consumers are willing to pay a premium to get a greener home. If a builder is going to build greener housing, then potential buyers need to know and understand the features included. To develop a market niche, it is important to differentiate greener houses from others on the market.

Builders should also look to material and product manufacturers for assistance when developing green building plans. Most leading manufacturers offer environmentally improved products, and can also provide useful information on selecting and promoting green building features.

Builders need to ensure that any green claims are real, significant and can be substantiated. While consumers are increasingly interested in green products, research shows that they are also skeptical about the green claims that businesses make.

Incorporating a few greener products in an otherwise conventional home will not significantly reduce its environmental impact. Most consumers understand this.

As discussed previously, the operational energy and water use in a home has the most significant impact on the environment. A home that is not energy-efficient simply cannot be called green.

For builders wanting to develop greener homes, the most accessible option is to get involved in a voluntary, market-driven and industry-supported process such as the R-2000 Program, CHBA's Net Zero Energy Housing, or other regional initiatives that are based upon R-2000's *House as a System* approach. This will provide builders with the information, learning opportunities and support needed to become a successful green home builder.

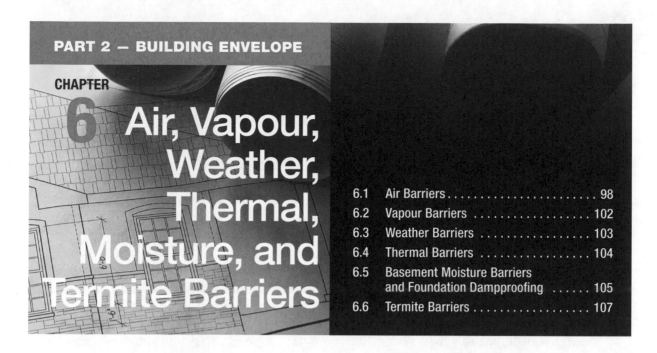

PART 2 — BUILDING ENVELOPE

CHAPTER

6 Air, Vapour, Weather, Thermal, Moisture, and Termite Barriers

Chapter 3 outlined many of the factors that need to be considered during the general design process. To develop the final plans for a building and to schedule construction, a builder needs to determine the exact materials and construction methods to be used.

Houses are subjected to a range of weather conditions. Building assemblies must include elements to protect the structural members from exposure to excessive humidity levels and to ensure that wind does not adversely affect the performance of thermal insulation materials. This chapter defines these barriers and provides guidelines to help ensure that structures will be durable and will perform as expected over the service life of the building. Figure 6.1 is a legend for the key elements used in figures showing barriers. Chapter 8 provides further detail for the air barrier principles presented in this chapter.

Figure 6.1 Key to illustrations for Chapters 6 to 13

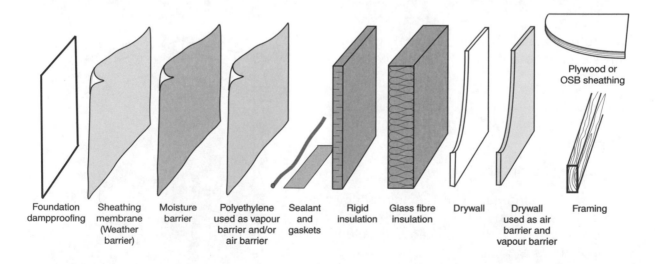

Foundation dampproofing   Sheathing membrane (Weather barrier)   Moisture barrier   Polyethylene used as vapour barrier and/or air barrier   Sealant and gaskets   Rigid insulation   Glass fibre insulation   Drywall   Drywall used as air barrier and vapour barrier   Framing   Plywood or OSB sheathing

6.1 Air Barriers

In cold climates, air barriers are designed to reduce the outward migration of moisture-laden air through the envelope structure and to reduce the inward migration of cold air. Since almost all interior water vapour is carried outwards by air movement and only a small amount diffuses through materials, the air barrier is the most important component in the building envelope for preventing condensation in insulated cavities. The air barrier is the designated air leakage control system for the building, and is comprised of a collection of materials and components that must be continuous at all corners, partition walls, floors and ceiling/wall junctions, windows, doors and other openings. The air barrier system is comprised of a main air barrier material that forms the principal plane of airtightness and is made continuous through the use of tapes, caulks, foams, gaskets and other accessories.

An effective air barrier system:

- Has a low air leakage rate;

- Is continuous over the entire envelope;

- Has strength to withstand the forces that may act on it during and after construction; and,

- Is durable over the expected lifetime of the building.

In addition to controlling air leakage, air barriers provide a number of other benefits including:

- Reducing wind-driven rain penetration in walls when used as part of a rainscreen system;

- Reducing heating loads in winter;

- Allowing maintenance of healthy indoor relative humidities when used in combination with a correctly designed and installed ventilation system;

- Reducing cooling loads in summer;

- Reducing outside noise penetration; and,

- Increasing occupant comfort by eliminating drafts.

There are several different building techniques used to achieve a continuous air barrier. Polyethylene (Figure 6.2) is commonly used as the primary interior air barrier in combination with sealants and rim (header) wraps. Common rim wraps are sheathing membranes (house wraps) that have qualified for use as an air barrier material. In this manual, polyethylene used for the air barrier is referred to as the sealed polyethylene approach (SPA). A second technique uses drywall in combination with sealants, gaskets, framing members and other rigid materials. Commonly known as a structural air barrier or the airtight drywall air barrier, throughout this Manual it is referred to as the airtight drywall approach (ADA). There are also two common exterior air barrier approaches: the exterior insulation approach (EIA) uses rigid foam insulation board, and the house wrap approach (HWA) uses a flexible sheathing membrane. Chapter 8 provides details for each of these four air barrier approaches.

Figure 6.2 Air barrier

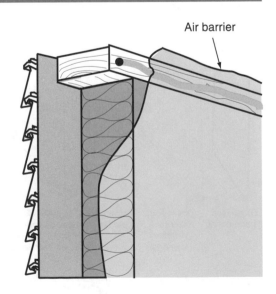

Air barrier

Air barrier material can be installed at any location in the wall, floor or ceiling assembly. The only restriction is that if an air barrier is also a vapour barrier (i.e., has a water vapour permeance less than 60 ng/Pa·s·m2) it must be kept on the warm side of the assembly. Interior-applied air barrier systems have the following advantages:

• Located on the inside of the insulation, they are in a stable, warm environment;

• They have a good performance record; and,

• They can prevent particles, fibres, gases emitted from building materials and mould spores within the construction assembly from entering the indoor environment.

Exterior-applied air barrier systems have their own advantages:

• Labour and material costs are lower because there are fewer connections, joints and penetrations to seal; and,

• The building can be tested for airtightness before the drywall is completed.

There are two basic types of air barrier materials: sheet membrane and rigid panel. Both are effective if installed properly, used in the appropriate building type and suited for the expected wind pressures. Air barriers, being the most airtight component of the building envelope, take the brunt of wind pressures on the building. In a low-rise building, pressures of more than a 1,000 Pascals (20 psf) can be caused by wind, depending on building height and wind exposure. The air barrier must be structurally strong enough to withstand these pressures without damage over the life of the building. In addition, the NBC specifies that the air barrier must not adversely affect nonstructural elements (for example, compress insulation) at code-factored wind loads. Membrane air barriers are more appropriate for one- and two-storey buildings in wind-shaded locations. Rigid air barriers or structurally supported membrane air barriers

are best used in three- to four- storey buildings, as well as those with high wind exposure.

Chapter 7 discusses specific physical properties and characteristics of air barrier materials and compatible sealant, tape and gasket options. Specific detailing, sequencing and installation procedures are described in Chapter 8.

6.1.1 Interior membrane air barrier—sealed polyethylene approach (SPA)

Polyethylene is one of the most common air barrier materials in energy-efficient houses. Its primary advantage is its capability of providing both the air and vapour barriers. If it is the designated air barrier system, it must be continuous and sealed throughout the building envelope. If it serves solely as the designated vapour barrier, it needs to be continuous, but does not need to be sealed. To ensure an effective air barrier, seams in the polyethylene should occur over solid backing, be overlapped and caulked with an acoustical caulking, and be stapled and sandwiched between rigid materials. Detailing at penetrations through the envelope for electrical boxes and ducting requires special attention. In many instances, a sheathing membrane (house wrap) having low air permeance is used as a rim wrap across floors, to maintain the continuity of the polyethylene installed on the interior of exterior walls.

Because of its location in the building envelope, the polyethylene air barrier cannot be easily accessed after construction. Therefore, specific steps must be taken to ensure its long-term effectiveness. Standard installation practices include:

• Ensuring that polyethylene is located on the warm side of the wall assembly at all times.

• Using UV-stabilized 6 mil polyethylene (CAN/CGSB-51.34-M86).

• Ensuring compatibility of sealants with the polyethylene.

- Ensuring polyethylene is not exposed to sunlight for extended periods prior to the installation of covering materials.

- Minimizing seams in the polyethylene by using the largest sheets possible.

- Overlapping seams of polyethylene by a minimum of 100 mm (4 in.).

- Ensuring seams are located over rigid backing such as studs.

- Caulking polyethylene seams with a flexible, non-drying sealant (such as acoustical sealant) and stapling seams through the sealant into solid backing.

- Sealing seams with an appropriate construction tape.

- Sandwiching polyethylene seams between two solid materials (for example, stud/drywall, stud/strapping, etc.).

- Ensuring that polyethylene is not in direct contact with heat-producing surfaces (e.g. chimneys, hot-water pipes, baseboard heaters, etc.).

In addition to polyethylene, interior membrane air barriers can also be comprised of aluminium foil and tape. Like polyethylene, this can also serve as the vapour barrier, but needs to be supported on both sides to resist wind billowing.

6.1.2 Interior membrane air barrier— airtight drywall approach (ADA)

This rigid air barrier approach was developed as an alternative to the use of polyethylene. The approach stresses the use of rigid materials, usually drywall, as components of the air barrier system. By sealing the drywall at all junctions and by incorporating subfloors, rigid insulations and framing members as part of the system, an effective air barrier can be achieved.

The rigid air barrier offers several advantages over its membrane counterpart:

- It is not easily damaged during construction

- It will stand up to high wind pressures

- It is accessible from the interior and can be repaired after construction

The vapour barrier can be provided by a variety of means, such as polyethylene, expanded polystyrene insulation, foil-backed drywall, or low water vapour permeance interior paints.

Chapter 7 provides information on the materials used in the ADA system and Chapter 8 provides further details. In addition, some general installation procedures are as follows:

- Seams between all components of the air barrier must be adequately sealed.

- Drywall is usually sealed to the framing or subfloor parts of the air barrier system by using adhesive-backed foam tape. The tape must be soft and resilient so that it will accommodate movement and fill all gaps. The gasket must be stapled to wood framing to ensure it will stay in place during drywall installation. It is important that the drywall be screwed or nailed at 200 mm (8 in.) spacing over the gasket to provide an airtight seal.

- Caulking must be flexible, durable and adhere well to wood, drywall, foam insulations and metals.

- One-part urethane caulking has the best performance, but should not be used where chemical sensitivity is a concern. Flexible panel adhesives can be used to seal small gaps between framing members. As an alternative to one-part urethane caulking, a neutral cure formulation silicone caulking can be used, but with a reduction in performance quality.

6.1.3 Exterior air barrier systems

Installation of the air barrier on the exterior of the framing assembly is a more recent development. Several exterior air barrier systems have been used, including:

- A flexible exterior membrane comprised of house wrap that meets the requirements of a sheathing membrane (weather barrier) and that has been qualified by the Canadian Construction Materials Centre (CCMC) to serve as an air barrier. (See HWA details in Chapter 8.) The membrane must be systematically sealed at all joints and penetrations through the exterior wall and to the upper storey ceiling and foundation air barriers. With this type of system, a vapour barrier must still be used on the warm side of the insulation. The sheathing membrane air barrier must be supported structurally on both sides.

- A rigid exterior insulation system in which rigid insulation is applied as an exterior sheathing and is sealed at all joints and penetrations. As builders move towards Net Zero levels of energy efficiency, thicker levels of exterior insulation are likely to be the approach chosen. While thicker insulation may provide advantages of reducing thermal bridging at studs and increasing overall insulation levels, it may also provide practical challenges of fastening it to the wall and fastening of the strapping and cladding materials.

- Liquid-applied exterior air barrier systems can be sprayed or pressure-rolled on to a variety of substrates and are increasingly being used.

In the case of vapour permeable exterior air barriers, a vapour barrier must be located on the inside of the assembly. Alkyd paints or vapour retarding drywall sealers and paints, polyethylene, aluminium or foil-backing on drywall can be used as the designated vapour barrier.

The National Building Code of Canada calls for air barrier materials to have an air permeability of no more than 0.02 L/(s·m2) measured at 75 Pascals (Appendix 2). To produce an effective air barrier system as required by the Code, the designated air barrier materials and components must be systematically sealed at all joints and penetrations, and made continuous throughout the envelope.

The building code also states that if an exterior element has a water vapour permeance of less than 60 ng/(Pa·s·m2), it is deemed to be a low-permeance material. As a result, the interior vapour barrier must have a greater resistance to vapour permeance and must be designed by a professional engineer or architect.

6.1.4 Insulated concrete forming systems

Insulated concrete form (ICF) systems are of concrete construction. Concrete is a good air barrier, provided the details at penetrations and junctions with other materials are made airtight. Refer to manufacturer's information for specific air sealing details. In addition, the foam material of the form is a vapour barrier.

6.1.5 Aerosol Air Barrier

This is relatively new application of an existing technology. It is mentioned here because it is gaining traction with builders. The product enhances the air tightness of the building and seals cracks and holes that cannot be seen or reached by workers.

The process is completed after the air barrier has been installed and at a time before the house is completed. Often this is after the installation of the drywall but before finishes. The intentional openings are sealed (windows, fans, HRV ducts, etc.). An aerosol-based sealant is sprayed into the air and a blower door is used to pressurize the house. As the sealant leaks out through the unintentional cracks and holes, the sealant sticks to the edges of the hole and eventually seals the hole. Using the blower door for pressurization allows for the process to be continuously monitored during the sealing process and the improvement in air tightness can be seen in real-time. Levels of air tightness below 0.5 ACH50 are being achieved.

Up to this point in time, air tightness was achieved based on the experience of the crew and their attention to detail during the installation, caulking and taping of the air barrier. The success in meeting the air tightness target was usually determined after the house was completed. Failure to achieve the air tightness target often resulted in repairs being needed to the air barrier, which was by that time, inaccessible behind walls and ceilings. Fixing the problem often resulted in the deconstruction of parts of the house to get to the hole. This new approach incorporates the measurement of the air tightness at the same time as the sealing is occurring. It provides the builder with certainty that the air barrier is in place and it provides the tightness of the house metric. Since the air tightness is being measured at the time of sealing, the sealing process can be extended to achieve a tighter house or meet the target required.

As homes move towards Net Zero Energy, builders and energy advisors are seeing an increased importance in air-sealing and in achieving air tightness targets that are much less than 1.0 ACH50. Being able to predict the air tightness with certainty assists in the design and energy evaluation of the house to meet the energy target. R-2000 demonstrated that houses with improved air tightness have enhanced durability along with improved interior comfort levels. The levels of air tightness achievable with this approach is a significant improvement on the R-2000 targets so builders expect to see even more improvement in durability and indoor comfort.

As the air barrier continues to rise in importance it is expected that other innovations to improve the air barrier will emerge.

6.2 Vapour Barriers

A vapour barrier is a membrane, material or coating that slows the diffusion of interior water vapour into insulated exterior assemblies such as walls, ceilings and exposed floors, and that helps prevent condensation of water vapour on cold surfaces in these areas. Polyethylene, aluminium foil and certain kinds of paint can be used as vapour barriers (see Chapter 7).

Whereas an air barrier needs to be continuous and sealed, a vapour barrier needs only to be continuous, and the joints and penetrations do not need to be sealed. In residential construction, polyethylene is often used as the designated air barrier, but also performs the role of the vapour barrier.

Depending on the vapour permeance of the interior air barrier, alkyd paints or vapour retarding drywall sealers, polyethylene, or foil-backing on drywall can also be used as the vapour barrier. Vapour barriers are classified according to their water vapour permeability and measured in ng/(Pa·s·m2) "perms." The lower the perm rating of a material, the more effectively it will retard diffusion. If paint or sealer is used as the vapour barrier, it must be applied evenly to the thickness required to obtain the correct rating.

New materials called "smart" vapour barriers are materials that have the physical property of changing their vapour permeance depending on relative humidity. The goal of the "smart" vapour barrier is to have high permeance when there is low RH to prevent vapour from warm indoor air penetrating the wall interior, and low permeance during high humidity periods, where both interior and exterior drying are desirable.

A vapour barrier must have a water vapour permeance no greater than 60 ng/(Pa·s·m2), but is subject to the climatic location of the building and the anticipated indoor relative humidity. In colder regions in Canada and in milder regions where the indoor RH is more than 60 %, a professional engineer or architect must determine the appropriate water vapour permeance level required.

Condensation will occur on any surface that is below the dew point temperature. The vapour barrier can be located anywhere within the assembly if enough insulation is on the cold side to keep the assembly warm and prevent condensation. In most regions of Canada, this amounts to two-thirds of the insulating value of the insulation on the cold side (Figure 6.3).

In northern areas, it may be necessary to put as much as four-fifths of the insulating value on the cold side of the vapour barrier.

In areas where there are periods of hot and humid weather in the summer, especially when a central air conditioning unit is installed, locating the vapour barrier on the inside would put it on the "wrong" side of the wall (i.e. the cold side) in the summer. In these circumstances, a "smart" vapour barrier, where permitted by code, should be considered.

Figure 6.3 Recessed vapour barrier

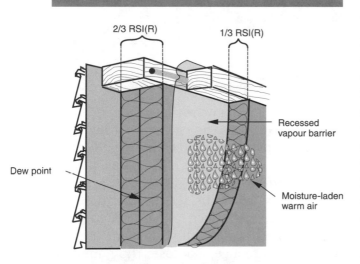

6.3 Weather Barriers

Weather barriers, also called sheathing membranes or sheathing barriers, protect the components of exterior walls from the effects of wind, rain, snow and sun. They can help block wind passing into and out of the wall cavity (called wind washing), which reduces the thermal effectiveness of fibrous insulations such as fibreglass (Figure 6.4). If rain or snow penetrates the weather barrier, the insulation may become wet, resulting in reduced thermal effectiveness, and structural members may be damaged.

Figure 6.4 Weather barrier

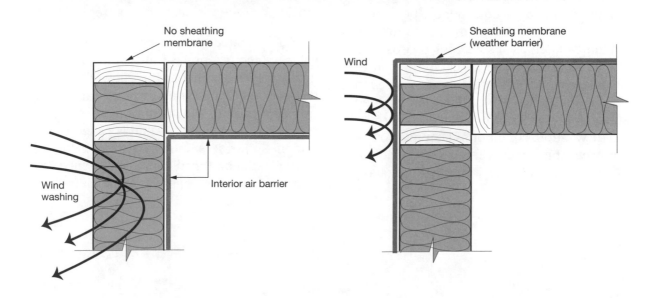

There are two types of weather barriers: building papers that are specified in the NBC, and proprietary house wraps which are not specified in the building code but are qualified by the Canadian Construction Materials Centre (CCMC) to perform as a water-resistant barrier.

Building papers should be installed horizontally and lapped to ensure shedding of water towards the exterior. If kept in a wet environment over a prolonged period of time, building papers can deteriorate. Building papers will last longer if they are allowed to drain freely.

House wraps will perform best as weather barriers if they are sealed at all joints and penetrations with a compatible, durable tape. If a house wrap is also qualified for and installed to be the designated air barrier, sealing is mandatory and structural support must be provided on both sides.

Rain passing through cedar, wood or wood-based siding, or absorbent claddings can potentially absorb small amounts of natural oils and chemicals. When these cladding materials are directly applied onto house wrap, the dissolved chemicals can be deposited on the house wrap, acting as surfactants, making it easier for the water to penetrate the pores of the plastic house wraps, thus reducing the water resistance characteristics of the house wrap. Current accepted liquid water diffusivity test protocols do not consider the performance of the house wraps in direct contact with cladding materials or sheathing boards; furring should be used to keep the cladding away from the house wrap. Similar issues have arisen from the inappropriate use of detergents added to stucco mixes to improve workability in cooler (cold) weather conditions. Damage to house wrap can be circumvented by providing an air space as explained in the next paragraph.

The NBC designates the weather barrier as the 'inner boundary' of the second plane of protection from rain penetration as part of the cladding performance requirements. Depending on the climatic location (such as wetter coastal areas), claddings must have a secondary plane of protection that includes a 10 mm (13/32 in.) air space capillary break and a sheathing membrane. Furring must be provided over the weather barrier to provide the drainage/air space behind the cladding. For non-coastal areas, the 10-mm air space is waived for code-specified building paper sheathing barriers.

Sheathing barrier materials are described in more detail in Chapter 7.

6.4 Thermal Barriers

There are two main ways that heat is lost from buildings. Heat loss can occur as a result of air leakage (convection), and can be significantly reduced by means of an effective air barrier. The second way heat is lost is through conduction; all walls, ceilings and floors separating heated space from unheated space need to be provided with sufficient thermal insulation to reduce heat loss. The minimum amount of insulation required is determined by climate and local codes. However, the cost of additional insulation can often be recouped quickly by reduced heating requirements.

Insulation is rated based on its thermal resistance value, which is a precise measurement of the insulation's resistance to heat flow. The higher the resistance value, the slower the rate of heat transfer through the insulating material. In metric units, insulation value is called RSI; in imperial units, it is known as the R-value. For example, the batt insulation used to fill a 38 x 140 mm (2 x 6 in.) cavity has an insulting value of about RSI 3.70 (R-21). Appendix 1 provides insulation values for a number of materials and Table 9.2 (see Chapter 9) shows suitable uses for various types of insulation. R-values do not consider the effects of air convection. Some insulations lose significant amounts of their thermal resistance if subjected to wind-washing.

It is important to remember that the R-value of *insulation* material is not necessarily the R-value that an assembly will achieve, especially for frame construction. At the locations of framing members, there is a lower R-value than between the framing members where only insulation material is present. The higher rate of heat transfer at framing members is called thermal bridging. Framing materials, which can account for 20% or more of the surface area of the wall, have a significant effect on the thermal resistance of the assembly. Rigid insulation on the exterior of the wall framing increases the overall R-value and reduces the effects of thermal bridging of the wall studs.

The overall thermal performance of an assembly depends on the combined effect of the framing and insulation. For this reason, new energy codes stipulate the *effective* R-value of assemblies needed to meet thermal insulation requirements. Effective R-value takes into consideration the thermal effect of all the materials in the assembly.

6.5 Basement Moisture Barriers and Foundation Dampproofing

Moisture can move from the ground through the foundation wall and slab by diffusion, as well as by capillary action. The moisture can then be released into the air in the basement. To avoid this, dampproofing is required on the exterior of foundation walls located below grade. The application of a bitumen coating can prevent water in the soil from penetrating the concrete walls. A drained bed of crushed rock or clean gravel base with no fine particles beneath a slab will provide a capillary break that prevents groundwater from passing through the slab (see Chapter 9).

Dampproofing is also required on the below-grade portion of interior foundation walls where wood framing or batt insulation is in contact with the concrete. A moisture barrier acting as dampproofing is usually provided on the interior of the foundation wall, using building paper or house wrap that is approved for this use. One or the other is required on the below-grade portions of the foundation wall (Figure 6.5). To ensure good coverage, the number of seams in the barrier should be minimized. Any seams should overlap to deflect water away from the wall and be sealed with a compatible material (Chapter 7).

Figure 6.5 Interior basement moisture barrier

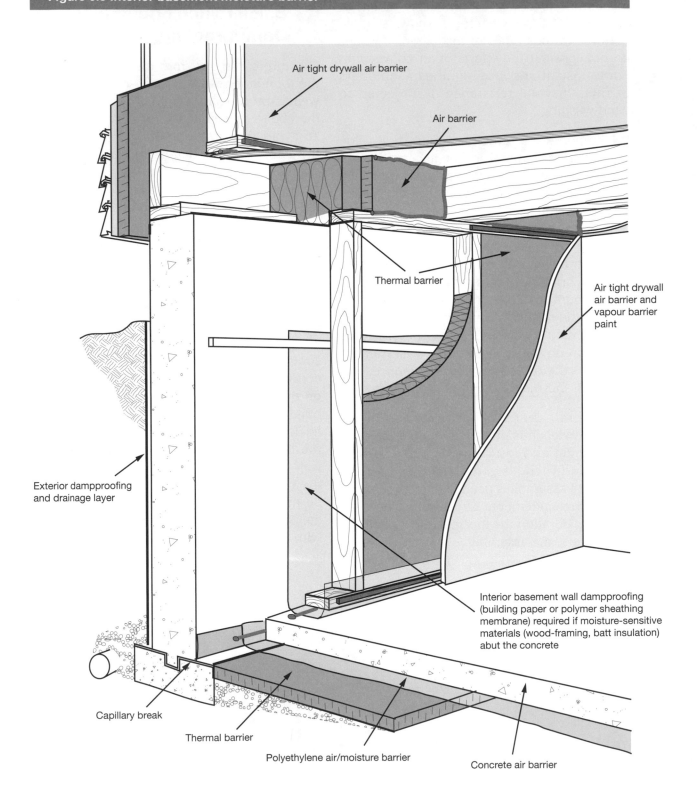

Air tight drywall air barrier

Air barrier

Thermal barrier

Air tight drywall air barrier and vapour barrier paint

Exterior dampproofing and drainage layer

Interior basement wall dampproofing (building paper or polymer sheathing membrane) required if moisture-sensitive materials (wood-framing, batt insulation) abut the concrete

Capillary break

Thermal barrier

Polyethylene air/moisture barrier

Concrete air barrier

6.6 Termite Barriers

Termites are present in the southernmost regions of Canada-southwest Ontario and pockets of southern Manitoba, Saskatchewan, Alberta and British Columbia. The National Building Code of Canada has established requirements to protect against termite damage in areas where termites are known to occur:

- The clearance between structural wood elements and the finished ground level directly below them needs to be at least 450 mm (18 in.).

- All sides of the supporting foundation need to be visible to permit inspection so the tubes constructed by termites to move between the ground and their food sources can be seen.

- Structural wood members supported by elements in contact with the ground or exposed over bare soil need to be pressure-treated with a chemical that is toxic to termites.

- In cases where the foundation is insulated or finished in a manner that could conceal a termite infestation, a metal or plastic barrier needs to be installed through the insulation and any other separation or finish materials above finished ground level to control the passage of termites behind or through the insulation or finish materials.(Figure 6.6)

In addition, backfill needs to be free of woody material that could serve as a food source and encourage infestation close to a house. It is important to keep in mind that these are minimum requirements; there are additional measures that can be taken to improve protection. Chemical poisoning of the soil around a foundation is no longer considered safe or environmentally acceptable. Modern acceptable barriers include:

- A termite-resistant stainless-steel mesh barrier placed under and around the foundation.

- A layer of specially sized sand under and around the foundation that discourages termite movement.

Figure 6.6 Termite Shield

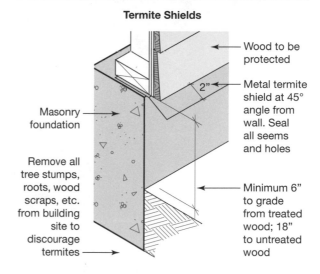

Termite Shields

Wood to be protected

Metal termite shield at 45° angle from wall. Seal all seems and holes

2"

Masonry foundation

Remove all tree stumps, roots, wood scraps, etc. from building site to discourage termites

Minimum 6" to grade from treated wood; 18" to untreated wood

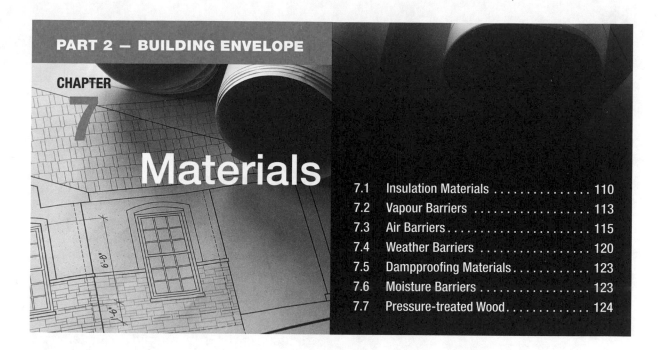

Materials

This chapter describes the materials used to control heat loss and moisture movement in houses. It provides general information for comparison purposes only; detailed information about any product should be obtained from product manufacturers and distributors. In addition, readers are encouraged to consult product evaluations issued by the Canadian Construction Materials Centre.

7.1 Insulation Materials

An insulating material slows the rate of heat flow from a warmer to a cooler area. Building envelopes generally consist of several components that act in different ways to slow heat flow:

- Most insulation materials block heat flow by *radiation*. They may be opaque to radiation, much as dark glass is opaque to light transfer, or they may act to reflect heat back, as with reflective foil sheeting.

- Insulation material contains tiny pockets of air or other gas(es) that reduce the *conduction* of heat.

- The air or gas pockets should be small enough and separated so that the possibility of heat flow via *convection* is reduced.

The thermal resistance of insulation materials depends on:

- Cell structure-the smaller the cells, the more effective they are in reducing heat transfer.

- The gas contained in the insulation-some gases, such as refrigerant gases, have proven to be more effective than air at stopping heat transfer by conduction.

- Moisture content-any water trapped in an insulating material will tend to fill the spaces that are normally occupied by air or gas, reducing the material's ability to block heat flow by conduction.

Heat transfer through the building envelope is probably most affected by the way the insulation is used and installed. First, the insulated space must be completely filled with material – there must be no gaps or voids. Second, the insulation must be kept dry.

Insulation materials available include batt-type, loose-fill, boardstock, spray-type, and radiant barriers. Table 7.1 summarizes the characteristics, advantages and disadvantages of these various types of insulation. Products with increased density generally have higher insulating value and, at the same time, reduce convective air movements within a building cavity.

7.1.1 Batt insulation

Batt-type insulation is made from glass or mineral fibres. These materials are suitable for interior use in walls, ceilings, and floors and for the interior insulation of foundations. Insulation values of the various products are a function of the density of the materials.

The performance of batt-type insulation products is directly related to installation practices. Gaps and compression around wiring and plumbing must be avoided, and the insulation must fill cavities completely and evenly.

7.1.2 Loose-fill insulation

Glass fibre, mineral wool and cellulose insulations are available in loose-fill form. The insulation material is chopped, mixed with air, and blown into place using special machinery. It can be used in attics and inside above-grade exterior walls. Loose-fill materials in walls require the installation of a mesh or other material over the face of a wall to temporarily contain the insulation material prior to the installation of the finished wallboard. The insulation must be applied at the correct density to attain good performance. Manufacturers' literature will provide information on the recommended application procedure and density for a given product.

Cellulose fibre insulation is made from recycled newsprint. The raw material is shredded and treated with chemicals to control flammability, to prevent the growth of moulds and fungi, and to deter rodents from nesting in the material.

Table 7.1 Properties of insulation materials

Insulation Type	RSI/mm (R/in.)	Density kg/m³ (lb/ft³)	Permeance ng/Pam²s (grain/ft² hr (in.Hg))	Flame Spread	Smoke Develop-ment	Advantages	Disadvantages
7.1.1 Batt						• widely available • relatively non-combustible	• moisture and air infiltration reduce performance • compression due to weight of multiple layers of batts can reduce performance
Glass fibre	0.022 (3.2)	24-40 (1.5-2.5)	1666 (29)	15	0		
Mineral fibre	0.024 (3.5)	24-64 (1.5-4.0)	1666 (29)	15	0		
7.1.2 Loose-fill						• widely available • relatively non-combustible • more impervious to air flow if installed at high density (56 kg/m³–3.5lb/ft.³	• settling and voids can occur if not applied at the correct density • moisture and air infiltration reduce performance
Glass fibre	0.020 (2.9)	9.8-40 (0.61-2.5)	1666 (29)	15	0		
Mineral fibre	0.023 (3.3)	24-64 (1.5-4.0)	1666 (29)	15	0		
Cellulose fibre	0.025 (3.6)	35-48 (2.2-3.0)	1666 (29)	75	15		
7.1.3 Boardstock (rigid and semi-rigid)						• variety of facing materials can provide air and moisture resistance and protection against ultraviolet rays • available in several densities for use in different applications • moisture resistant • resistant to airflow	• combustible
Expanded polystyrene (Types I and II)	0.026 (3.8) to 0.030 (4.4)	14.4-25.6 (0.9-1.6)	115-333 (2.0-5.8)	200	500		
Extruded Polystyrene	0.035 (5)	16.01 (2.2)	60-90 (1-1.5)	200	500		
Semi-rigid glass or mineral fibre	0.029-0.031 (4.2-4.5)	48-144 (0.3-9.0)	1725 (30)	15	0	• can serve as a drainage layer • suitable for below grade, exterior use	• requires mechanical fastening
Mineral fibre insulating sheathing	0.029 (4.0)	128 (8.0)	1768 (30.9)	5	10	• non-combustible • water repellent	• not suitable for below grade, exterior use
7.1.4 Spray-applied						• impervious to airflow water repellent but vapour permeable • fills irregular voids	• combustible • application only by qualified installers
Polyicynene	0.62 (3.6)	8 (0.5)	941 (16)	20	400		
Polyisocyanate (polyurethane)	0.96 (5.5) to 1.1 (6.25)	24-40 (1.5-2.5)	1.7(2)	25-500	400		
7.1.5 Radiant barrier	varies					• vapour impermeable barrier can be air and vapour barrier • can reduce summer cooling loads	• requires an air space on the warm side

7.1.3 Boardstock insulation

There are several types of rigid and semi-rigid boardstock insulations used for residential construction. The R- value per unit of thickness is different for each type. Representative values are listed in Appendix 1.

Expanded polystyrene (EPS)

Expanded polystyrene (EPS) is made by expanding polystyrene beads in a mold. Low-density polystyrene (Type I) is suitable for use as a sheathing material for both below- and above-grade exterior walls. It can also be used to insulate interior basement walls, flat roofs and cathedral ceilings. High-density (Type II) material will withstand fairly high pressures, so it can be used to insulate below-grade walls on the exterior and under slabs- on-grade. The higher the type number, the higher the density of the material. Both materials can be used to insulate the interior of walls above and below grade level. Because these materials are combustible, they must be covered with a fire-protective covering such as 12.7 mm (1/2 in.) drywall when installed in living spaces.

Extruded polystyrene (XPS)

This product is available as Type II, III and IV insulation and is suitable for use in the same applications as Type II expanded polystyrene. It has a higher thermal resistance per unit thickness than expanded polystyrene boardstock.

Type IV is also suitable for use in built-up roofing applications. It is available with a bonded felt layer suitable for hot tar. As all cellular plastics are combustible, this material must be covered with a fire-protective covering when in exposed locations. It also must be covered with a fire-protective covering if used in living spaces.

Semi-rigid glass or mineral fibre

Glass and mineral fibre insulation can also be manufactured as a semi-rigid boardstock. It is compressed to a higher density than batt-type insulation (typically three to five times more), and is generally held together using a combustible organic binder. Rigid glass fibre insulation can be used in built-up roofing applications and as exterior wall sheathing. It can also be used as below-grade exterior wall insulation. The fibres of this product are aligned vertically so that any water that penetrates the insulation will run down the fibres, making it serve as a drainage layer.

Mineral fibre insulating sheathing

Mineral fibre insulating sheathing board mineral is semi-rigid, non-combustible, water repellent, and fire resistant and suitable for above-ground exterior use or below-ground, interior use.

Polyisocyanurates (polyurethanes)

Polyisocyanurate (polyurethane) boardstock can be used for the same applications as Type II expanded polystyrene. As noted earlier, these cellular plastics are combustible and must be covered with a fire-protective coating such as 12.7 mm (1/2 in.) drywall if used in exposed locations. Gases produced by burning this product are very toxic. Scraps should be sent to landfill.

7.1.4 Spray-type insulation

Three different spray-type insulations are available to the residential construction industry.

Spray cellulose insulation

Spray cellulose insulation is available in a variety of formulations to suit specific applications. The material is applied using special applicators that mix the insulation material with water-based adhesives, allowing it to hold together and adhere to the surface to which it is applied. Wet spray materials are gaining broader market acceptance because they offer thorough cavity coverage, reducing envelope air leakage characteristics. Some spray-applied materials require the installation of a mesh over the face of the wall to contain the insulation material prior to the installation of the finished wallboard. Cellulose fibre spray-type insulation can only be used on the interior of the building envelope, and requires the addition of air and vapour barriers.

Spray polyurethane foam (SPF)

Spray-applied polyurethane foam (SPF) is produced by a chemical reaction when two liquid components are combined. There are two main formulations and both require a fire-protective covering:

- Low-density foam (0.5 lbs/ft.2) is typically installed in one pass. When installed between framing members, it is sprayed to slightly overfill the wall cavity and then is trimmed flush to the stud face. It typically has an R-value of about 3.6 to 3.8 per inch. Low-density foam is open-celled and very vapour permeable. Therefore, it requires a vapour barrier.

- Medium-density foam (2 lbs/ft.2) generates high heat and therefore is applied in multiple lifts to achieve the thickness required for the desired R-value. The lifts are usually 50 mm (2 in.) to allow heat to dissipate before the next layer is applied. Medium-density foam is closed-cell and resists water absorption. For a 75 mm (3 in.) thickness, it has a low enough vapour permeance that it can be used without a separate vapour barrier.

Single-component polyurethane foam is available in cans with gun-type dispensers, or in 4.5 kg (10 lb.) canisters for small applications. Low-expansion formulations are available for uses around doors and windows to minimize pressures on frames, which could result in binding of window and door units or void warranties.

7.1.5 Radiant barrier insulation

A radiant barrier is a sheet of reflective material that is installed between a heat-radiating surface such as a roof heated by the sun and a heat-absorbing surface such as a ceiling. Radiant barriers must always have an air space and a clean, shiny surface to be effective. The reflective material stops the radiant transfer of heat between two surfaces.

Radiant barriers can be used to reduce cooling loads in summer by reducing the radiation of heat from the attic through the ceiling. The RSI (R) value provided by a radiant barrier depends on the direction of the heat flow.

Radiant barriers have limited application for winter heat insulation. R-value claims by manufacturers should not be used for thermal performance calculations, because they are not based on or computed the same way as the R-values for conductive insulation products. However, in applications where the radiant barrier is placed on the interior of the structure, inside the thermal insulation and strapped to create an air space, they can function as both a radiant barrier and a vapour barrier.

Because radiant barriers reflect infrared heat energy that is travelling through air, there must be an air space on the warm side of the barrier. For this reason, radiant barriers used beneath concrete floors are ineffective in reducing heat transfer.

7.2 Vapour Barriers

Vapour barriers (also known as vapour diffusion retarders) are materials that resist the diffusion of water vapour through the building envelope. Vapour diffusion resistance ratings are listed in Appendix 2. To qualify as a vapour barrier, a material must have a permeance of 60 ng/(Pa.s.m2) or less. Although a number of materials can be used to provide the vapour diffusion resistance required, polyethylene films and vapour- resistant paint are the most commonly used materials. In all cases, careful application is essential.

Polyethylene film is very resistant to the flow of water vapour and is suitable for use as a vapour barrier. Polyethylene that is used to provide the air barrier function as well as vapour diffusion resistance must comply with the Canadian General Standards Board (CGSB) standard for 0.15 mm (6 mil) polyethylene (CAN/CGSB-51.34-M86) and should be so indicated on the product label.

The vapour barrier can be placed on the inside of the wall or ceiling assembly, or partway into the assembly. However, the placement of the vapour barrier relative to the interior is dependent on the amount of insulation on either side of the vapour barrier and the climate in which the building is built. In general, the more severe the climate, the more thermal insulation there should be to the exterior of the vapour barrier. The NBC provides a table that indicates the minimum ratio of the outboard insulation value to the inboard insulation value that is dependent on the heating-degree days for a given location.

Vapour retarding paints will provide the required resistance to the flow of water vapour and also serves as the drywall finish. Care is required to ensure adequate coverage to attain a suitable perm rating. If paint is used as the vapour barrier, it must meet the requirements of CAN/CGSB-1.501-M89 *Method for Permeance of Coated Wallboard*.

As we contruct houses with more insulation the wall becomes less "forgiving" in terms of being able to dry. Older buildings may not have had perfect flashings and the walls got wet. The low levels of insulation in the walls allowed for a lot of energy to flow from indoors to outdoors in the winter. This energy caused the walls to dry. With poly on the inside, the wall had to dry to the outside. With Net Zero levels of insulation, there is nowhere near the same level of energy flowing through the wall as in older homes. This means even more care is needed in detailing flashings and installing caulk. However, sooner or later every wall will get wet. This means that it is even more important that walls can dry to the inside, to the coutside or both. A "smart" vapour barrier can help. This is a vapour barrier whose permeance (a measure of how readily water vapor can pass through) varies based on the humidity. The materials should have low permeance in the winter when humidity is low but it's important to block moisture flow and prevent condensation. In summer it should have high permeance when humidity is higher so that there is drying potential to both the interior and exterior

The National Building Code, when it refers to permeance values, are reported from a 'dry cup' test. However, 'wet cup' ratings are more representative of in-service conditions. Water vapor transmission (WVT) is the rate of water transmission through a material of a constant thickness at a given time. Water Vapor Transmission is calculated using the formula: $WVT = G / t A = (G / t) / A$ (G = weight gain; t = time tested; A = area of the test area or dish opening).

Dry Cup vs Wet Cup Testing

There are two methods to test the water vapour transmission of a material; desiccant (dry cup) and water (wet cup). These two tests are similar in setup but the service conditions are different and the results are not comparable in any way. The dry cup is designed to simulate a heated dry building during a pouring rain, measuring the drive into the building. The water, or wet cup measures the vapour drive moving in the opposite direction. Another way to think about this is the dry cup method measures the vapour permeance of a material when the material is dry and the wet cup method measures the vapour permeance of the material when it is damp.

To set up for these tests, the desiccant or water is placed in a dish leaving a small gap (0.25" to 0.75") of air space between it and the material being tested. The test chamber is maintained at a constant temperature of 23°C (73.4°F) and a relative humidity of 50 ± 2%. An initial weight is taken of the apparatus and during the course of the test the weight change of the complete test assembly is measured until the results become linear.

The wet cup assembly measures weight loss due to water vapour from the cup transmitting through the material to the test chamber atmosphere as well as the humidity of the test chamber.

The dry cup assembly measures weight gain due to water vapor from the chamber atmosphere transmitting through the material due to the desiccant in the cup absorbing any moisture from the material sample and the humidity from the test chamber that is being absorbed by the material.

Low vapour permeance numbers mean the material is a vapour barrier and higher vapour permeance numbers mean that the material is vapour open. For some materials such as asphalt felt, plywood and OSB, the vapour permeance is variable; meaning that when they are dry, the vapour permeance is low, but when they are damp, the permeance rises. These products are known as variable permeance vapour retarders. Some materials are designed to change vapour permeance with RH, and these are known as "smart" vapour retarders. If we look at water movement through a building assembly over time, we realize that the direction of vapour transport frequently changes. Inside your walls and ceilings, a constant vapour movement is underway, as moisture condenses, evaporates, diffuses through materials, and diffuses back again the other way. It is important that consideration be made to ensure that building materials can dry if they become wet. What is the primary direction that drying will occur; to the inside or to the outside in the area where the building is being constructed? If a building is located in a maritime climate and sees 200 + days of rain a year, most of the drying will be to the inside. That moisture movement will largely be driven by the mechanical, space conditioning equipment making the indoors "drier" than the outdoors.

Practically, knowing the dry cup number for a material will tell you how well warm, moist, indoor air will move into a wall when the exterior vapour pressure is lower than the indoor (winter). Knowing the wet cup number for a material will tell you whether the material will allow drying if the wall gets wet.

7.3 Air Barriers

Air barriers resist the movement of air through the building envelope. Air barriers may be a single material, or a combination of materials that are installed and sealed together in a manner to resist air movement through the system.

7.3.1 Air barrier materials

As noted in Chapter 6, air barriers can be either membrane or rigid barriers. Polyethylene film is often used as a membrane air barrier material. In many cases, it also functions as the vapour barrier. It must be properly situated in the wall or ceiling assembly and sealed with compatible materials. With the rigid air barrier approach, drywall, wood panel sheathing or certain boardstock insulations such as extruded polystyrene, foil- faced polyurethane and polyisocyanurate boardstocks can be used as the air barrier, as long as they are sealed with appropriate gaskets and sealants (see details in Chapter 8 and Chapter 9).

7.3.2 Gasket materials

Gaskets can be used to seal joints between materials to prevent air leakage. They are most commonly used in the sill plate area, but are also used extensively to seal rigid air barriers. The method of attachment must be compatible with the gasket profile and must not compromise the integrity of the air seal.

Desirable characteristics of gaskets are as follows:

- Gaskets must be sufficiently resilient to maintain their seal while accommodating changes in the dimensions of the materials they are intended to seal. These changes can result from seasonal changes in building frame moisture content, building movement due to settlement, and wind and snow loads.

- Gaskets must be thick and wide enough to effectively seal the cavity between the two materials, and must be sufficiently compressible to not cause visible deformations in interior panel materials.

- Gaskets must be made of a material that does not degrade or break down over the service life of the building.

- Gaskets should not be water-soluble nor give off toxic fumes. They should not chemically attack or be affected by the building materials they join or abut.

- Gaskets must be sufficiently durable to withstand the construction process.

Materials that have been employed effectively as gaskets include open- and closed-cell polyethylene, butyl glazing tapes, neoprene, and other polymer-type gaskets.

7.3.3 Caulking and sealant materials

Caulking is used to seal joints between materials to prevent air leakage, sound transmission, and penetration by snow and rain. Most caulks should be applied at temperatures above 15°C (59°F). Manufacturers provide directions for application and storage.

A wide variety of caulking materials are available, each suited to certain applications. They tend to be high VOC emitters; therefore, builders need to be aware of possible indoor air quality problems that can result from the use of a particular sealant, especially in housing for chemically sensitive people. The following table provides some guidelines. (Table 7.2)

Table 7.2 Features of Caulking and sealant materials

Type	Bonds to	Application	Maximurn joint	Comments
Acoustical sealant	• metal, concrete, gypsum board and polyethylene	• use only where sandwiched between two materials (not exposed to the exterior) • staples required when sealing joints in polyethylene • can be reapplied over itself	• 16 mm ($^5/_8$ in.) • accepts 10% joint movement	• good durability: 20 years • non-hardening • not paintable
Butyl rubber caulk (synthetic rubber sealant)	• most surfaces but particularly suited to metal and masonry	• generally used on exterior • ventilation required during application and curing (up to three days) • difficult to smooth	• 13 mm (½ in.) • accepts 5 to 10% joint movement	• low to moderate durability: 5 to 10 years • available in a variety of colours • paintable after curing
Silicone sealant caulk	• most non-porous surfaces • primers may be required on wood, steel or anodized aluminum • cannot be used over existing silicone	• interior and exterior grades • ventilation required during application • easy to smooth • flexible, watertight seal when cured	• 25 mm (1 in.) with backer rod • accepts 12 to 50 % joint movement • excellent for large moving joints	• good durability: 20+ years • available with fungicide for wet locations and in a high-temperature type for use around chimneys/vents • available in colours and clear • most types not paintable • paintable types less durable

Table 7.2 Features of Caulking and sealant materials

Type	Bonds to	Application	Maximurn joint	Comments
Polysulp hide caulk (synthetic rubber sealant)	• stone, masonry and concrete surfaces when usedwith a special primer • may attack some plastics	• generally used on exterior • can be used below grade • ventilation required while curing • moderately easy to smooth • flexible upon curing	• 25 mm (1 in.) with backer rod • accepts 12 to 25% joint movement	• very good durability: 25+ years • available in several colours • paintable
Polyurethane caulk (urethane)	• most surfaces • preferred choice of window and door installers	• exterior use only • ventilation required while curing • long curing time • can be hard to smooth • flexible upon curing • can be reapplied over itself	• 25 mm (1in.) with backer rod • very stretchable: up to 50 % joint movement	• very good durability: 25+ years • limited colours • paintable
Acrylic latex caulk	• most surfaces	• interior and exterior use • ventilation required when curing • easy to smooth	• 10 mm ($^3/_8$ in.) • accepts 7 to 10% joint movement	• low to moderate durability (varies by brand): 5 to 25 years • water cleanup • comes in colours • paintable
Acrylic latex with silicone caulk	• most surfaces	• interior and exterior use • ventilation required when curing • easy to smooth • can be reapplied over itself	• 13 mm (½ in.) • accepts 10 to 15% joint movement	• very good durability: 30 + years • water cleanup • paintable
Elastomeric latex sealant	• most surfaces	• interior (some brands only) and exterior use • ventilation required when curing • flexible upon curing • moderately easy to smooth • can be reapplied over itself	• 25 mm (1 in.) with backer rod • accepts 50 % joint movement	• very good durability: 30+ years • water cleanup limited colours • paintable

Table 7.2 Features of Caulking and sealant materials

Type	Bonds to	Application	Maximurn joint	Comments
Urethane foam sealant (low, medium and high expansion types)	• most surfaces except Teflon, polyethylene or silicone plastics	• interior and exterior use • use only low expansion type around window and door frames or risk bowing • can be used below grade • ventilation required during installation • can be reapplied over previous foam • protect from sunlight	• check the can for expansion rates and sizes of cracks that can be filled • very good for filling larger joints and cavities like header/ joist intersections, around indoor and outdoor plumbing and vent openings, and wiring holes	• good durability: 10 to 20 years • available in individual aerosol spray cans and dispensing systems with spray nozzles • hard consistency when cured • use gloves and a drop cloth: impossible to remove residue after curing • use acetone to clean up uncured foam • paintable
Latex foam sealant	• most surfaces	• interior and exterior use • must be covered for exterior use due to open-cell structure • not for use below grade • ventilation required during installation • extremely flammable during application: read precautions on the product label • can be applied in successive layers • difficult to smooth	• will not over expand – reaches 75% of size upon application • recommended around window and door frames, but requires a vapour barrier	• good durability: 10 to 20 years • cleans up with water • soft, spongy consistency when cured • paintable
High-temperature stove or muffler cements and non-combustible sealants	• most materials • typically used in conjunction with other materials for sealing around masonry or factory-built chimneys	• interior and exterior use • for use in high temperature applications • easy to smooth	• no joint movement	• very good durability • compatible with high-temperature silicone sealant • check product for CSA or UL rating for high-temperature use • available at heating equipment supply stores

7.3.4 Weatherstripping materials

This section provides information on five types of the "active" material used in the manufacture of weatherstripping. Weatherstripping also typically includes a fastening system made from wood, vinyl, or metal, or simply grooves cut into a window or door frame.

The effectiveness of the seal depends on the weatherstripping material, the fastening system and the design of the seal. Hinged units, such as casement windows and entrance doors, work on the principle of compression to create a seal when closed. Sliding units, such as sliding patio doors and horizontally sliding windows, use a friction seal. In general, compression units provide a better seal than friction units, as long as there is no warping.

Before purchasing and installing a window or door system, it is important to assess the effectiveness and durability of the seals and designs used, and obtain information on air leakage characteristics and long-term performance.

Neoprene rubber is used in compression seals. This material is often used in automobile door gaskets. It has good "memory" and compression set resistance-the ability to return to its original shape. It offers superior resistance to the effects of heat, cold, oxidation and ultraviolet light. It does not shrink or crack. It also has excellent impact resistance and good abrasion resistance.

PVC, TPR and polypropylene plastics do not perform as well as rubber products. PVC may shrink or lose flexibility over time. It can be affected by heat, cold and ultraviolet light. If exposed to high temperatures, which sometimes occur between glazing panels, the PVC can set in the compressed form and not return to its original shape. It also becomes brittle over time. Polypropylene has the best performance characteristics of the three. These materials are generally used in compression applications, although some are also used in friction seals.

Steel, bronze and brass do not shrink and are not affected by environmental conditions. They are generally used in friction applications and are very durable. However, since they are easily deformed and rendered ineffective, the design of any window or door system using metal strips is critical.

Pile is particularly suited for use in sliding seals. It is very effective when dry and new, but wears and loses its memory. Some pile products incorporate a central PVC fin that improves durability and performance.

Magnetic strips are two-part systems. A metal strip is attached to the frame of the window or door. A magnetic strip held in vinyl is attached to the face of the window or door. When the unit is closed, the metal and magnet come together to form the seal. This system works well in moderate climates, but the adhesive fastening strips become stiff and perform poorly in cold weather.

7.3.5 Specialty items

Urethane foam is especially good for sealing sill plates, rough-frame openings around windows and doors, and other openings too large to be sealed with caulking or gasket materials.

Figure 7.1 Cap Nails

Sheathing tape is specially designed to provide long service life for sealing housewrap that is approved to serve as a weather barrier and external air barrier, and for sealing exterior rigid insulation. The tape must have excellent adhesion to insulation materials, good low-temperature performance, good ultra violet (UV) stability, and good high-temperature performance. Suitable sheathing tapes are those that have CCMC or other evaluation. Some insulation manufacturers and housewrap manufacturers have come out with their own specialty tapes both for providing better adhesion to their products and to work as flashing materials.

Manufacturers of housewrap recommend the use of cap nails (Figure 7.1) or button staples to affix the material to sheathing. These help ensure a tear-free and air tight application of housewrap.

7.4 Weather Barriers

A weather barrier is a water-resistant material that will allow water vapour to pass through from a high humidity zone to a lower humidity zone. It is used on the exterior of frame walls under the exterior cladding and has three functions:

1. Shed moisture so as to restrict water entry from the exterior.

2. Allow moisture trapped in the wall assembly to escape to the exterior.

3. Act as a wind barrier to restrict air movement into the wall assembly.

The NBC requires a weather (sheathing) barrier to resist the passage of liquid water but to allow the passage of water vapour. It references CAN 2-51.32-M *Sheathing, Membrane, Breather Type*, which covers asphalt- impregnated building paper. Other sheathing membrane materials such as house wrap must be qualified by the Canadian Construction Materials Centre (CCMC) for use as sheathing membrane. Some house wraps are also qualified as air barriers.

Spunbonded polyolefin and woven polypropylene

These materials (commonly referred to as house wraps) shed liquid water and resist airflow but are permeable to the diffusion of water vapour. The woven products may not be tough enough to withstand severe wind and the rough handling they might receive during the construction process. House wraps should be covered within 60 days to prevent potential deterioration caused by ultraviolet radiation. Special sheathing tape is used to seal seams, holes, and openings around windows, doors and service penetrations.

Experience has shown that the performance of plastic house wrap products can be affected by some cladding materials. Minute amounts of natural oils in cedar or acrylic additives used in stucco can dissolve in water. These act as surfactants, reducing the surface tension of water drops, thus making it easier to penetrate the pores of the plastic house wraps. To avoid the problem, cladding materials should not be in direct contact with the house wrap materials.

Building papers

Asphalt-impregnated building papers have been used as weather barriers for decades. Both solid and micro- perforated building papers are available. They must be lapped, shingle fashion, and secured to perform adequately. Some manufacturers recommend two layers. Strapping is most commonly used to hold the paper in place before the siding is applied.

30-minute and 60-minute building paper is a U.S. designation based on a moisture resistance test. The designation is not officially recognized in Canada.

Liquid-applied weather resistive barriers

Liquid-applied weather resistive barriers (WRBs) are applied to wall sheathing by roller, trowel or spray to form a continuous membrane over water-sensitive substrates that is the second plane of protection against water infiltration. Liquid-applied WRBs are most often used in conjunction with proprietary exterior insulation finishing systems (EIFS). In order to provide the intended level of protection against water infiltration, some liquid- applied WRBs are two-coat applications. The continuity of the second plane of protection across joints and junctions at openings, penetrations and expansion joints is maintained by means of accessories such as self- adhering membranes, tapes, etc. as specified by the manufacturer.

Flashings

A Fundamental Part of a Weather Barrier

"Flashing" refers to a thin sheet of water-impervious material used to direct bulk water away from building materials. The fundamental principle is to direct water away from the building. The driving force of bulk water is gravity. Flashings use gravity to help direct water down and out, away from enclosure assemblies, openings, components and materials.

Where possible, the sooner water can be directed away from the building, the better. Since water is one of the most significant causes of building damage, the importance of proper flashing cannot be over-stated. "Proper flashing" is integrated with drainage planes in the buildings.

Flashing has the following functions:

- It protects the interface between two different building elements (roof-wall junctions, for example)

- To direct away water that has penetrated behind the cladding (at the base of a wall)

- To direct water over building protrusions (windows, doors, vents)

Flashings are also required where a drainage plane terminates or is interrupted. (the bottom of a wall, edge of a roof, intersections of assemblies) But flashings must never concentrate water at any part of the building.

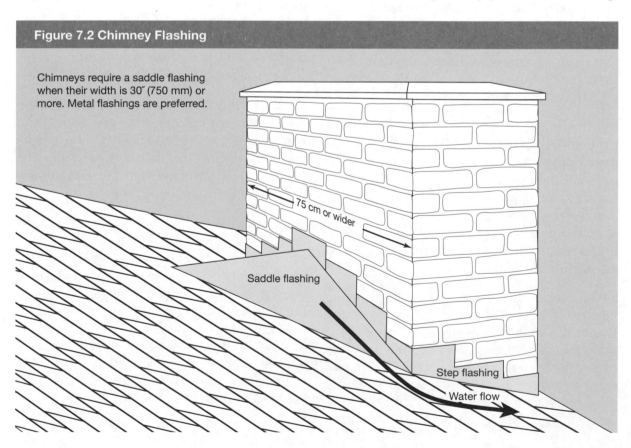

Figure 7.2 Chimney Flashing

Chimneys require a saddle flashing when their width is 30″ (750 mm) or more. Metal flashings are preferred.

75 cm or wider

Saddle flashing

Step flashing

Water flow

Over the years, many different materials have been used for flashing. Modern flashing techniques usually involve a combination of materials. The way these materials work together always follows the fundamental principle: down and out.

Historically, most flashing was made of sheet metal such as copper, lead or zinc, (although aluminum and stainless steel were also used). Before the availability of sheet metals, other flashing strategies were employed. For windows, awnings were used. For chimneys, many strategies were employed such as angling roof shingles away from the penetration, ensuring the chimney was placed at the peak of a gabled roof, and dense mortar at the seals. When the chimney could not be placed strategically at the peak and the chiminey is more than 75 cm (30"), a saddle is constructed to avoid a build up of water behind the chimney. (Figure 7.2)

By the 20th century, various types of putty were employed in flashing systems. White lead putty was used around windows and, by the 1950s asbestos-infused oil-based putties were used. Old caulking around windows degrades with time, but because of asbestos and lead, should be handled with care.

By the early 1960s, putties containing polysulfides were employed. While not presenting the hazards of earlier putties, polysulfide-based sealants were messy to handle and degraded over time. They also often lost their adhesive properties when installed in cold or hot weather. By the 1980s, silicone-based sealants had almost completely replaced polysulfide sealants.

Sealing tape revolutionized flashing. Sealing tape is a thin sheet of aluminum (or something similarly flexible and air- and water-tight) backed with adhesive. Flashing tape is easy to use, easy to store and comes in convenient pre-cut widths from about 5 cm to 60 cm. Materials used for both the tape and the adhesive are constantly being improved and today's tapes are much better than tapes used even ten years ago.

Many tapes are stretch-able, making them easy to apply around window corners. Not all flashing tapes are equal, and their various properties are rated by testing done by ASTM (American Society of Testing and Materials). ASTM has a range of tests for flashing tapes that measure such things as peel adhesion and strip adhesion.

The performance of a tape over time depends on many things including its exposure to UV radiation, temperature and the surface it is applied to.

Flashing terminology

Step flashing interweaves flashing material with roof cladding. It is used where a sloped shingled roof intersects a vertical wall. (Figure 7.3) The flashing acts like a shingle, but with an upturned leg to allow the transition of the vertical drainage plane of the walls to the sloping drainage plane of the roof. The roof drainage plane should terminate with "kick-out" flashing, which directs water away from the wall and ensures moisture will not concentrate on the surface of the wall.

Head flashings are those used to direct water away from openings such as doors and windows. The key to head flashings it to ensure a positive slope that leads away from the building. Head flashings should extend laterally past the opening on either side.

Many wall penetrations, such as dryer vents or air vents, have flanged insets, which must be integrated into the drainage plane. Where building paper or housewrap is used, flashing tape can be applied over the flange, taping from the bottom, so the top of the flange is taped last, adhering to the fundamental principle of down and out. Flashings must always be applied so that water is directed out over the cladding or drainage plane without allowing the water to be directed back into the wall.

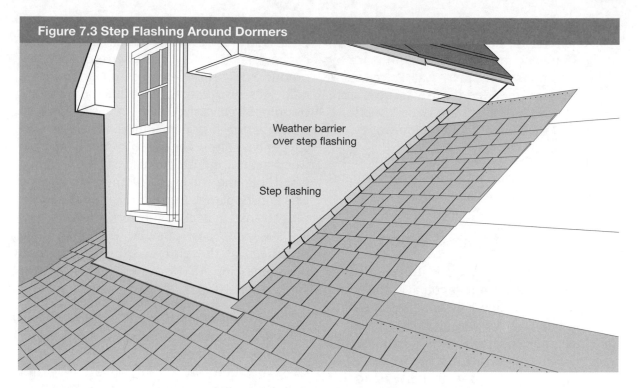

Figure 7.3 Step Flashing Around Dormers

Weather barrier over step flashing

Step flashing

7.5 Dampproofing Materials

Dampproofing materials are applied to the exterior, below-grade portion of foundation walls to repel water. The material most commonly used is a spray- or mop-applied bituminous substance. It fills the pores in the concrete or parging, reducing the penetration of liquid water due to pressure against the wall and capillary action. This material has been used by builders for many years. It is easy to apply, effective and very durable.

Specially designed foundation membranes that provide both moisture protection and free flow drainage capabilities are also available. However, the combined use of dampproofing and free-draining backfill or drainage plane provide additional protection.

Slabs-on-grade can be dampproofed with polyethylene sheet at least 0.15 mm (6 mil) thick.

7.6 Moisture Barriers

A moisture barrier (Chapter 6) is a material, membrane or coating used to keep moisture that might penetrate a foundation wall or floor from contacting interior foundation insulation or the wood framing members supporting the insulation and interior finishes. It is installed only to the below-grade portion of the foundation walls or floor slabs. Materials that can be used as moisture barriers for walls include:

* Paint- or spray-applied asphalt emulsions used on the interior surface of the wall to provide a continuous membrane. Bituminous (creosote) coating is not recommended because it often produces an objectionable odour and can contribute to indoor air quality problems.

* Sheet materials, such as house wrap or building paper. All seams must be overlapped and sealed. Sheet materials can be fastened

to the wall using adhesives or a cold asphalt mastic such as plastic roof cement. Alternatively, they can be held in place by furring strips secured to the wall. Polyethylene is not recommended for use as a moisture barrier because it entraps excess moisture emitted by concrete foundation walls.

- Specially designed foundation membranes that both provide moisture protection and free-flow drainage capabilities.

7.7 Pressure-treated Wood

Most pressure-treated wood for residential applications sold prior to January 1, 2004 used CCA (chromated copper arsenate). Since then, CCA has been replaced by alternatives such as alkaline copper quaternary (ACQ) and copper azole (CA) formulations for residential applications. Framing and plywood for permanent wood foundations (Chapter 9) is still treated using CCA based on CAN/CSA-O80.15-M *Preservative Treatment of Wood for Building Foundation Systems, Basements and Crawl Spaces by Pressure Processes*.

Like CCA, ACQ and CA are water-borne preservatives. This means that they have the ability to chemically attach to the wood cell walls, but some leaching into the environment is possible. Wood preservative manufacturers continue to seek chemicals with lower toxicity profiles that can provide a high level of protection.

ACQ- and CA-treated wood products tend to be more corrosive to metal fasteners and connectors. Therefore, it is important to follow producer recommendations on appropriate nails, screws, plates and other connectors. Hot-dipped galvanized steel, types 304 or 316 stainless steel fasteners (nails and screws) and copper have always been recommended by the wood-treating industry for use with CCA-treated wood, but the thickness of the zinc coating was not stipulated. Current recommendations for galvanized steel connectors and fasteners are similar to past practice, except that the thickness of the zinc coating is governed by referencing ASTM (American Society for Testing Materials).

Connectors used for ACQ- or CA-treated wood should be manufactured from steel either galvanized in accordance with ASTM A653, G185 designation, or be galvanized after manufacture in accordance with ASTM A123. Stainless steel connectors (type 304 or 316) are recommended for maximum service life or severe applications. Borate-treated wood used inside buildings can use the same connectors as those used for untreated wood.

Galvanizing is a sacrificial coating and the presence of some white corrosion product on the surface is normal. However, red rust is an indicator of coating failure. Electroplate galvanized steel and aluminium have never been and are not recommended for use in contact with treated wood.

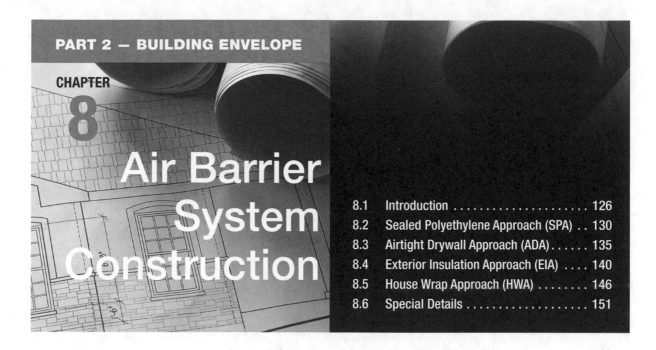

This chapter is devoted to the important subject of constructing houses with effective air barriers. In previous chapters, the principles and materials for use in air barrier systems were introduced. In this chapter, key elements for various air barrier approaches are presented. This information provides guidelines to help builders assess the most appropriate approach. Selection should consider the home's location, climate exposure, design, construction method, and the availability of materials and skilled trades. Special features (e.g., jogs, projections, bump outs, cantilevers, transitions from cathedral ceilings abutting a wall separating interior and exterior or attic space, bay windows under a cantilevered floor) and stacked town houses require particular attention to ensure continuity of the air barrier system. As housing moves to increasing levels of energy efficiency designers will be counting on improved airtightness of the building envelope for some the energy savings. Uncontrolled air leakage is the major contributor to energy loss in a house. Airtightness is tested using a blower door and the results are reported as Air Changes per Hour at 50 Pascals depressurization (ACH50). To get a sense of what this means, the following table has some general values:

Table 8.1 Typical Airtightness by Building Age		
House Type	**Typical ACH50**	**Testing Mandated**
1950's Farm House	10+	no
1970 Detached House	6+	no
2015 Code Built	4+	no
R-2000 House	less than 1.5	yes
Energy Star – Attached	less than 3.5	yes
Energy Star – Detached	less than 2.5	yes
Net Zero/Net Zero Ready	less than 1.0	yes – requirement is < 1.5
PassivHaus	Less than 0.6	yes

8.1 Introduction

It is helpful to think that a house can never be "too tight", it can only be "under-ventilated". Tightening of the house is the only way that uncontrolled air infiltration can be controlled. In addition, a tight envelope and a balanced ventilation system means that all the fresh air entering the house will need to come through the ventilation inlet. This provides the ideal point for a filtration system to ensure that any contaminants are removed from the outdoor air. The move to Net Zero has builders and designers looking for energy savings anywhere they can get them and improving the tightness of the house is one of their first requests to builders, since the air barrier is already being installed – just do it better. This chapter looks at the most common approaches to air barriers.

8.1.1 Air Barrier Basics

The air barrier is one of the most critical components in the construction of a home for controlling moisture movement, drafts and the infiltration of outdoor contaminants. Attention to detail in the construction and sealing of the air barrier has been shown to increase the durability of the house. Some simple rules for air barriers are as follows:

- The air barrier must be continuous.

- The builder is encouraged to plan the path of the air barrier at the design stage so that continuity can be ensured in the construction stage. The air barrier is too important to be left to chance or to on-site improvisation.

- The builder must be able to trace the air barrier completely around any cross-section drawing of the house, at transitions in plane and corners, from top to bottom of the building without any gaps.

- The builder must ensure that the trades working on the building understand the air barrier system to ensure they can implement it properly throughout the building.

- The air barrier can be on the inside or the outside of the building assembly, or anywhere between.

- The air barrier can transition from outside to inside to within the assembly. The key is continuity.

- There can be more than one air barrier.

- The air barrier, if used on the outside of the assembly or within the assembly, must not be a vapour barrier. Or, stated differently, only an air barrier on the warm side of the building envelope can use a material that is both an air and vapour barrier.

This section of the Manual focuses on four different approaches for constructing the air barrier on site. They vary depending on the location of the air barrier (interior or exterior) and the type of material used for the air barrier (flexible or rigid) as follows:

- The **sealed polyethylene approach (SPA)** is applied on the interior and involves the application and sealing of polyethylene, a flexible membrane. Unlike the other three air barrier approaches listed here, the polyethylene can also serve as the designated vapour barrier. For this reason, care is required to ensure the polyethylene is always kept on the warm side of the envelope to prevent condensation from occurring within a wall or roof assembly.

- The **airtight drywall approach (ADA)** is applied on the interior and makes use of rigid drywall (gypsum board) and taping, sealing and gasketing to provide an airtight barrier on the interior.

- The exterior insulation approach (EIA) involves the application and sealing of rigid insulation or other types of panels on the building exterior.

- The **house wrap approach (HWA)** makes use of the application and sealing of a flexible house wrap sheathing membrane to provide the airtight barrier.

For any approach, a successful air barrier is essential to constructing an energy-efficient and healthy home. Builders should plan the approach to constructing the air barrier and ensure it is compatible with the other building techniques that will be used.

An exterior air barrier offers the benefit of allowing air tightness to be tested prior to completion of the house, in which case, the air barrier may be the responsibility of the exterior cladding installers. An interior air barrier offers the benefit of installation protected from weather conditions. In this case, the air barrier may be the responsibility of the insulation team or the drywall crew.

There are other approaches for providing an effective air barrier including insulated concrete forms (ICFs), cast-in-place concrete, spray foam or structural insulated panels (SIPs). This Manual focuses on those air barrier approaches most compatible with frame construction. However, the basic principles of sealing and continuity need to be applied to all air barrier approaches.

8.1.2 Foundation air barriers

The four approaches of constructing air barriers described in this chapter apply to the building envelope above the foundation. It is essential that the foundation be airtight, especially to prevent the infiltration of soil gas. Another crucial element is to ensure that the foundation air barrier is effectively transferred to the envelope above the foundation.

Figure 8.1 Foundation — concrete wall air barrier

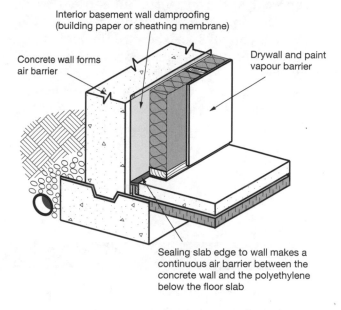

Interior basement wall dampproofing (building paper or sheathing membrane)

Concrete wall forms air barrier

Drywall and paint vapour barrier

Sealing slab edge to wall makes a continuous air barrier between the concrete wall and the polyethylene below the floor slab

Figure 8.2 Foundation – drywall air barrier

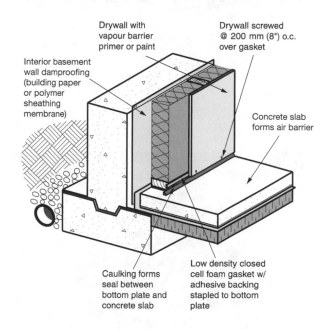

Drywall with vapour barrier primer or paint

Drywall screwed @ 200 mm (8") o.c. over gasket

Interior basement wall dampproofing (building paper or polymer sheathing membrane)

Concrete slab forms air barrier

Caulking forms seal between bottom plate and concrete slab

Low density closed cell foam gasket w/ adhesive backing stapled to bottom plate

For the foundation portion of the envelope, there are two methods for providing an air barrier. First, the poured concrete foundation can serve as the designated air barrier (Figure 8.1). Second, the airtight drywall approach (ADA) (Figure 8.2) can be used. In both cases, floor joints such as drains, sump pumps and the floor slab-to-wall interface must be sealed. As explained in Chapter 9, it is no longer recommended that polyethylene be used for the wall air barrier in a below-grade basement.

8.1.3 Attic/ceiling air barriers

Of the four air barrier approaches, only two approaches – the interior air barriers – are practical for conventional attic ceilings: the sealed polyethylene approach (SPA) and the airtight drywall approach (ADA). Figures 8.3 to 8.7 show how penetrations and junctions in the attic ceiling are air sealed.

Figure 8.3 Air barrier at fan enclosure

Airtight drywall approach (ADA)

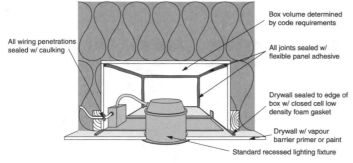

All wiring penetrations sealed w/ caulking

Box volume determined by code requirements

All joints sealed w/ flexible panel adhesive

Drywall sealed to edge of box w/ closed cell low density foam gasket

Drywall w/ vapour barrier primer or paint

Standard recessed lighting fixture

Sealed polyethylene approach (SPA)

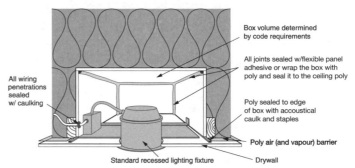

All wiring penetrations sealed w/ caulking

Box volume determined by code requirements

All joints sealed w/flexible panel adhesive or wrap the box with poly and seal it to the ceiling poly

Poly sealed to edge of box with accoustical caulk and staples

Poly air (and vapour) barrier

Standard recessed lighting fixture

Drywall

Figure 8.4 Air barrier at prefabricated chimney

Airtight drywall approach (ADA)

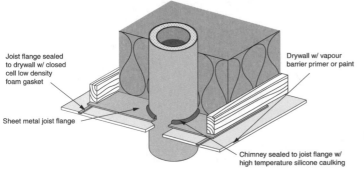

Joist flange sealed to drywall w/ closed cell low density foam gasket

Sheet metal joist flange

Drywall w/ vapour barrier primer or paint

Chimney sealed to joist flange w/ high temperature silicone caulking

Sealed polyethylene approach (SPA)

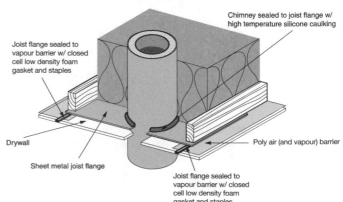

Joist flange sealed to vapour barrier w/ closed cell low density foam gasket and staples

Chimney sealed to joist flange w/ high temperature silicone caulking

Drywall

Sheet metal joist flange

Poly air (and vapour) barrier

Joist flange sealed to vapour barrier w/ closed cell low density foam gasket and staples

Figure 8.5 Air barrier at plumbing stack penetration

Airtight drywall approach (ADA)

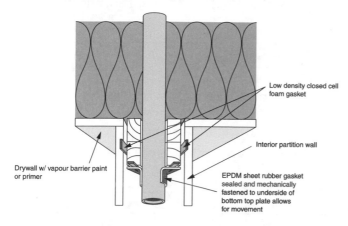

Low density closed cell foam gasket

Interior partition wall

Drywall w/ vapour barrier paint or primer

EPDM sheet rubber gasket sealed and mechanically fastened to underside of bottom top plate allows for movement

Sealed polyethylene approach (SPA)

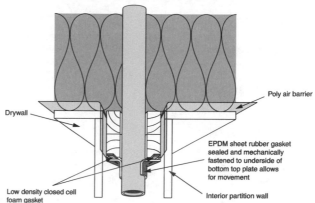

Poly air barrier

Drywall

EPDM sheet rubber gasket sealed and mechanically fastened to underside of bottom top plate allows for movement

Low density closed cell foam gasket

Interior partition wall

Figure 8.6 Air barrier at ventilation intake

Airtight drywall approach (ADA)

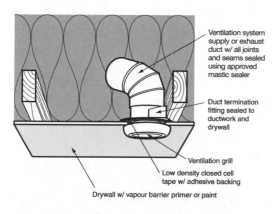

Ventilation system supply or exhaust duct w/ all joints and seams sealed using approved mastic sealer

Duct termination fitting sealed to ductwork and drywall

Ventilation grill

Low density closed cell tape w/ adhesive backing

Drywall w/ vapour barrier primer or paint

Sealed polyethylene approach (SPA)

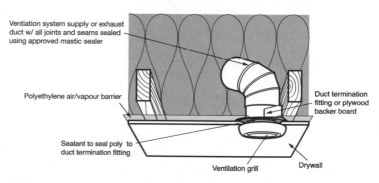

Ventiation system supply or exhaust duct w/ all joints and seams sealed using approved mastic sealer

Polyethylene air/vapour barrier

Duct termination fitting or plywood backer board

Sealant to seal poly to duct termination fitting

Ventilation grill

Drywall

Figure 8.7 Air barrier at recessed light

Airtight drywall approach (ADA)

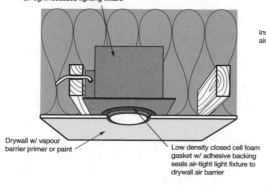

Insulation Cover (IC) rated, air-tight recessed lighting fixture

Drywall w/ vapour barrier primer or paint

Low density closed cell foam gasket w/ adhesive backing seals air-tight light fixture to drywall air barrier

Sealed polyethylene approach (SPA)

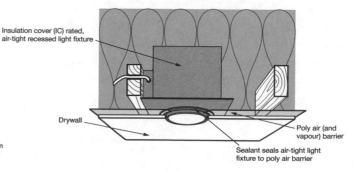

Insulation cover (IC) rated, air-tight recessed light fixture

Drywall

Poly air (and vapour) barrier

Sealant seals air-tight light fixture to poly air barrier

8.2 Sealed Polyethylene Approach (SPA)

Polyethylene air/vapour barriers have been widely used in Canada. When used in low-rise construction in wind- shaded locations, polyethylene air vapour barriers can perform adequately.

SPA Advantages	SPA Disadvantages
• Provides an air barrier using a standard construction material. • Allows for conventional scheduling of sub-trades. • Is known by most trades. • Is located on the interior and will block the entry of air pollutants emitted by building materials located in the insulated cavity.	• Does not provide a rigid air barrier that can withstand wind pressures without damage and without compressing cavity insulation. • Is subject to construction damage. • Cannot easily be repaired over the life of the building. • Needs to be supported on both sides to prevent billowing and tearing.

8.2.1 SPA materials

Air barrier sheet and panel materials

The barrier materials are 6 mil polyethylene complying with CGSB standard CAN2-51-34M86, plywood or OSB floor sheathing, extruded polystyrene foam board, house wrap and rim wrap.

Mechanical fasteners

Polyethylene is typically fastened to framing members with randomly spaced staples. At joints, it is usually lapped one stud space and stapled through a sealant bead located over framing or blocking. The drywall then acts as a clamp to secure the laps against the framing.

Caulkings and tapes

Polyethylene film can be sealed to itself with a butyl-based, non-curing acoustical sealant if the sealant is covered with polyethylene on all sides and the polyethylene is mechanically fastened with staples every 150 mm (6 in.) through the sealant bead. Polyethylene can also be sealed with high quality sheathing tape manufactured for use with polyethylene.

Foam sealants

Self-expanding polyurethane foams are often used to seal window and door frames to rough openings. Care must be taken to ensure that the foam used does not cause the window or door frame to bow. Expanding foams can also be used to seal gaps between the top of the foundation and the sill plate. Expanding foams will not adhere to polyethylene, so additional materials such as sheathing tape must be used to complete the air barrier system.

Spray foam insulation can also be used in spaces between floor joists to form an air barrier (and a vapour barrier) from the top plate of the lower wall to the underside of the floor sheathing. This would negate the need to have a rim wrap and poly vapour barrier as shown in Figure SPA 9.

Vapour barriers

The polyethylene forms both the air barrier and the vapour barrier. If polyethylene is used as the vapour barrier for other air barrier approaches, it should be continuous but does not need to be sealed. When it is acting as both the air barrier and the vapour barrier as in the case of the sealed polyethylene approach (SPA), it needs to be sealed to fulfill the air barrier requirements.

8.2.2 SPA details

The reference diagram for the sealed polyethylene approach (SPA) air barrier details is Figure 8.8. The corresponding wall details dealing with air barrier intersections and penetrations are shown in Figures SPA 1 to 10. In addition, because polyethylene is commonly used for air barrier construction and for providing the vapour barrier, several figures in Chapters 9, 10, 11 and 12 also show the SPA method.

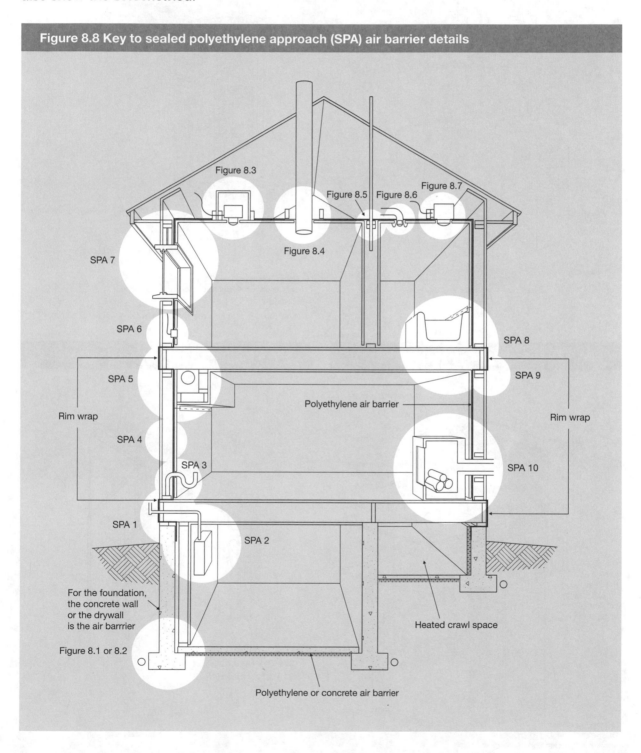

Figure 8.8 Key to sealed polyethylene approach (SPA) air barrier details

SPA 1 Basement wall/floor junction

Rim wrap sealed to polyethelene

Rim wrap sealed to concrete or drywall, depending on which is the designated air barier

SPA 3 Plumbing penetration

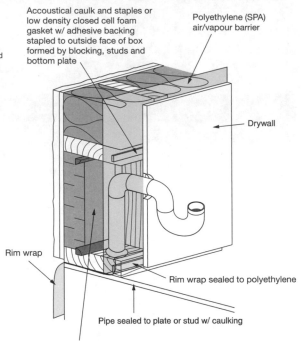

Accoustical caulk and staples or low density closed cell foam gasket w/ adhesive backing stapled to outside face of box formed by blocking, studs and bottom plate

Polyethylene (SPA) air/vapour barrier

Drywall

Rim wrap

Rim wrap sealed to polyethylene

Pipe sealed to plate or stud w/ caulking

Airtight box formed by XPS or foil faced foam insulation, compatible caulking and blocking

Note: Pipes in exterior walls should be avoided whenever possible

SPA 2 Electrical service panel

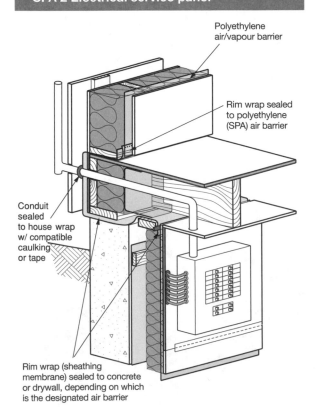

Polyethylene air/vapour barrier

Rim wrap sealed to polyethylene (SPA) air barrier

Conduit sealed to house wrap w/ compatible caulking or tape

Rim wrap (sheathing membrane) sealed to concrete or drywall, depending on which is the designated air barrier

SPA 4 Partition wall intersection

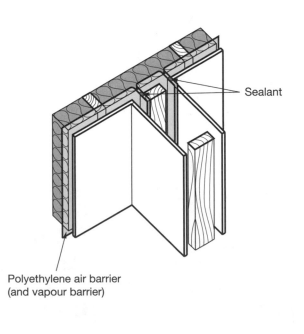

Sealant

Polyethylene air barrier (and vapour barrier)

SPA 5 Dropped ceiling

SPA 7 Window

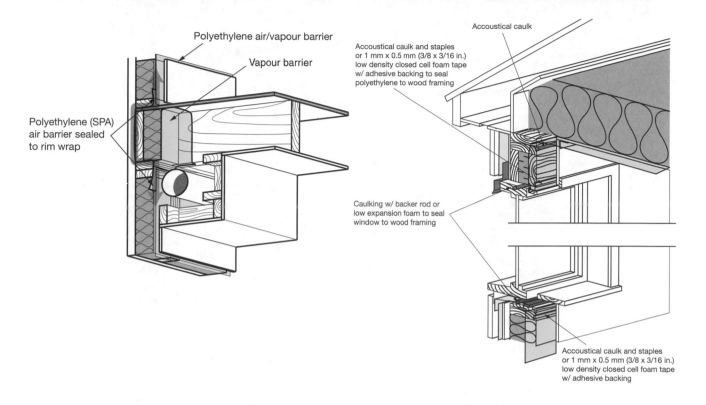

Polyethylene air/vapour barrier

Vapour barrier

Polyethylene (SPA) air barrier sealed to rim wrap

Accoustical caulk

Accoustical caulk and staples or 1 mm x 0.5 mm (3/8 x 3/16 in.) low density closed cell foam tape w/ adhesive backing to seal polyethylene to wood framing

Caulking w/ backer rod or low expansion foam to seal window to wood framing

Accoustical caulk and staples or 1 mm x 0.5 mm (3/8 x 3/16 in.) low density closed cell foam tape w/ adhesive backing

SPA 6 Electrical box

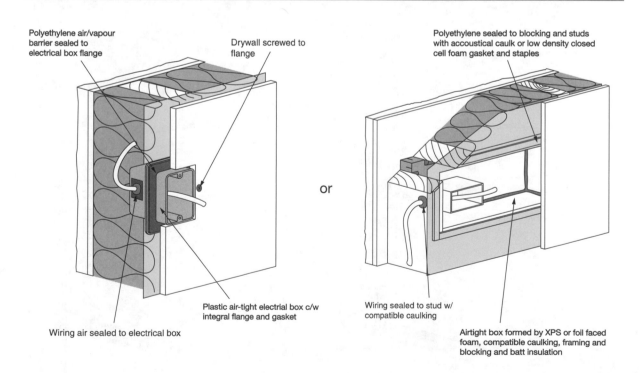

Polyethylene air/vapour barrier sealed to electrical box flange

Drywall screwed to flange

Polyethylene sealed to blocking and studs with accoustical caulk or low density closed cell foam gasket and staples

or

Plastic air-tight electrial box c/w integral flange and gasket

Wiring air sealed to electrical box

Wiring sealed to stud w/ compatible caulking

Airtight box formed by XPS or foil faced foam, compatible caulking, framing and blocking and batt insulation

SPA 8 Bathtub

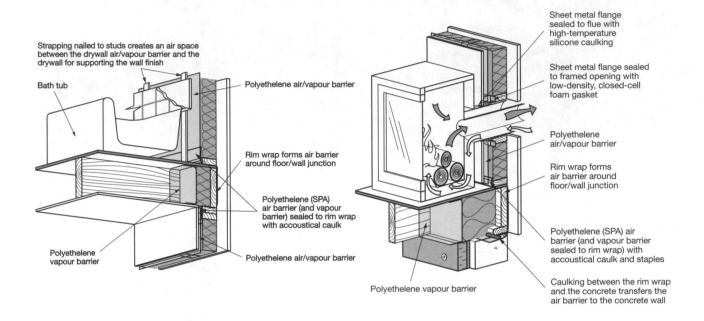

Strapping nailed to studs creates an air space between the drywall air/vapour barrier and the drywall for supporting the wall finish

Bath tub

Polyethelene vapour barrier

Polyethelene air/vapour barrier

Rim wrap forms air barrier around floor/wall junction

Polyethelene (SPA) air barrier (and vapour barrier) sealed to rim wrap with accoustical caulk

Polyethelene air/vapour barrier

SPA 10 Direct-vent gas fireplace

Sheet metal flange sealed to flue with high-temperature silicone caulking

Sheet metal flange sealed to framed opening with low-density, closed-cell foam gasket

Polyethelene air/vapour barrier

Rim wrap forms air barrier around floor/wall junction

Polyethelene (SPA) air barrier (and vapour barrier sealed to rim wrap) with accoustical caulk and staples

Caulking between the rim wrap and the concrete transfers the air barrier to the concrete wall

Polyethelene vapour barrier

SPA 9 Floor intersection

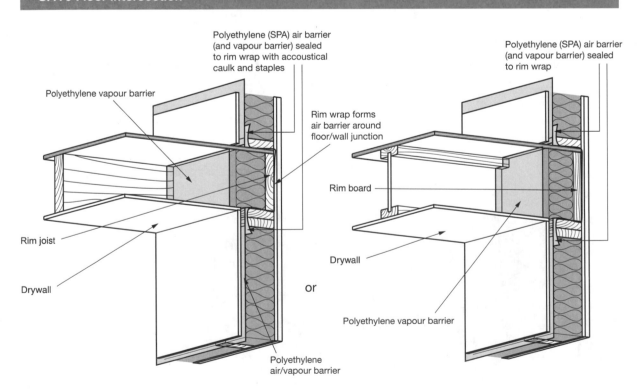

Polyethylene (SPA) air barrier (and vapour barrier) sealed to rim wrap with accoustical caulk and staples

Polyethylene vapour barrier

Rim wrap forms air barrier around floor/wall junction

Rim joist

Drywall

Polyethylene air/vapour barrier

or

Polyethylene (SPA) air barrier (and vapour barrier) sealed to rim wrap

Rim board

Drywall

Polyethylene vapour barrier

8.3 Airtight Drywall Approach (ADA)

8.3.1 ADA materials

Air barrier panel materials

The air barrier and panel materials are 12 or 15 mm (1/2 or 5/8 in.) drywall, plywood or OSB floor sheathing or extruded polystyrene foam board.

Gaskets

The typical materials used is 9 x 5 mm (3/8 x 3/16 in.) closed-cell, low-density, self-adhesive neoprene foam strip for sealing drywall to framing.

Mechanical fasteners

Self-adhesive foam gaskets should be stapled in place to ensure they are not knocked off during drywall installation. Where drywall is in contact with a gasket, drywall screws must be affixed every 200 mm (8 in.) to ensure full compression of the gasket and sealing of the joint.

Caulkings

One-part urethane or silicone can be used for sealing the sole plate to the floor sheathing, sill plate to concrete foundation, framing to metal, and for electrical and plumbing penetrations. One-part urethane is a highly durable and flexible sealant and will adhere well to many materials. It should only be used where it will be concealed. Installers should wear rubber gloves and refer to the Materials Safety Data Sheet supplied by the manufacturer for correct handling. One-part urethane should not be used in housing for people who are chemically hypersensitive.

Foam sealants

Expanding foams are used to seal gaps between the top of the foundation and the sill plate. Non-expanding foams should be used to seal window and door frames to rough openings so that the frames do not distort.

Spray foam insulation can also be used in spaces between floor joists to form an air barrier (and a vapour barrier) from the top plate of the lower wall to the underside of the floor sheathing. This would negate the need to use the rim joist as the air barrier as shown in Figure ADA 9.

Tape

Exterior air barrier systems typically rely on tape to transfer the barrier between insulation panels. See Section 7.3.5.

Vapour barriers

Vapour barriers used with ADA include water-based vapour barrier drywall sealers, aluminium foil, either installed separately or supplied as backing on the drywall, or polyethylene. The vapour barrier sealers are most commonly used with this system due to ease and simplicity of installation. Polyethylene is another option but is typically not used because it interferes with gasket and sealant installation.

8.3.2 ADA details

The reference diagram for the airtight drywall approach (ADA) air barrier details is Figure 8.9. The corresponding details dealing with air barrier intersections and penetrations are shown in Figures ADA 1 to 10. The details shown here have been successfully used in the field. Some of the details can be customized to work better for local situations.

Figure 8.9 Key to airtight drywall approach (ADA) air barrier details

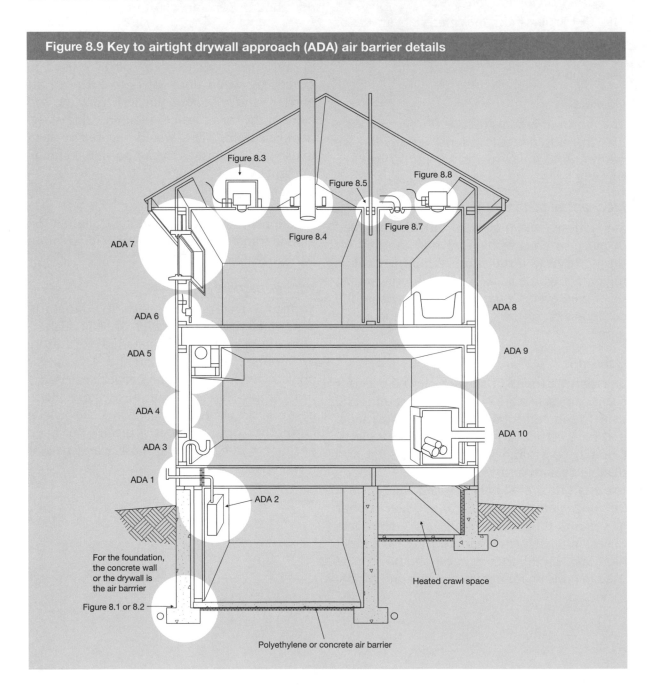

ADA 1 Basement wall/floor junction

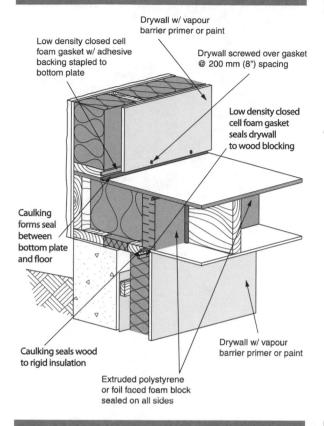

Drywall w/ vapour barrier primer or paint

Low density closed cell foam gasket w/ adhesive backing stapled to bottom plate

Drywall screwed over gasket @ 200 mm (8") spacing

Low density closed cell foam gasket seals drywall to wood blocking

Caulking forms seal between bottom plate and floor

Caulking seals wood to rigid insulation

Drywall w/ vapour barrier primer or paint

Extruded polystyrene or foil faced foam block sealed on all sides

ADA 3 Plumbing penetration

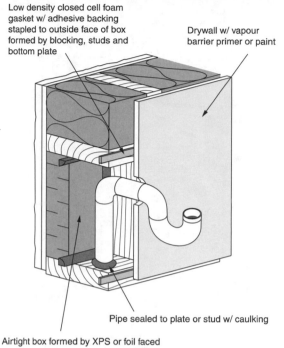

Low density closed cell foam gasket w/ adhesive backing stapled to outside face of box formed by blocking, studs and bottom plate

Drywall w/ vapour barrier primer or paint

Pipe sealed to plate or stud w/ caulking

Airtight box formed by XPS or foil faced foam insulation, compatible caulking and blocking

Note: Pipes in exterior walls should be avoided whenever possible

ADA 2 Electrical service panel

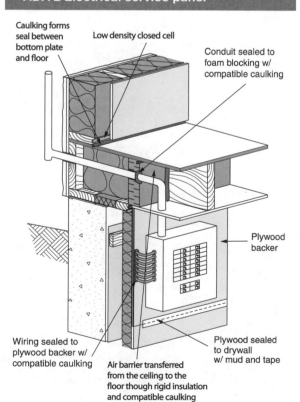

Caulking forms seal between bottom plate and floor

Low density closed cell

Conduit sealed to foam blocking w/ compatible caulking

Plywood backer

Wiring sealed to plywood backer w/ compatible caulking

Air barrier transferred from the ceiling to the floor though rigid insulation and compatible caulking

Plywood sealed to drywall w/ mud and tape

ADA 4 Partition wall intersection

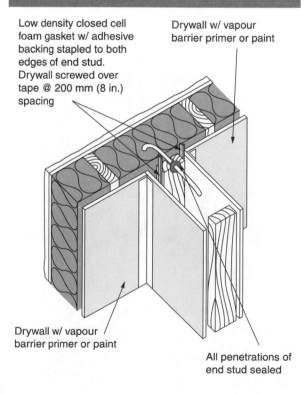

Low density closed cell foam gasket w/ adhesive backing stapled to both edges of end stud. Drywall screwed over tape @ 200 mm (8 in.) spacing

Drywall w/ vapour barrier primer or paint

Drywall w/ vapour barrier primer or paint

All penetrations of end stud sealed

ADA 5 Dropped ceiling

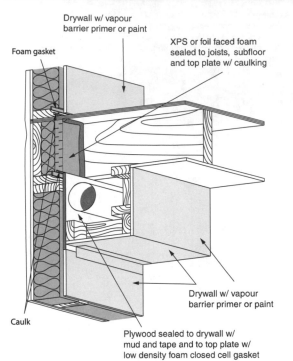

Drywall w/ vapour barrier primer or paint

Foam gasket

XPS or foil faced foam sealed to joists, subfloor and top plate w/ caulking

Drywall w/ vapour barrier primer or paint

Caulk

Plywood sealed to drywall w/ mud and tape and to top plate w/ low density foam closed cell gasket

ADA 7 Window

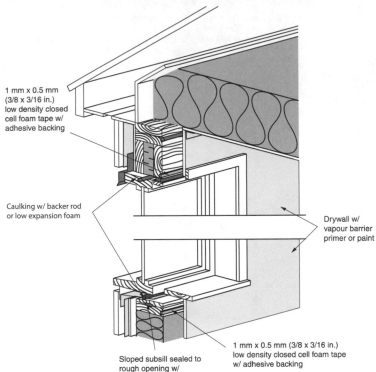

1 mm x 0.5 mm (3/8 x 3/16 in.) low density closed cell foam tape w/ adhesive backing

Caulking w/ backer rod or low expansion foam

Drywall w/ vapour barrier primer or paint

Sloped subsill sealed to rough opening w/ flexible panel adhesive

1 mm x 0.5 mm (3/8 x 3/16 in.) low density closed cell foam tape w/ adhesive backing

ADA 6 Electrical box

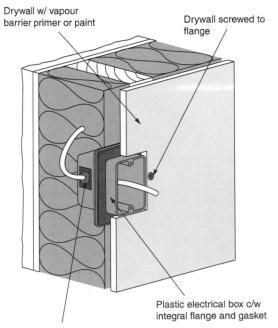

Drywall w/ vapour barrier primer or paint

Drywall screwed to flange

Wiring air sealed to electrical box

Plastic electrical box c/w integral flange and gasket

or

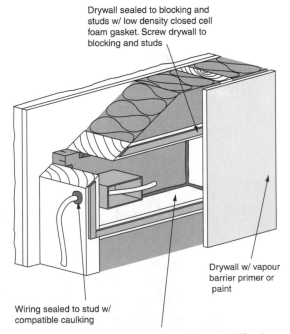

Drywall sealed to blocking and studs w/ low density closed cell foam gasket. Screw drywall to blocking and studs

Drywall w/ vapour barrier primer or paint

Wiring sealed to stud w/ compatible caulking

Airtight box formed by XPS or foil faced foam, compatible caulking, framing and blocking and batt insulation

ADA 8 Bathtub

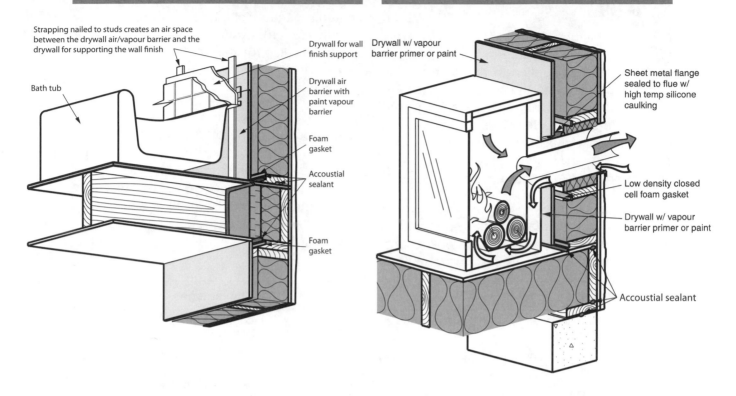

Strapping nailed to studs creates an air space between the drywall air/vapour barrier and the drywall for supporting the wall finish

Bath tub

Drywall for wall finish support

Drywall air barrier with paint vapour barrier

Foam gasket

Accoustial sealant

Foam gasket

ADA 9 Direct-vent gas fireplace

Drywall w/ vapour barrier primer or paint

Sheet metal flange sealed to flue w/ high temp silicone caulking

Low density closed cell foam gasket

Drywall w/ vapour barrier primer or paint

Accoustial sealant

ADA 10 Floor intersection

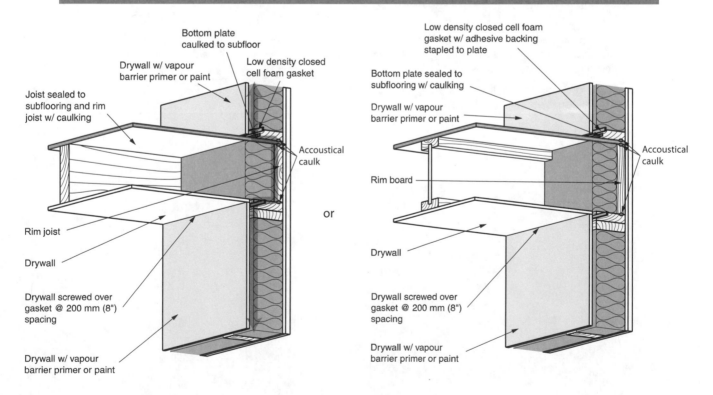

Drywall w/ vapour barrier primer or paint

Bottom plate caulked to subfloor

Low density closed cell foam gasket

Joist sealed to subflooring and rim joist w/ caulking

Accoustical caulk

Rim joist

Drywall

Drywall screwed over gasket @ 200 mm (8") spacing

Drywall w/ vapour barrier primer or paint

or

Low density closed cell foam gasket w/ adhesive backing stapled to plate

Bottom plate sealed to subflooring w/ caulking

Drywall w/ vapour barrier primer or paint

Accoustical caulk

Rim board

Drywall

Drywall screwed over gasket @ 200 mm (8") spacing

Drywall w/ vapour barrier primer or paint

8.4 Exterior Insulation Approach (EIA)

Exterior insulation air barrier systems consist of rigid, air impermeable exterior insulated sheathing that is applied to the wall framing and sealed at all joints and penetrations to form a continuous air barrier. The air barrier used in the ceiling could also consist of an insulated sheathing, but more typically consists of a polyethylene air/vapour (SPA) barrier or an airtight drywall (ADA) air barrier.

The EIA typically uses an extruded polystyrene insulation with shiplap joints sealed with a foamed polyethylene gasket or construction tape. The insulated sheathing must also have a high enough thermal resistance to ensure that the framing it covers stays above the dew point temperature of indoor air during heating season. (See NBC Appendix A and Section 6.2 for guidance on the correct location of vapour barriers in relation to inboard and outboard insulation values.)

If the exterior insulation is also functioning as the second plane of protection for water intrusion from the exterior, care must be taken at all butt joints and flashing details to ensure they are watertight. This can easily be accomplished by also using a house wrap weather barrier on the exterior of the insulating sheathing.

EIA Advantages	EIA Disadvantages
• Eliminates the need for air sealing interior electrical and plumbing penetrations.	• Is recognized by the NBC, but not all building code officials are familiar with this air barrier system.
• Allows for conventional scheduling of sub-trades.	• Is located on the exterior, and will not block the entry of air pollutants emitted from building materials located in the insulated cavity into the indoor air.
• Provides a rigid air barrier that can withstand wind pressures without damage and without compressing cavity insulation.	
• Is rigid and therefore can form part of a pressure-equalized rainscreen system.	
• Can be easily repaired before being covered.	
• Is both an insulation and exterior sheathing system, and keeps the framing warmer than conventional sheathing. This reduces the likelihood of condensation forming in the wall due to the entry of interior moisture into the wall cavity.	
• Allows airtightness of the envelope to be tested before substantial completion of the house.	

8.4.1 EIA materials

Sheets and panels

The air barrier material is 25, 37.5 and 50 mm (1, 1.5, and 2 in.)-thick extruded polystyrene insulated sheathing with a maximum air permeance of 0.02 L/s-m2 @ 75 Pa and a water vapour permeance of at least 57.5 ng/Pa.m2s (0.75 imperial perms) or higher, low expansion foam insulated sheathing, plywood and OSB subflooring, polyethylene (SPA) or drywall (ADA) for ceiling air barrier.

Gaskets

The gaskets are 89 mm (3.5 in.) wide foamed-polyethylene.

Tape

EIA air barrier systems typically rely on tape to transfer the barrier between insulation panels. See Section 7.3.5.

Mechanical fasteners

The foamed polyethylene gaskets are usually stapled in place to ensure they are not knocked off during sheathing installation. Steel wire or spiral nails with minimum 25 mm (1 in.) diameter galvanized steel or plastic washers are used. To ensure full compression and sealing of sheathing with gaskets, the board must be nailed every 150 mm (6 in.) along all joints. All joints must be supported with framing or blocking. An approved construction tape is also used to seal the joints in the insulating sheathing.

Caulkings

Extruded polystyrene should only be in contact with compatible caulkings such as latex and silicone-based products or acoustical caulking. One-part urethane or silicone can be used for sealing framing to floor sheathing, sill plate to concrete foundation, framing to metal, and electrical and plumbing penetrations. One-part urethane is a highly durable and flexible sealant and will adhere well to many materials. It should only be used where it will be concealed. Installers should wear rubber gloves and refer to the Materials Safety Data Sheet supplied by the manufacturer for correct handling. One-part urethane should never be used in housing for the chemically hypersensitive. Silicone caulking will not perform as well as one-part urethanes, but is odourless once cured.

Foam sealants

Expanding foams are used to seal gaps between the top of the foundation and the sill plate. Expanding foams may also be used to seal joints in extruded polystyrene sheathings at other than 90-degree corners, such as at bay windows. Non-expanding foams should be used to seal window and door frames to rough openings so that the frames do not distort.

Vapour barriers

A wide range of vapour barriers can be used with EIA including water-based vapour barrier drywall sealers, alkyd paints, and aluminum foil either installed separately or supplied as backing on the drywall or polyethylen.

8.4.2 EIA details

The reference diagram for the exterior insulation approach (EIA) air barrier details is Figure 8.10. The corresponding details dealing with air barrier intersections and penetrations are shown in Figures EIA 1 to 10.

Figure 8.10 Key to exterior insulation approach (EIA) air barrier details

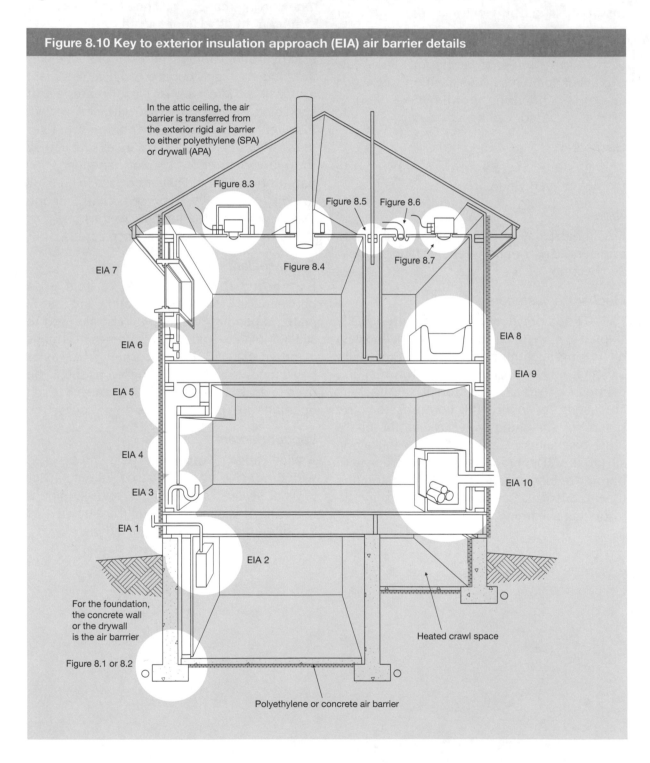

In the attic ceiling, the air barrier is transferred from the exterior rigid air barrier to either polyethylene (SPA) or drywall (APA)

Figure 8.3

Figure 8.5   Figure 8.6

Figure 8.4

Figure 8.7

EIA 7

EIA 8

EIA 6

EIA 9

EIA 5

EIA 4

EIA 3

EIA 10

EIA 1

EIA 2

For the foundation, the concrete wall or the drywall is the air barrrier

Heated crawl space

Figure 8.1 or 8.2

Polyethylene or concrete air barrier

EIA 1 Basement wall/floor junction

XPS foam insulated sheathing sealed at all joints, connections and penetrations

Polyethelene vapour barrier

Nail w/ washer

Gasket transfers the air barrier from the sill plate to the rigid insulation

Concrete wall forms air barrier

Sill plate sealed to concrete wall w/ one-part urethane caulking transfers the barrier from the concrete wall to the sill plate

Drywall with vapour barrier paint

EIA 3 Plumbing penetration

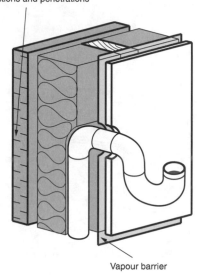

XPS foam insulated sheathing sealed at all joints, connections and penetrations

Vapour barrier

Note: Pipes in exterior walls should be avoided whenever possible

EIA 2 Electrical service panel

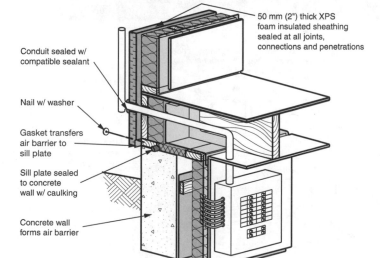

Conduit sealed w/ compatible sealant

Nail w/ washer

Gasket transfers air barrier to sill plate

Sill plate sealed to concrete wall w/ caulking

Concrete wall forms air barrier

50 mm (2") thick XPS foam insulated sheathing sealed at all joints, connections and penetrations

EIA 4 Partition wall intersection

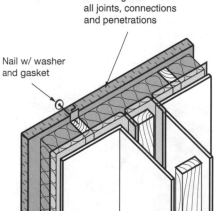

XPS foam insulated sheathing sealed at all joints, connections and penetrations

Nail w/ washer and gasket

Vapour barrier

EIA 5 Dropped ceiling

EIA 7 Window

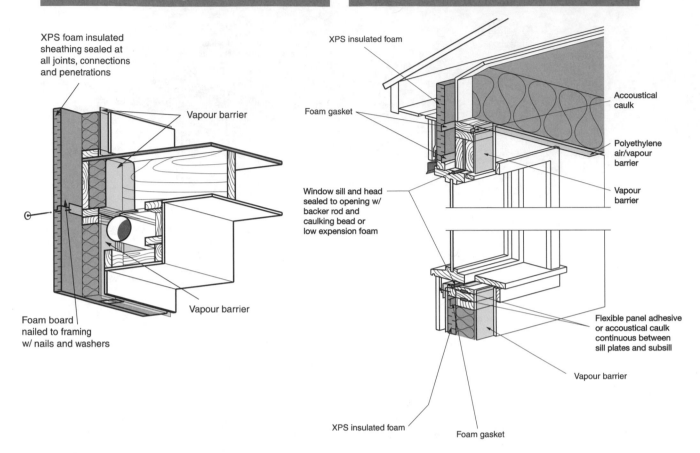

XPS foam insulated sheathing sealed at all joints, connections and penetrations

Vapour barrier

Vapour barrier

Foam board nailed to framing w/ nails and washers

XPS insulated foam

Foam gasket

Window sill and head sealed to opening w/ backer rod and caulking bead or low expension foam

Accoustical caulk

Polyethylene air/vapour barrier

Vapour barrier

Flexible panel adhesive or accoustical caulk continuous between sill plates and subsill

Vapour barrier

XPS insulated foam

Foam gasket

EIA 6 Electrical box

EIA 8 Bathtub

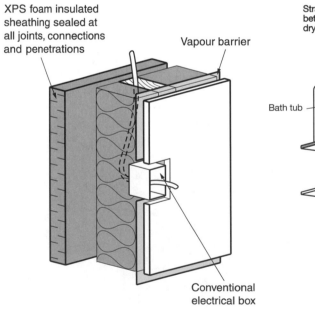

XPS foam insulated sheathing sealed at all joints, connections and penetrations

Vapour barrier

Conventional electrical box

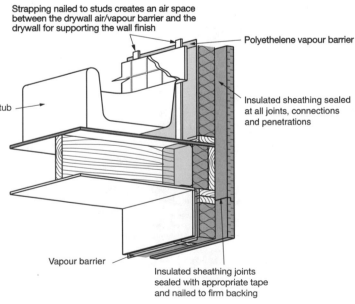

Strapping nailed to studs creates an air space between the drywall air/vapour barrier and the drywall for supporting the wall finish

Bath tub

Vapour barrier

Polyethelene vapour barrier

Insulated sheathing sealed at all joints, connections and penetrations

Insulated sheathing joints sealed with appropriate tape and nailed to firm backing

EIA 9 Floor intersection

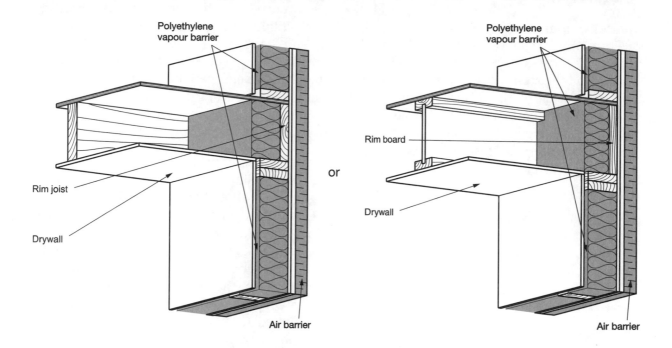

Polyethylene vapour barrier

Rim joist

Drywall

or

Air barrier

Polyethylene vapour barrier

Rim board

Drywall

Air barrier

EIA 10 Direct-vent gas fireplace

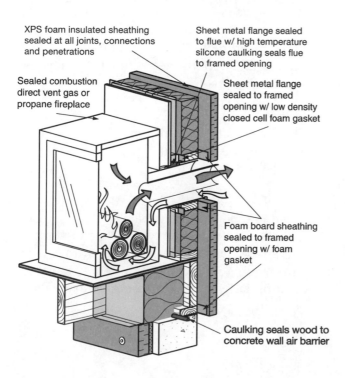

XPS foam insulated sheathing sealed at all joints, connections and penetrations

Sealed combustion direct vent gas or propane fireplace

Sheet metal flange sealed to flue w/ high temperature silcone caulking seals flue to framed opening

Sheet metal flange sealed to framed opening w/ low density closed cell foam gasket

Foam board sheathing sealed to framed opening w/ foam gasket

Caulking seals wood to concrete wall air barrier

8.5 House Wrap Approach (HWA)

House wrap air barrier systems consist of an air-impermeable (i.e., air leakage below $0.02 L/s \cdot m^2$) exterior house wrap membrane that is applied to the exterior structural sheathing of a home and sealed at all joints and penetrations to form a continuous air barrier. The air barrier used in the ceiling could also consist of a house wrap membrane, but it is more typical to use a polyethylene air/vapour barrier or an airtight drywall air barrier.

The HWA typically uses a spunbonded polyolefin sealed at all joints with a high quality sheathing tape or compatible sealant and mechanical fasteners.

8.5.1 HWA materials

Air barrier sheet and panel materials

The air barrier materials are spunbonded polyolefin house wrap with a maximum air permeance of 0.02 L/s-m2 @ 75 Pa, plywood or OSB subflooring, polyethylene or drywall for ceiling air barrier. The house wrap must be qualified by the Canadian Construction Materials Centre (CCMC) for use as an air barrier.

Mechanical fasteners

The spunbonded polyolefin is typically stapled securely to the structural exterior sheathing. In some cases, the house wrap is held between two layers of a highly vapour permeable wall sheathing material such as asphalt impregnated fiberboard. This provides structural support for the house wrap so that the air barrier can resist wind pressures.

Caulkings

Spunbonded polyolefin house wrap should only be in contact with manufacturer-approved, compatible caulking such as acrylic latex, polyurethane and acoustical sealant. One-part urethane or silicone can be used for sealing framing to floor sheathing, sill plate to concrete foundation, framing to metal, electrical and plumbing penetrations. Silicone should not be used in contact with spunbonded polyolefins.

One-part urethane is a highly durable and flexible sealant that will adhere to many materials. It should only be used where it will be concealed. Installers should wear rubber gloves and refer to the Materials Safety Data Sheet supplied by the manufacturer for correct handling. One-part urethane will release a slight odour that can be objectionable to some people, in which case silicone can be substituted. One-part urethane should never be used in housing for chemically hypersensitive occupants. Silicone caulking will not perform as well as one-part urethanes, but is odourless when cured.

Foam sealants

Expanding foams are used to seal gaps between the top of the foundation and the sill plate. Non-expanding foams should be used to seal window and door frames to rough openings so that the frames do not distort.

Tape

HWA air barrier systems typically rely on tape to transfer the barrier at house wrap joints. See Section 7.3.5.

Vapour barriers

A wide range of vapour barriers can be used with HWA, including water-based vapour barrier drywall sealers, alkyd paints, and aluminum foil either installed separately or supplied as backing on the drywall or polyethylen.

8.5.2 HWA details

The reference diagram for the house wrap approach (HWA) air barrier details is Figure 8.11. The corresponding details dealing with air barrier intersections and penetrations are shown in Figures HWA 1 to 10 illustrate the HWA for a series of typical scenarios.

Figure 8.11 Key to house wrap approach (HWA) air barrier details

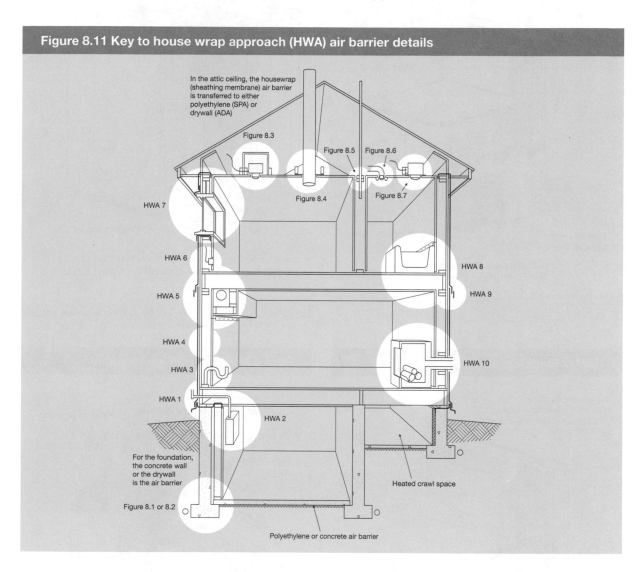

HWA 1 Basement wall/floor junction

House wrap (sheathing membrane) air barrier sealed to the foundation concrete air barrier

Sheathing

Vapour barrier

Concrete wall forms air barrier

Drywall and vapour barrier paint

Sill plate sealed to concrete wall w/ one-part urethane caulking

HWA 3 Plumbing penetration

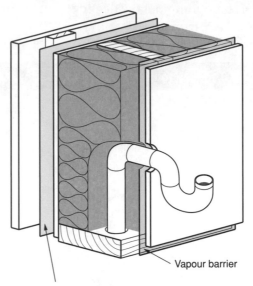

Vapour barrier

House wrap air barrier (sheathing membrane) sealed at all joints and penetrations w/ compatible caulking and tape

Note: Pipes in exterior walls should be avoided whenever possible

HWA 2 Electrical service panel

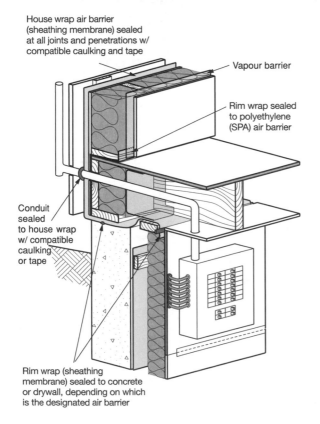

House wrap air barrier (sheathing membrane) sealed at all joints and penetrations w/ compatible caulking and tape

Vapour barrier

Rim wrap sealed to polyethylene (SPA) air barrier

Conduit sealed to house wrap w/ compatible caulking or tape

Rim wrap (sheathing membrane) sealed to concrete or drywall, depending on which is the designated air barrier

HWA 4 Partition wall intersection

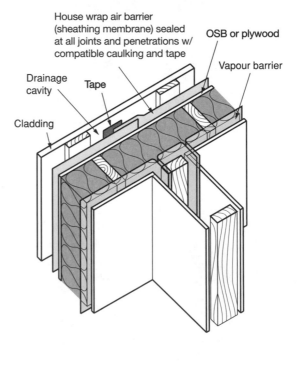

House wrap air barrier (sheathing membrane) sealed at all joints and penetrations w/ compatible caulking and tape

OSB or plywood

Vapour barrier

Drainage cavity

Tape

Cladding

HWA 5 Dropped ceiling

Cladding

Vapour barrier

Tape

Vapour barrier

Drainage cavity

House wrap air barrier (sheathing membrane) sealed at all joints and penetrations w/ compatible caulking and tape

HWA 7 Window

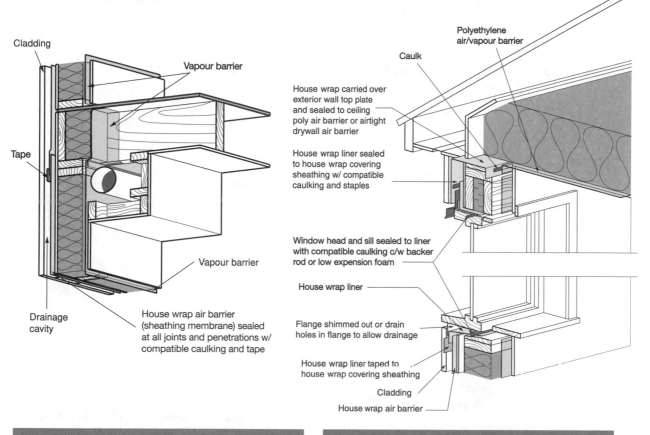

Polyethylene air/vapour barrier

Caulk

House wrap carried over exterior wall top plate and sealed to ceiling poly air barrier or airtight drywall air barrier

House wrap liner sealed to house wrap covering sheathing w/ compatible caulking and staples

Window head and sill sealed to liner with compatible caulking c/w backer rod or low expansion foam

House wrap liner

Flange shimmed out or drain holes in flange to allow drainage

House wrap liner taped to house wrap covering sheathing

Cladding

House wrap air barrier

HWA 6 Electrical box

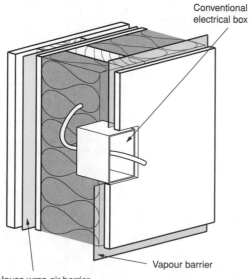

Conventional electrical box

Vapour barrier

House wrap air barrier (sheathing membrane) sealed at all joints and penetrations w/ compatible caulking and tape

HWA 8 Bathtub

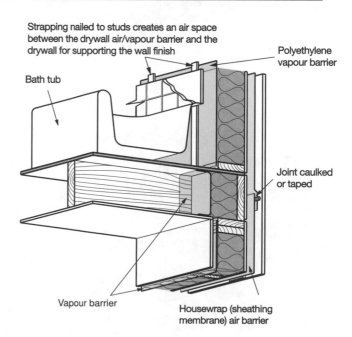

Strapping nailed to studs creates an air space between the drywall air/vapour barrier and the drywall for supporting the wall finish

Bath tub

Polyethylene vapour barrier

Joint caulked or taped

Vapour barrier

Housewrap (sheathing membrane) air barrier

HWA 9 Floor intersection

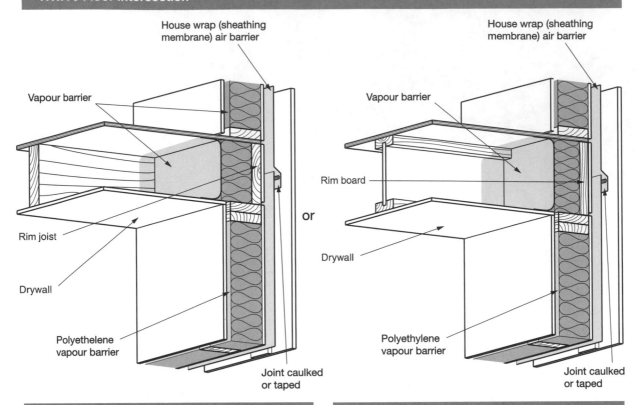

House wrap (sheathing membrane) air barrier

Vapour barrier

Rim joist

Drywall

Polyethelene vapour barrier

Joint caulked or taped

or

House wrap (sheathing membrane) air barrier

Vapour barrier

Rim board

Drywall

Polyethylene vapour barrier

Joint caulked or taped

HWA 10 Direct-vent gas fireplace

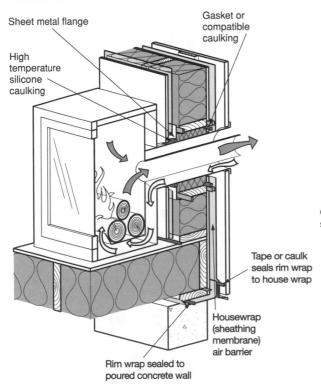

Sheet metal flange

High temperature silicone caulking

Gasket or compatible caulking

Tape or caulk seals rim wrap to house wrap

Housewrap (sheathing membrane) air barrier

Rim wrap sealed to poured concrete wall

Figure 8.12 Connecting a bay or bow window to the air barrier system

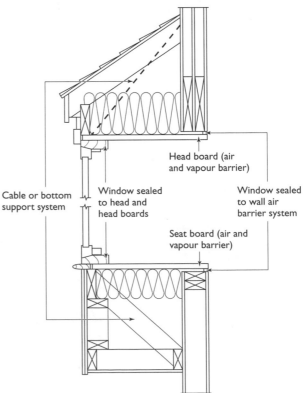

Cable or bottom support system

Window sealed to head and head boards

Head board (air and vapour barrier)

Window sealed to wall air barrier system

Seat board (air and vapour barrier)

8.6 Special Details

8.6.1 Attached garages

Attached garages have the potential to transfer vehicle exhaust and evaporative emissions from gas-powered equipment and stored solvents into living areas of a house. The required gas-tight barrier between a dwelling unit and an attached garage is intended to provide protection against the entry of carbon monoxide and gasoline fumes into a dwelling unit. The air barrier system will provide an adequate degree of gas-tightness provided all joints in the airtight material are sealed and reasonable care is exercised where the wall or ceiling is pierced by building services. The gas-tight construction is required for walls and ceilings that are shared between the attached garage and the house. In addition, a door between an attached or built-in garage and a house is required to be tight-fitting and weather-stripped to provide an effective barrier against the passage of gas and exhaust fumes, and be equipped with a self-closing device.

8.6.2 Cantilevered floors

A cantilever floor requires that the air barrier be transferred from the lower wall, to the cantilever floor, and back to the upper wall (See Figures 10.9 and 10.10).

8.6.3 Bay and bow windows

Bow and bay windows are usually attached to the headboards and the seatboards at the factory but the window units are not necessarily sealed to the boards. If the manufacturer does not indicate that the entire bay or bow window can be considered a sealed unit, apply sealant in the locations shown on the installation instructions. Once this is done, the bay or bow window unit needs to be sealed to the house air barrier system around its perimeter (Figure 8.12).

8.6.4. Multiple windows

Although window standards have criteria for the air-tightness of individual window units, it is important for a builder to ensure there is an air seal between windows. Check with the manufacturer to ensure that two or more windows that have been mulled (joined) in the factory are sealed between adjacent windows. Seal between windows that are mulled on site.

8.6.5 Cathedral ceiling/wall junction

The air barrier system for a cathedral ceiling is similar to that of a ceiling below an attic (Figure 8.13).

Figure 8.13 Air barrier at the wall / cathedral ceiling intersection

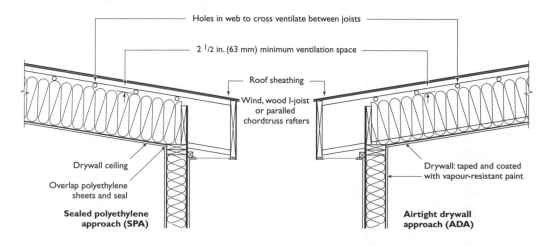

Figure 8.14 Air barriers for bulkheads and cabinetry

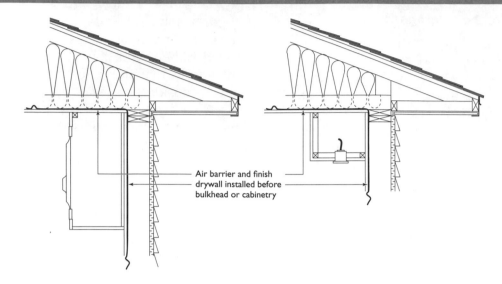

Air barrier and finish drywall installed before bulkhead or cabinetry

8.6.6 Bulkheads and Cabinetry

The simple way to deal with bulkheads and cabinets is to first construct the air barrier system, add wall and ceiling gypsum board, and then any structure inside the air barrier does not need to be sealed (Figure 8.14).

8.6.7 Emerging Technology

The importance of air sealing is being recognized as a key feature of Net Zero Energy Housing. As such, alternative techniques, products and processes are expected to be developed. At the time of writing, one such new, emerging technology is just beginning to make market inroads. The technology uses a liquid based air sealing material which is sprayed into the air of a closed house. This material has a very high air suspension factor. The house is pressurized to 100 Pa and the the air leaks out, taking with it the air sealing liquid suspended in the air. As the air passes through the unintended holes and cracks a small amount of the air sealing material clings to the side of the hole and hardens. Slowly, drop after drop, the air sealing material collects sufficiently to seal the hole. The process takes 1-3 hours and is delivering significant improvements in air tightness. Reportedly levels of air tightness in the range of 0.2 ACH50 are not out of the ordinary.

No matter which of the conventional air barrier approaches are used as described in this Manual, air tighness levels of just under 1.0 ACH are about the practical limit of the technology and time and attention needed by the trades. In addition, air barriers are traditionally a joint effort by many trades, all taking responsibility for ensuring that they achieve a good seal for their penetrations. This emerging technology is the first of its kind where a trade takes responsibility for the "final" sealing. During the sealing process the house is monitored and the air tightness is continuously being measured and monitored during the air sealing process. This allows the operator of the sealing equipment to continue until the desired (or specified) air tightness is achieved. If this technology is successfully adopted by builders, no longer will an air test at the end of construction be the first time that a builder knows if their air sealing has been successful. Conceptually, even for builders who are currently building to a 3.5 ACH50 level can reach tightness levels of 0.5 ACH50 after a few hours of air suspended, pressurized air sealing.

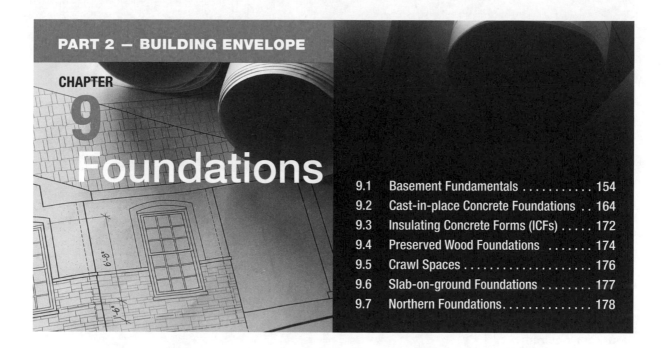

In Canada, a foundation provides not only structural support for the building above, but also commonly houses a basement. When a foundation also serves as a basement, successful performance can be a challenge. It is located, for the most part, below ground. It abuts earth that can be dry, moist, wet or frozen. It is subjected to greater structural, water and moisture loads than the above-grade portions, and soil and groundwater conditions can vary from site to site.

Consumer expectations for basements have increased in the last few decades, with basements used more and more as living spaces requiring the same degree of temperature and humidity comfort as the rest of the house. When a problem occurs with a foundation/basement, it can be expensive to rectify, especially if the foundation function is compromised. Attention to design and construction is required to ensure basements meet performance requirements and consumer expectations.

9.1 Basement Fundamentals

Performance expectations for environmental separation have become more demanding as basements are used more as living spaces. Table 9.1 presents a list of requirements basements should fulfill.

Table 9.1 Functions of the basement envelope system

Performance Requirements
Provide structural support for the building and earth pressure
Control heat loss
Control air leakage including soil gas
Control moisture flow in and out
Meet other code requirements (sound, fire, etc.)

Construction Requirements
Be economical and fast to construct
Use durable materials that can withstand storage and handling
Accommodate services—electrical, plumbing, HVAC, etc.

Market Requirement
Provide market value by being usable for its intended purpose

---

The National Building Code of Canada (NBC) provides minimum requirements for basements that will suit many, but not all, site and climate conditions. In good building conditions, minimum requirements can perform well. However, when minimum requirements are used in less than ideal conditions, failure of the basement system may occur. This means the designer and builder need to recognize conditions that require additional measures so that a basement meets all the performance requirements. Sometimes site assembly practices defeat the intended functions, resulting in a poorer envelope than is expected with a 'minimum basement configuration.'

There are many different approaches to building a successful basement envelope and each has advantages and disadvantages. Usually, basement envelopes featuring multiple materials must be specified to make sure that all of the functional requirements expected of the envelope are covered by at least one of those materials or systems of materials.

Although polyethylene has been used to provide the air/vapour barriers in basements, moisture problems have been encountered. Modern construction can result in basements that are ready for finishing before excess moisture has had a chance to escape from the concrete, which can take up to two years after concrete placement. Installing polyethylene while the concrete moisture is still present traps the moisture. For this reason, polyethylene should not be used below grade until the majority of water in the concrete has escaped.

This chapter does not attempt to provide a single solution. To do so would result in a foundation that might not perform in certain conditions and might be over-designed and expensive for other applications. Instead, this chapter provides information to help the designer/builder understand building physics, performance requirements, functions of building elements (dampproofing, insulation, vapour barrier, etc.), materials, and finishing details so that the appropriate materials and methods can be selected.

While other possibilities do exist, this chapter focuses on basement systems most commonly used, which are cast-in-place concrete with:

- Exterior insulation; and/or

- Interior insulation.

This chapter also provides basic information about ICFs (insulating concrete forms), which provide insulation on both the interior and the exterior, and PWF (preserved wood foundation) with an insulated cavity. Canada's North presents special foundation challenges; this chapter also provides information on northern construction.

9.1.1 Water management

Moisture condensing on basement walls and floors and water leaking through the foundation from the outside can be major problems. Water can enter basements and crawl-spaces in several ways (Figure 9.1):

- Water is released through the curing of concrete in walls and slabs, increasing indoor humidity levels.

- Water may diffuse inward through improperly dampproofed walls and slabs.

- Water vapour is carried by infiltrating humid air in summer, which condenses on cooler surfaces. Effective air sealing techniques and proper ventilation strategies can control this problem.

- The common practice of constructing a stand-off wall 1" away from the concrete wall, filling it with full- height insulation and facing it with polyethylene, has been problematic and has led to moisture problems in the stand-off wall (Figure 9.2).

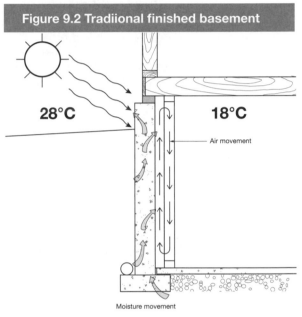

Figure 9.2 Tradiional finished basement

28°C   18°C

Air movement

Moisture movement

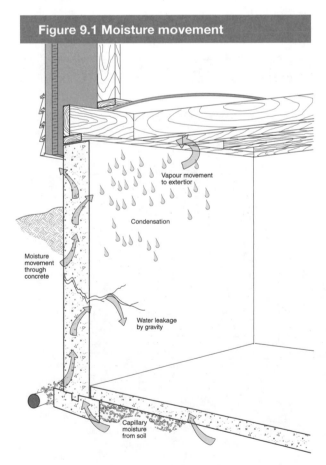

Figure 9.1 Moisture movement

Vapour movement to extertior

Condensation

Moisture movement through concrete

Water leakage by gravity

Capillary moisture from soil

Analysis

Assume the outdoor temperature is 28°C and the indoor temperature in the basement is 18°C because it is summer time and the air conditioner is on. Moisture is somehow getting into the space between the foundation wall and the polyethylene. This could be due to capillary movement if the soil is wet under the footings, or it could be the drying of the foundation if the construction is new. The foundation wall is at 28°C or higher depending on whether it is in the sun or not. The polyethylene is at 18°C. The RH is 100% at the inside surface of the polyethylene because water is condensing. At the inside surface of the foundation wall the

RH is less than 100% because the water is not condensing on the foundation wall. The warm foundation wall is warming the air and causing it to rise. As the air rises along the foundation wall, the air is absorbing moisture from the wall. As the air curls at the top of the cavity and comes into contact with the cool polyethylene. The air cools and falls towards the basement floor. As the air cools, it reaches the "dew point" (the temperature at which the water vapour in the air condenses). This causes water droplets to form on the polyethylene. Once the air reaches the basement floor it curls towards the basement wall, where it is warmed and again absorbs moisture. And so, the process repeats.

Using the psychrometric chart, assume the concrete wall is at 28°C and the RH of the air in the space near the concrete wall is at 80% or higher. Enter the chart at 28°C and move upward to the 80% RH line. Then left to the 100% RH line, then straight down to determine the temperature at which condensation will occur. In this case it is roughly 24°C. But the polyethylene

is at 18°C because the air conditioning is on. Therefore condensation forms.

Three Potential Solutions:

1. The polyethylene is a vapour barrier. Remove the polyethylene and use an approved "smart" vapour barrier to allow the wall to dry to the inside of the building.

2. Install rigid foam insulation to the full height of the basement wall on the inside, then install the stand off wall, the batt insulation, and a "smart" vapour barrier.

3. Use insulated concrete forms for the basement wall system.

Of note, is that the phenomenon described here is usually evident on the east, south or west walls. Why? Because these are the walls that "see" the sun and the sun raises the temperature of the walls above the ambient temperature. On the north wall the temperature will be closer to ambient.

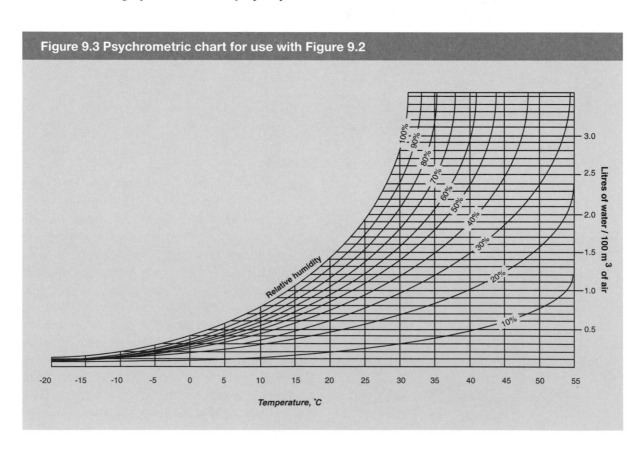

Figure 9.3 Psychrometric chart for use with Figure 9.2

Figure 9.4 Water management

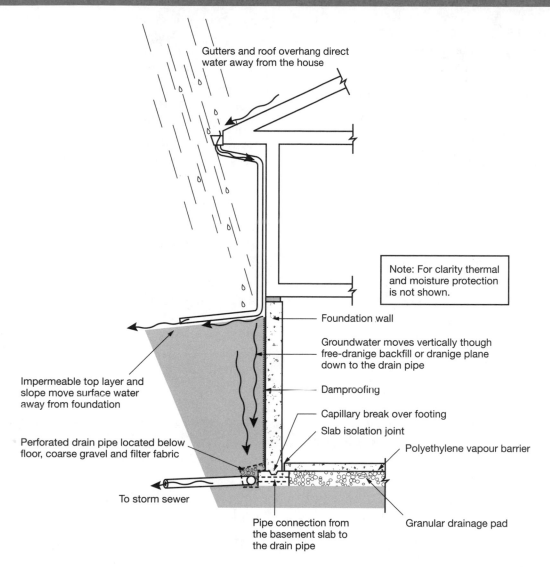

Gutters and roof overhang direct water away from the house

Note: For clarity thermal and moisture protection is not shown.

Foundation wall

Groundwater moves vertically though free-dranige backfill or dranige plane down to the drain pipe

Damproofing

Impermeable top layer and slope move surface water away from foundation

Capillary break over footing

Slab isolation joint

Polyethylene vapour barrier

Perforated drain pipe located below floor, coarse gravel and filter fabric

To storm sewer

Granular drainage pad

Pipe connection from the basement slab to the drain pipe

Water can leak through cracks in the foundation. Proper construction techniques and exterior drainage can prevent leakage.

Insulation, dampproofing and drainage systems can reduce foundation moisture problems.

Careful design and construction of the foundation can be compromised if the fundamental principles of keeping water away from the exterior wall are ignored (Figure 9.4). While this may seem elementary, failure to manage rain and snow melt continues to result in call-backs. It is important to remember that poorly compacted or frozen backfill placed around the foundation will settle and leave a flat or depressed area that directs water toward the foundation wall. In addition, settlement can occur around the foundation for several years after backfilling and cause water to not drain away from the foundation. If settlement does occur, proper drainage should be restored.

Proper water management includes:

• Surface drainage to direct water away from the foundation;

- Free-draining backfill or a drainage plane next to the foundation;

- Properly graded drainage pipe system protected from plugging by fine soil particles; and

- Effective means of conveying water away from the foundation drainage system to the municipal storm sewer or to open space.

There are two strategies for dealing with surface and groundwater that does come into contact with the foundation wall.

1. Continuous and effective wall drainage, interconnected to a compatible drainage system, to prevent accumulation of water against the outer surfaces of the envelope (walls and floor slab)-exterior drainage and dampproofing.

2. Full and continuous barrier to water penetration-waterproofing.

In soil conditions where water cannot reliably be removed from the foundation wall, waterproofing is required to keep the basement dry. Complete waterproofing systems wrap the entire envelope exposed to bulk water, including beneath floor slabs, between footings and walls, penetrations, and the exterior of walls up to the high groundwater level. Waterproofing should only be installed by specialty contractors. Groundwater pressure increases the lateral load on foundation walls, and this must be taken into account in the structural design of the foundation walls and floor.

Hydrostatic Pressure

If water is unable to get away from the foundation, it can exert a significant force on the walls and uplift on the floor because of hydrostatic pressure. This is a condition that can happen when water is trapped along side a foundation wall and cannot escape. This condition can be caused by failed drainage/

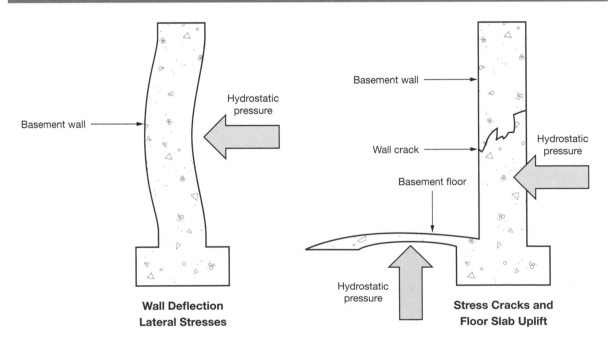

Figure 9.5 Effects of hydrostatic pressure

Basement wall

Hydrostatic pressure

**Wall Deflection
Lateral Stresses**

Basement wall

Wall crack

Hydrostatic pressure

Basement floor

Hydrostatic pressure

**Stress Cracks and
Floor Slab Uplift**

weeping tiles, combined with surface grades towards the house and/or downspouts that discharge to the weeping tile instead of away from the house. If the wall is watertight and and the hydrostatic pressure is high enough, it can cause the wall to deflect or crack. While this is a condition that can lead to structural failure of the wall, it is more common that the hydrostatic pressure forces water through cracks in the wall, around form ties, around sub-surface penetrations, through the wall to footing connection, or under the footing and through cracks in the basement floor slab or between the floor slab and the basement wall (Figure 9.5).

The significance of the the hydrostatic pressure can be seen in the following calculation. Refer to Figure 9.6.

Calculation Information

Note that the pressure exerted against the wall is dependent on the height of the water. The pressure is greatest at the bottom of the wall and 0 at the top of the water. The pressure against the wall also increases, with the depth of the water. The specific weight of water is a constant at 62.4 lb/ft³ (9.807 kN/m³).

Pressure = Specific weight of Water x h where:

h = depth of water in m or feet – for this example lets assume this is 4 feet.

The pressure against the wall at the top of the water is 0.

The pressure at the bottom of the wall is = 62.4 lb/ft³ x 4 ft = 249.6 lb/ft². This converts to 1.73 lb/in².

The force on the wall can be assumed be applied at 1/3 the height of the pressure distribution triangle. To calculate the force on the wall we need to imagine a 1 ft slice of wall and calculate the area of the pressure distribution triangle.

Area of the triangle = 1/2 x base x height = 1/2 x 249.6 lb/ft² x 4 ft = 499.2 lb per lineal foot of the wall. If the wall is (assume 25 ft) then the force on the wall is F = 12,480 lbs.

With these types of pressures and forces acting on the wall when water builds up against it, there is little wonder that foundation leaks occur or walls crack. Ensuring water gets away from the house and the foundation is critical. The hydraulic pressure on walls and floors from even a small depth of water needs to be avoided.

Figure 9.6 Calculation of hydrostatic pressure

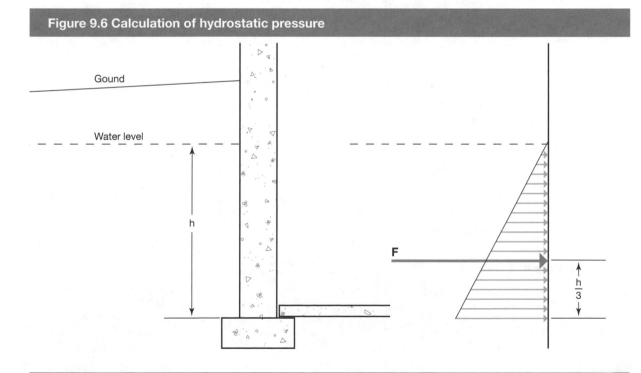

Curing concrete

As concrete cures, it releases large amounts of excess water in the form of vapour, especially in the first few months. If the interior surfaces of the foundation walls and floor are left uncovered, this moisture will be released into the house. If the concrete surfaces are covered, the moisture may move into other areas in the walls or floor, causing problems such as staining and mould growth.

To reduce these problems:

- Allow concrete foundations to dry for as long as possible before placing the interior insulation and vapour barrier.

- Place a moisture barrier over the inside surface of the concrete walls from the footing up to grade level.

- Insulate the floor slab.

- Leave above-grade sections of the concrete wall uncovered as long as possible to allow moisture to escape.

Reducing condensation

Condensation on the interior of basement or crawl space walls and floors can be reduced by:

- Insulating on the exterior. This will keep the concrete wall warm and reduce the likelihood of condensation.

- Placing a continuous air barrier and a vapour barrier over the inside of all insulation when insulating on the interior, even though the foundation wall acts as an air barrier.

- Sealing the bottom plate/floor slab junction to keep humid air from leaking behind the wall and condensing on the cold concrete.

- Conditioning the interior air by cooling in summer months or lowering the humidity.

9.1.2 Soil conditions

Local experience is a good indicator of whether difficult soil and groundwater conditions are likely. If there is any doubt, it is important to engage a geotechnical expert. Groundwater conditions can vary significantly within a given area due to pockets of poorly draining soil and perched or fluctuating water tables. Difficult conditions may affect the structure and drainage system, and indicate whether dampproofing alone is adequate or whether waterproofing is required.

Swelling or shrinking soils present a challenge and can result in foundations that move and cause cracks in walls, ceilings and basement floors, as well as uneven floors and doors that bind. Generally, volume changes in expansive soils are caused by changes in moisture content; therefore, extra attention to the design and installation of foundation drainage is essential for providing a foundation that is stable. Difficult soil conditions require design by a geotechnical engineer. One approach is supporting the foundation on piles (Figure 9.7) and providing a void beneath a lightweight suspended floor so that subsoil shrinkage and expansion does not act on the basement floor.

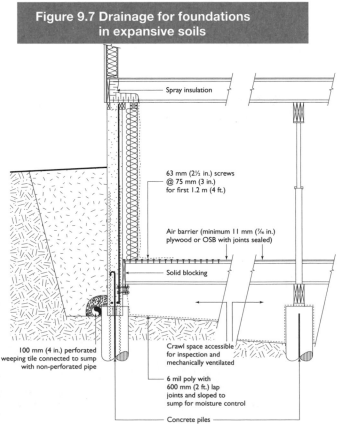

Figure 9.7 Drainage for foundations in expansive soils

Spray insulation

63 mm (2½ in.) screws @ 75 mm (3 in.) for first 1.2 m (4 ft.)

Air barrier (minimum 11 mm (⁷⁄₁₆ in.) plywood or OSB with joints sealed)

Solid blocking

100 mm (4 in.) perforated weeping tile connected to sump with non-perforated pipe

Crawl space accessible for inspection and mechanically ventilated

6 mil poly with 600 mm (2 ft.) lap joints and sloped to sump for moisture control

Concrete piles

9.1.3 Managing heat loss

Heat loss from the foundation can account for a significant amount of total heat loss in the average house. The rate of heat loss is proportional to the difference in temperature between the heated living space and the temperature of the outdoor air as well as to the temperature of the ground and soil water in contact with the foundation. There are three basic arrangements for wall insulation coverage used in Canada:

1. Full coverage.

2. Majority coverage: a gap of about 200 mm (8 in.) is left uninsulated above the basement floor.

3. Partial coverage: insulated to 600 mm (24 in.) below grade (for interior insulation).

Full coverage provides the best energy-efficiency and makes it easier to apply wall finishes for livable spaces. If the desired outcome is a Net Zero Energy House, full coverage will be required.

Most heat loss (Figure 9.8) occurs due to:

• Air leakage through the sill plate/header/subfloor floor assembly

• Conduction through above-grade sections of foundation walls

• Conduction below grade to the surrounding soil and to groundwater

Foundations can be insulated on the outside, on the inside, on both the outside and the inside, or in the centre. Each approach has advantages and disadvantages. In all cases, control joints should be used where required to control cracking. Exterior insulation needs to be able to function in wet conditions, must be shielded above ground to prevent damage, needs to be insect-resistant, and needs to be able to resist uplift from frost action.

Interior insulation is the most economical, but moisture management is a challenge. Insulation installed in the centre of a foundation wall is the most expensive and difficult to construct, but does away with some of the challenges posed by internal and exterior systems. Insulating on both sides has the same challenges as exterior insulation, and the additional cost of the internal insulation. Insulating concrete forms (ICFs) are a special case of insulating on both sides and offer some advantages.

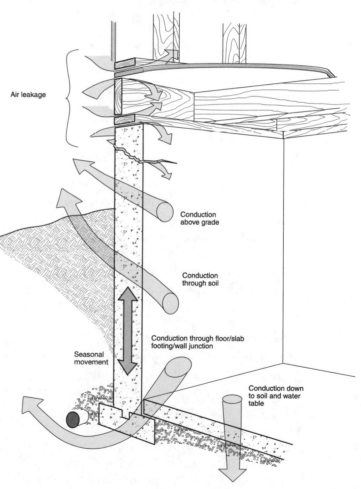

Figure 9.8 Heat loss through the foundation wall and floor

Air leakage

Conduction above grade

Conduction through soil

Conduction through floor/slab footing/wall junction

Seasonal movement

Conduction down to soil and water table

Heat loss above grade

Heat loss through foundation walls above grade is directly affected by the temperature difference between inside and outside, and the resistance to heat loss of the foundation wall. It tends to be significant even though only a small portion of the foundation wall is exposed to the outside air. This is because the materials used for foundation walls have a lower insulating value than those used for the main building envelope, and winter air temperature is usually much lower than soil temperature. In addition, wind adds to heat loss above grade if the air barrier is incomplete.

Heat loss below grade

Several factors influence heat loss below grade:

- Depth: soil temperature increases with depth during winter months. Those parts of the foundation close to the surface have higher heat loss rates than those at the footings. But even at the footing and foundation floor level, the soil is colder than the interior living space, causing conductive heat flow.

- Presence of water: a high water table within 600 mm (24 in.) of the slab will increase heat loss from the slab because water passing by the slab will carry heat away with it. Similarly, surface water draining to the weeping tile will carry heat away from the foundation wall.

Air leakage

Air leakage can occur both above and below grade. Cold air will tend to enter through the lower portions of a house because of negative pressures created by stack action and mechanical exhaust equipment (see Section 2.2). The foundation/sill plate/joist header junction has multiple joints and connections through which air can move. Cracks and joints in poured concrete and concrete block walls, and openings around service penetrations and windows increase the number of paths for air leakage. Air will leak in through a floor drain if it does not have a trap, or if the trap is dry. Air will also leak through the weeping tiles if they are connected to an unsealed sump chamber.

Reducing heat loss

Proper insulation can greatly reduce heat loss from the foundation. Proper foundation insulation can improve thermal comfort, reduce surface condensation on walls, and add protection for the structure, as well as reduce energy costs. Table 9.2 lists common types of insulation and where they can be used.

The amount of insulation required and its location depends on local soil conditions, the method of construction, construction budget, and how the space is to be occupied. The following points apply to non-permafrost regions and to all construction practices.

- Full-depth foundation insulation is now common in Canada and will be standard for Net Zero construction.

- Basement walls, especially the basement floor header area, should be insulated to the same level as exterior walls.

- Insulation is desirable for comfort reasons if the basement is to be a finished space. Basement floor slabs should be insulated with RSI 1.8 (R-10) for a minimum 1.0 m (3 ft.) width of insulation around the entire slab perimeter but it is recommended that the entire floor slab should be insulated. If in-floor heating is to be used, then the entire floor slab must be insulated to minimum RSI 1.8 (R-10).

- Foundation wall/sill plate/joist header junction must be airtight. Airtight construction details should be used throughout the rest of the foundation wall, floor, and wall/floor junction.

- Net Zero building experience is showing designers using at least RSI 4.2 + (R-24 +) on the basement walls and RSI 1.76 + (R-10 +) under the basement floor slab.

Check local code requirements or NBC 9.36 to establish the amount of insulation required.

Table 9.2 Permitted placement of thermal insulation

Insulation Type	Permitted Placement	
	Interior	Exterior, below grade
Glass or mineral fibre batt	Yes	No
Glass or mineral fibre loose-fill	Yes	No
Cellulose loose-fill	Yes	No
Glass or mineral fibre boardstock (semi-rigid)	Yes	Yes
Expanded polystyrene boardstock (Types I, II and III)	Yes*	Yes
Extruded polystyrene boardstock (Types II [manufacturer may still restrict to interior and exterior above-grade applications], III and IV)	Yes*	Yes
Glass or mineral fibre spray type	Yes	No
Cellulose spray type	Yes	No
Polyurethane spray type	Yes*	Yes
Insulating concrete forms (ICF)	Yes*	Yes

* A fire-protective covering such as drywall is required.

9.1.4 Managing air movement

As for other parts of the building envelope, managing air movement in a basement system is essential for reducing heat loss and moisture deposition, and for minimizing infiltration of radon or other soil gas. This means that the walls and floor and their junctions must be sealed for airtightness. Where a sump pump is required to remove water from around the foundation, its chamber must also be sealed (Figure 9.9).

Radon

Protection from soil gas ingress is now required in all buildings (see Section 4.1.6). This protection is achieved by installing a continuous air/soil gas barrier. The 2015 NBC provides further protection against future radon ingress into conditioned spaces in Part 9 buildings (houses and small buildings) by requiring one of two methods.

The first method uses a gas-permeable layer between the undisturbed ground and the air barrier that allows for depressurization of the space below the soil gas barrier. This layer

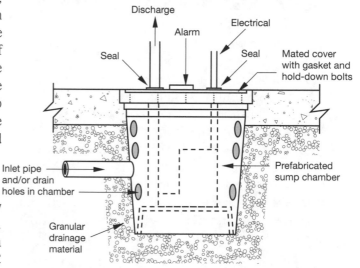

Figure 9.9 Airtight sump pump chamber

could be coarse sand, stone or a dimpled membrane or another product that allows the collection and extraction of gas. An inlet needs to be provided that allows for effective depressurization of the gas-permeable layer. An outlet needs to be provided that permits connection to depressurization equipment sealed to maintain the integrity of the air barrier system. The outlet should be clearly labelled to indicate that it is intended for the removal of radon from below the floor-on-ground. An example of this method would be a sump chamber that is sealed to the air barrier, which can be connected and used to exhaust air from beneath a floor-on-ground.

The second method requires a 100-mm (4 in.) layer of clean, granular material under the floor on ground and a pipe at least 100 mm (4 in.) in diameter through the floor. The lower end of the pipe extends into the required granular layer. The top of the pipe must be fitted with an air-tight cap. If it is desired to locate the pipe rough-in close to an exterior wall or into the service area of a basement, a Schedule 40 PVC plumbing pipe is typically used to connect the vertical pipe to the center of the sub-floor. If the sub-floor space is interrupted by internal footings, it is important to ensure that the collection system is capable of depressurizing all areas.

Continuity of Sub-slab Air Barrier to the Wall Air Barrier

It is important that the sub-slab air/gas barrier is adequately connected to the foundation wall air barrier system. In the event that the air/gas barrier continuity is faulty, the depressurization system for removing radon will also be able to extract air from the basement area. Since the radon depressurization system typically operates 100% of the time, this can lead to conditioned air being removed from the basement. This example illustrates the importance of having a plan, before construction starts, of how the continuity of the air barrier will be achieved.

9.2 Cast-in-place Concrete Foundations

9.2.1 Externally insulated concrete foundations

Rigid insulating board can be fixed to the exterior basement wall (Figure 9.10) using

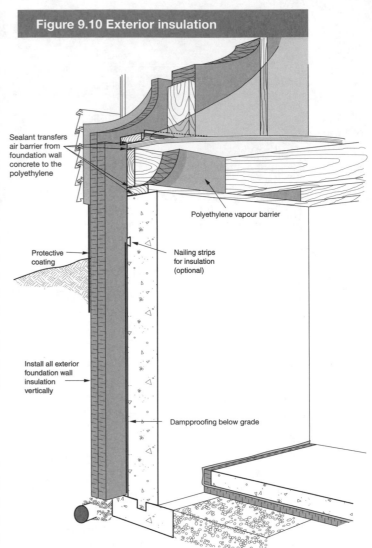

Figure 9.10 Exterior insulation

Sealant transfers air barrier from foundation wall concrete to the polyethylene

Polyethylene vapour barrier

Protective coating

Nailing strips for insulation (optional)

Install all exterior foundation wall insulation vertically

Dampproofing below grade

adhesive or mechanical fastening techniques and protective coverings. Rigid insulation needs to be affixed to the foundation wall to resist frost action from soil that may become frozen to the insulation. As with all foundation work, good dampproofing and drainage techniques are important for long-term performance. The amount of insulation installed depends on regional climate, soil conditions, and desired energy performance. Refer to local code requirements or NBC 9.36.

Spray-on insulations are a relatively recent innovation in residential construction. There are three different types used in basement construction: spray cellulose insulation;

spray mineral fibre insulation; and spray polyurethane foam. Only polyurethane is approved for exterior insulation. Spray-on insulation must be applied by a certified applicator. As for rigid insulation, compatible dampproofing and protection of the above-grade portion is required.

Externally-insulated concrete foundation	
Advantages	**Disadvantages**
• Reduced condensation problems, as the wall is kept warmer.	• Higher material costs are probable, including above-grade insulation protection.
• Reduced potential for "adfreezing" (where the soil freezes to the surface of the foundation and may lift it).	• Unfinished interior surface.
• Reduced labour requirements.	• Possible thermal bridging from the warm foundation to the cold brick veneer.
• Improved airtightness and reduced thermal bridging at the header joist.	• Dislodged insulation could result from adfreezing.
• Improved temperature stability, as the thermal mass of the foundation wall is inside the house.	• Extra care is required during backfilling.

Dampproofing

It is essential to use dampproofing material that is compatible with the board insulation. Some dampproofing materials such as asphalt emulsion react with foam insulations while curing, so manufacturer's information should be consulted.

Drainage

Membrane drainage materials must be flashed to prevent above-grade water from entering behind the materials. Many of the systems require special detailing at the footing/foundation wall junction. Where free-draining backfill materials are available, they may prove less expensive than membrane drainage materials. Figure 9.11 shows the interface of an externally insulated concrete foundation with a wall with cladding.

Insulation

Type I and II expanded polystyrene and Types III and IV extruded polystyrene are suitable for exterior insulation (see Table 9.2). Rigid glass-fibre or mineral fibre insulation can provide excellent drainage even without free-draining backfill if detailing at the footing allows water to flow into the perimeter drain or weeping tile. Both rigid polystyrene and glass fibre boardstock must be installed vertically.

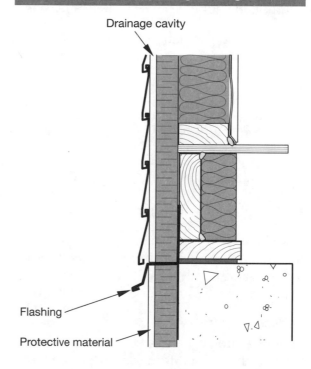

Figure 9.11 Externally insulated foundation wall supporting a siding-clad wall

Drainage cavity

Flashing

Protective material

Where free-draining backfill or materials are employed, free-flowing access to weeping tiles must be maintained.

Fastening

Board insulation needs to be secured to the foundation to resist shifting due to frost action. Nailing strips can be cast into poured concrete foundations at locations dictated by the amount of exposure above grade and special-purpose, large-headed fasteners or galvanized nails with plastic washers are used to hold the insulation in place. Other fastening systems connect directly to masonry surfaces. Manufacturers' information can provide guidance on the most suitable fastening system to use. Fastening is also required above grade. If above-grade exposure is not significant, the insulation can be affixed to the sill plate.

Protective covering

The above-grade area of exterior insulation must be protected from solar radiation, rodents, insects and damage, and several protective coverings are suitable for this purpose, including:

- Galvanized wire lath and stucco (additional fasteners may be needed to make the lath rigid);

- Fibre-reinforced, polymer-modified cement or other foundation coating;

- Fibre-cement mill board;

- Pressure-treated plywood; and

- Galvanized sheet metal.

For some arrangements, metal flashing is required to keep water from leaking between the insulation and the foundation wall. Even where it is not required, it is recommended.

Service penetrations

Conduits should be sealed where they pass through the foundation wall or joist headers, and inside the conduit where they terminate in the electrical panel, to prevent moist air travelling through the conduit and causing condensation damage. Sealing should be done inside conduits with approved sealants, such as duct-sealing putty or specialized

mechanical inserts. Service penetrations through externally insulated foundation walls below grade (Figure 9.12) should be sealed with polysulphide or high solids content butyl. Service penetrations through the joist header (Figure 9.13) should be sealed with an acrylic, silicone or butyl sealant that is compatible with wood and with the conduit material.

Figure 9.12 Sealing service penetration below grade (exterior insulation)

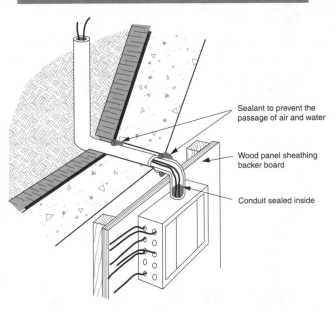

Figure 9.13 Sealing service penetration through the rim joist below grade (exterior insulation)

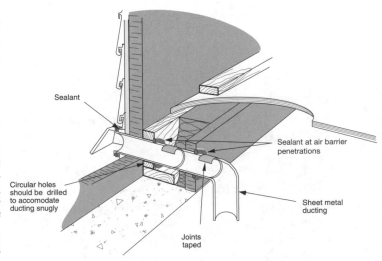

Sheet metal ducting for dryers, heating and heat recovery ventilator systems or make-up air may pass through the joist header. These penetrations should be sealed with a rubber gasket (such as an elastomeric roofing membrane), or with acrylic, silicone, or high solids content butyl caulking material suitable for the duct temperature. Of these, silicone is best suited for high temperature.

Below-grade openings in the foundation wall for plumbing should be sealed the same way as penetrations for electrical conduits.

Copper piping should be isolated from the wall concrete to avoid deterioration of the copper due to galvanic action.

9.2.2 Internally insulated concrete foundations

There are several different ways to insulate the foundation from the interior. The thickness of insulation required depends on the RSI (R) value of the particular product or system, the potential loss of interior space, ease of installation, regional climate, and desired energy performance.

Internally-insulated concrete foundation	
Advantages	**Disadvantages**
• Insulation is provided as part of the interior finishing. • No changes to exterior finishing details. • Space is provided for mechanical and electrical services. • Thermal bridging with brick veneer cladding is prevented.	• Potential for concealed condensation exists, so a continuous interior air barrier and a vapour barrier are required. • Foundation wall exterior is exposed to temperature fluctuations and there is potential for adfreezing. • Sill plate/header joist assembly sealing can be difficult.

Where brick veneer is used, interior insulation (Figure 9.14) will eliminate thermal bridging through the brick, as this is very difficult to control with exterior insulation.

Figure 9.14 Brick veneer with interior basement insulation

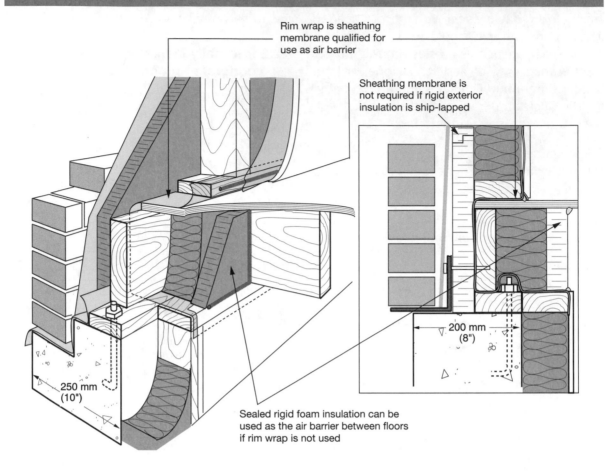

Rim wrap is sheathing membrane qualified for use as air barrier

Sheathing membrane is not required if rigid exterior insulation is ship-lapped

250 mm (10")

200 mm (8")

Sealed rigid foam insulation can be used as the air barrier between floors if rim wrap is not used

Moisture barrier

If the insulating method considered involves placing fibre insulation or untreated wood in contact with the concrete below grade, an interior moisture barrier is required. This is in addition to, and does not replace, the exterior dampproofing. According to the NBC, this interior moisture barrier/sheathing membrane should be tar-impregnated building paper (CGSB 51.32) or other approved layer, for example, CCMC-evaluated sheathing membranes such as spun-bonded polyolefin.

Many houses have been constructed in Canada using polyethylene for this purpose. While this has worked well in many cases, it has also caused mould and water condensation problems in the insulation cavity, particularly where polyethylene has also been used as the vapour barrier over the insulation. This combination can prevent moisture in the insulating cavity from escaping. Where the concrete and wood framing were relatively dry at the time of completing the interior insulating assembly, this combination has worked successfully. However, where closing is completed while the concrete is relatively new, expensive remedial work may be necessary later.

Recent research concludes that the use of polyethylene in basements requires careful consideration and should not be used until the concrete has lost all excess moisture. This process can be accelerated by using commercial dehumidifiers or electric heaters. Fuel-fired construction heaters, on the other hand, can make the problem worse because these combustion-type heaters generate humidity.

Two tested alternatives to the use of polyethylene are suggested. They are based on the fact that a) moisture needs to be able to escape from materials in the months after construction, and b) moisture vapour from the interior needs to be restricted from moving into the internally insulated foundation wall assembly. Figure 9.15 shows the use of batt insulation and the avoidance of polyethylene. The vapour barrier is provided by a vapour-barrier paint applied to the drywall. The drywall is made airtight and constitutes the air barrier.

Figure 9.15 Batt-insulated foundation

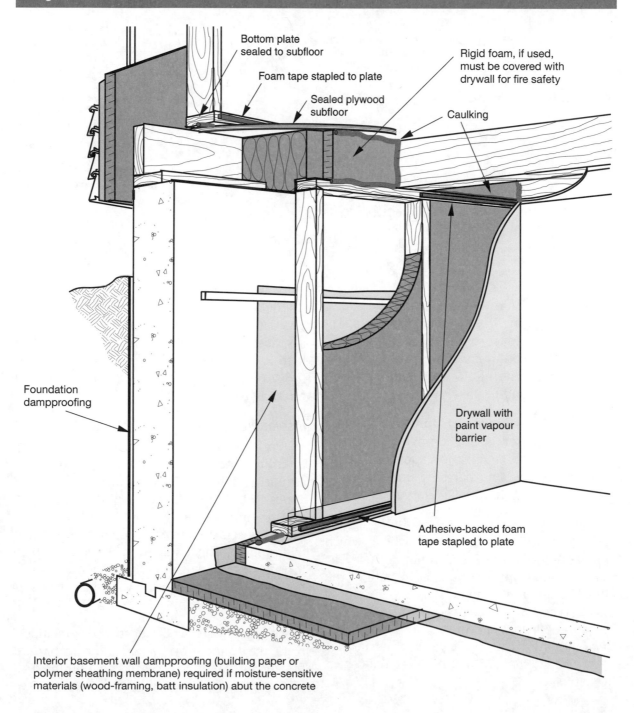

Bottom plate sealed to subfloor

Foam tape stapled to plate

Sealed plywood subfloor

Rigid foam, if used, must be covered with drywall for fire safety

Caulking

Foundation dampproofing

Drywall with paint vapour barrier

Adhesive-backed foam tape stapled to plate

Interior basement wall dampproofing (building paper or polymer sheathing membrane) required if moisture-sensitive materials (wood-framing, batt insulation) abut the concrete

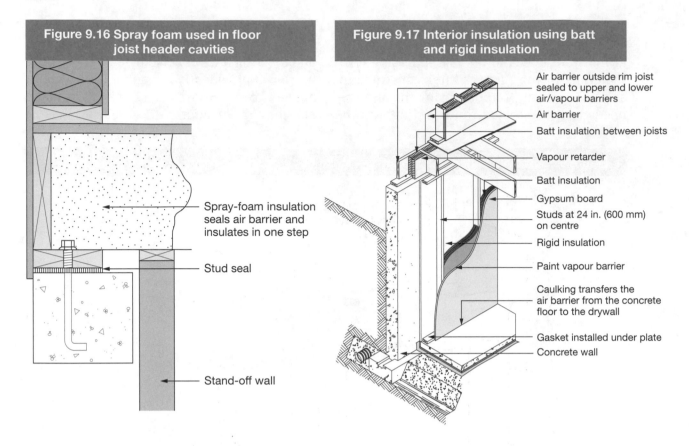

Figure 9.16 Spray foam used in floor joist header cavities

Spray-foam insulation seals air barrier and insulates in one step

Stud seal

Stand-off wall

Figure 9.17 Interior insulation using batt and rigid insulation

Air barrier outside rim joist sealed to upper and lower air/vapour barriers

Air barrier

Batt insulation between joists

Vapour retarder

Batt insulation

Gypsum board

Studs at 24 in. (600 mm) on centre

Rigid insulation

Paint vapour barrier

Caulking transfers the air barrier from the concrete floor to the drywall

Gasket installed under plate

Concrete wall

A slight variation on Figure 9.16 is the use of spray foam in the floor joist cavity. The spray foam fills the space between the joists, and maintains the continuity of the air barrier from the basement stand-off wall to the poured concrete wall and to the rim joist.

Figure 9.17 is similar to Figure 9.15 but the moisture barrier is a 25 mm (1 in.)-thick rigid insulation. Again, the vapour barrier is provided by a vapour-barrier paint applied to the drywall and the drywall serves as the air barrier.

Today, "smart" vapour barriers, those which change permeance based on humidity levels, make another option possible. In both of the above cases, the vapour barrier paint could be replaced with a smart vapour barrier membrane installed on the studs, behind the drywall. One such smart vapour barrier has been evaluated by CCMC and has a data sheet available.

Framing

The use of a pressure-treated bottom plate or a spacer under the bottom plate to separate it from the concrete can reduce problems if moisture is present while the concrete is still emitting excess moisture.

Insulation

Several types of insulation are suitable for interior foundation insulation (see Table 9.2). Any rigid board insulation-polystyrene Types I, II, III and IV-can be directly fastened to the foundation wall with adhesive or mechanical fasteners or placed between layers of strapping. The insulation will require either furring or cross-strapping to provide support for drywall unless the drywall finish is glued to the insulation.

Wood-frame walls can be constructed to standoff from the foundation walls to accommodate thicker insulation. The wall can be nailed to joists above and fastened with concrete nails to the floor slab. Since wood materials must not be in direct contact with concrete below grade unless treated, place polyethylene sheeting or gaskets between the wood and the concrete. Installing batt insulation in two steps, with one layer horizontally between the frame and foundation and the other vertically in the stud cavity, will reduce convection loops behind the studs where the batt insulation does not completely fill the cavity. It is important to note that a dampproofing material (polyethylene or asphalt-infused building paper) be be installed on the concrete wall to protect the batt insulation from absorbing moisture from the concrete wall. Since the wall is not load-bearing, framing can be 38 x 64 mm (2 x 3 in.) lumber at 600 mm (2 ft.) centres. RSI 3.5 (R-20) can be achieved if the horizontal layer has a value of RSI 2.1 (R-12) and the layer between the studs is RSI 1.4 (R-8).

All three types of spray-on insulations – cellulose, mineral fibre insulation and spray polyurethane – are suitable for interior insulation. Spray-on polyurethane is usually applied to wood framing kept back 25 mm (1 in.) from the foundation wall. With this arrangement, the foam creates a moisture barrier between the wall and the framing. Polyurethane foam must be covered with a fire-protective covering, such as 12.7 mm (1/2 in.) drywall.

Air sealing

There are three ways to air seal interior insulated foundations. Figure 9.15 shows the airtight drywall approach (ADA). As mentioned, polyethylene can be used over the insulation as an air barrier, but the cautions explained in Moisture Barrier must be heeded. The third method involves using the concrete wall as the air barrier and providing adequate sealing at the top and bottom. Because the concrete needs to be sealed at the floor wall interface to prevent soil gas infiltration, it is convenient to make the concrete the designated air barrier.

In all cases, special attention is required to ensure the area between the concrete and the upper building envelope is air-sealed. This is done by:

- Using a sill plate gasket to provide a seal between the sill plate and the concrete;

- Using spray-on insulation between the joists;

- Installing and sealing a polyethylene air/vapour barrier where rigid or batt insulation is used; and

- Sealing service penetrations through externally insulated concrete and masonry walls to prevent air and water leakage.

It is important to note that concrete can serve as part of the air barrier system, but masonry block is not considered an air barrier material.

Service Penetrations

Electrical and other service penetrations should be minimized in interior insulated basements. Where they are necessary, they should be located where they will not be affected by drifting snow. Penetrations can often be placed in above-grade frame areas such as headers or suspended floor assemblies, as long as the design has taken this placement into account.

Where possible, electrical circuits should be kept on interior basement walls. Electrical boxes in exterior basement walls must be sealed to the air barrier (see Chapter 8). Where drywall is used as the air barrier, penetrations must be air and vapour sealed to reduce the risk of moisture entering the insulated cavity. Penetrations can be minimized by providing a single, dedicated through-wall conduit for telecommunication services such as telephone and cable. This will prevent installers from damaging the air sealing and vapour barrier details after the house has been completed.

For basement walls insulated using the airtight drywall approach (ADA), the main electrical service box should be mounted on a plywood backing board fastened to the drywall in a way that does not damage the air barrier. Wiring from the box should be kept in front of the backing board, except those wires that run into the frame walls of the basement itself. Wire penetrations need to be sealed (see Chapter 8, ADA 2) with caulking where wiring runs through the framing. All service penetrations must be sealed where they pass through the air barrier. After the vapour barrier is in place, it should be sealed to the plywood backing board with caulking and staples. Where the conduit or duct passes through the plywood, it should be sealed with caulking.

Windows

Windows are part of the air barrier system, and the designated air barrier must be transferred to the window. If the concrete foundation wall is the designated air barrier, the window frame is sealed to the air barrier or directly to the concrete foundation wall. Since most basement windows are mounted in the exterior foundation wall, the air barrier must span from the inside wall to the outside wall. Figure 9.18 shows sealing the window with a plywood liner for the airtight drywall approach (ADA). Alternative air sealing details are provided in Chapter 13.

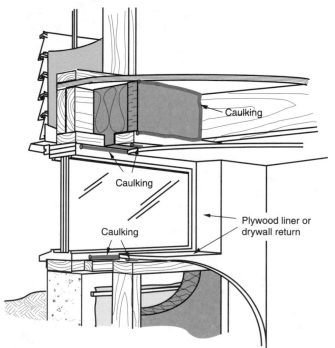

Figure 9.18 Interior insulation – basement window

Caulking

Caulking

Caulking

Plywood liner or drywall return

9.3 Insulating Concrete Forms (ICFs)

Insulating concrete forming systems are increasingly used for foundation wall construction. Thermal insulation (usually expanded polystyrene) is molded to create formwork for cast-in-place concrete. After placement and curing of the concrete, the formwork remains in place to provide interior and exterior insulation of the typically reinforced concrete foundation structure. The ICF system may be used for upper walls as well as foundation walls. Typically, one storey is constructed at a time.

The NBC permits any ICF system having a solid concrete core to be designed in accordance with Part 9 ICF prescriptive requirements. ICF systems permitted for use in Canada generally require CCMC (Canadian Construction Material Centre) evaluations containing usage and limitations criteria, but may be based on Part 4 engineering specifications. There are currently several ICF products with CCMC evaluations, and each manufacturer provides installation information for forms, bracing, windows, dampproofing and finishing inside and above grade on the exterior. There are three categories of insulating concrete form types (Figure 9.19):

- Panel Systems have the largest ICF components. The units are 300 to 1200 mm (12 to 48 in.) tall and 2.4 to 3.6 m (8 to 12 ft.) long.

- Plank Systems are 200 to 300 mm (8 to 12 in.) tall, and 1.2 to 2.4 m (4 to 8 ft.) long. The main difference between the panel and the plank system is the assembly method.

- Block Systems have blocks sizes 200 to 450 mm (8 to 18 in.) tall, and 1.2 to 2.4 m (4 to 8 ft.) long. They have interlocking edges.

Figure 9.19 Types of ICF

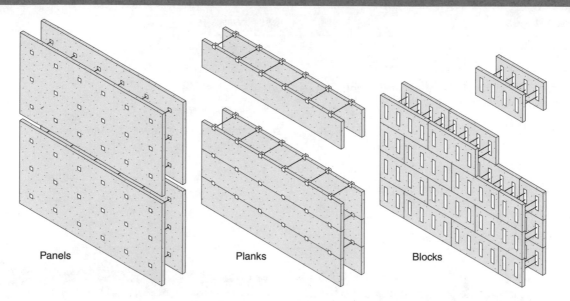

Panels

Planks

Blocks

Planks rely on rigid polystyrene panels that may be notched or specially molded to interlock and receive plastic or nylon spacers and ties. These systems resemble conventional form work. Blocks are factory-assembled units that may resemble a large hollow concrete block. Most have a design with interlocks so that the modules are stacked on site. A typical basement wall section is shown in Figure 9.20. Special units are available that form a flair at the top of the wall for supporting brick veneer.

It is important to ensure footings are level, square, and wide enough to support the insulating forms. Once the forms are assembled, a workable and flowable concrete mix is placed into the forms (usually by pump) to create a solid insulated wall. The concrete producer and the ICF supplier will recommend the proper concrete mix to ensure proper placement. The slump of most mixes should not exceed 150 mm (6 in.) so that excessive pressure is not exerted on the forms during the placement.

Generally, the pour rate is slower than for conventional forms to avoid placing high pressures on the forms. To ensure wall

Figure 9.20 Typical ICF basement section

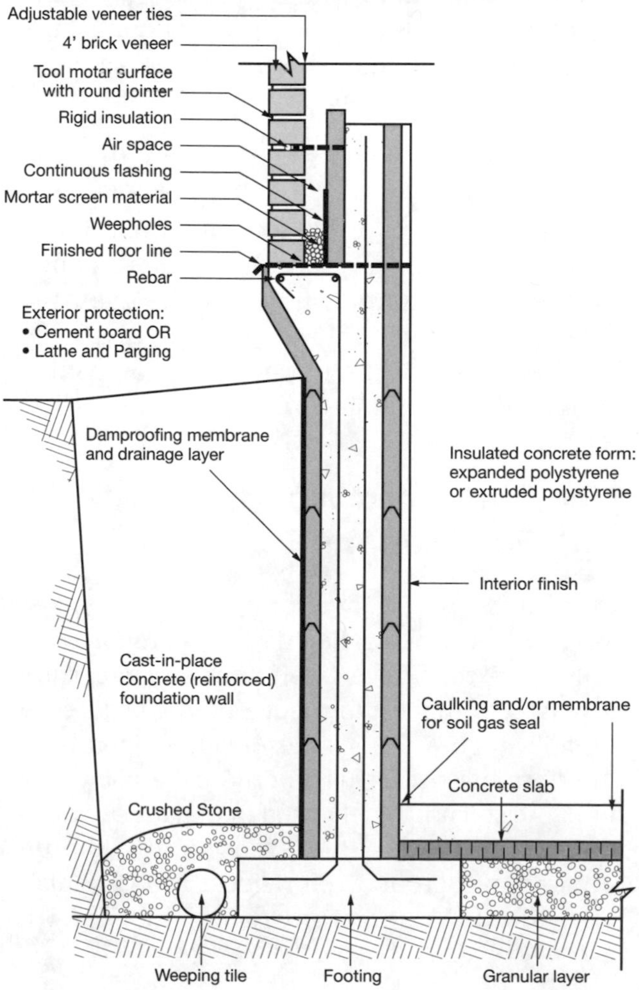

Adjustable veneer ties
4' brick veneer
Tool motar surface with round jointer
Rigid insulation
Air space
Continuous flashing
Mortar screen material
Weepholes
Finished floor line
Rebar
Exterior protection:
• Cement board OR
• Lathe and Parging

Damproofing membrane and drainage layer

Cast-in-place concrete (reinforced) foundation wall

Crushed Stone

Insulated concrete form: expanded polystyrene or extruded polystyrene

Interior finish

Caulking and/or membrane for soil gas seal

Concrete slab

Weeping tile   Footing   Granular layer

Insulating concrete forms (ICFs)

Advantages	Disadvantages
• Forms are lightweight.	• Care is required in layout and leveling of footing.
• No specialized labour or tools are required.	• Higher initial costs.
• Framing, insulation sheathing and vapour and air barriers are combined into one easy step.	• Less robust forms.
• R-values are high.	• Slower pour rates.
• Construction can be done year-round.	• Staging and rebar bending is required.
• No concrete form rental required.	
• Provides an airtight wall and air sealing is only required around penetrations.	
• Forms provide a good concrete curing environment in both summer and winter	

uniformity and to prevent honeycombing and voids, the concrete must be consolidated by internal or external vibration. However, internal vibration must be done carefully because the polystyrene cannot take the pressures and motion of careless concrete vibration. Excess pressure can damage the insulation and lead to a blow-out.

ICF systems provide a uniform thermal resistance of about RSI 3.5 (R-20). ICFs cannot be left exposed to the soil; the below-grade portion must be covered with a waterproofing membrane compatible with the foam as described in the CCMC evaluations – typically a peel-and-stick membrane or a compatible spray-on membrane.

9.4 Preserved Wood Foundations

Preserved wood foundations (PWF) consist of wood-frame walls made of lumber and plywood that have been specially pressure-treated to make them suitable for use below grade (Figure 9.21). These foundations have performed successfully for more than 50 years, but are still not widely used in Canada. Builders unfamiliar with PWF techniques should obtain background references. The Canadian Standards Association (CSA) publication,

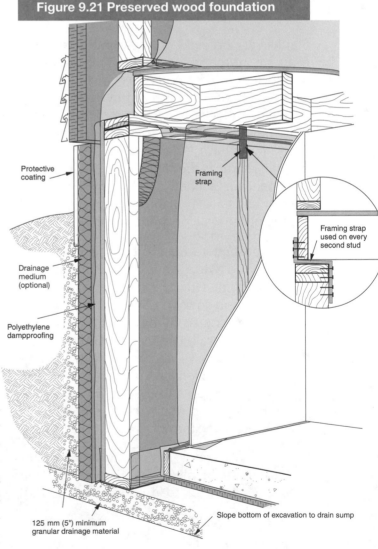

Figure 9.21 Preserved wood foundation

Protective coating

Framing strap

Framing strap used on every second stud

Drainage medium (optional)

Polyethylene dampproofing

125 mm (5") minimum granular drainage material

Slope bottom of excavation to drain sump

Preserved wood foundations	
Advantages	**Disadvantages**
• Can be built by a standard framing crew.	• Has low market acceptance in some areas.
• Are especially useful where concrete is difficult to obtain or place.	• May require additional site supervision.
• Can install high levels of batt insulation in the foundation walls.	• Must carefully design foundation to resist the pressure of backfill and hydrostatic pressures.
• Can use the same air sealing techniques as for above-grade walls.	• Require specialized pressure-treated materials. Particular grades and dimensions of pressure- treated lumber may require lead-time to order.
• Can have high floor insulation levels for crawl space basement floors using batt insulation.	• Need to make alterations to first floor joist framing to account for horizontal loads.
	• Must slope the bottom of the excavation toward a drain.

Construction of Preserved Wood Foundations (CAN3-S406), provides complete information on preserved wood foundations.

Preserved wood foundations can be built using a variety of floor systems, including a concrete slab, a wood sleeper floor, or a suspended wood floor.

9.4.1 System considerations

Design

The size and spacing of the wall studs depend on the backfill height. The Canadian Wood Council's *Permanent Wood Foundations* provides tables for selecting sizes.

Materials

Lumber and plywood used in PWF systems must conform to CSA O80.15 *Preservative Treatment of Wood for Building Foundation Systems, Basements and Crawl Spaces by Pressure Process*. Lumber suitable for use in preserved wood foundations is stamped accordingly. If the lumber is cut in the field, the cut surfaces must be thoroughly saturated with special purpose preservative by brushing or dipping. There are specific requirements for the types of fasteners such as nails, staples, joist hangers and straps.

Installation

Initial levelling for crushed gravel and wood footings must be accurate. Standard techniques can be used to frame and sheath walls, but framing straps must be used to connect the joist header to the foundation wall.

Air sealing

An interior air barrier system should be used with preserved wood foundations so that emissions are kept out of the house. If concrete is used for the floor slab, it can be sealed by laying polyethylene sheeting under the slab and sealing it to the polyethylene sheeting in the walls. If pressure-treated plywood floor is used as the air barrier, all joints and seams must be caulked. As with a concrete floor, a polyethylene sheet is required over the granular layer. A better seal is made if the polyethylene ground cover is extended to the polyethylene vapour barrier. If sheet material is used around the sill plate/floor joist assembly, it should be sandwiched to the sheet between double top plates to prevent excessive wear during joist installation.

Dampproofing

Dampproofing for preserved wood foundations is provided by using:

• 0.15 mm (6 mil) polyethylene or commercial membranes for exterior.

• Exterior joint sealants for the preserved plywood sheathing that are compatible with the sheathing and exterior dampproofing.

- Polyethylene dampproofing over the crushed-gravel drainage layer under the floor to keep moisture from diffusing in from the soil. The polyethylene should be lapped but not sealed to allow for drainage.

- Installation of a drainage membrane or suitable draining insulation against the wall to provide a free passage for water to drain to reduce hydrostatic pressures against the foundation wall and to protect the polyethylene during backfill.

Conventional drainage tiles are not required. Instead, a granular drainage layer is installed over undisturbed soil to a depth of at least 125 mm (5 in.) and a central gravity drained sump is used to provide drainage. If concrete footings are used, the concrete is placed over undisturbed soil and drainage pipes are provided through the footings. It is best practice to install a dimpled drainage layer adjacent to the walls.

Other barriers, combinations of films and coatings can be used subject to the approval of the building authority having jurisdiction. These barriers must also be compatible with the treated wood and caulking, and have good adhesion to the PWF sheathing.

9.5 Crawl Spaces

A crawl space is a type of shallow foundation, usually with the floor at grade and with low headroom, typically less than 1200 mm (4 ft.). They are commonly used in areas where there is a high water table, or where services are shallow (as in milder climate zones). They can also be found where deep excavation is not needed to provide structural support, where the frost line is shallow, or where ground conditions are inappropriate for a full in ground basement-for example, where there is considerable bedrock or permafrost near the surface.

Many problems found in crawl spaces are related to a misunderstanding of how crawl spaces work. Essentially, there are two types of crawl spaces: conditioned (i.e., heated) and unconditioned. The National Building Code of Canada has recognized this distinction by incorporating requirements based on whether the crawl space is heated or not heated.

Since crawl spaces are essentially "short" foundations, for Net Zero Energy Houses, it is recommended that the crawl space be insulated and heated as it would be if it were a full-height basement.

9.5.1 Heated crawl spaces

Heated crawl spaces are not separated from heated/conditioned portions of the house. The crawl space temperature may be cooler than the main portion of the house, but the space is still connected to the house air. A heated crawl space is essentially a basement with a low height. Therefore, all the requirements of a basement apply.

9.5.2 Unheated crawl spaces

Although building codes permit unheated crawl spaces and specify ventilation requirements, they pose potential moisture accumulation problems. For this reason, they should be avoided. The exception is in northern construction where there is no basement, in which case the crawl space is open and completely ventilated. Where an unheated crawl space is constructed, the floor separating it from conditioned space above must be insulated and have suitable air and vapour barriers.

Any crawl space that contains heating ducts and pipes is considered to be heated, unless the services are fully sealed and insulated. For this reason, advanced planning is required to ensure a high level of insulation around heating ductwork.

9.6 Slab-on-ground Foundations

A slab-on-ground foundation consists of a slab with perimeter edge reinforcing, or a slab and a perimeter foundation wall. This type of foundation may be insulated beneath the slab and at the slab edge, or an insulated plywood floor may be placed over the slab.

Slab-on-ground construction must be designed to resist frost heave. This design includes protecting footings from freezing and properly draining surrounding soils (Figure 9.22). These foundations are commonly insulated below the slab with rigid board insulation. Several points must be considered:

- The floor slab should be isolated from the soil and outdoor air temperatures with insulation.

- The greatest heat loss occurs at the slab edge. It should be insulated to levels equal to the exterior walls, or as high as practical. A thermal break of rigid insulation should be placed between the slab edge and the footing.

- Foundation walls supporting a slab or the above-grade walls should be insulated from the exterior to reduce the chance of frost penetration.

- The slab should be placed on a 125 mm (5 in.) bed of compacted gravel, which can be covered with high compressive-strength rigid insulation. The gravel will provide a capillary break. Do not use sand because the sand will not provide a capillary break.

- A polyethylene moisture barrier must be installed beneath the slab.

- In most parts of Canada, at least RSI 1.8 (R-10) of rigid board insulation should be installed under the entire slab. Higher levels may be necessary to achieve Net Zero Energy levels or depending on climate, soil and groundwater conditions or if the slab is heated. In frost-susceptible soils, the footing should be further protected by an insulating skirt (A in Figure 9.22). The length of the skirt is determined by the Climate Zone in which you are building.

- Heat loss from the underside of the slab is high, particularly at the edge. If the entire slab is not being insulated, at least a 600 mm (2 ft.)-wide strip of insulation should be placed around the slab perimeter (B in Figure 9.22). A vertical band of rigid insulation in the exterior wall will also cut heat loss and reduce the chance of frost penetration under the slab (C in Figure 9.22). If a foundation wall is used at the perimeter of the slab, then the vertical frost protection insulation should run to the footing.

- An alternative insulation strategy is to place insulation between strapping placed above the slab. This provides a surface better suited for some wood and resilient flooring options. However, moisture management must be considered to avoid moisture that could wick up through the concrete.

Slab-on-ground foundations	
Advantages	**Disadvantages**
• May be cheaper to build than framed floors in some areas.	• Is generally not insulated to the same levels as floors over unheated crawl spaces.
• Can provide heat storage for solar and internal gains.	• Can lead to frost heaving if improperly installed.
• Is less susceptible to moisture damage than an unheated crawl space.	• Requires specialized design and construction to ensure stability of slab-on-ground foundations in areas with clay soils.
• Is well suited to in-floor heating.	• Requires engineered specification.

Figure 9.22 Slab-on-grade: slab insulation and sealing

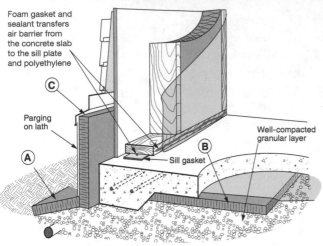

Foam gasket and sealant transfers air barrier from the concrete slab to the sill plate and polyethylene

Parging on lath

C

A

Sill gasket

B

Well-compacted granular layer

Slab-on-grade sealed polyethylene approach (SPA)

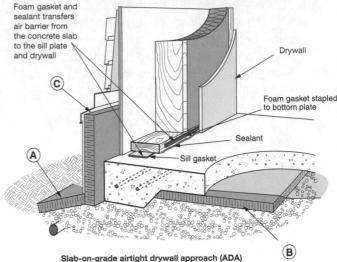

Foam gasket and sealant transfers air barrier from the concrete slab to the sill plate and drywall

Drywall

Foam gasket stapled to bottom plate

Sealant

C

A

Sill gasket

B

Slab-on-grade airtight drywall approach (ADA)

Figure 9.23 Slab-on-grade with foundation wall

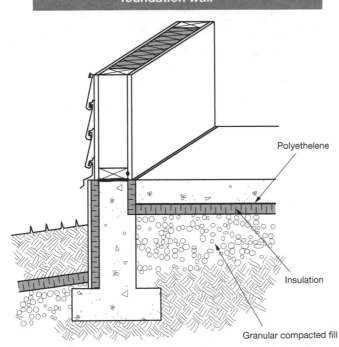

Polyethelene

Insulation

Granular compacted fill

Figure 9.23 shows a slab-on-grade with a shallow foundation wall. Insulation is important to deter frost penetration under the wall and the slab. The insulation on the foundation wall reduces heat flow through the foundation wall and buried, horizontal insulation reduces heat flow under the foundation wall. The insulation on the above grade concrete wall should have approximately the same insulation value as the above grade house walls.

9.7 Northern Foundations

Foundation design in northern areas presents special problems, partly because of difficulties in access, availability of materials and the short construction season, but mainly because of the difficult environmental and soil conditions.

9.7.1 Soil conditions

In the northern parts of many provinces, there are large areas of muskeg or soils with high water tables. Other areas with deeper water tables may have frost-susceptible soils and/or conditions that encourage ice lensing. These conditions, combined with deep frost penetration, make it difficult to build foundations not subject to failure.

Conditions are even more challenging further north where there are areas of discontinuous or continuous permafrost. Permafrost is soil with a high water content that remains below 0°C (32°F) throughout a year. It can occur in scattered patches surrounded by soil that experiences normal freeze-thaw cycles, but further north it occurs as large continuous areas of frozen soil, several hundred metres thick.

In all cases, permafrost is covered by a layer of soil that experiences normal freezing and thawing through the seasons. This active layer can vary in thickness from a few centimetres

to several metres. Soils in the active layer may be partially or fully saturated. If they are frost-susceptible, considerable movement may be expected in this layer.

It is essential to avoid thawing the permafrost, which will produce an unstable soil. Different soil conditions require different approaches to foundation design (Table 9.3).

Table 9.3 Foundation design for Northern soil conditions		
	Soils Not Susceptible to Frost	**Frost-susceptible Soils**
Non-permafrost	• Use normal foundation techniques. • Shallow footings are possible.	• Techniques used are similar to those used for southern foundations. • Use deeper footings to reach below the frost line. • Consider clear span joists in crawl spaces to reduce differential settlement. • Use a basement only if water or moisture penetration problems can be handled. • Provide frost protection for shallow footings at the day-lighted area of walk-out basements.
Discontinuous permafrost	• The approach recommended for permafrost with frost-susceptible soils may be necessary. • Carry out a detailed soils study and consult local expertise before deciding on an approach.	
Permafrost beneath the "active layer" of soil	**High water table** • Minimize heat transmission from the building through the active layer to the permafrost. • Basements and heated crawl spaces are not advisable. • Open or ventilated crawl spaces are the best solution. Place a gravel pad on the surface to provide a stable and well-drained top layer. **Water table well below the top of the permafrost** • Footings and foundation practices used in southern Canada may be used. • Also consult local practice.	• Minimize heat transmission from the building through the active layer to the permafrost. • Basements and heated crawl spaces are not advisable. • Open or ventilated crawl spaces are the best solution. Place a gravel pad on the surface to provide a stable and well-drained top layer.

9.7.2 Types of Northern foundations

A number of foundation systems have been developed specifically for Northern use. The North has challenges not encountered in more southern latitudes. Specifically, Northern foundations must account for the stability of the ground where ice rich permafrost thaws or the active layer with ice lenses is prone to frost heaving. If no permafrost exists in the foundation area, almost any foundation type is possible depending on local materials available, the cost of purchase and shipping, labour skills availability, and ultimately the soil testing results per site (e.g. load bearing capacity or soil deformation calculations). Piles, pads and wedges, grade beams and even spaceframes offer suitable support for different types of permafrost conditions and active layers; provided any seasonal soil movement from freeze/thaw cycles or even wetting and drying of the soils of the active layer is taken into consideration when preparing for the footings.

Planning to build on permafrost is always discouraged. However, in some cases, non-permafrost sites can be more challenging to build on such as nearby areas with frost susceptible soils. If building on permafrost is the best or only option, consider the consequence of failure specific to the type of building before starting. The foundation budget and its subsequent monitoring, maintenance and related costs must be factored together to protect the durability of the building it supports. If regular maintenance is questionable or not available, consider more rigid foundations such as piles or more rigid surface foundations like spaceframes. Alternatively, design a very rigid building which can be supported with adjustable systems like jack screws or pad and wedges. When designing the foundations, keep in mind that concrete is often not a viable option.

Ensure soil investigations are undertaken by subject matter experts before proceeding with design and calculations. Investigations from as short as ten years ago may no longer be valid due to dramatically changing climate conditions

in the North. Piles may need to be deeper and larger in diameter. Foundation pads may have to be larger in area, require more insulation, or allow for more adjustment capacity. Surface gravel or granular pads may also need to be larger, deeper, further insulated or even include geotextile membranes. Furthermore, the site may require more precautions to protect it from running or ponding water as these can quickly degrade the permafrost; and once the permafrost starts to degrade, it is very difficult to reverse the process.

Well designed and efficient active and passive artificial cooling techniques can help keep the ground frozen using thermosiphons and mechanical refrigeration, but they can be expensive to install and maintain while prone to failure. They are more commonly used with high risk buildings but they can also be used to help remediate the permafrost below existing housing.

Buildings in the North that are located on frost susceptible soils, permafrost, flood areas or high wind regions may require elevated and vented foundations with suspended floors as a first design strategy. This vented space helps to cool and preserve any permafrost and maintain the structure's design life. Some of the advantages of open and elevated foundations include:

- Less site preparation and changes to existing ground that may affect its stability;

- Allowing the wind to blow unimpeded to reduce snow drifting in the vicinity;

- Preventing snow from accumulating under the building which insulates the ground and reduces refreezing of the active zone; and

- Reducing labour and material costs, relative ease for transporting materials, simplicity, and ease to maintain.

However, suspended floors can result in them being cold so well insulated and air sealed floor systems are required. Skirting the exposed foundation may help to keep the floors warmer, but skirting must not restrict the passage of wind in areas where drifting snow is a problem. Care must also be taken that the skirting does not promote thawing of the permafrost below the house. Building occupants may find access to raised buildings more difficult and those with disabilities may require ramps.

Piles

For deep foundations, piles are used to transfer building loads through weak, compressible or ice susceptible ground to prevent excessive settlement or heaving. Pile types include driven piles, slurry backfilled adfreeze piles, screw piles, end bearing piles, rock socketed piles and thermopiles. Piles can be made of wood (Figure 9.24) concrete or steel. (Figure 9.25)

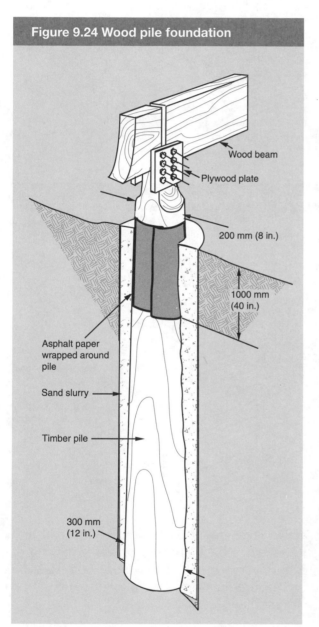

Figure 9.24 Wood pile foundation

Wood beam

Plywood plate

200 mm (8 in.)

1000 mm (40 in.)

Asphalt paper wrapped around pile

Sand slurry

Timber pile

300 mm (12 in.)

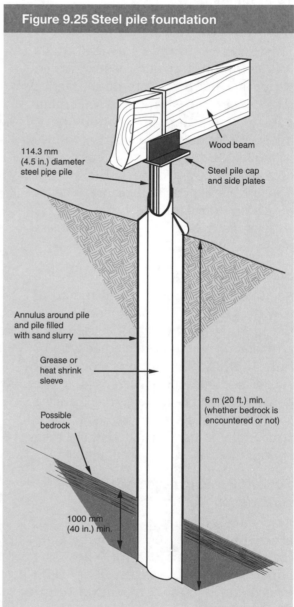

Figure 9.25 Steel pile foundation

114.3 mm (4.5 in.) diameter steel pipe pile

Wood beam

Steel pile cap and side plates

Annulus around pile and pile filled with sand slurry

Grease or heat shrink sleeve

Possible bedrock

6 m (20 ft.) min. (whether bedrock is encountered or not)

1000 mm (40 in.) min.

Lifting forces on piles known as "frost jacking" can be caused by freeze and thaw cycles. Uplift problems can be overcome by various methods such as adding a mechanical anchor to the pile below the active layer, wrapping a plastic bond-breaking sheet or membrane around the pile in the active layer and if using a wood pile, place its large end down. Piles should be designed by an engineer familiar with local conditions.

Grade beams

This shallow foundation system is less common and not recommended where permafrost exists or the active layer experiences large displacement due to heave and thaw annually. It involves placing concrete strip footings or laminated wood grade beams on top of a prepared gravel pad. The system is relatively expensive because it relies on concrete or laminated wood, and is susceptible to uneven settlement unless the pad is very stable.

Shallow foundations

Adjustable foundations can accommodate a wide variety of soils including ice rich permafrost and can be used as a remediation method when other systems fail. Shallow foundations consist of subsurface and surface types that can both accommodate for releveling. Leveling systems consist of wedges, screw jacks and structurally enhanced foundations such spaceframes on multipoint foundations.

Subsurface adjustable pads and cribbing foundations

Adjustable subsurface pads consist of a wood pad sitting on undisturbed and frozen permafrost (Figure 9.26). The construction process involves rapid excavation of a hole to a level below the active layer, rapid placement of the pad and post, and quick backfilling to prevent thawing of the exposed frozen soil. Site supervision must be good to ensure that work is completed before the permafrost thaws.

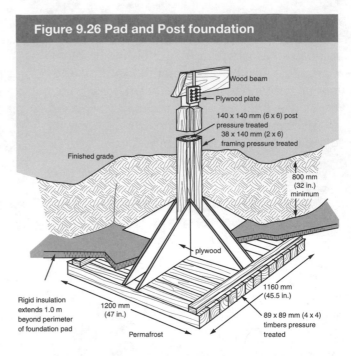

Figure 9.26 Pad and Post foundation

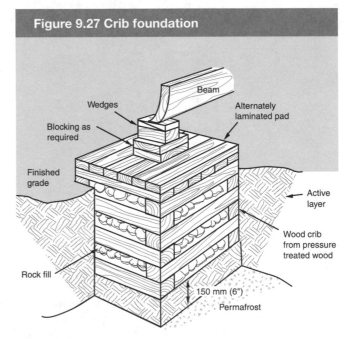

Figure 9.27 Crib foundation

Similar to subsurface pads, pressure-treated wood cribs are set into excavated holes on prepared gravel pads and filled with coarse gravel or rocks (Figure 9.27). This is a more permanent solution than the pad and wedge method that also offers additional lateral and wind support. This system also requires undisturbed permafrost.

Adjustable surface foundations

Commonly used pad and wedge and screw jack raised foundation systems are cost effective for building on unstable or low bearing capacity soil where they are situated on top of a thick well-compacted gravel pad. Using adjustable wedges or saddle brackets on a rigid wood frame designed to thermally isolate small buildings from the soil, they allow the building to respond to changes in the ground though they do not have as much adjustability built in as do piles. Surface foundations may also require additional lateral load and seismic restraint systems. The pad and wedge system consists of pressure-treated timbers laid in alternating layers on a prepared gravel pad or exposed rock outcrop (Figure 9.28). Since a large volume of wood is required, transportation of materials must be considered if choosing this option.

Screw jack systems are set on wood platforms also on top of a gravel pad to help disperse the load (Figure 9.29). Screw jacks can simplify the leveling of the building and may reduce shipping volumes and cost.

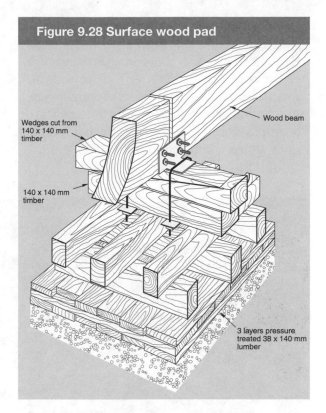

Figure 9.28 Surface wood pad

Wedges cut from 140 x 140 mm timber

Wood beam

140 x 140 mm timber

3 layers pressure treated 38 x 140 mm lumber

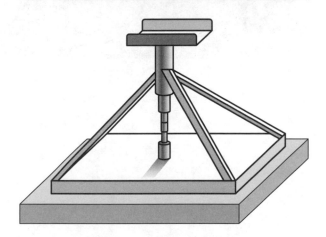

Figure 9.29 Screw jack system

Spaceframes

Spaceframes or triodetic foundations are used in Northern areas to overcome problems with permafrost and movement of foundation supports. A spaceframe consists of prefabricated, rigid galvanized steel or aluminum frame members connected by simple mechanical joints using hand tools (see figure 9.30).

The frame is very rigid and every module can adjust in many directions to compensate for ground movement. Spaceframes, though more expensive than other adjustable surface foundations, can reduce maintenance costs for leveling and, and if done when needed, reduce the chance of building damage. The modular design of its components can also reduce shipping costs.

Figure 9.30 Spaceframes or triodetic foundations

Credit: Triodetic

PART 2 — BUILDING ENVELOPE

CHAPTER 10

Floors

Floors are important elements of a well-built house. They must support loads without undue deflection, and must also limit vibration and sound transmission. In cases where floors extend over unheated areas, they must provide the same resistance to air, heat and vapour movement as exterior walls and ceilings. Their intersections with exterior walls need to maintain proper insulation levels and continuity of the air barrier. Doing the job correctly during construction can reduce the much greater cost of remedial measures after completion of a house.

This chapter examines approaches for main floors, intermediate floors, cantilever floors and floors over unheated crawl spaces and garages. It includes an introduction to the special requirements of floors in multi-unit buildings, and techniques to be used with floor trusses. In addition to the figures in this chapter, the figures in Chapter 8 dealing with wall/floor intersections also apply.

10.1 Design Considerations

Whether floor members are dimension lumber, parallel-chord trusses, wood I-joists or steel framing, the allowable span is determined by several factors that are built into span tables. In the 1980s, span tables were adjusted to take vibration into account. This was because, even though floors were strong enough to carry loads, satisfaction was at times adversely affected by vibration. For example, footfall impact in the centre of a floor could cause dishes in cabinets to rattle. Vibration can be minimized by any combination of:

- Using a thicker subfloor;

- Adding a concrete topping to the sub-floor;

- Attaching a ceiling directly to the bottom of the joists;

- Gluing the subfloor to the top of the joists; and

- Installing continuous bridging, blocking and/or strapping.

Span tables provide minimum standards, and performance can be improved by using a given design over a shorter span. Framed floors are load-sharing systems and, therefore, performance is improved by increasing the ability of more framing members to share loads. For this reason, span tables allow increased spans when the sub-floor is glued or screwed to the joists, if bridging and/or strapping is used, or if a thicker sub-floor sheathing is used.

The perimeter of floors is referred to as the rim framing. When lumber joists are used, the rim framing is called a rim joist. When wood I-joists are used, the specialized rim framing manufactured for use with I-joists is called a rim board.

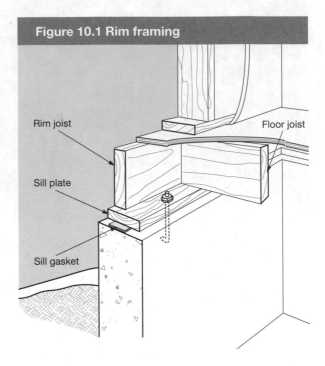

Figure 10.1 Rim framing

Rim joist

Floor joist

Sill plate

Sill gasket

10.1.1 Main floor assembly options

The main floor is usually the floor assembly that rests on the foundation wall. It is typically framed in one of two ways. In the first method (Figure 10.1), the sill plate is levelled on top of the foundation wall. The rim framing and all floor joists are installed and then the subfloor is applied. The second method (Figure 10.2) is used in parts of the Western provinces. Two plates are embedded in the concrete when the foundation walls are poured, and the rim and floor joists are then anchored to the plates.

Regardless of which method is used, the rim framing area must be insulated and air-sealed for the building to perform well. Sill gasket materials are used to reduce the potential for air leakage between the framing materials and the foundation wall.

Membrane air barrier approach

Figure 10.3 illustrates a technique that can be used to seal and insulate the rim framing area when the sealed polyethylene approach (SPA) is used as both the air barrier and the vapour barrier. If polyethylene is used to wrap the rim framing, there must be at least twice

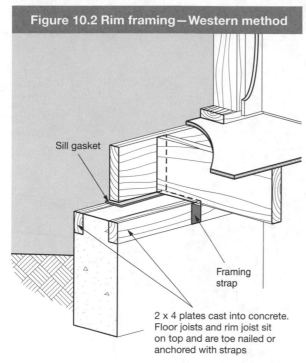

Figure 10.2 Rim framing—Western method

Sill gasket

Framing strap

2 x 4 plates cast into concrete. Floor joists and rim joist sit on top and are toe nailed or anchored with straps

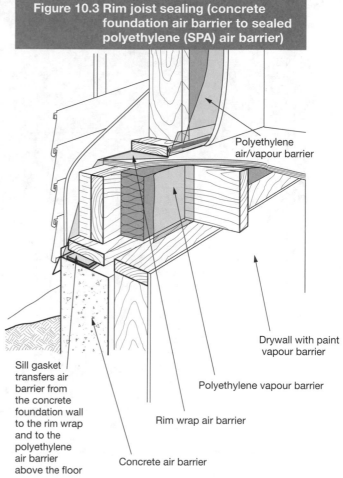

Figure 10.3 Rim joist sealing (concrete foundation air barrier to sealed polyethylene (SPA) air barrier)

Polyethylene air/vapour barrier

Drywall with paint vapour barrier

Polyethylene vapour barrier

Rim wrap air barrier

Sill gasket transfers air barrier from the concrete foundation wall to the rim wrap and to the polyethylene air barrier above the floor

Concrete air barrier

the insulating value on the cold side of the polyethylene as on the warm side. Where this cannot be provided or where all the insulation is on the warm side, the rim framing should be wrapped with sheathing membrane that is qualified for use as an exterior air barrier.

Some, but not all, house wrap materials can be used for rim wrapping, but products should be verified by checking Canadian Construction Materials Centre (CCMC) listings. The sheathing membrane is brought inside the wall either above or below the sill plate. In either case, anchor bolt projections through the membrane need to be sealed. Above and below the floor, a sealed connection is made between the sheathing membrane rim wrap and the wall polyethylene air/vapour barrier.

Rigid air barrier approach

If the airtight drywall (ADA) method is used, batt insulation can be applied to inside the rim framing area (Figure 10.4). The batt insulation is covered with an air barrier (such as rigid insulation) cut to fit between the joists. The air barrier is sealed to the adjacent floor joists, to the subfloor, and to the air barrier system on

the foundation wall. All cracks and joints in the subfloor that are on the cold side of the air barrier must also be sealed. This approach is not recommended if plank subflooring is used because of the difficulty of ensuring airtight joints between the planks.

With this method, the wood members and panel products such as subflooring are used as part of the air barrier. Gasketing and/or sealing is applied between the plates, the rim framing, and the subfloor. Any vertical joints in the rim framing must also be sealed.

If the subfloor is being glued (in addition to being screwed or nailed) to the floor joists, a continuous bead of the glue, instead of the caulking or gasket, is applied between the rim framing and the subfloor. The gasket under

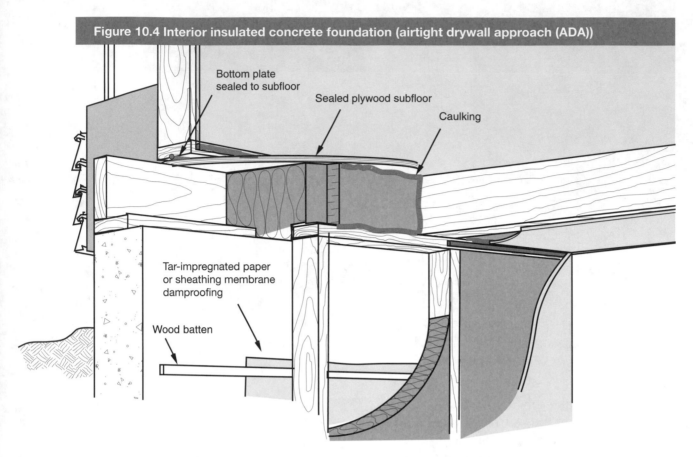

Figure 10.4 Interior insulated concrete foundation (airtight drywall approach (ADA))

Bottom plate
sealed to subfloor

Sealed plywood subfloor

Caulking

Tar-impregnated paper
or sheathing membrane
damproofing

Wood batten

the bottom sill plates of the exterior perimeter walls may also be replaced with a bead of caulking at the inside edge of the bottom sill plate where it meets the subfloor. This bead of caulking is normally installed along with the other gaskets and sealants after the framing is complete and before drywall is installed.

Spray Foam

Another option being used by builders is spray foam. As construction components change from dimensioned lumber to wood-I joists and open-web joists the geometry of this cavity becomes more complicated to seal with traditional, rectangular materials. To address this builders are increasingly using specialists to install spray foam insulation into this cavity. This approach can seal from the concrete wall, the sill plate, the rim joist to the plywood floor decking. A 2-part, closed cell foam is recommended for this application because it provides both air and vapour barrier functions.

10.1.2 Intermediate floor assembly options

Membrane air barrier approach

Figure 10.5 shows a method that can be used to frame intermediate floors while maintaining continuity of the air barrier. A 600 mm (24 in.) strip of sheathing membrane approved for use as an air barrier is sandwiched between the top plates during wall assembly and is draped to the outside before the floors are constructed. After the subfloor is laid, the strip of sheathing membrane is wrapped around the sub-floor wood panel sheathing before the next wall is framed in place. Rigid insulation is installed in the space provided by recessing the rim joist 38 mm (1-1/2 in.) from the exterior of the wall plates. Batt insulation representing no more than one-third of the thermal resistance value of the exterior insulating sheathing can be placed in the interior joist cavities. A vapour barrier is installed between the joists.

Figure 10.5 Intermediate floor/wall junction (single-stud, exterior-insulated wall)

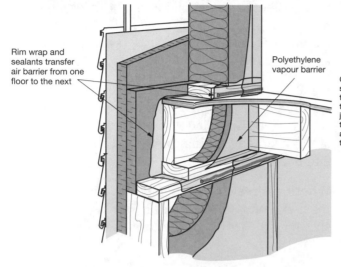

Rim wrap and sealants transfer air barrier from one floor to the next

Polyethylene vapour barrier

Figure 10.7 Intermediate floor joists parallel to wall (airtight drywall approach (ADA))

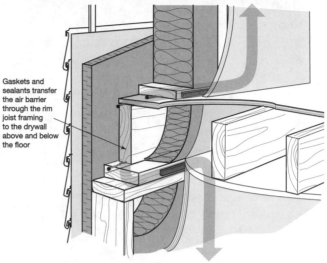

Gaskets and sealants transfer the air barrier through the rim joist framing to the drywall above and below the floor

Figure 10.6 Intermediate floor joists perpendicular to wall (airtight drywall approach (ADA))

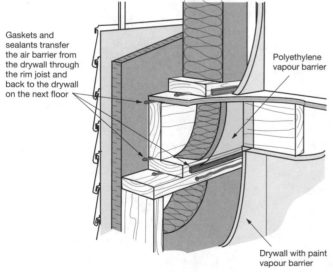

Gaskets and sealants transfer the air barrier from the drywall through the rim joist and back to the drywall on the next floor

Polyethylene vapour barrier

Drywall with paint vapour barrier

Figure 10.8 Intermediate floor with dropped ceiling (airtight drywall approach (ADA))

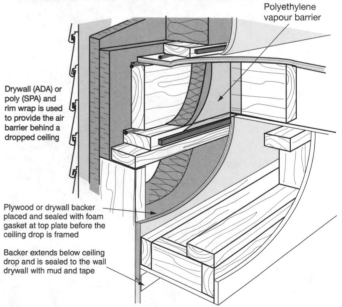

Polyethylene vapour barrier

Drywall (ADA) or poly (SPA) and rim wrap is used to provide the air barrier behind a dropped ceiling

Plywood or drywall backer placed and sealed with foam gasket at top plate before the ceiling drop is framed

Backer extends below ceiling drop and is sealed to the wall drywall with mud and tape

Rigid air barrier approach

Figure 10.6 shows how to maintain air seals at floors between storeys when using the airtight drywall approach (ADA) air barrier where the joists are perpendicular to the wall. Where floor joists run parallel to the exterior perimeter walls, the details shown in Figure 10.7 can be used to maintain the continuity of the air barrier. In both cases, the drywall must be sealed to the top and bottom plates. Where a ceiling drop is required, the method shown in Figure 10.8 may be used.

10.2 Cantilever Floors

If a strip of sheathing membrane (approved for use as an air barrier) is not laid under the subfloor during construction of a cantilever floor or an exterior air barrier is not used, then the seams in the subfloor must be sealed to serve as the air barrier. Before insulating a cantilever, it must be ensured that there is no water trapped between the subfloor and the sheathing membrane. Insulation should be placed to fill the entire cavity, from the header joist to the inside face of the wall below (Figure 10.9).

Blocks of wood or rigid polystyrene insulation can be installed between the floor joists. The edges of the blocking must be sealed to the subfloor above, to the floor joists on either side, and to the air barrier from the wall below to make the air barrier continuous. The polyethylene from the wall above is sealed to the subfloor. The underside of the overhang must be protected by a weather barrier connected to the weather barriers of the walls above and below.

If the floor joists run parallel to the exterior wall (Figure 10.10), the cantilever must be constructed using 'ladders' in the same way a roof overhang is built to pass over the gable end of a house.

Where cantilevers support roof loads, they must extend into the interior framing at least six times the length of the cantilever.

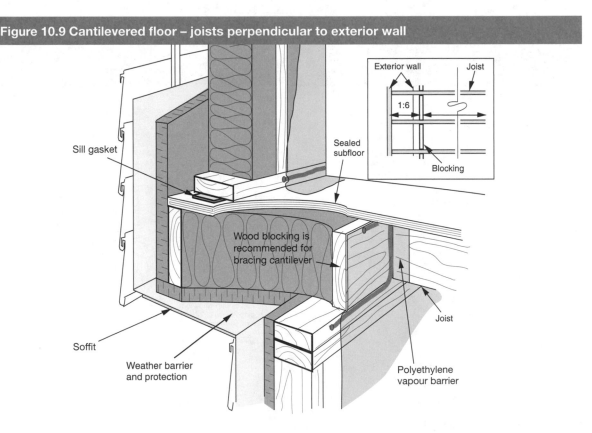

Figure 10.9 Cantilevered floor – joists perpendicular to exterior wall

Sill gasket

Sealed subfloor

Exterior wall   Joist

1:6

Blocking

Wood blocking is recommended for bracing cantilever

Joist

Soffit

Weather barrier and protection

Polyethylene vapour barrier

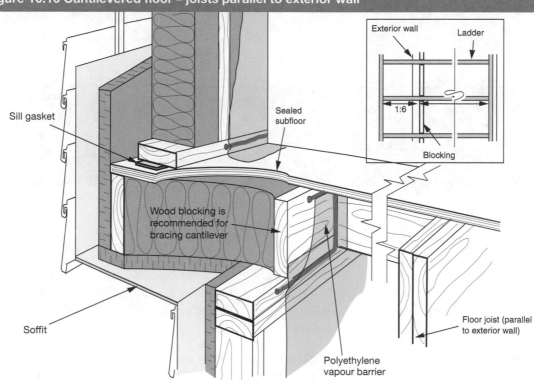

Figure 10.10 Cantilevered floor – joists parallel to exterior wall

Sill gasket

Sealed subfloor

Exterior wall

Ladder

1:6

Blocking

Wood blocking is recommended for bracing cantilever

Soffit

Floor joist (parallel to exterior wall)

Polyethylene vapour barrier

10.3 Floors over Unheated Spaces

Although unheated crawl spaces are permitted, they pose potential moisture accumulation problems (see Section 9.5.2). For this reason, they should be avoided. The exception is in northern construction where there is no basement, in which case the crawl space is open and completely ventilated. If they are used, care is required to ensure a good air, vapour and thermal barrier is in place and that adequate ventilation is provided to remove moisture from the crawl space. The insulation should be installed snugly to the subfloor after the services have been installed. Ductwork must be insulated to the same level as the floor. The insulation should be protected by an effective weather barrier to keep wind out of the insulated space. Spray-in-place foam insulation can be used to reduce air leakage while providing high insulation levels.

Whether a garage is heated or not, air leakage around garage doors and the likelihood of the door being left open long enough to cool the space means that all garages and the floors above them should be designed as though the space were unheated.

Floors over garages should be protected by drywall for fire resistance and be air sealed to stop air leakage into the garage and to keep automotive exhaust gases out of the dwelling unit. Floors over garages must be insulated (Figure 10.11) to required levels and the joint between the rim framing and the subfloor must be sealed to keep cold air from infiltrating into the floor assembly. Rigid insulation should be provided under the floor joists to reduce thermal bridging. All air leakage sites in the floor must also be sealed. These include plumbing and electrical penetrations, and all openings where heating ducts pass through the floor into the space above, including garage door hardware.

Figure 10.11 Floor over unheated space

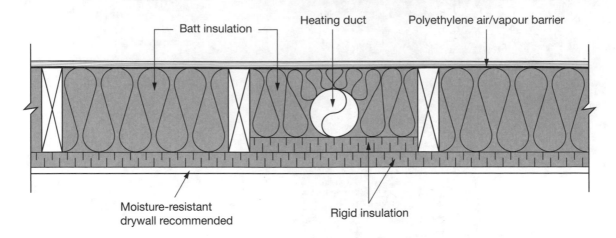

Batt insulation

Heating duct

Polyethylene air/vapour barrier

Moisture-resistant
drywall recommended

Rigid insulation

If polyethylene is not installed under the subfloor, all the seams in the subfloor sheathing need to be sealed. Ductwork must be sealed along all seams and at each joint. Because ductwork reduces the space available for batt insulation, rigid insulation should be placed below the duct so that the floor area over the ductwork stays warm (Figure 10.11).

A garage is a high moisture potential area due to the snow and rain brought in on vehicles. For this reason, drywall used in garages should be moisture-resistant, or better yet, be suited for exterior applications.

Figure 10.12 Multi-unit construction—masonry walls, with sealing at the foundation/party wall junction

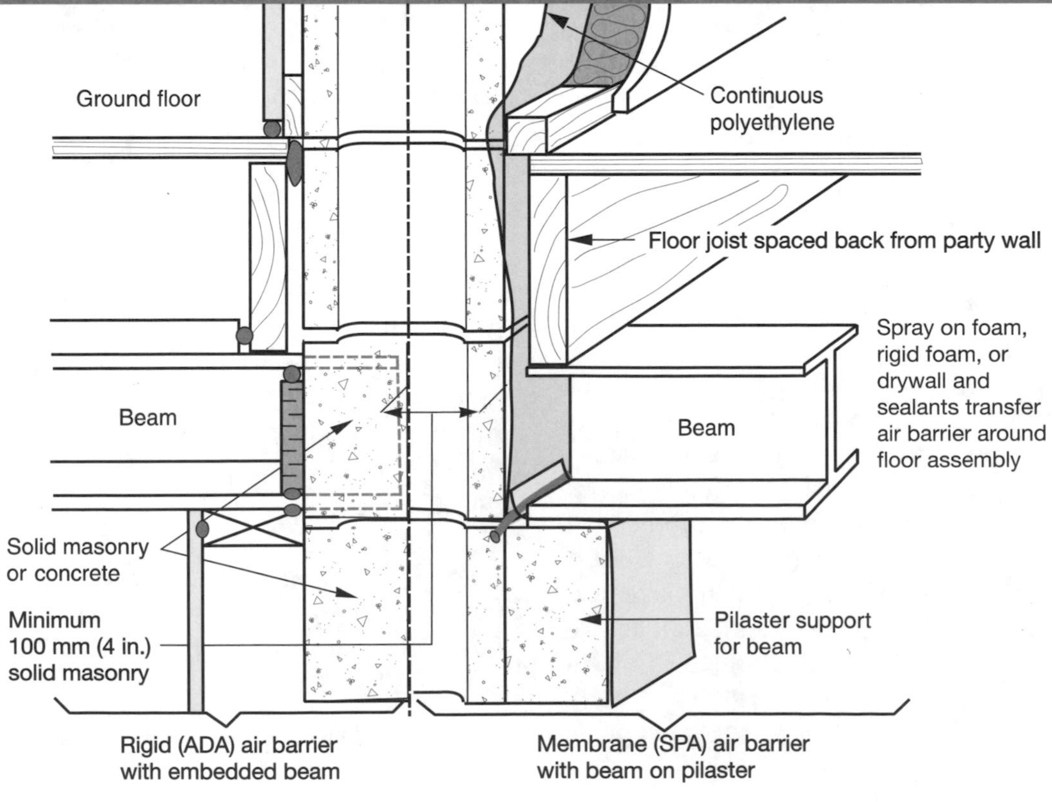

Ground floor

Continuous
polyethylene

Floor joist spaced back from party wall

Spray on foam,
rigid foam, or
drywall and
sealants transfer
air barrier around
floor assembly

Beam

Beam

Solid masonry
or concrete

Minimum
100 mm (4 in.)
solid masonry

Pilaster support
for beam

Rigid (ADA) air barrier
with embedded beam

Membrane (SPA) air barrier
with beam on pilaster

10.4 Floors in Multi-unit Buildings

Floors in multi-unit buildings require special attention to reduce sound transmission from one unit to another, and to lessen the potential of fire spreading between units. This section is not intended to provide comprehensive coverage of these topics, but rather, to indicate some of the additional requirements for floors in multi-unit buildings.

10.4.1 Beam/party wall details

The main floor can be framed in a fashion similar to that used for single-family houses (Figure 10.12). Beams abutting at the party wall must be separated by 100 mm (4 in.) of solid masonry to minimize sound transfer between units, and all gaps in the masonry should be sealed. The beams should be supported on pilasters or columns rather than set into the foundation wall.

Air leakage up the party wall from the basement can be eliminated by building the floor assembly as shown in Figure 10.13. The left half of the illustration shows the rigid air barrier approach and the right half illustrates the membrane air barrier approach. Note how the subfloor is discontinuous and separate bottom plates are used to reduce sound transmission from one unit to another.

Figure 10.13 Multi-unit construction—wood-frame walls, with sealing at the foundation/party wall junction

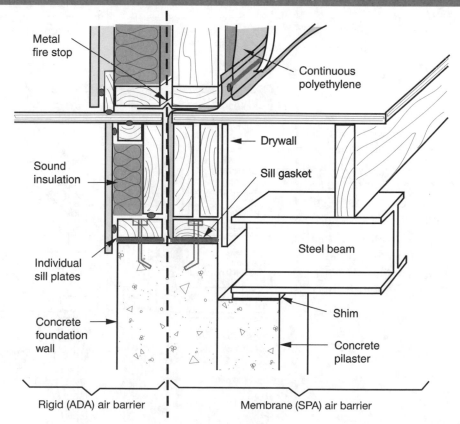

Metal fire stop

Continuous polyethylene

Drywall

Sound insulation

Sill gasket

Individual sill plates

Steel beam

Shim

Concrete foundation wall

Concrete pilaster

Rigid (ADA) air barrier

Membrane (SPA) air barrier

10.4.2 Floor/party wall details

If the floor joists run perpendicular to the party wall and are supported by masonry, they must rest on a solid bearing support (Figure 10.14, left side). The joist ends must be fire cut so that, in the event of a fire, collapsing joists will not put upward and outward pressure on the masonry wall.

The party wall between the joist ends should be at least 100 mm (4 in.) thick, and all gaps around the joists must be sealed to minimize sound transfer and smoke or fire movement between units. Sound transmission will be further reduced if the floor joists run parallel to the party wall and the subfloor is kept away from the wall (Figure 10.14, right side). Care must be taken to eliminate air leakage at this location. Techniques for sealing the bottom plate/subfloor joint are described in Chapter 11.

Figure 10.15 illustrates another approach to framing floors where they connect to party walls. A strip of polyethylene is placed so that it can be folded around the header after the upper floor has been framed (the right half of the illustration). The vertical air space should also be blocked by a metal fire stop. The left-half of the illustration shows how the detail can be framed using a rigid air barrier. Sound insulation is placed in the rim framing area.

Figure 10.14 Multi-unit construction—masonry walls, floor/party wall junction

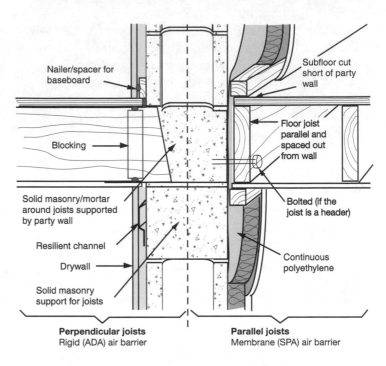

Perpendicular joists
Rigid (ADA) air barrier

Parallel joists
Membrane (SPA) air barrier

Figure 10.15 Multi-unit construction—wood-framing, floor/party wall junction

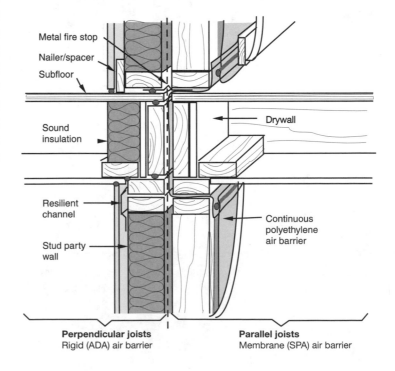

Perpendicular joists
Rigid (ADA) air barrier

Parallel joists
Membrane (SPA) air barrier

10.5 Engineered Wood Floor Systems

Many builders are using a variety of engineered framing systems to replace standard dimension lumber floor joists. These systems generally make use of engineered wood products such as parallel-chord wood trusses, open-web wood joists and wood I-joists (Figure 10.16). One type is a wood I-joist with a reinforced opening for running services. These systems include the use of beams and headers made from parallel strand lumber (PSL) and laminated veneer lumber (LVL).

Figure 10.16 Types of engineered floor joists

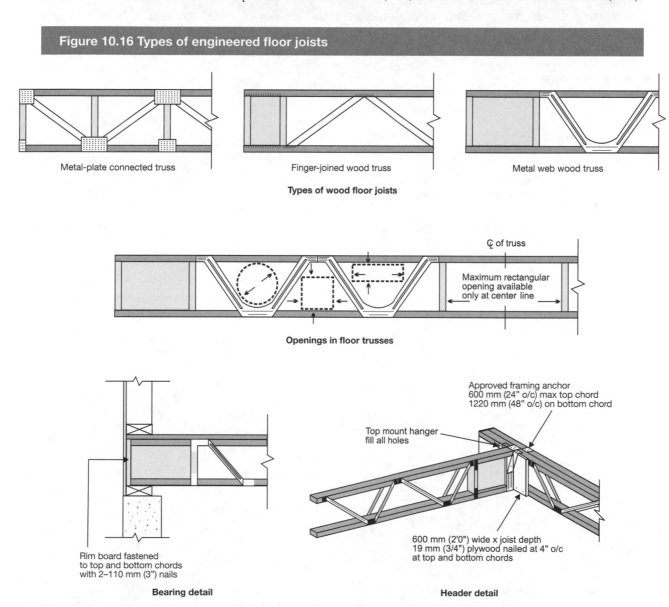

Metal-plate connected truss

Finger-joined wood truss

Metal web wood truss

Types of wood floor joists

₵ of truss

Maximum rectangular opening available only at center line

Openings in floor trusses

Rim board fastened to top and bottom chords with 2–110 mm (3") nails

Bearing detail

Approved framing anchor 600 mm (24" o/c) max top chord 1220 mm (48" o/c) on bottom chord

Top mount hanger fill all holes

600 mm (2'0") wide x joist depth 19 mm (3/4") plywood nailed at 4" o/c at top and bottom chords

Header detail

Engineered wood members are lightweight and in many cases cost-effective alternatives to dimension lumber floors. They are also a good environmental option because their manufacture does not require large trees.

Oriented strandboard lumber (OSL) rim boards are made specifically for use with engineered floor joists. Most engineered wood floor systems are proprietary and the manufacturer's directions for spans and connections must be followed.

Wood I-joists have gained a large share of the flooring market. Wood I-joist floors behave differently than dimension lumber floors, and some basic installation details need to be applied (Figure 10.17). While rim framing is designed to transfer distributed wall loads around the ends of I-joists, other devices such as squash blocks, blocking or web stiffeners may be required to handle special vertical loading conditions such as point loads from columns.

Figure 10.17 Typical details for wood I-joist floors

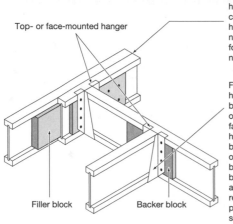

Top- or face-mounted hanger

Double I-joist header: The capacity of I-joist headers and the nailing requirements for the filler block need to be checked.

For top-mounted hangers, a backer block is required on one side. For face-mounted hangers, backer blocks are required on both sides. The backer blocks must be wide enough to accommodate the required nailing pattern without splitting.

Filler block   Backer block

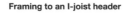

Framing to an I-joist header

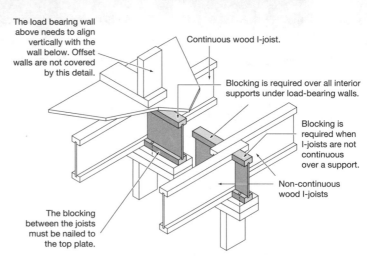

The load bearing wall above needs to align vertically with the wall below. Offset walls are not covered by this detail.

Continuous wood I-joist.

Blocking is required over all interior supports under load-bearing walls.

Blocking is required when I-joists are not continuous over a support.

Non-continuous wood I-joists

The blocking between the joists must be nailed to the top plate.

Framing over interior load-bearing wall

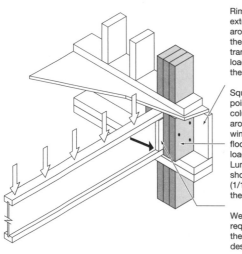

Rim framing transfers exterior wall loads around the I-joists to the wall below. Blocking transfers interior wall loads around I-joists to the wall or beam below.

Squash blocks transfer point loads from columns or framing around doors and windows from one floor to the next without loading the I-joists. Lumber squash blocks should be 0.15 mm (1/16 in.) longer than the I-joist depth.

Web stiffeners may be required if the load on the joist exceeds the design capacity

Transferring loads past wood I-joist floors

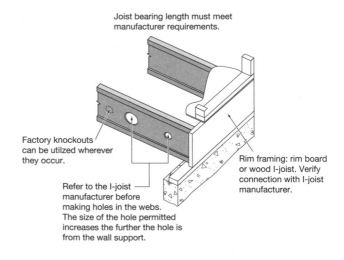

Joist bearing length must meet manufacturer requirements.

Factory knockouts can be utilzed wherever they occur.

Refer to the I-joist manufacturer before making holes in the webs. The size of the hole permitted increases the further the hole is from the wall support.

Rim framing: rim board or wood I-joist. Verify connection with I-joist manufacturer.

Rim framing

* Refer to manufacturer requirements for specific connections and details.

Because wood I-joists shrink less than sawn lumber and their thin webs have limited capacity to carry vertical point loads, specialized rim boards (PSL, LVL or OSL) must be used to ensure loads from the floor above are transferred from one wall to the one below, around the joists rather than through them (Figure 10.18). If dimension lumber rim framing were used, wood shrinkage would result in overloading the wood I-joist webs at supports. If the rim joist is not adequate to transfer vertical loads, squash blocks are required to transfer loads through the I-joists.

Recently, insulated rim boards with Canadian Construction Materials Centre (CCMC) evaluations have been introduced. These rim boards have been evaluated only for strength- not for insulating properties or long-term performance of the foam core. Therefore, it is important to assess whether the insulation in the rim board is adequate to meet thermal requirements.

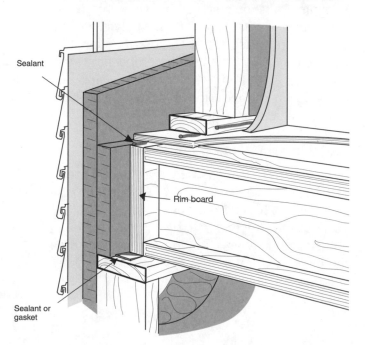

Figure 10.18 Rim framing for wood I-joist floors

Sealant

Rim board

Sealant or gasket

Both parallel chord floor truss and wood I-joists systems can provide a wide range of benefits over standard floor systems, most notably the increased span they provide for the same depth of floor assembly. In many cases, these floor systems can be used to span across the entire width of the house, allowing greater flexibility in the placement of partitions. This capability means that larger loads are transferred to the perimeter foundation walls, and footing size may have to be increased to distribute the loads to the ground under the footings.

Engineered wood floor members are less prone to shrinkage and twisting because they are manufactured at a low moisture content compared to dimension lumber. As a result, engineered floor systems tend to experience less squeaking. Built in a factory using accurate fabrication and constant quality control, members tend to be uniform in size and shape, reducing the likelihood of on-site framing problems.

Engineered wood floor systems can be easily designed to accommodate heating and ventilating ducts without compromising headroom or requiring the construction of bulkheads. Electrical wiring and plumbing can run between the top and bottom chords of trusses or through knock-outs in I-joists without requiring drilling.

Wood I-joist floors differ from wood joist floors in several ways. The following will help ensure a quality floor:

- Always follow manufacturer's instructions for spans and the provision of squash blocks and blocking.

- Holes cut into the web of wood I-joists should be sized and placed according to the manufacturer's instructions. Overcut or improperly placed holes can seriously compromise the strength of the floor system and possibly result in collapse.

- Top and bottom flanges and members should never be cut or notched.

- Top flanges of wood I-joists should never be cut back from the bearing point of the bottom flange.

- Engineered wood products usually involve a cost premium. This investment should be protected by storing members in dry conditions and protecting them against damage during handling and installation.

- Use the same principles for air and vapour barrier installation as for wood joist floor systems.

10.6 Modified Balloon Framing

Prior to World War II, many of the houses built in Canada were balloon-framed, whereby the wall studs are continuous from the sill plate up to the double top plate, even in a two-storey house.

Balloon framing has some advantages. Most notably, it provides for complete insulation of the wall, except for the thermal bridges created by studs and plates, without the problems caused by the floor assemblies in platform framing. However, because the floor joist ends extend into the wall cavity, fire stops are required and special care is needed to achieve a good air seal when an interior air barrier is used.

10.6.1 Foundation wall/main floor detail

A modified balloon framing technique can be used to ensure continuity of the air barrier as well as full depth insulation at the basement wall/main floor junction (Figure 10.19). A 38 x 190 mm (2 x 8 in.) sill plate is installed on top of the foundation wall. Prior to floor assembly installation, a strip of polyethylene (the polyethylene is on the warm side of the wall) is laid around the rim joist that is wide enough to overhang both the top and bottom sides of the floor. The polyethylene should be protected with building paper during assembly of the floor and wall systems.

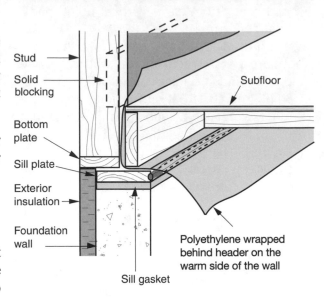

Figure 10.19 Foundation/floor intersection

Stud

Solid blocking

Bottom plate

Sill plate

Exterior insulation

Foundation wall

Sill gasket

Subfloor

Polyethylene wrapped behind header on the warm side of the wall

The floor system is then installed but is kept back 100 mm (4 in.) from the outer edges of the plates. The subfloor is installed, and the polyethylene is brought up to wrap the joist and lie on top of the subfloor. The wall is framed on the deck and set down onto the sill plate outside the floor assembly. Blocking or strapping must be installed between the studs to provide fastening points for the polyethylene, drywall and baseboard. Insulation can be installed outside of the floor assembly between the studs. Insulating sheathing can also be installed on the exterior to provide a higher RSI (R) value.

10.6.2 Intermediate floor detail

Intermediate floors can also be framed using a modified balloon framing technique (Figure 10.20). The first-floor walls are framed and erected. A strip of polyethylene is installed, leaving enough hanging over the top plate to wrap around the ledger to seal to the polyethylene that will be applied to the second-storey walls.

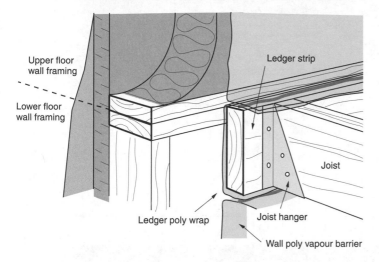

Figure 10.20 Modified balloon framing

Upper floor wall framing

Lower floor wall framing

Ledger strip

Joist

Ledger poly wrap

Joist hanger

Wall poly vapour barrier

The polyethylene strip should also be wide enough to hang down below a ledger strip made of lumber with the same dimensions as the floor joists. This ledger strip is installed so that its top edge is flush with the top edge of the single top plate of the first-storey walls. The floor joists are then installed using joist hangers. The bottom plate of the second-storey wall provides support for the membrane and drywall.

10.7 Steel-frame Floors

Builders in many regions of Canada are using light gauge steel as a substitute for wood. Currently the design of steel-framed houses falls within the scope of Part 4 of the National Building Code, making engineering design necessary, although prescriptive methods may become available that will largely eliminate this.

The Canadian Sheet Steel Building Institute (CSSBI) has produced a number of publications that facilitate design and construction of steel-framed houses. These publications provide details that are important to avoid potential problems. Framing with steel normally requires more control over the design process. Pre-planning is necessary to establish a cut list that is used to order material from a steel fabricator. Steel framing members are then delivered pre-cut and colour-coded according to steel thickness, ready for assembly.

C-channel and track sections of lightweight, cold-formed steel of varying depths and thickness are assembled into a structural frame (Figure 10.21) that supports interior and exterior finishes. Built-up steel beams normally consist of floor joist and track sections that are fastened together as a box section. Like wood built-up beams, these can be assembled as needed to support the building loads.

Unlike wood framing, steel framing requires all structural members to be placed in-line to allow loads to be transferred from one member to another. In other words, floor joists must be installed directly over load-bearing studs the same as advanced wood framing. As well, flanges of the C-channel joists must point in the same direction and web knock-out holes must align.

Figure 10.21 Typical steel-frame floor sections

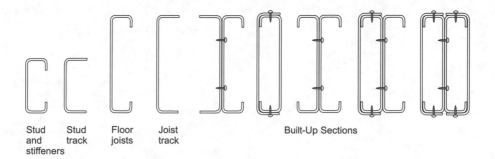

Stud and stiffeners

Stud track

Floor joists

Joist track

Built-Up Sections

Steel-frame floors

Advantages	Disadvantages
• Steel joists can be fabricated to span the entire length of the building, avoiding the need for intermediate support from beams or partitions. • Steel members are not subject to moisture-related shrinkage, warping or twisting. • Steel members are not subject to attack or damage from insects or vermin. • Services are easily accommodated through pre-punched holes in web elements of steel framing members. • Steel framing is considered to be a non-combustible material.	• Engineered design is required. • Reinforcing elements must be installed to support superimposed point loads. • More attention to the proper installation of insulation is required-steel framing can cause thermal bridging if appropriate insulation detailing is not followed. • Some additional details and materials are required.

Figure 10.22 Typical steel-floor framing details

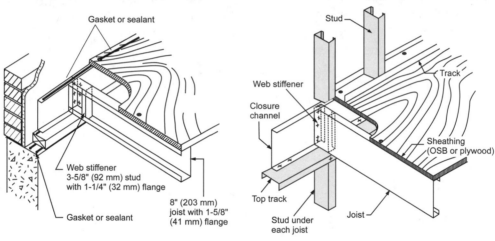

Main-Floor Framing

Second-Floor Joist Framing

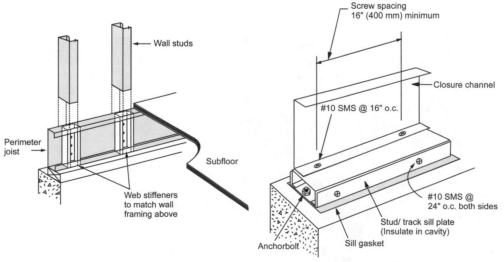

Web Stiffeners and Perimeter Joists

Floor System Anchorage - Still Sill Plate

Steel-framed floors are normally constructed with steel floor joists that frame into closure channels that function as rim joists do in wood-frame construction. The closure channels are attached to wood or steel sill plates that are anchored to the foundation. Alternatively, the channel can be attached directly to the foundation. The wooden subfloor is attached to the top of the steel floor joists while floor finishes are installed conventionally on the subfloor (Figure 10.22).

Unlike floor construction with lumber, steel-framed floors require web stiffeners to be installed in all steel joists at locations where point loads are transferred into or out of the joists. Stiffeners prevent the thin web of the joist member from deforming or buckling due to concentrated loads. This is similar to the role of squash blocks in engineered wood construction. Typically, stiffeners are required where bearing occurs (at each joist end and over supporting beams) and at the intersection of the joists and load-bearing walls supported above.

Floor vibration is also of concern. The NBC allows floors to deflect L/360; where L is the length of the joists. For an 8 m (26') span the deflection could be 22mm or almost 1". While this deflection may not pose a safety risk to the occupants, the deflection may be of concern. To address this, a more restrictive deflection limit of L/480 is often imposed. For deeper joist sections spanning longer distances, a more detailed vibration analysis can be carried out utilizing existing design procedures appropriately modified for steel framing.

All floors framed using steel framing must be braced with flat strap bracing, notch channel bridging or solid C-channel blocking for stability. CSSBI publications provide additional details on size and location of the bracing that is required.

10.7.1 Insulation, air and vapour barriers

Steel framing conducts heat much more readily than wood framing. To avoid condensation problems on the interior of the building, all steel must be covered with rigid or spray foam insulation. The insulation acts as a thermal break and prevents the steel from cooling interior surfaces of the building, except in those small areas where fasteners intrude.

The exterior of steel floor headers must be covered by at least 25 mm (1 in.) of rigid or spray foam insulation. The exterior insulation is in addition to required cavity insulation that may be needed to satisfy the minimum provisions of building codes, energy codes or standards for given locations.

The installation of vapour barriers on the warm side of the insulation is equally important in steel construction. Floor header areas, as in wood-frame construction, require protection from vapour movement. Where exterior sheathings with low vapour permeance are used on the outside of the building envelope, the warm-side vapour barrier must have a permeance not greater than 15 ng/Pa.s.m2. In practice, this means that where extruded polystyrene sheathings (Type IV) are used, polyethylene sheeting must be installed on the warm side of the insulation. Normally, the polyethylene can be fixed to the floor joists with adhesive.

Air sealing practices for steel-framed floors are similar to those used for floors framed with wood. Sheet or panel-type air barrier systems are acceptable for use in steel houses. Continuity of the air barrier system must be maintained by lapping and sealing air barrier materials with gaskets or sealants. The steel framing members, like those made of wood, can be used as integral elements of the air barrier system.

10.8 Telegraphing of Underlay in Finished Flooring

Expansion and shrinkage of underlay sheathing can be telegraphed through the floor finish, leading to homeowner complaints and premature deterioration of the finished floor. Sheet vinyl floors are most susceptible to this problem because discontinuities are more apparent on glossy surfaces.

Particleboard and oriented strandboard (OSB), the most commonly used underlay materials, are sensitive to moisture changes. Consecutive wetting of the underlay edges during construction or in areas such as bathrooms and entrances where water may occasionally be present can result in linear expansion and edge swelling. To minimize the problem, the joints in the underlay should be filled and sanded as suggested by the underlay manufacturer. Seams in the resilient flooring must be well sealed, and traffic delayed until the adhesive is fully cured.

Underlay panels must be stored flat over three supports in a dry, covered area protected from heat and moisture extremes prior to installation. Underlay manufacturers recommend specifically how and where their products should be installed. They also require the conditioning or acclimatizing of panels before installation.

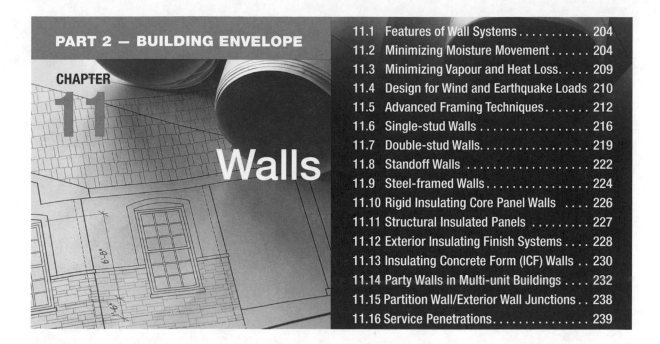

In addition to providing structural support, exterior walls must provide a thermal, weather, humidity, noise and dust barrier between the interior and exterior. To perform these functions properly, exterior walls must:

• Resist external forces such as wind, rain, snow and sun;

• Resist the outward migration of both conditioned air and water vapour; and

• Resist heat flow in both directions.

This chapter outlines several approaches for constructing insulated exterior walls with effective insulation and air and moisture barriers which can be effective options for Net Zero Energy builders.

It is important to recognize that as walls become thicker and the use of insulation sheathing increases to achieve the Net Zero Energy targets, it becomes extremely important to manage water ingress into walls. This Manual spends significant time describing the building science of water vapour movement into walls through air leaks and simple diffusion. Water can also enter walls through bulk transfer. Experience has shown that this is caused by a lack of attention to detail on site when installing weather barriers and flashings. Older buildings were subject to the same bulk water problems but the walls were comparatively less-insulated than the Net Zero Energy buildings we are describing in this Manual. As such, significant energy was lost through the walls and as this energy passed through the assembly it dried the assembly. With Net Zero Energy walls, the transfer of energy will not be anywhere near as significant to provide this drying. Therefore attention to detail will be as important as ever. Keep in mind that people make mistakes, caulking fails, wind and snow move flashings, and water gets in – it must be able to dry. Largely that drying will be by diffusion. Think about where you are building – is the building more likely to dry to the inside or the outside on an annual basis (maritime vs prairie climate)? Think about how drying will be accomplished if your wall was to unexpectedly become wet – will drying be driven by nature or by the operation of mechanical systems?. The following pages in this chapter describe high performance walls and you, as builders, choose the materials that will best perform in your area and building.

11.1 Features of Wall Systems

To meet modern design requirements, exterior walls have, as a minimum, the following components:

- External skin or cladding;

- Weather barrier;

- Structural components including framing members, sheathing, etc.;

- Insulation;

- Air barrier;

- Vapour barrier; and,

- Interior finish.

These components work together to produce a durable, structurally sound assembly that is resistant to heat, air and moisture flows. Wall selection is based on climatic and seismic conditions, the level of thermal performance required and material availability and cost.

Most walls are built on-site, but there are advantages to using factory-made walls. Most builders already make use of engineered wood trusses, and for some, factory-made wall panels offer many advantages.

Factory-made wall panels can be "open" and comprised of framing and sheathing, or they can be "closed" and include all the envelope elements – interior drywall, air and vapour barriers, framing sheathing, sheathing membrane and exterior cladding. Whether the certification standards in Chapter 14 apply depends on the local jurisdiction and the extent of completion before the panels arrive on-site. Panels consisting only of framing and sheathing may require only on-site inspection. Closed wall panels will likely require factory certification so that local inspectors can be assured that all required components have been correctly installed.

The purchase of wall panels usually includes a shop drawing that shows the assembly sequence for each of the numbered panels. If the panels are closed, the shop drawing should include instructions for ensuring insulation and air barrier continuity between panels.

11.2 Minimizing Moisture Movement

11.2.1 Moisture considerations with exterior sheathing

A wall assembly can get wet as a result of water entry from inside or outside the wall, or from the release of moisture from wet building materials in the wall assembly, such as wood framing. If damp or wet conditions occur in a wall, several factors influence the rate at which the wall cavity will dry:

- The permeability of the exterior sheathing/cladding system;

- The number and location of joints in the exterior sheathing/cladding system;

- The length of the drying season, temperature and orientation of the wall; and

- The relative humidity of the outside air during the drying season.

Research on moisture in wall systems resulted in the development of Moisture Indices (MI) for Canadian locations. These were subsequently included in the NBC along with requirements for a second plane of protection (rainscreen) for certain climate conditions.

11.2.2 Minimizing rain penetration

Wind-driven rain is a primary cause of wall deterioration. It can occur anywhere rainfall takes place, but is especially prevalent in wet, coastal climates. Three conditions must occur for rain to penetrate a wall assembly:

- There must be water on the surface of the cladding;

- There must be an opening in the cladding; and,

- There must be force, from a pressure difference, pushing or drawing the water through the opening.

If any one of these can be eliminated, rainwater will not penetrate an exterior wall. For example, water can be kept away from exterior wall cladding through the use of overhangs. The larger the overhang, the more protection it will provide. For this reason, one- and two-storey buildings with large overhangs have traditionally had few water penetration problems.

In some situations, overhangs are not used or cannot provide protection for the entire wall area. In these cases, cladding materials must either be sealed or the pressure differences driving water through the cladding must be equalized.

Face sealing is a technique for reducing water penetration by sealing all cracks, penetrations and joints in a cladding. Face sealing requires a high level of workmanship and is very difficult to achieve, so it is not a recommended approach for most applications. It is also very difficult to maintain a face seal over time, because the cladding expands and contracts with temperature changes, and the sealants and gaskets age as they are exposed to sunlight, temperature changes and chemical attack.

Face sealing also causes the cladding to become an air barrier in the wall assembly. As wind blows against the wall, the highest pressures will occur on the surface of the cladding and will force water into the wall where an opening does exist and the pressure is not equalized.

11.2.3 The mechanics of rain penetration

The forces that cause water penetration through cladding are:

- Kinetic energy (the force of moving rain)

- Capillary action and surface tension

- Gravity

- Wind pressure

If these forces can be controlled, water will not be drawn or forced into the wall. This is the objective of a rainscreen.

Kinetic energy

Pushed by wind, raindrops can hit a wall with considerable speed so that their momentum carries them through openings. Or they can shatter on impact and the resulting droplets can be forced through small openings and wet the inside of the wall. Rainwater ingress due to kinetic energy can be minimized by the use of battens, splines, baffles, interlocks and overlaps at joints and connections (Figure 11.1).

Figure 11.1 Minimizing kinetic energy

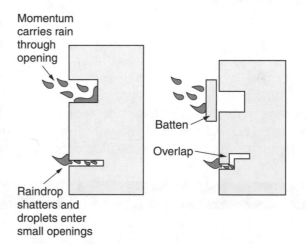

Momentum carries rain through opening

Batten

Overlap

Raindrop shatters and droplets enter small openings

Kinetic energy · · · · · · · · Minimizing kinetic energy

Capillary action

Capillary action draws or holds water in cracks and openings that are 0.5 mm (less than 1/32 in.) or less in width. Water held by capillary action can then be forced into the wall by pressure differences caused by wind, or gravity. If the backside of the cladding is tight against the weather barrier, water can travel in all directions by capillary action. Capillary action can also hold water between the cladding and weather barrier for long periods, leading to degradation of the weather barrier and/or cladding. Water ingress into a wall assembly due to capillary action can be minimized through the use of an air space of 10 mm (3/8 in.) or more between the cladding and the weather barrier/sheathing (Figure 11.2). A smaller air space may be appropriate for some exterior insulated finishing systems (EIFS) that have been performance tested (see Section 11.12).

Figure 11.2 Minimizing capillary action

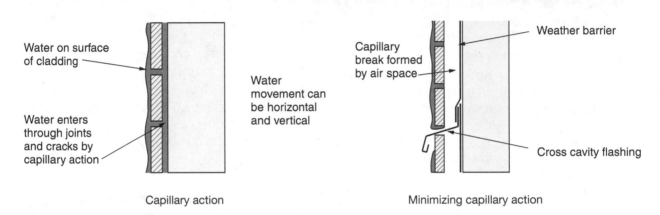

Water on surface of cladding

Water enters through joints and cracks by capillary action

Water movement can be horizontal and vertical

Capillary break formed by air space

Weather barrier

Cross cavity flashing

Capillary action

Minimizing capillary action

Gravity

Gravity pulls water into any opening that is sloped downward. Preventing water entry by gravity is achieved by using sloped flashings and the shingling of materials. Most openings that allow water entry by gravity appear after construction due to shrinkage of framing and cladding materials. This leakage can be minimized by the use of a drainage plane or air gap behind the cladding that allows water to drain down the backside of the cladding, and the use of flashings that carry the water out at each floor line, at horizontal junctions and at the base of the wall (Figure 11.3). The wall/window interface is known to have a high risk for water ingress (see Chapter 13 for window installation details).

Figure 11.3 Minimizing the effect of gravity

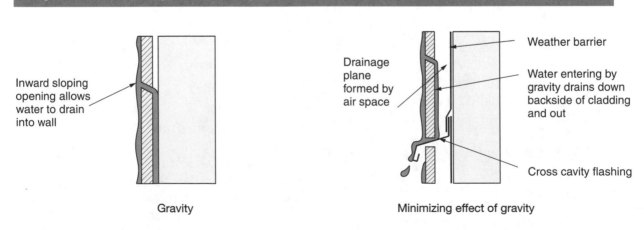

Inward sloping opening allows water to drain into wall

Drainage plane formed by air space

Weather barrier

Water entering by gravity drains down backside of cladding and out

Cross cavity flashing

Gravity

Minimizing effect of gravity

Wind pressure

The air pressure caused by wind blowing against a wall causes a pressure drop across the wall. If the pressure drop occurs behind the cladding, and there are openings in the cladding and water on the surface, the water will be driven through the cladding. To minimize the effect of the force of wind pressure across the cladding, the air pressure on the back of the cladding must be the same as the pressure on the outside face of the cladding. This is accomplished by providing an air space behind the cladding, compartmentalizing the air space, placing enough openings in the cladding to allow wind to pressurize it, and providing an air barrier behind the air space on the wall (Figure 11.4).

Figure 11.4 Minimizing the effect of wind pressure

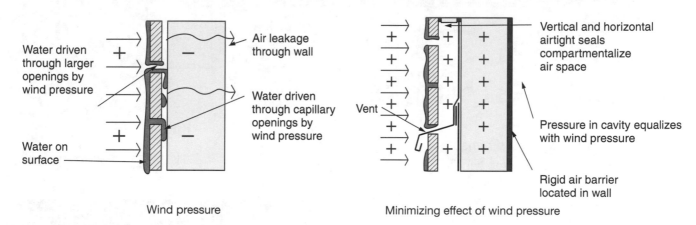

Wind pressure

Minimizing effect of wind pressure

11.2.4 Second planes of protection

If there is no space between the cladding and the weather barrier and sheathing, the exterior wall has a single plane of protection. This leaves a wall more susceptible to rain penetration due to driving forces. A rainscreen is a second plane of protection against water ingress. The NBC requires that exterior walls that are exposed to precipitation have a second plane of protection with a capillary break, based on the number of degree days and the moisture index (MI) for a given location (see NBC Appendix C, Table C-2). The MI is an indicator of the moisture load imposed on buildings by the climate and is used to define the minimum levels of protection from precipitation to be provided by cladding assemblies.

Simple rainscreens

Effects from capillary action and gravity can be minimized by placing an air space (drainage plane) behind the cladding (Figure 11.5). The drainage plane is drained to the outside at the floor line and/or base of the wall with flashings. The simple rainscreen drainage plane uses 19 mm (3/4 in.) vertical battens, and an air/weather barrier membrane is located between the sheathing and the battens. Pressure-treated or naturally decay-resistant materials (such as red cedar) should be used for the battens, and fasteners must be corrosion-resistant.

Figure 11.5 Simple rainscreen (without compartmentalization)

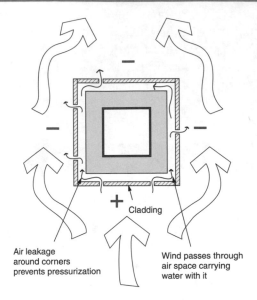

Cladding

Air leakage around corners prevents pressurization

Wind passes through air space carrying water with it

be continuous or evenly spaced across the width of the wall. The bottom vents should have an insect barrier.

Figure 11.6 Pressure-equalized rainscreen

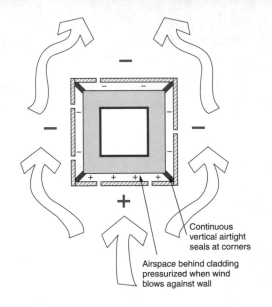

Continuous vertical airtight seals at corners

Airspace behind cladding pressurized when wind blows against wall

Pressure-equalized rainscreen

To effectively manage wind-driven rain, a more sophisticated rainscreen is required. It must be built in a way that causes the air space behind the cladding to become pressurized to equal the wind air pressure when the wind blows against the wall (Figure 11.6). This is done by:

- Placing airtight vertical seals at a maximum spacing of 6 m (20 ft.) and at all corners to ensure wind and air pressure entering the air space does not pass around the corners of the building (Figure 11.7).

- Placing a horizontal seal at the top of the air space. The horizontal air seal can be formed by the floor-line flashing incorporated for drainage for the storey above.

- Incorporating a continuous, structurally supported air barrier in the wall.

- Incorporating vent openings in the face of the cladding that allow for rapid pressure equalization. The size of the vents is related to the volume of the air space, the airtightness of the air barrier and the rigidity of the cladding. The vents should

Figure 11.7 Rainscreen

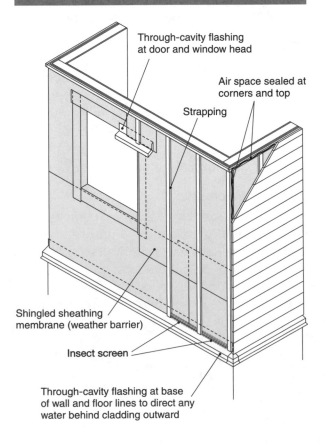

Through-cavity flashing at door and window head

Air space sealed at corners and top

Strapping

Shingled sheathing membrane (weather barrier)

Insect screen

Through-cavity flashing at base of wall and floor lines to direct any water behind cladding outward

11.3 Minimizing Vapour and Heat Loss

Water vapour can enter wall cavities from the interior as a result of vapour diffusion and air leakage. The NBC requires that a vapour barrier be installed on the high vapour pressure (warm) side of any walls sheathed with low-permeance materials. The proper installation of air barriers is also critical for reducing heat loss and the associated flow of warm, moist air into cold wall assemblies where it can condense and result in damage. In residential construction, the roles of vapour and air barriers are often served simultaneously through the installation of a polyethylene air/vapour barrier. The air barrier must be made continuous at window and door openings, electrical boxes, plumbing and all other penetrations.

In colder climates, the polyethylene air barrier must be installed on the warm side of the dew point. In most regions of Canada, this means no more than one third of the RSI value of the wall should be on the warm side of the polyethylene. In cold, northern regions, the limit might be one-fifth or less, depending on local climate conditions. The NBC provides a table showing the ratio for various climate conditions (outboard to inboard ratios).

Of importance to Net Zero Energy builders, is a recent change made to the NBC relating to low permeance insulation and the trigger for the outboard to inboard calculation. This was was changed from 60 to 30 ng/(Pa.s.m2). Practically, what this means is that builders can use an insulating sheathing with a vapour permeance above 30 ng/(Pa.s.m2) as long as it has a thermal resistance of at least R-4. This can be done in all Heating Degree Day zones less than 6000 without having to comply with the minimum outboard to inboard ratio by climate zone. This approach works because the low permeance insulation on the exterior makes the wall cavity warmer and the sheathing is much more vapour permeable than the polyethylene vapour barrier on the

inside. The experience to date of Net Zero Energy builders and energy advisors has been that exterior insulation has been the method of choice to increase the overall effective R-value of the wall system and reduce thermal bridges.

The air barrier must be continuous at foundations and intermediate floors. If the air barrier is polyethylene or another flexible sheet material, it needs to be sealed to a house wrap qualified as an air barrier at the floor/wall junctions. It must also be protected from damage during construction.

Advanced framing techniques such as those described later in this chapter (Section 11.5) can reduce the quantity of lumber used in walls. Since insulation has a higher RSI value than lumber, advanced framing techniques can reduce heat loss through walls by up to 10%. Some of the techniques described increase wall thickness, which allows for more insulation.

Adding a second, continuous layer of insulation can reduce thermal bridging through the framing members. Because wood and steel framing have lower insulation values than materials manufactured specifically for thermal insulation, they reduce the *effective* insulation value of an assembly. This is why steel framing requires exterior rigid insulation, and why the same treatment improves the insulation value of wood-frame walls.

Whatever technique is used, the insulation must be installed properly to obtain the full benefit. It must fill the entire cavity, leaving no gaps where convection currents could form. In double-stud and standoff walls, different batt thicknesses may be required in different parts of the wall to completely fill the cavity. Walls must also be constructed to prevent cold air from circulating through or around the insulation.

Various blown and spray insulations are available. Spray foam insulation and wet and dry cellulose and fibreglass systems, when applied correctly, can fill cavities and control convection. Some spray insulations are also effective in reducing air leakage in the wall assembly.

Walls represent a significant surface area of the building envelope and play a large role in the overall heat loss of the building. Moving toward Net Zero Energy housing means that attention must be paid to minimizing the heat loss in any way possible. As a result, designers are looking for every bit of energy savings that they can get. This means thicker walls in some cases, almost always continuous, exterior insulation to reduce thermal bridging through studs, advanced framing to minimize the amount of wood because wood is not a good insulator and details to improve air tightness. Experience is showing builders achieving Net Zero Energy or Net Zero Energy Ready are targeting RSI 6.5 + (R-37 +) in their walls. The wall systems shown in this chapter are appropriate with achieving this level of insulation.

11.4 Design for Wind and Earthquake Loads

Buildings need to be able to resist lateral forces due to wind and earthquake loads. Prior to 2010, the National Building Code, Part 9, did not explicitly include prescriptive requirements for lateral resistance. The requirements introduced in the 2010 NBC (seismic hazard values were updated in the 2015 NBC) reflect the fact that house construction has changed. Older houses tended to have small rooms meaning there were more interior walls to provide rigidity. They also tended to have a moderate number and size of windows and doors, which left ample exterior wall space to add rigidity. The NBC does not address the issue of bracing of a structure during construction. Until interior finishes or sheathing are installed, temporary bracing should be used to provide support for the structure.

Depending on building location and design features, new houses may need some additional bracing to resist wind and earthquake loads.

To ensure adequate resistance to lateral loads, it is necessary that:

- Walls be strong enough to resist cumulative lateral loads;

- Walls be arranged and configured to allow load transfer between floors; and,

- Connections be strong enough to transfer forces between roof, walls, floors and foundations.

The construction required to provide resistance to lateral loads will depend on whether the climatic data for a region establishes it as having *low to moderate*, *high* or *extreme* exposure to wind or earthquake loads. It also depends on building complexity. NBC Appendix C, "Climatic and Seismic Information for Building Design in Canada" provides the 1-in-50 hourly wind pressures that determine wind load, and the seismic spectral response acceleration that determines earthquake exposure for low-rise buildings. The higher a building, the heavier the materials used or the more complex a building is in terms of shape and the size of openings, the more likely it is that engineered solutions will be required.

11.4.1 Areas with low to moderate exposure

Of the 640 locations identified in NBC Appendix C, 588 fall into this category. This means that for most locations in Canada, bracing requirements can be met by using acceptable materials and fastening methods that have traditionally been used for housing – exterior sheathing, panel-type cladding, or gypsum board finish. Using more than one of these options will increase resistance. There is also the option of designing according to Part 4 of the National Building Code or following good engineering practice.

11.4.2 Areas with high exposure

For wind, 19 locations in Newfoundland, Quebec, Alberta, Nunavut, and Northwest

Territories are affected. Of the 33 locations affected by seismic risk, 29 are located in the coastal region of British Columbia and 4 are located in the lower St. Lawrence region of Quebec.

Buildings in this exposure category require additional features to provide required resistance to lateral loads. The NBC provides prescriptive solutions based on providing strong portions of walls called 'braced panels.' There are limitations for using these prescriptive solutions based on building height and whether the construction is comprised of heavy materials. There is also the option of designing according to Part 4 of the National Building Code or following good engineering practice.

Braced panels are portions of wood-frame walls where bracing, sheathing, cladding or interior finish is installed to provide the required resistance. If a given wall is required to have a certain number of braced wall panels it is optional to provide only the required panels or to construct the entire wall using the same construction technique as for the braced panels. They must meet requirements for location, spacing and construction.

To provide a continuous lateral load path, braced wall panels must be located within braced wall bands and must extend from the top of the supporting foundation, slab or sub-floor to the underside of the floor, ceiling or roof framing above (Figure 11.8). As exterior walls must provide bracing, the perimeter of the building must be located within the braced wall bands. Interior bands may be required to respect the maximum spacing allowance between bands, as measured from centre-to-centre.

Figure 11.8 General concept of braced wall panels within braced wall bands

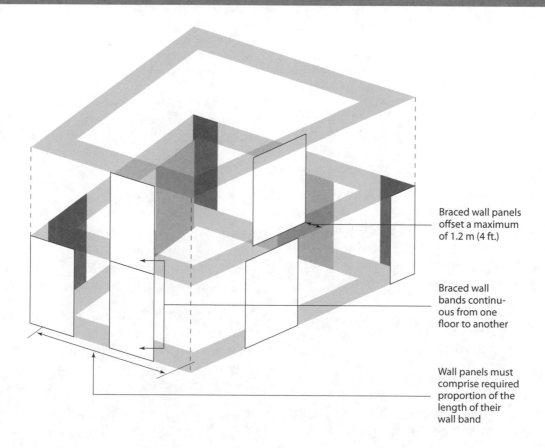

Braced wall panels offset a maximum of 1.2 m (4 ft.)

Braced wall bands continuous from one floor to another

Wall panels must comprise required proportion of the length of their wall band

Perimeter concrete or masonry foundation walls provide significant lateral resistance compared to above- ground frame walls. Therefore, interior braced wall bands can be terminated at the floor above the basement or crawl space provided the remaining braced wall bands are spaced not more than 15 m (49 ft.) on centre or 15 m (49 ft.) from a perimeter braced wall band.

Identifying adjacent braced wall bands and determining the spacing of braced wall panels and braced wall bands is not complicated where intersecting walls are perpendicular, but becomes more complicated where buildings have irregular shapes (See NBC Appendix A).

The front walls of one storey attached garages that serve a single dwelling unit do not require braced wall panels if:

- The distance between the front and back walls of the garage does not exceed 7.5 m (25 ft.);

- There is not more than one floor above the garage;

- Not less than 50% of the length of the back wall is constructed of braced panels; and

- Not less than 25% of the length of side walls is constructed of braced panels.

11.4.3 Areas with extreme exposure

Only 3 locations fall into this category for seismic value and only 1 for wind. Buildings in this exposure category are required to be designed according to Part 4 of the National Building Code or following good engineering practice.

11.5 Advanced Framing Techniques

Conventional wood-frame construction results in the use of more material than is necessary for structural rigidity, convenience or code compliance. These additional materials and labour may serve no purpose and add to the cost of a project. Advanced framing techniques can provide the same level of performance, and provide labour and material savings. They are recognized in building codes; however, in areas where special structural provisions are required to meet wind and seismic requirements, it is essential to ensure that advanced framing measures comply with these provisions.

Examples of advanced framing techniques are:

- Increasing the spacing of structural members to 490 or 600 mm (19.2 or 24 in.) centres. The larger dimension simplifies framing layout and uses less material-therefore more insulation can be added. It also reduces the number of drywall attachments and locations for nail popping.

- Aligning all floor, wall, and roof framing. When the respective members bear directly over each other, the more efficient structure can eliminate the need for some framing such as double top plates.

- Coordinating the openings in the wall to line up with the modular stud spacing on at least one side of an opening.

- Eliminating unnecessary cripples and jack studs in both load-bearing and non-load-bearing walls. If cripples are needed, they only have to be 38 x 89 mm (2 x 4 in.).

- Designing and placing beams to allow for even-length floor joists.

- Using diagonal bracing in conjunction with insulating sheathing to eliminate the need for structural sheathing and to reduce thermal bridging through wall systems.

- Eliminating backers and studs at exterior wall corners (Figure 11.9)-a three-stud exterior corner is not structurally necessary. Drywall support can be provided by one stud, and drywall clips used for the other side.

- Eliminating partition posts at exterior walls (Figure 11.10) and ceiling

Figure 11.9 Two-stud corner with drywall clips

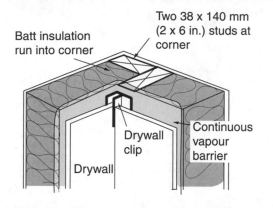

Two 38 x 140 mm (2 x 6 in.) studs at corner

Batt insulation run into corner

Drywall clip

Continuous vapour barrier

Drywall

Figure 11.10 Interior wall junction

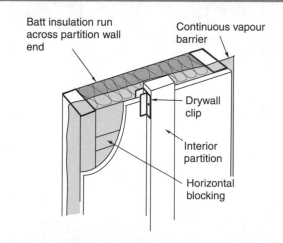

Batt insulation run across partition wall end

Continuous vapour barrier

Drywall clip

Interior partition

Horizontal blocking

Figure 11.11 Modified balloon framing

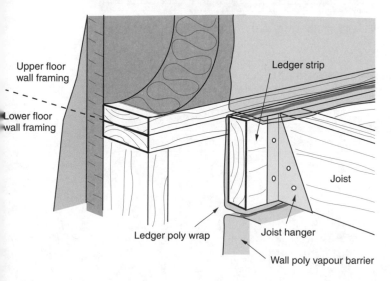

Upper floor wall framing

Lower floor wall framing

Ledger strip

Joist

Ledger poly wrap

Joist hanger

Wall poly vapour barrier

- Reducing the size of built-up posts. In a 38 x 139 mm (2 x 6 in.) exterior wall, a 3 – 38 x 89 mm (2 x 4 in.) built-up post may be sufficient to carry loads from above. This saves material and allows for insulation to be installed behind the post, reducing thermal bridging.

- Eliminating lintels in gable end walls where there is no vertical load or where trusses are parallel to the wall in which the opening is located.

- Using modified balloon framing techniques to reduce thermal bridging through top and bottom plates (Figure 11.11).

11.5.1 More on Thermal Bridging & Net Zero

Achieving Net Zero Energy requires builders and energy advisors being very focused on energy efficiency. Net Zero Energy means that the house produces as much energy as it uses over the course of a year. Some days the house produces more energy than it needs and some days it produces less. Net Zero Energy is achieved when the annual, overall energy produced is more than the annual energy consumed. Recognizing this fact, builders are evaluating the cost of a GJ of energy saved and comparing it with the cost of installing the equipment to produce a GJ of energy. As long as the cost of installing insulation, air sealing or purchasing more efficient mechanical equipment to save a GJ is less than the cost of installing a photovoltaic system to produce a GJ, then energy conservation is where the money should be spent. The cost of the systems to produce energy (PV) has been falling in recent years, so this strategy requires keeping current on technology and prices in order to achieve Net Zero Energy in the most cost-effective manner.

Appendix 1 of this Manual shows an example of calculating the Effective RSI (R) value of a wall, taking into account the thermal bridging of the studs making up the wall. As builders look for ways to improve the thermal performance of the house, advanced framing (reducing the amount of wood) is one technique that can improve the R-value of the wall while reducing the amount of wood. This section will take a more detailed look at this.

Example Insulation Basics (working in imperial units)

The dimensioned lumber we use for building has an R-value of approximately R-1.3/inch.

Fibreglass batt insulation typically has an R-value of R-3.2/inch. If we can replace a piece of wood with insulation we will have a better performing wall, no matter how thick the wall is (i.e 2x4, 2x6, 2x8). The table below shows how significant this is for walls with stud spacing of 12", 16" and 24", all of which are commonly used by builders today. The wall being analyzed is a 12' long by 8' high wall built with 2 top plates and a single bottom plate. Note that pre-cut studs are 92.5" long.

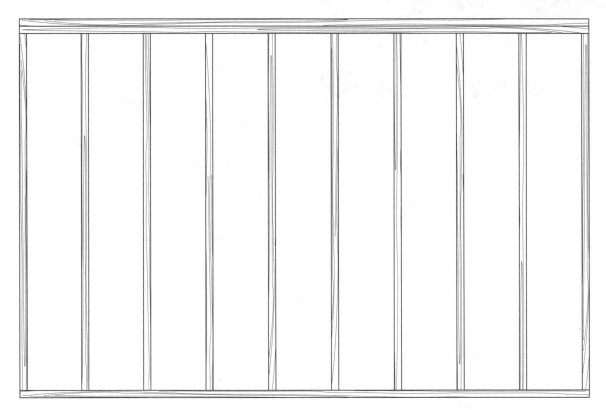

Example: 12' long x 8' high wall with studs at 16" o/c

Stud Spacing	# of studs	Surface Area of Wood in 2	% of Wall that is Wood
12" o/c	13	2451.75	17.6
16" o/c	10	2035.50	14.6
24" o/c	7	1619.25	11.6

Background Calculations

Surface area of one stud = 1.5" x 92.5" = 138.75 in²
Surface area of wooden plates = 1.5" x 144" x 3 pieces = 648 in²
Surface area of wood in entire 16" o/c wall = (138.75 in² x 10 studs) + 648 = 2035.5 in²
Surface area of the entire wall = 97" x 144" = 13,968 in²
% of wall which is wood = 2035.5 in²/13,968 in² = 14.6%

Observations

A savings of 3% of the wall surface area of wood can be made switching from 16" stud spacing to 24" stud spacing. Refer to the example in Appendix 1 for the calculation procedure. This means that for a 2"x6" wall, the Reff (effective R-value) of the wall with the studs at 16" is R-24.45 while the Reff for the wall with the studs at 24" is R-25.06. While this may seem small, achieving Net Zero Energy in a cost-effective manner is largely about getting the most out of the materials and construction techniques. When this is applied to all the walls of a house it may make the difference between changing to 2"x8" studs, double wall construction or some other technique that may cost more to create a larger cavity to hold more insulation.

Note also that as the wall becomes shorter in length the percentage of wood increases. For example, for a 4' long wall, with studs on 16" o/c, the percentage of wood in the wall is 16.6% using the same calculations as used in the table above. Therefore, the amount of wood increases as a percentage of the surface area of the wall as the wall becomes shorter in length. A house with exterior walls with many jogs in them will will have a higher percentage of the wall face that is wood. A house design with a simpler geometry using longer walls will improve the energy efficiency by reducing thermal bridging but the result is a more "boxy" looking house.

If a window is added, the percentage of wood increases. For example, if the same 12' wall used above includes a window with a Rough Stud Opening of 48" x 48", the percentage of wood in the wall becomes 19.8%. Note that this is over 5% more wood than in the same wall with no window.

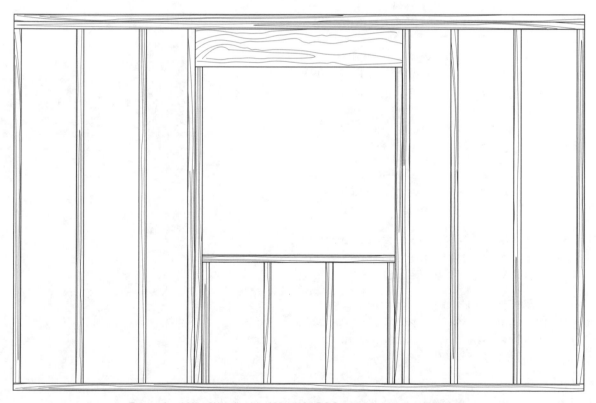

Example: 12' x 8' wall with 48" x 48" RSO window, studs at 16" o/c

Continuous Exterior Insulation

The case for continuous, exterior insulation should be becoming clear at this point. Note that the full insulation value of continuous insulation is applied directly to the effective R-value number. Because the continuous insulation covers the studs and it covers the cavity, it is directly added to the R effective.

From the example in Appendix 1, the wall with studs on 24" spacing, with the addition of 2" of extruded foam insulation (R-5/inch) would increase from Reff of 25.06 to Reff = 35.06.

11.6 Single-stud Walls

11.6.1 Single-stud wall with exterior insulating sheathing

A common way to thermally upgrade typical 2 x 6 R-20 single-stud walls is to add continuous, insulating sheathing (rigid or semi-rigid boardstock insulation) on the outside. Modified balloon framing can also reduce thermal bridging. Exterior insulated sheathing can be used with either a membrane or a rigid air barrier approach. However, to reach Net Zero Energy insulation levels (near RSI 7.04 (R-40)) on a single-stud wall a 2 x 8 wall may be needed. Insulation of R-28 is available for the cavity and with 2" of rigid foam on the exterior, there is a nominal R-38.

A common stud wall can easily be enhanced by the addition of exterior insulating sheathing (Figure 11.12) and the following modifications:

- The 38 x 140 mm (2 x 6 in.) studs are placed 600 mm (24 in.) on centre (depending on the requirements of the siding).

- Structural sheathing is replaced with diagonal bracing (wood or preformed metal) and insulating sheathing, except where the structural panel sheathing is required for structural purposes.

- The rim joist is recessed to allow higher insulation levels at the floor junctions.

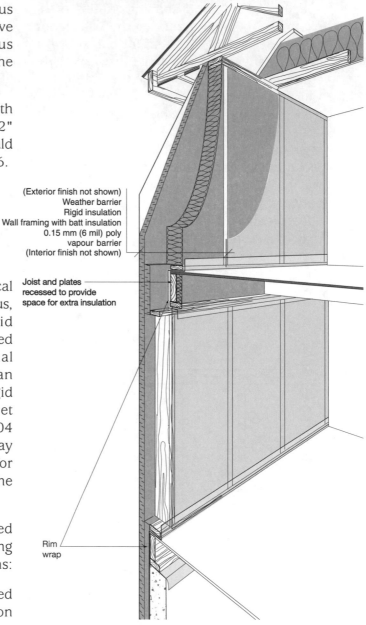

Figure 11.12 Single-stud wall with exterior insulating sheathing

(Exterior finish not shown)
Weather barrier
Rigid insulation
Wall framing with batt insulation
0.15 mm (6 mil) poly
vapour barrier
(Interior finish not shown)

Joist and plates recessed to provide space for extra insulation

Rim wrap

Single-stud wall with exterior insulating sheathing	
Advantages	**Disadvantages**
• Uses readily available construction materials. • Is a simple way to reduce thermal bridging through framing. • Small incremental costs compared to standard framing. • Requires little change from standard framing practices.	• Net Zero Energy levels of insulation will require thicker wall systems • Can cause problems for the attachment of siding to some exterior insulated sheathings due to their compressibility. • Creates a requirement to build out around window and door openings. • Penetrations for items such as hose bibs, heating intakes etc. need solid blocking and preplanning is required. • Reduces the ability of a wall to dry to the exterior.

Exterior sheathing options

Several types of board insulations can be used (see Chapter 7), and selection depends on:

- Insulation level required;

- Means of mechanical attachment;

- Product durability during construction;

- Cost of the installed system;

- Air and vapour permeability of the material and its sealing requirements;

- Compatibility of the sheathing with the proposed siding installation; and

- Product availability.

Upgraded insulation between the studs

The space between the studs is often filled with batt insulation. However, spray insulation can also be used. These products provide a uniform insulation level and help to reduce air leakage. Some spray-applied materials may also provide higher thermal resistance per unit thickness than batt insulations. Since they are denser than batt-type insulations, they tend to reduce structure-borne sound transmission through wall assemblies.

Spray insulation requires the expertise of a certified applicator. Some spray insulation needs to be trimmed even with the stud surfaces after the materials have expanded in place. The installer is responsible for applying the appropriate density and coverage. The builder may need to leave the walls exposed for a longer period than normal to allow for adequate drying or curing if a wet system is used.

Windows and doors

Procedures for installing windows and doors in this type of wall system are provided in Chapter 13.

11.6.2 Single-stud wall with interior strapping and insulation

Additional insulation space is created inside by installing 38 x 38 mm (2 x 2 in.) or 38 x 64 mm (2 x 3 in.) strapping horizontally on the interior of stud walls. Either a rigid or a membrane air barrier can be used. If polyethylene is used as the air/vapour barrier, it is usually placed on the inside face of the studs before the strapping is installed.

Single-stud walls with interior strapping and insulation can also be built with insulating sheathing on the exterior (Figure 11.13). This could increase the total RSI value of the wall to between 6.1 and 7.0 (R-35 and R-40), depending on the materials used.

Strapping and insulation

In addition to the regular runs of strapping, additional strapping is required to support:

- Drywall around windows and doors;

- Drywall at inside and outside corners, unless drywall clips are used to support the drywall;

- Kitchen cupboards, closet rods, etc.;

- Baseboards; and

- Electrical boxes.

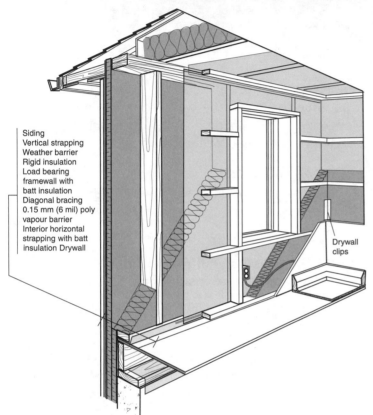

Figure 11.13 Single-stud walls with interior strapping and insulation

Siding
Vertical strapping
Weather barrier
Rigid insulation
Load bearing
framewall with
batt insulation
Diagonal bracing
0.15 mm (6 mil) poly
vapour barrier
Interior horizontal
strapping with batt
insulation Drywall

Drywall
clips

RSI 1.4 (R-8) batts can be friction fit into the cavities created by 38 x 64 mm (2 x 3 in.) strapping. Standard batt sizes are not generally available for 38 x 38 mm (2 x 2 in.) strapping.

Electrical and plumbing

Electrical work must be modified to fit in the strapping space. For the most part, electrical installation is simplified by the space between the horizontal strapping and the wall studs, but the following points should be considered:

- Shallow electrical boxes are required if 38 mm (2 in.)-deep strapping is used. Only two connections are allowed inside shallow boxes.

- Plastic boxes are preferable because they are less likely to harm the polyethylene. If metal boxes are used, care must be taken to ensure the air barrier is not breached by clamps and grounding screws.

- Strapping should only be drilled where wiring is necessary.

- Wiring staples should be fixed to the cross-strapping and should not penetrate the air/vapour barrier.

- A gap between the strapping and the wall top plate reduces the need to drill studs for wire runs.

Low-voltage wiring for telephone, cable TV, data and home automation, requires similar consideration.

Single-stud wall with interior strapping and insulation	
Advantages	**Disadvantages**
• The combination of insulation in a 38 x 140 mm (2 x 6 in.) main wall and a 38 x 64 mm (2 x 3 in.) strapped space provides a thermal resistance of RSI 4.9 (R-28).	• If horizontal interior strapping is used, blocking must be used to provide support for kitchen cabinets, baseboards and other fixtures.
• The extra layer of insulation that covers the inside face of the studs and the horizontal strapping reduces thermal bridging.	• In some places, the strapping will have to be drilled to allow the passage of wiring, unless it is staggered at the wall studs, and wiring must be protected from finish nailing and drywall screws.
• Electrical services can be installed on the interior side of the strapped space to minimize penetrations.	• Drywall must be installed vertically.

11.7 Double-stud Walls

Double-stud wall systems were developed to accommodate very high levels of insulation.

They should be considered if the climate is extremely cold or fuel costs are exceptionally high, and are likely to be used more as the quest for energy reduction continues. They are another option available to Net Zero Energy builders.

A double-stud wall consists of a load-bearing, structural wall and a lighter, non-bearing wall section. The thickness of the wall assembly, and therefore the amount of insulation that can be installed, is up to the builder. Either a rigid or a membrane air barrier can be used.

Location of air barrier

If a polyethylene air/vapour barrier is used, it is essential to locate it on the warm side of the assembly dew point.

Windows and doors

Double wall systems are wide and special attention is required for window installation. If the windows are installed on the interior face of the wall, a sloped metal flashing or an adequate slope for wood sills is required to promote rapid runoff. If the windows are installed on the outside face of the wall, the detailing of sills and trim is more conventional (Figure 11.14). However, as explained in Chapter 13, window

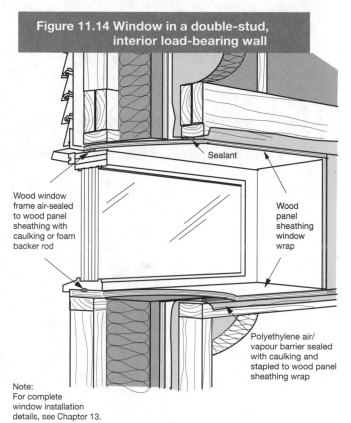

Figure 11.14 Window in a double-stud, interior load-bearing wall

Sealant

Wood window frame air-sealed to wood panel sheathing with caulking or foam backer rod

Wood panel sheathing window wrap

Polyethylene air/ vapour barrier sealed with caulking and stapled to wood panel sheathing wrap

Note:
For complete window installation details, see Chapter 13.

installation aligned with the exterior wall reduces the movement of warm air on the window interior and increases condensation. This condition is made worse as the thickness of the exterior wall increases. For this reason, if a window is located at the exterior wall, a double wall is another application where triple-glazed windows would be beneficial.

Double-stud walls	
Advantages	**Disadvantages**
• Conventional platform framing techniques can be used to construct the load-bearing wall. • Smaller dimension lumber can be used. • Flexible spacing can be used to accommodate the requirements of the cladding system. • Wide range of insulation values is possible. • Thermal bridging through wood framing is minimized. • Minimal penetrations, and good air barrier continuity can be maintained.	• Labour and material costs will be higher than for other systems. • Platform framing techniques may not be suitable for erecting the exterior wall. • The additional thickness of the wall reduces interior floor dimensions. • Thicker walls require special details for finishing windows and doors.

11.7.1 Exterior load-bearing

Double-stud walls can have an exterior structural wall with a second wall erected independently on the house interior (Figure 11.15).

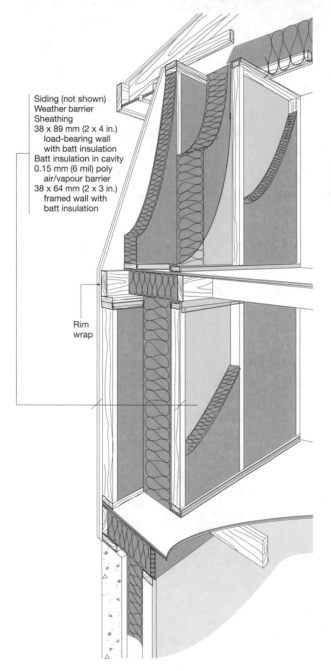

Figure 11.15 Double-stud, exterior load-bearing wall

Siding (not shown)
Weather barrier
Sheathing
38 x 89 mm (2 x 4 in.)
  load-bearing wall
  with batt insulation
Batt insulation in cavity
0.15 mm (6 mil) poly
  air/vapour barrier
38 x 64 mm (2 x 3 in.)
  framed wall with
  batt insulation

Rim
wrap

The exterior wall is framed, sheathed, and insulated. Then a second stud wall is framed and installed on the house interior, spaced to create a cavity for additional insulation. If polyethylene is used as the air barrier, it may be installed on either side of the interior frame wall and be supported by a solid panel-type material.

This system requires additional work to seal floor joist assemblies, but it eliminates complex details. The interior wall, which is not load-bearing, can be framed with smaller dimension lumber such as 38 x 64 mm (2 x 3 in.) at 600 mm (24 in.) on centre. Figure 11.16 shows a corner detail for an exterior load-bearing, double-stud wall.

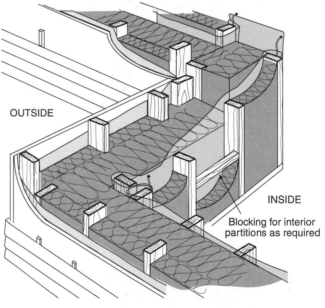

Figure 11.16 Corner details for a double-stud, exterior load-bearing wall

OUTSIDE

INSIDE

Blocking for interior partitions as required

11.7.2 Interior load-bearing

This double-stud wall system incorporates an interior load-bearing wall and an exterior non-bearing wall that supports exterior finishes (Figure 11.17). The two walls are connected by top and bottom plates made from wood panel sheathing and are spaced to contain the required thickness of insulation.

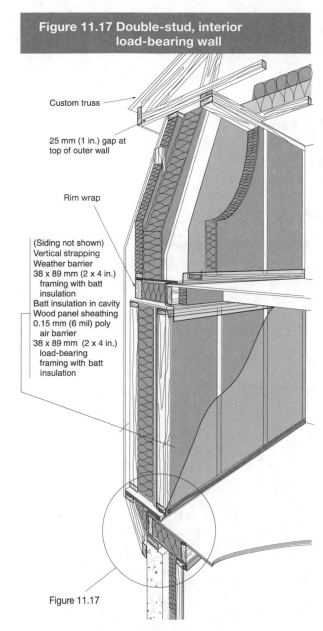

Figure 11.17 Double-stud, interior load-bearing wall

Custom truss

25 mm (1 in.) gap at top of outer wall

Rim wrap

(Siding not shown)
Vertical strapping
Weather barrier
38 x 89 mm (2 x 4 in.) framing with batt insulation
Batt insulation in cavity
Wood panel sheathing
0.15 mm (6 mil) poly air barrier
38 x 89 mm (2 x 4 in.) load-bearing framing with batt insulation

Figure 11.17

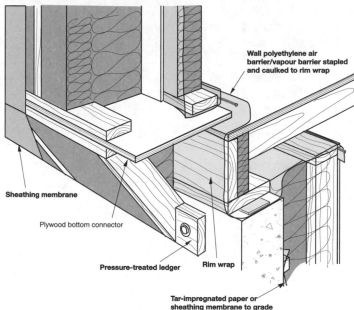

Figure 11.18 Double-stud, interior load-bearing wall: support for exterior wall

Wall polyethylene air barrier/vapour barrier stapled and caulked to rim wrap

Sheathing membrane

Plywood bottom connector

Pressure-treated ledger

Rim wrap

Tar-impregnated paper or sheathing membrane to grade

If polyethylene is used as the vapour barrier or air barrier, it can be installed on the outside of the inner stud wall and be protected by solid panel-type sheathing. This placement reduces the likelihood that the polyethylene will be damaged during the construction process. The placement of the polyethylene must respect its location relative to the wall dew point. This assembly requires the installation of the outer insulation from the exterior-a disadvantage in the north where rapid close-in is desirable. In addition, support is required at the bottom of the outer wall to carry its weight (Figure 11.18).

Differential expansion will occur between the inner and outer wall assemblies because of their different temperatures and relative humidities. Consequently, the non-bearing wall must be able to float relative to the load-bearing wall. The interior load-bearing wall should have a plywood or OSB spacer so that it is 13 mm (1/2 in.) higher than the outer non-load-bearing wall to ensure the vertical load from the roof is transferred appropriately.

The rough openings in the inner and outer walls are joined with a wood panel sheathing liner that provides support for interior finishes and ties the two walls together only at that point. Insulation can be installed when the wall is laid out on the subfloor, as long as an adequate weather barrier is installed before the wall is erected. The insulation must fill all wall cavities. The centre cavity will generally be 89 or 140 mm (3-1/2 or 5-1/2 in.), which will fit RSI 2.1 or 3.5 (R-12 or R-20) insulation batts. This layer of insulation should be installed horizontally in the cavity and vertically between the studs.

Spray insulation can also be used. It may be a foamed insulation, or loose-fill fibre or cellulose designed for such applications. For spray applications, at least one side, usually the exterior, must be a solid surface to act as a backing for the insulation.

Corner details

Figure 11.19 shows the inside and outside corners for a double-stud, interior load-bearing wall. Where partition walls intersect exterior walls, horizontal blocking is installed between the studs. This blocking allows insulation to run past the end of the partition.

11.8 Standoff Walls

A standoff wall is a double-stud wall with the interior wall being the load-bearing system. In addition to wood studs, wood I-joists or parallel chord trusses on the vertical can be used to create the insulation space. Standoff walls use standard framing techniques for a single-stud, load-bearing wall with sheathing. Intermediate floor assemblies and partition walls are all independent.

Either a rigid or a membrane air barrier can be used. If a polyethylene air barrier is used, it should be installed over the sheathing, from the top of the completed wall to the foundation wall. However, there must be enough insulation to the exterior to ensure that the polyethylene is maintained above the dew point. A truss wall is then anchored, through the polyethylene and sheathing, into the wall studs (Figure 11.20). Alternatively, the wood panel sheathing or house wrap can be used as the air barrier, as long as all joints are sealed.

Figure 11.20 Standoff wall system

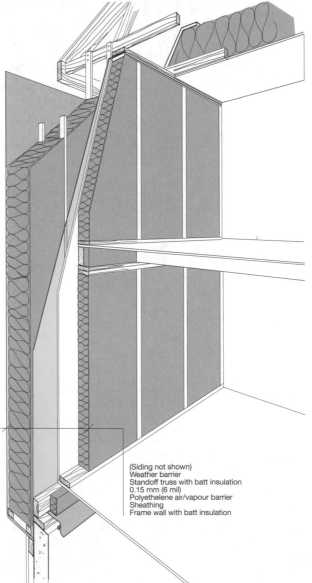

(Siding not shown)
Weather barrier
Standoff truss with batt insulation
0.15 mm (6 mil)
Polyethelene air/vapour barrier
Sheathing
Frame wall with batt insulation

Figure 11.19 Corner details for a double-stud, interior load-bearing wall

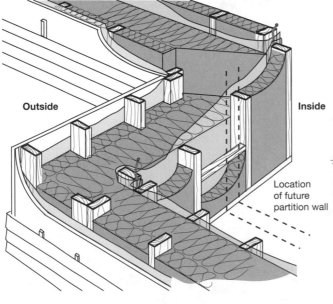

Outside

Inside

Location of future partition wall

Standoff walls

Advantages	Disadvantages
• The load-bearing frame uses standard framing. • The wall can be designed to accommodate high insulation levels and be used with vertical siding when the wall is horizontally strapped. • A polyethylene air barrier can be applied as one large single sheet, with a minimum number of seams and penetrations.	• Gaps may occur in the insulation if trusses are not correctly spaced and insulation is not properly installed. • Differential shrinkage between the inner and outer truss members and the header joist can cause deformation and cracking of the interior finish material at the ceiling/wall joint. • Vapour barrier and insulation materials are exposed to weather during installation.

Figure 11.21 Window framing in a standoff wall

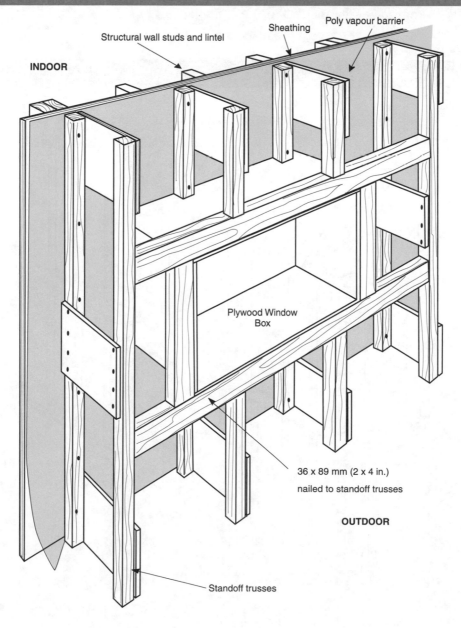

Wall trusses can be either site-fabricated or manufactured using a variety of designs and mechanical fastening techniques. The outer member can be built of smaller dimension lumber since it is not load-bearing. Trusses should be designed to minimize gaps in the insulation behind framing members. They should be spaced to accommodate the required thickness and width of insulation.

If polyethylene is used, it should be an ultraviolet-stabilized material (meeting standard CGSB 51.34-M), as it may be exposed to sunlight for a long period during construction. Rigid board insulation can be installed between chords of the standoffs to minimize air pockets in the insulation.

If the wall trusses are nailed to the rafter or truss tails, the base should be free-floating to accommodate differential movement. Figure 11.21 shows the framing around a window in a standoff wall.

11.9 Steel-framed Walls

The NBC provides size and spacing information for non-load-bearing walls and partitions. Load-bearing walls require engineering design.

Steel-frame construction requires that the webs of all studs and joists align to transfer load from one member to the other (Figure 11.22). Joists must never bear on track members between

---

Figure 11.22 Steel-frame walls

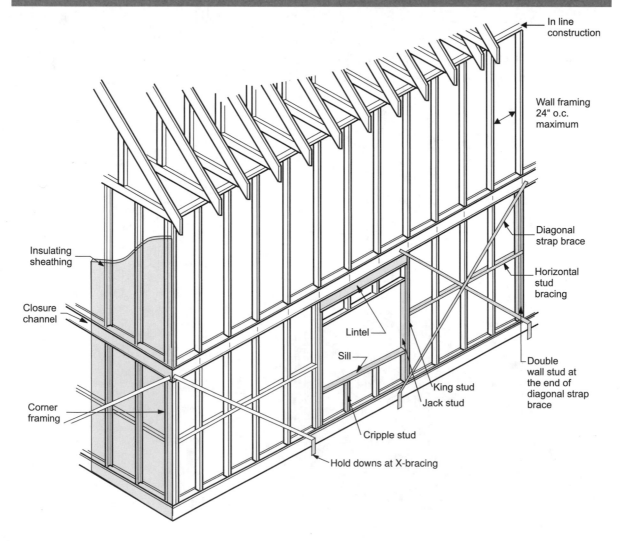

studs, since the track is not designed to support these loads.

Studs are typically ordered to the required lengths and thickness. Where on-site cutting is necessary, a chop saw with a metal cut-off blade or power shears can be used.

Steel-frame walls are normally built on-site and tilted into place in the same way as wood-frame platform construction. Each stud is fitted into the top and bottom track and screwed to each of the track's exterior flanges. Studs must all face in the same direction, and are fitted to bear directly onto the bottom track. Knock-out holes in the studs are aligned to allow the easy passage of services within the wall. Exterior insulating sheathing is attached to the outside of the stud wall before it is tilted into place.

When the exterior wall is tilted into place and plumbed, it is fastened with a temporary brace at each end. The track is then screwed into the floor joist below and the inside flange of the stud is screwed to the top and bottom flanges of the track. Typically, one additional stud is required at corners to provide support for the drywall.

Steel-framed walls must be supported with horizontal bracing installed on each side of the exterior wall and connected to each stud. Diagonal bracing is required at each corner of the building to resist wind pressures and provide racking resistance.

Lintels that support loads over windows are made of built-up steel sections fastened either back-to-back or toe-to-toe to form a closed box section. The spaces are filled with insulation after assembly. Lintels need to be supported by jack studs that extend from the lintel down to the track. Jack studs need to be supported by steel members in the floor system. King studs on the outside of the lintel and jack stud support loads from the floor above and provide additional lateral support to the lintel and to the jack stud.

Walls that support roofs must be constructed with double top plates of wood or steel, unless all structural roof elements are lined up directly with the studs. Roofs can be framed in steel or, as is more common, with wood trusses. Roof trusses can be connected to steel top plates with clip angles or hangers or, where wooden top plates are used, be nailed directly into the plate.

All exposed steel must be covered with rigid or spray foam insulation providing 25% of the required RSI value. The exterior insulation covering the wall provides a thermal break and prevents cold interior surfaces that could cause condensation.

Cavity insulation is installed the same way as for wood-frame construction. When glass or mineral fibre batts are used, it is important that the cavity be filled completely, including the space within the lip of each stud flange.

Studs are sometimes assembled in such a way that they create an inaccessible space that, if left uninsulated, will create cold spots on the interior surfaces of the house and potentially lead to condensation. Studs at corners, at windows and at doors are often configured this way. These spaces must be fitted with insulation before they are enclosed. Similarly, lintels or other doubled elements must also be filled with insulation before enclosed.

Vapour barriers must be installed on the warm side of the insulation and be attached to the wall studs with sealant or screws. Where exterior sheathings with low vapour permeance are used (e.g., Type IV extruded polystyrene or foil-back urethane foam), the warm-side vapour barrier must have a permeance not greater than 15 ng/Pa.s.m2 (e.g., polyethylene or foil-backed drywall).

As is the case for wood-frame walls, air barriers for steel-frame walls can be interior or exterior, sheet or panel-type, and continuity and sealing is essential.

11.10 Rigid Insulating Core Panel Walls

Rigid insulating core wall panels (Figure 11.23) are made of foam, framing members and foam-insulated panels, and have locking details at the edges so that joints fit together to make an airtight seal. Standard framing techniques can then be used to erect a load-bearing wall system.

Manufacturers use various techniques to build the framing into the wall system and in some cases provide space for electrical wiring and

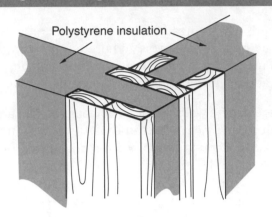

Figure 11.23 Rigid insulating core wall panels

Polystyrene insulation

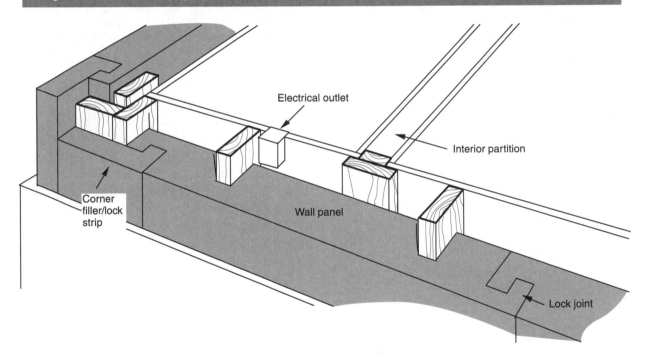

Figure 11.24 Interlocking rigid insulating core wall panels

Electrical outlet

Interior partition

Corner filler/lock strip

Wall panel

Lock joint

Rigid insulating core wall panels

Advantages	Disadvantages
• Uniform insulation of the wall assembly is assured-there are no voids.	• Other trades may have to cut or groove the material to install wiring, plumbing, etc.
• Good air barrier is provided if the joint system seals well.	• Plumbers and other trades must be careful not to ignite the insulation.
• Thermal break is provided behind all studs.	• Thermal bridging may occur through top and bottom plates.
• Low installation labour requirements since studs and insulation are erected at the same time.	• Drawings and estimates must be precise to ensure accurate production.
• Reduced waste-manufacturers can recycle scraps.	

other services. The studs are set into pre-grooved channels that provide a 50 mm (2 in.) gap on the interior side of the insulation to run wires, while still providing a complete thermal break behind the studs. If a greater insulating value is desired, this space can be filled with insulation prior to installing the interior finish.

Figure 11.24 shows another system that places the insulation between the framing members to provide a thermal break, except at the corner. This system must be cut or grooved to make room for electrical and plumbing services. Doors and windows can be cut into the system on-site, and framed using standard methods.

11.11 Structural Insulated Panels

Structural insulated panels (SIPS) are polystyrene, polyurethane or glass fibre insulating cores sandwiched between skins of plywood, OSB or drywall (Figure 11.25). The panels are available in a wide range of configurations depending on the insulating core, the type of skin applied to either side, and whether or not stiffeners are installed in the panels to make them more rigid. If the panels are not rated for load-bearing applications, they are used as in-fill panels in post and beam construction.

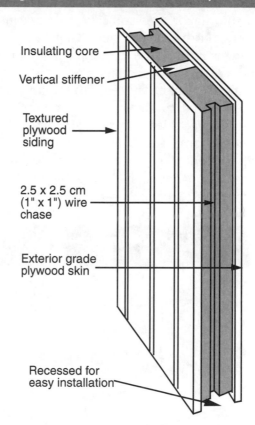

Figure 11.25 Structural insulated panel

Insulating core

Vertical stiffener

Textured plywood siding

2.5 x 2.5 cm (1" x 1") wire chase

Exterior grade plywood skin

Recessed for easy installation

SIPs use either polystyrene or polyurethane as the insulating core. Polystyrene has a lower RSI (R) value per unit thickness than polyurethane. The insulations also behave differently in fire, but panels made from either core can meet fire safety requirements.

Sandwich panel systems	
Advantages	**Disadvantages**
• Uniform insulation of the wall assembly is assured-there are no voids.	• Other trades may have to cut or groove the material to install wiring, plumbing, etc.
• Good air barrier is provided if the joint system seals well.	• Plumbers and other trades using hot tools must be careful not to ignite the insulation
• Structural support provided to wall system by panels.	• Thermal bridging may occur through top and bottom plates, and through vertical "stiffeners" if they are used.
• Rapid construction, early close-in.	• Drawings and estimates must be precise to ensure accurate production.
• Minimal waste.	• Joint design needs to be air- and vapour- tight.

Some SIPs use a wood spline to join panels together (Figure 11.26). However, full splines act as thermal bridges and can cause cracking on interior finishes if their dimensions vary due to changes in moisture content. Air sealing is required at all spline locations. Some systems use a double-spline system; the splines are installed with their long dimension parallel to the wall surface, leaving room for insulation between them. The thermal performance of this system depends on the thickness of the insulation between the splines and the effectiveness of the joint sealing.

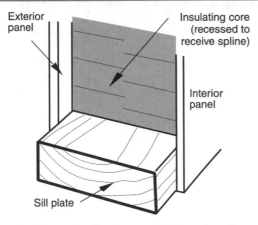

Figure 11.26 Sandwich panel bottom and side joint

Exterior panel

Insulating core (recessed to receive spline)

Interior panel

Sill plate

Panel is "notched" to fit over sill plate and receive spline that joins panels together

Strapping is often used on the exterior to provide a second plane of protection against rain penetration. Some structural insulated panels have raceways for installing electrical wiring.

11.12 Exterior Insulating Finish Systems

An exterior insulation and finish system (EIFS) is a type of exterior wall cladding system that provides an insulated finished surface in an integrated composite material system. EIFS can be installed over concrete and masonry and be attached to substrate sheathings fastened to either steel or wood framing.

EIFS are proprietary and system manufacturers must always be consulted about their material properties, performance, and regulatory implications. If a system is altered or constituent components are substituted that have not been tested and approved by the manufacturer, performance may be unpredictable and not covered by warranties.

EIFS incorporate the following components (Figure 11.27):

• Insulation board, fastened mechanically and/or with an adhesive;

• Base coat with reinforcement (typically, alkali-resistant glass fibre or coated glass mesh), typically adhered to the insulation;

• Surface finish, sometimes with a primer, adhered to the base coat;

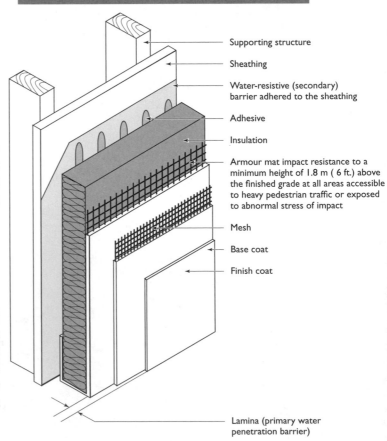

Figure 11.27 General arrangement of a drained and pressure-moderated EIFS

Supporting structure

Sheathing

Water-resistive (secondary) barrier adhered to the sheathing

Adhesive

Insulation

Armour mat impact resistance to a minimum height of 1.8 m (6 ft.) above the finished grade at all areas accessible to heavy pedestrian traffic or exposed to abnormal stress of impact

Mesh

Base coat

Finish coat

Lamina (primary water penetration barrier)

- Joint treatments, drainage accessories, seals, and sealants may also form part of the system.

Though finished with a stucco-like covering, EIFS differ from stucco in many respects. EIFS elements are bonded together and supported by adhesive. Stucco is more massive and is hung from mechanically secured lath. Stucco also requires joints to reduce cracking because of movement within the stucco. EIFS only requires joints where movement is expected, particularly at floor lines in wood frame construction.

EIFS incorporate proprietary constituent components that have been developed and tested to be compatible, and to fulfill specific building envelope performance requirements. They do not include components forming the substrate to which the cladding is applied. However, the substrate must be compatible with the EIFS, and be properly designed and installed for the EIFS to perform acceptably. EIFS are always applied to substrates treated with a moisture, air and/or vapour barrier. Barriers that are compatible with EIFS are provided or recommended by manufacturers. For some systems, the air and vapour barriers can be provided by a liquid-applied water-resistive barrier that also serves to bond the insulation to the substrate. Application with a grooved trowel can provide drainage paths. EIFS are available in a range of lamina thicknesses and cement/polymer ratios that affect the control of rain penetration, and impact resistance.

EIFS are always applied over a water resistive barrier. The standard approach is to use a CCMC-evaluated, liquid-applied, water resistive barrier as supplied by the EIFS manufacturer. Most EIFS systems rely on adhesive attachment.

EIFS offer the potential to provide supplemental insulation to meet or exceed Net Zero levels of insulation. Where spatial separation and fire spread are not an issue, insulation up to 150-mm (6-in.) (effective R24) can be used. Where fire spread is an issue, EIFS must be tested and in general, are limited to 100 mm (4 in.) (effective R16).

Properly applied and maintained EIFS lamina provide resistance to rainwater penetration. In addition, systems have been developed that provide protection in the event that water penetration does occur.

To improve the ability to tolerate periodic water ingress, EIFS are provided with a second weatherproof barrier behind the insulation (dual barrier and drained system) and a drainage path to collect and drain the water to the exterior. Drainage is generally accomplished by providing a drainage layer of slots/grooves or vertical ribbons of adhesive behind the EIFS insulation. The drainage system must be carefully detailed and installed at interfaces to assure water is properly managed to drain to the exterior.

Exterior insulated finishing systems (EIFS)

Advantages	Disadvantages
• Continuity of thermal barrier and additional insulating capacity to meet energy code requirements. • The insulation and air barrier are located on the exterior allowing a smaller stud space (2x4 studs) and ease of mechanical and electrical installation without affecting the air barrier. • Reduces thermal bridging through framing. • Properly applied and maintained EIFS provide good resistance to rain water penetration. • Wide range of finish colours and textures available.	• EIFS can be vulnerable to impact damage unless heavy duty reinforcing mesh is used in damage prone areas. • Relies on precision installation as small details are crucial to system performance.

To further improve the performance of a drained system, EIFS are available that apply the "rain screen" principle (Figure 11.27). The cavity is sized to facilitate effective drainage.

All EIFS manufacturers in Canada have CCMC Evaluation Reports that include a liquid-applied, water-resistive barrier (LA-WRB) and a tested means of drainage. The EIFS industry has developed three new standards for reference:

1. ULC S716.1-12 – EIFS materials – Materials and Systems;

2. ULC S716.2-12 – EIFS Installation – Installation of EIFS Components and Water Resistive Barrier; and

3. ULC S716.3-12 – Design Application – Design Application.

These standards are referenced in the 2015 NBC. In addition, the EIFS Council of Canada (ECC) (www.eifscouncil.org/) is preparing a Practices Guide that will provide detail not included in the standards. The ECC has also introduced the EIFS Quality Assurance Program, intended primarily for commercial and institutional construction but there is nothing stopping an owner from requesting it for a residential project.

11.13 Insulating Concrete Form (ICF) Walls

Concrete construction for small buildings and houses has been made easier with the development of insulating concrete forming systems (ICFs). The prescriptive design of ICFs is now permitted under Part 9 of the NBC for up to two storeys for areas that have low seismic risk. For other cases, engineering design is required. The materials are the same as those described in Chapter 9 for foundations, but used in above-grade walls. ICFs provide the formwork, insulation and sheathing in a single system that stays in position once the concrete has been placed.

Each manufacturer's details may vary, but the essential features are similar. Professional design input may be required, particularly where wall or window and door layouts differ from the prescriptive details provided in the NBC.

Figures 11.28 and 11.29 show a concrete wall system with interior floor framing. Figure 11.30 shows all-concrete construction, with pre-stressed concrete planks used for the floors. This is one system that could meet more stringent fire-resistant requirements, especially in multi-unit buildings.

Insulating concrete form (ICF) walls	
Advantages	**Disadvantages**
• Forming material is lightweight.	• More care in layout required.
• Little specialized labour or tools are required.	• Higher initial costs for some designs.
• Framing, insulation, sheathing and air barrier are combined into one easy step.	• Professional design input may be needed.
• Uniform R-values.	• Steel reinforcing required.
• Massive construction can improve sound insulation against exterior noise.	• Difficult to make changes on-site once concrete has been poured.
• The exterior foam insulation may be a satisfactory substrate for acrylic stucco finishes.	• Some care is necessary to get the concrete past the rebar and form ties to the bottom of the form.

Figure 11.28 ICF walls with wood-frame flooring

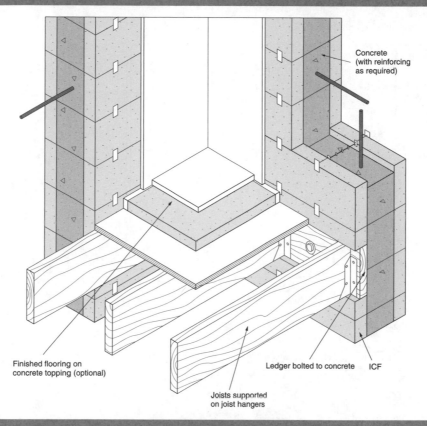

Concrete
(with reinforcing
as required)

Finished flooring on
concrete topping (optional)

Joists supported
on joist hangers

Ledger bolted to concrete ICF

Figure 11.29 Floor framing methods

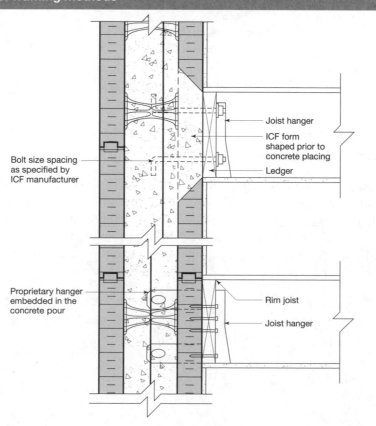

Bolt size spacing
as specified by
ICF manufacturer

Joist hanger

ICF form
shaped prior to
concrete placing

Ledger

Proprietary hanger
embedded in the
concrete pour

Rim joist

Joist hanger

Figure 11.30 ICF walls and concrete floor

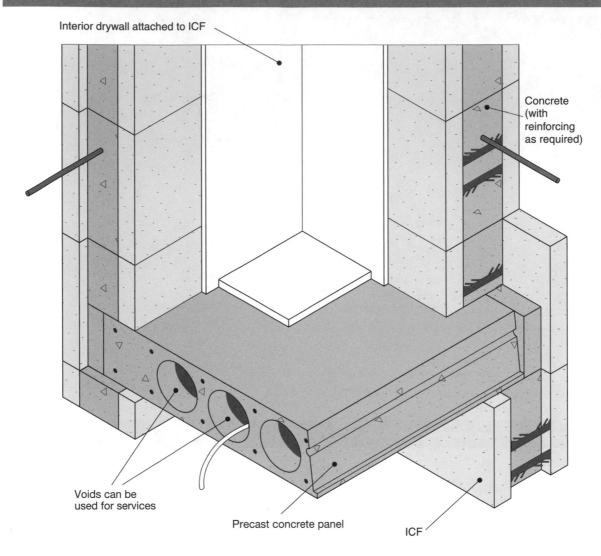

Interior drywall attached to ICF

Concrete (with reinforcing as required)

Voids can be used for services

Precast concrete panel

ICF

11.14 Party Walls in Multi-unit Buildings

This section focuses on the techniques that can be used to construct party walls that meet fire and sound transmission requirements, while reducing heat loss. The NBC provides fire and sound ratings for many floor and wall assemblies.

The code definition of a party wall is a wall jointly owned and used by adjoining parties. Party walls can be built with either combustible materials or with non-combustible materials that provide the required fire-resistance rating. They may terminate at the underside of the roof sheathing. Figures 11.31 and 11.32 illustrate the two methods commonly used to build party walls.

Air barriers are installed to provide a continuous barrier for each unit, independent of adjoining units.

Figure 11.31 Masonry block party wall

Figure 11.32 Wood-frame party wall

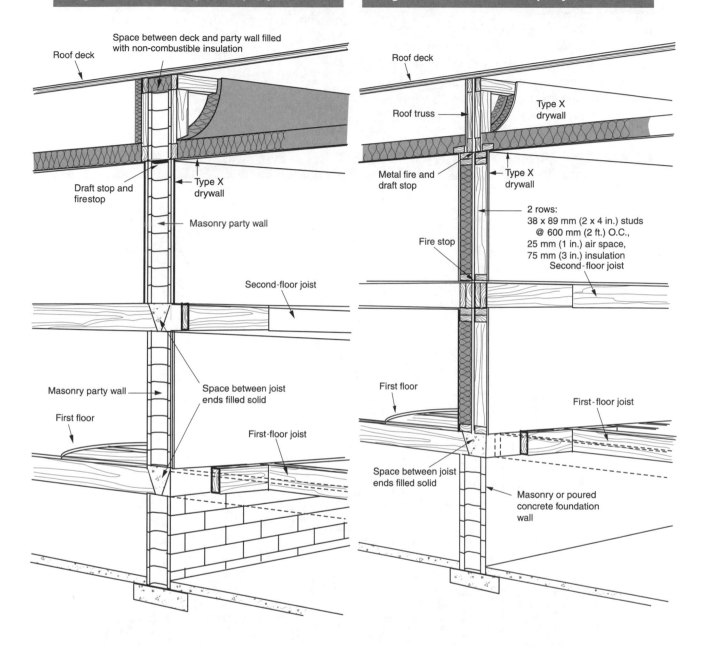

Figure 11.31 labels:
- Roof deck
- Space between deck and party wall filled with non-combustible insulation
- Draft stop and firestop
- Type X drywall
- Masonry party wall
- Second-floor joist
- Masonry party wall
- Space between joist ends filled solid
- First floor
- First-floor joist

Figure 11.32 labels:
- Roof deck
- Roof truss
- Type X drywall
- Metal fire and draft stop
- Type X drywall
- 2 rows: 38 x 89 mm (2 x 4 in.) studs @ 600 mm (2 ft.) O.C., 25 mm (1 in.) air space, 75 mm (3 in.) insulation Second-floor joist
- Fire stop
- First floor
- First-floor joist
- Space between joist ends filled solid
- Masonry or poured concrete foundation wall

11.14.1 Exterior wall junctions

Masonry block walls

Anchor rods are required every 900 mm (36 in.) to tie a masonry block party wall to the exterior wall. The joint between the party wall and the exterior wall can be sealed using either the membrane (Figure 11.33, right side) or the rigid (Figure 11.33, left side) air barrier approach. The end of the masonry wall is covered with non-combustible insulation to prevent it from acting as a thermal bridge. Firestop material such as 12.7 mm (1/2 in.) drywall or equivalent must be installed on both sides of the truss that separates two adjacent attic spaces. These firestops must extend out to the eaves.

Figure 11.33 Masonry block party wall: exterior wall junction

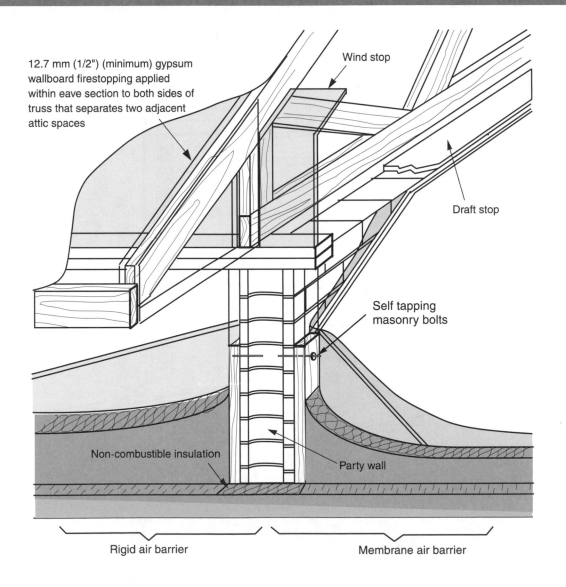

12.7 mm (1/2") (minimum) gypsum wallboard firestopping applied within eave section to both sides of truss that separates two adjacent attic spaces

Wind stop

Draft stop

Self tapping masonry bolts

Non-combustible insulation

Party wall

Rigid air barrier

Membrane air barrier

Figure 11.34 Masonry block party wall for offset units

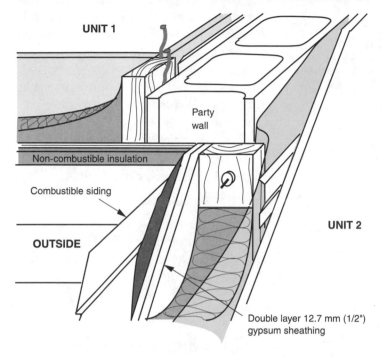

UNIT 1

Party wall

Non-combustible insulation

Combustible siding

OUTSIDE

UNIT 2

Double layer 12.7 mm (1/2") gypsum sheathing

Where adjacent units are offset, the party wall need not extend beyond the joint with the exterior wall of the innermost unit (Figure 11.34). A non-combustible thermal break should be installed across the end of the party wall.

Figure 11.35 Double wood-frame party wall: exterior wall junction

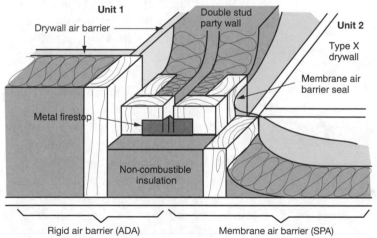

Unit 1

Drywall air barrier

Double stud party wall

Unit 2

Type X drywall

Membrane air barrier seal

Metal firestop

Non-combustible insulation

Rigid air barrier (ADA)

Membrane air barrier (SPA)

Double wood-frame party wall

Figure 11.35 shows the exterior wall junction for a double wood-frame party wall. The outermost stud spaces of both halves of a double wood-frame party wall should be insulated to ensure continuity of the exterior insulation across the party wall.

Figure 11.36 Double wood-frame party wall for offset units

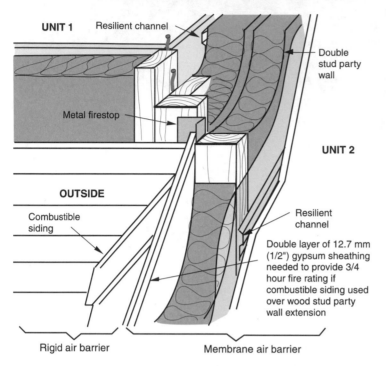

UNIT 1

Resilient channel

Double stud party wall

Metal firestop

UNIT 2

OUTSIDE

Combustible siding

Resilient channel

Double layer of 12.7 mm (1/2") gypsum sheathing needed to provide 3/4 hour fire rating if combustible siding used over wood stud party wall extension

Rigid air barrier

Membrane air barrier

Figure 11.37 Masonry block party wall: roof/ceiling junction

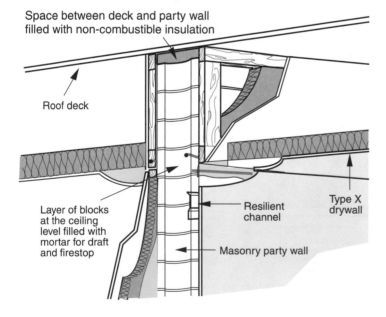

Space between deck and party wall filled with non-combustible insulation

Roof deck

Layer of blocks at the ceiling level filled with mortar for draft and firestop

Resilient channel

Type X drywall

Masonry party wall

Where adjacent units are offset, the double-stud party wall need not extend beyond the joint with the exterior wall of the innermost unit (Figure 11.36). A firestop should be installed across the 25 mm (1 in.) air space between the rows of studs. Both rows of studs should be insulated at least one stud space into the party wall. The 25 mm (1 in.) air space between the two rows of studs should be sealed. This can be done with a metal firestop, or by using firestop material as sheathing.

If combustible siding is used over a wood stud party wall extension, a double layer of 12.7 mm (1/2 in.) drywall should be used to provide the necessary 3/4-hour fire rating. This is not needed with brick veneer.

11.14.2 Attic penetrations

Block walls

Figure 11.37 shows how to minimize air leakage at the ceiling/party wall junction of a masonry block party wall. The layer of blocks at the ceiling level must be filled with mortar or solid masonry to prevent moisture-laden air in the cores from entering the attic space. A row of solid blocks would also serve the purpose. The blocks should terminate just below the line of the roof deck. When the trusses and sheathing are installed, a layer of non-combustible insulation material should be installed over the tops of the blocks to provide both a firestop and a thermal break. Both faces of the party wall in the roof space should be insulated to prevent thermal bridging through the masonry.

The joint between the ceiling and the wall must be sealed to stop air leakage into the attic. If a membrane air barrier is used, it should be sealed to the polyethylene on the wall surface. If drywall is being used as a rigid air barrier, the joint will be sealed when the corner is taped and finished. In either case, all penetrations into the space behind the drywall and into the party wall above the ceiling must be sealed to keep air from leaking into these spaces.

Wood-frame party wall

Figure 11.38 shows how to minimize air leakage into the attic space for a double wood-frame party wall. A metal firestop should be used to block air leakage through the 25 mm (1 in.) air space. Fire-rated gypsum board (Type X) should be used to continue the fire rating up to the underside of the roof sheathing. Insulation can be installed in the space created by the trusses above the top plate to reduce heat loss into the attic space.

11.14.3 Load-bearing partition wall junctions

Block walls

Load-bearing partition walls should be anchored to masonry party walls (Figure 11.39). If a membrane air barrier is used, it should be installed between the wall stud and the party wall. If a rigid air barrier is used, the edges of the drywall on both sides of the stud next to the party wall must be sealed to the stud, and be taped and finished.

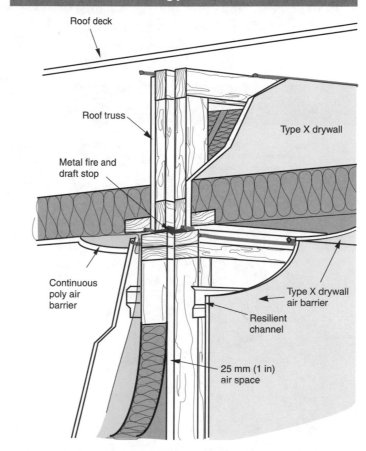

Figure 11.38 Double wood-frame party wall: roof/ceiling junction

Roof deck

Roof truss

Metal fire and draft stop

Continuous poly air barrier

Type X drywall

Type X drywall air barrier

Resilient channel

25 mm (1 in) air space

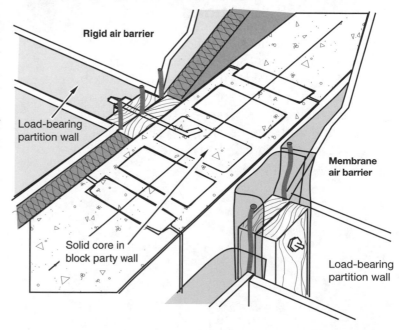

Figure 11.39 Masonry block party wall: load-bearing partitions

Rigid air barrier

Load-bearing partition wall

Membrane air barrier

Solid core in block party wall

Load-bearing partition wall

Double-stud walls

Backing should be placed in wood stud party walls to accommodate partition walls that are erected later in the process (Figure 11.40), and the air barrier must be made continuous.

Figure 11.40 Double wood-frame party wall/partition junction

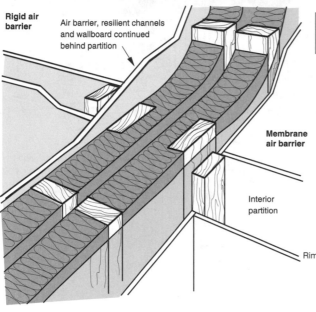

The partition wall must be recessed from the exterior wall by at least 16 mm (5/8 in.). Polyethylene is installed continuously over the exterior wall, and the drywall is slipped into the space between the partition and the exterior wall (Figure 11.42). This eliminates the need for drywall clips. Alternatively, the drywall can be caulked or gasketed on both sides of the interior partition.

Figure 11.41 Continuity of the air barrier at partition wall junctions

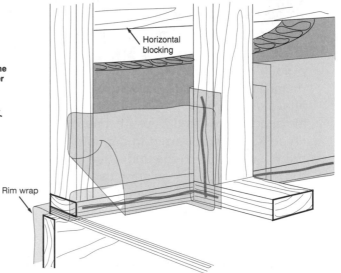

11.15 Partition Wall/Exterior Wall Junctions

There are several approaches for dealing with wall/partition wall intersections. Horizontal blocking is installed in the outside wall between the studs where partition walls intersect. A strip of polyethylene is wrapped behind the end partition wall stud before the wall is nailed to the blocking (Figure 11.41), and drywall clips are used to support the drywall.

Figure 11.42 Drywall installation at partition wall junctions

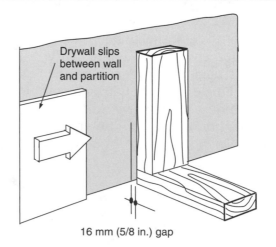

11.16 Service Penetrations

Several techniques can be used to ensure the continuity of the air barrier around service penetrations in exterior walls. In all cases, the number of penetrations should be minimized as much as possible.

11.16.1 Plumbing penetrations

Several types of plumbing components may penetrate exterior walls: drain pipes and vent stacks, water supply pipes, and gas line piping. Where plumbing components pierce the membrane air barrier, a wood panel sheathing backing board is mounted flush with the inside face of the studs (Figure 11.43, top). Where pipes pass through wood members, they may rub and squeak whenever hot water is used. The gap between the pipe and the hole should be sealed with a flexible sealant.

If a rigid air barrier is used, the wood panel sheathing is mounted onto the studs to be flush with the face of the drywall. Horizontal blocking should be placed between the studs as a backing for the seam between the sheathing and the drywall. This seam must be sealed to ensure continuity of the air barrier (Figure 11.43, middle).

Another rigid air barrier approach is to construct an airtight box which the plumbing penetrates vertically (Figure 11.43, bottom). Drywall is then sealed to the face of the box using foam tape. Direct-vented fans and their penetration of the air-barrier can be eliminated by using an HRV and placing the intakes on interior walls.

Figure 11.43 Plumbing penetrations

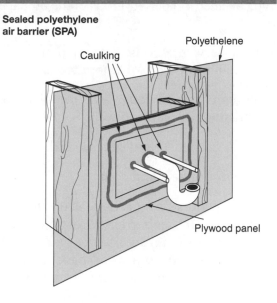

Sealed polyethylene air barrier (SPA)

Polyethelene

Caulking

Plywood panel

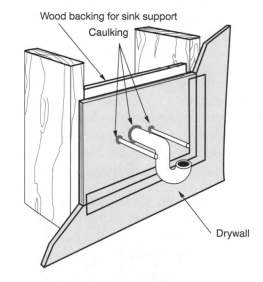

Air-tight drywall (ADA)

Wood backing for sink support

Caulking

Drywall

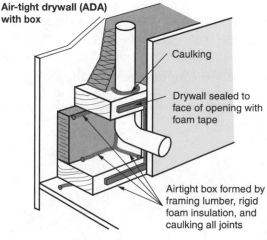

Air-tight drywall (ADA) with box

Caulking

Drywall sealed to face of opening with foam tape

Airtight box formed by framing lumber, rigid foam insulation, and caulking all joints

11.16.2 Electrical penetrations

Typical electrical penetrations of the air barrier include:

- Main service conduits and the main service box, if located on an exterior wall;

- Wires passing through wall top plates and end studs of partition walls;

- Electrical outlets and light switch boxes; and

- Exterior outlets and lights.

These penetrations must be sealed to maintain continuity of the air barrier. Wires and conduits running to the main service box can be sealed by caulking them to a wood panel sheathing backing board, onto which the main service box is mounted.

Wiring passing through top plates and end studs can also be sealed with caulking. Electrical boxes can be placed in site-built or prefabricated airtight boxes (Figure 11.44).

Wiring and electrical boxes inside or outside the air barrier do not require separate sealing. However, main service conduits passing through the air barrier must be sealed (Figure 11.45). The conduit must also be sealed inside with approved electrical sealant.

Wherever possible, lights, electrical outlets and switches should be kept on interior walls. Those installed on exterior walls and penetrating the air barrier must be sealed to the designated air barrier.

Other wiring, such as telephone, cable TV, data, home automation, security and entertainment requires similar consideration. Airtight outlet boxes should always be used where the outlet penetrates the air barrier in the wall or ceiling, even for those services that do not normally use boxes.

Figure 11.44 Electrical penetrations

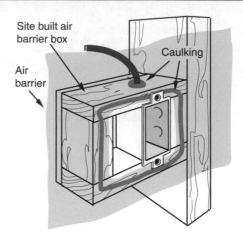

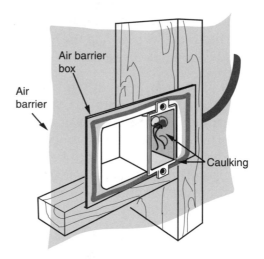

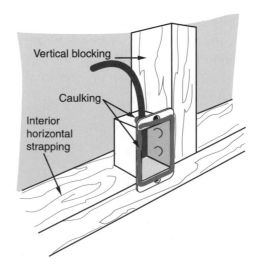

Figure 11.45 Double wood-frame party wall: electrical penetration

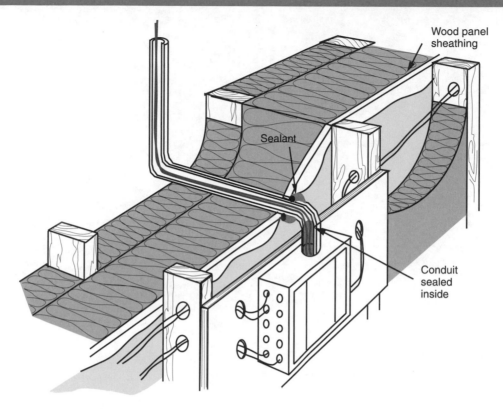

Wood panel sheathing

Sealant

Conduit sealed inside

11.16.3 Mechanical system penetrations

Ductwork for heat recovery ventilators (HRVs) and exhaust fans also require sealing. For penetrations such as chimney flues, sheet metal should be used and sealed to the metal duct with a caulk or sealant capable of withstanding the high temperature, such as silicone.

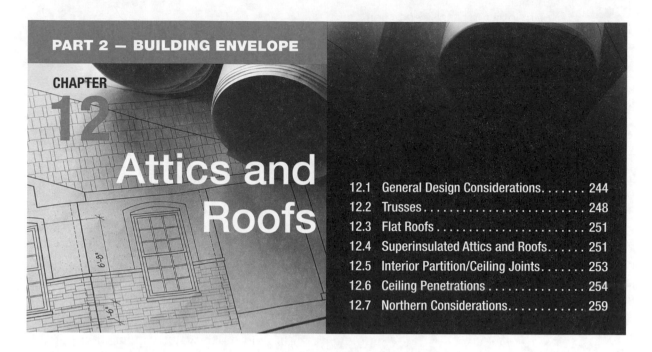

Attics and Roofs

The roofs of Canadian houses usually consist of a ceiling assembly, an attic and a roofing membrane. As with other components of the building envelope, proper insulation values, air leakage, and moisture control are essential.

12.1 General Design Considerations

12.1.1 Insulation

Attic spaces are generally accessible and therefore relatively easy to insulate to high levels. Insulation levels of RSI 7.0 (R-40) to RSI 10.5 (R-60) are common for ceiling/roof systems with Net Zero Energy builders on the high end of this range and beyond.

The quantity of insulation alone does not determine its effectiveness. Overall performance of the roof and attic also depends on:

- Installing a wind barrier at the eaves to allow air movement but prevent wind from blowing through the insulation.

- Sealing ceiling joints and penetrations to restrict air leakage around plumbing stacks, electrical wiring, junction boxes and recessed light fixtures, at partition wall top plates, around chimneys and flues, and at access hatches.

- Providing adequate and balanced attic ventilation.

- Exhausting bathroom fans to the exterior.

- Eliminating gaps in the insulation, particularly at truss webs.

- Maintaining full insulation thickness at the eaves-in no case should the amount of insulation over the top of the exterior walls be less than that of the exterior walls.

- Reducing thermal bridges through structural members.

12.1.2 Moisture control and ventilation

In addition to insulation, air leakage and moisture control are critical to ensure good roof performance and durability. Roof assemblies are vulnerable to moisture from three sources: rain penetration, water vapour entry, and ice damming.

Water vapour can enter the attic space in two ways:

- Warm, moist air from air leakage can be a major source of moisture movement from the living space to the attic, where it can condense on cold surfaces (Figure 12.1); and,

- Water vapour may diffuse into the attic through ceiling building materials.

Cold air cannot hold much water vapour; therefore, in cold temperatures, ventilation air may not be adequate to remove moisture that has moved into the attic space by air leakage or diffusion. The result is frost build-up in the attic space, which, when it melts, can damage wood framing, insulation, and drywall, and buckle the roof membrane as a result of sheathing movement.

Figure 12.1 Potential air/heat leakage points in attics

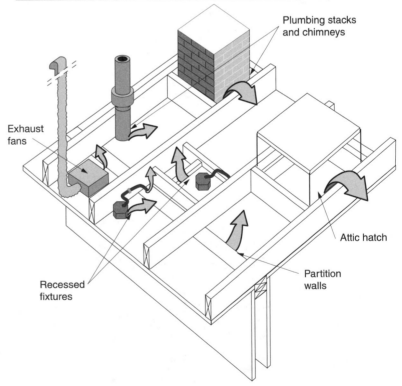

For this reason, it is essential to minimize the possibility of moisture accumulation in the attic space. This is done by installing effective air and vapour barriers (Chapter 8). One option is installing a polyethylene air/vapour barrier on the warm side in the following manner:

- Carry the polyethylene across the top plates of partition walls;

- Seal around chimney and ductwork using firestop materials;

- Seal around plumbing stacks and vents;

- Minimize ceiling-mounted electrical fixtures and penetrations in the ceiling. Where they are necessary, use airtight octagon boxes and lighting fixtures approved by the Canadian Standards Association (CSA) for insulated ceiling applications, and seal the units to create a continuous air barrier;

- Weatherstrip and latch attic access hatches, or place them on gable end walls outside the house; and,

- Seal electrical wiring and plumbing pipes where they penetrate through the ceiling or wall plates.

These measures will reduce the passage of water vapour through a ceiling and into a roof structure. To account for leakage through any imperfections in the air or vapour barrier, the next line of defence is to provide attic ventilation capable of removing moisture.

The National Building Code of Canada (NBC) requires the unobstructed vent area of a typical average pitched roof to be not less than 1/300 of the insulated ceiling area. Warranties for asphalt shingles are also based on adequate ventilation. Because the stack effect that moves air through the attic space is affected by the height between the eaves and the ridges, the amount of venting needs to be increased for flatter roofs, and can be decreased for steeper roofs. Screens and louvers obstruct the openings and must be taken into account when calculating the vent area. Other design considerations for roof ventilation are:

- Maximize airflow by locating vents at eaves and soffits and near the peaks or along ridges.

- Increase the vent area on roofs with pitches less than 6/12.

- Balance the areas of vent intakes (low points) and exhausts (high points).

Proper attic ventilation can remove water vapour from the attic space before condensation can cause trouble, and is essential for maximizing the service life of a roof assembly. Other benefits include a cooler attic in the summer, and a dryer attic during the winter. Both result in increased energy savings and greater occupant comfort.

During the summer months, radiant heat from the sun can cause high roof-deck temperatures. Gradually, the entire attic space is heated, and, in turn, the whole dwelling feels the effect of a hot roof. Research shows that prolonged exposure to high heat levels shortens the service life of asphalt roofing products. Heat build-up can be reduced by properly venting the underside of the roof deck.

There are two types of venting. Passive ventilators are low-profile vents like ridge-line ventilators and roof louvers. Unless wind direction conditions are ideal, passive ventilators do not freely promote airflow but merely allow air to disperse. Air enters through the soffit into the attic space, and then gradually dissipates out through the ridge vents. This type of vent meets code requirements for area, but its performance is questionable because it is unable to exchange or replace attic air at a sufficient rate. Low-profile ridge vents are easily buried by snow rendering the ventilation system inactive. And in windy conditions, they provide little protection from rain or snow infiltration.

Turbine-type or fixed deflector-type ventilators have a higher profile that allows them to function with some snow on the roof. The height creates additional stack effect to draw ventilation air from the soffit vents. In windy conditions, turbine-type ventilators can depressurize an attic space, which could potentially pull moist air from the heated spaces into the cold attic where condensation can occur. This highlights the need for a good air barrier.

Ventilation openings may admit small amounts of precipitation and therefore it is important to have conditions that allow an attic to dry – good air and vapour barriers and ventilation.

A balanced system combines equally sized soffit vents and vents high on the ridge to use stack effect to move air from the bottom to the top of the attic space. Louver and vent openings should be situated to allow ventilation when snow has accumulated on the roof. Baffles should be provided above the wall/ceiling intersection to allow room for air movement between the roof sheathing and insulation.

Raised-heel trusses should be used to permit full depth insulation and still provide room for air movement from the soffit vents to the ridge vents. Bathroom and kitchen mechanical vents should be vented to outside the roof. Power ventilators, while useful in the summer, should not be used in the winter. By creating negative pressure in the attic space, they could increase the flow of moist, warm air from the interior, and may suck snow into an attic.

12.1.3 Ceiling sag

Ceiling drywall can sag because of:

- The absorbtion by the drywall of its water-based textured finishes;

- High humidity from drying lumber and interior finishing materials;

- Condensation on the drywall; and

- Water damage caused by wind-driven rain and snow entering the attic or roof space.

These problems can be reduced or eliminated by:

- Using thicker drywall on ceilings (15.9 mm (5/8 in.)) and controlled-density or sag-resistant drywall in place of regular gypsum board, or reduced spacing of supports, for example, by strapping at 400 mm (16");

- Preparing the surface with a compatible primer before applying heavy water-based textured finishes;

- Providing ample ventilation during construction;

- Preventing wind-driven rain and snow from entering the space;

- Insulating the ceiling immediately after installing the drywall and before heating commences; and

- Ensuring installation of drywall sheets perpendicular to the strapping or framing to which they are attached.

12.1.4 Truss uplift

Truss uplift can occur in the winter when the upper chord of a truss contains more moisture than the lower chord. This is a result of differing temperature conditions whereby the upper chords are above the insulation, while the lower chords are insulated, and thus at a warmer temperature. The upper chord, being at a higher relative humidity compared to the lower chord, expands by lengthening and bowing upward, pulling up the webs and the lower chord and causing the ceiling to move upward.

Truss uplift can damage interior finishes, particularly where the ceiling and interior partition walls join. There are several ways to minimize the effects of truss uplift:

- Use half-span trusses supported on roof girders or interior load-bearing partitions;

- Use trusses manufactured with kiln-dried lumber and keep the trusses protected from wetting as much as possible during storage and installation;

- Ensure that the attic space is adequately ventilated and the vents provide balanced airflow;

- Ensure that soffit vents are not blocked by insulation; and

- Connect the ceiling drywall to the partition walls using drywall clips, and screw the ceiling drywall far enough from the partition wall intersection and float the corners at least 300 mm (12 in.) to allow for deflection without joint failure (Figures 12.2 and 12.3).

- Install 2 x 6 pieces to the top of partition walls and fasten the drywall to the lumber and not the trusses.

12.1.5 Ice damming

Ice damming (Figure 12.4) is the build-up of ice at the edge of the roof caused by heat escaping from the house and melting the snow that accumulates on the roof. This water flows down under the snow covering the roof; as it reaches the outer edge of the eave over the cooler soffit area, it freezes, creating an ice dam. The ice dam stops the melt water from reaching the eave. Ice then builds up in the form of icicles and slabs, and the melt water can back up under the shingles and leak into the attic if adequate eave protection was not used.

Ice damming can be prevented by:

- Maintaining adequate levels of insulation over the exterior wall in combination with ventilation between the insulation and roof sheathing;

- Minimizing heat loss due to air leakage at the ceiling/joist junction by providing a proper air barrier;

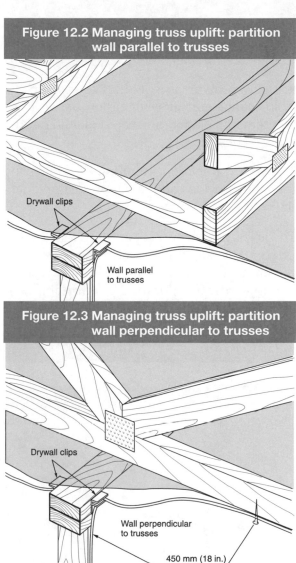

Figure 12.2 Managing truss uplift: partition wall parallel to trusses

Drywall clips

Wall parallel to trusses

Figure 12.3 Managing truss uplift: partition wall perpendicular to trusses

Drywall clips

Wall perpendicular to trusses

450 mm (18 in.)

Figure 12.4 Ice damming

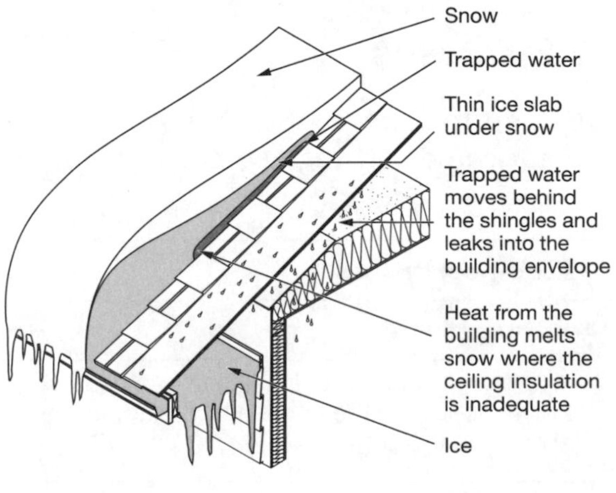

Snow

Trapped water

Thin ice slab under snow

Trapped water moves behind the shingles and leaks into the building envelope

Heat from the building melts snow where the ceiling insulation is inadequate

Ice

• Using raised-heel (also called "high heel") trusses to allow for additional insulation over the exterior wall; and

• Using prefabricated baffles to restrain the insulation and allow for airflow between the ceiling insulation and the underside of the roof sheathing.

The eave protection membrane required by the NBC provides additional protection if ice-damming does occur.

The levels of insulation being used for Net Zero Energy Housing, when done correctly using high heel trusses, will eliminate this problem, leading to more durable, comfortable and energy efficient housing.

Figure 12.5 Raised-heel truss

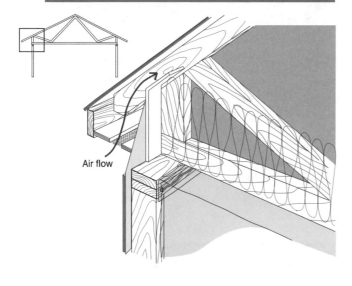

Air flow

12.2 Trusses

Most builders are accustomed to using prefabricated, or engineered, roof trusses.

There are many reasons why light-frame wood trusses are such an important component of residential construction:

• Truss design software enables the manufacture of almost any conceivable shape suited to local design loads.

• Specific lumber grades can be placed where needed in the trusses to maximize cost/benefit and reduce waste.

• Truss cutting and assembly equipment enables precise joints, plate alignment and quality control.

• Trusses can be installed quickly with light-duty lifting equipment.

This section discusses trusses that permit the installation of higher levels of insulation and enhance ventilation, particularly at the eaves. There may be a small cost premium for these trusses compared to standard trusses, but they provide several roof performance advantages.

12.2.1 Raised-heel trusses

A raised-heel truss (Figure 12.5) has a short, vertical chord member over the top plate bearing point that provides additional room for insulation over the wall/ceiling intersection. The higher the heel, the more space there is to add insulating value at the roof/wall junction.

A study on wall problems in a high rainfall area showed that problems decreased based on the ability of a roof overhang to protect walls from wetting (Figure 12.6). Keeping water off of walls goes a long ways to protecting the wall from bulk water ingress.).

Raised-heel trusses	
Advantages	**Disadvantages**
• A uniform thickness of insulation can usually be installed over the entire attic including above the top plates.	• The cost is higher than for standard trusses. • The design increases the height of the exterior stud wall, and therefore the siding area increases.

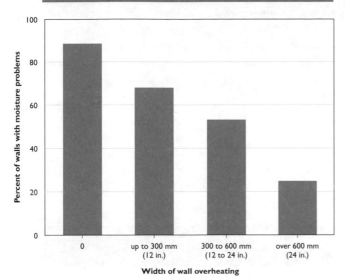

Figure 12.6 Relationship between width of roof overhang and wall moisture problems

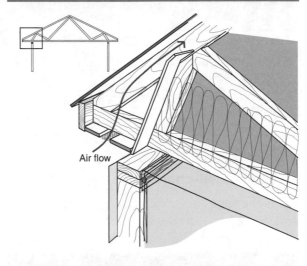

Figure 12.7 Cantilever truss

Air flow

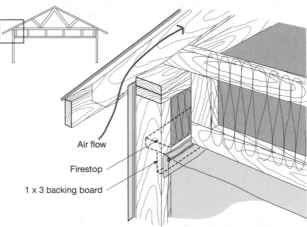

Figure 12.8 Dropped chord truss

Air flow
Firestop
1 x 3 backing board

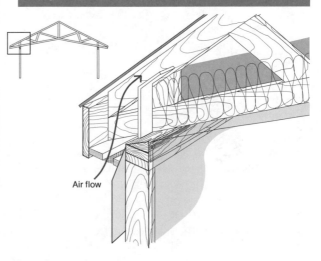

Figure 12.9 Scissor truss

Air flow

12.2.2 Cantilever truss

A cantilever truss has a short, inclined chord member over the top plate bearing point and the bottom chord projects to the eave (Figure 12.7). Whether there is adequate room for full depth insulation over the wall/ceiling intersection depends on the length of the cantilever and the length of the chord; there may not be enough space above the top plate to allow for full-depth insulation.

12.2.3 Dropped-chord truss

This truss has an additional bottom chord (Figure 12.8). The space between the structural bottom chord of the truss and the dropped chord is filled with insulation.

12.2.4 Scissor truss

Scissor trusses have a sloped bottom chord (Figure 12.9) and provide a cathedral ceiling without a supporting beam or wall at mid span. This type of truss can be modified to accommodate higher levels of insulation by increasing the height of the raised-heel over the top plate wall/ceiling intersection.

Scissor trusses

Advantages	Disadvantages
• Provides a free-spanning cathedral ceiling. • Accommodates higher levels of insulation than a rafter/cathedral ceiling. • Can provide full-depth insulation up to the perimeter walls.	• Less access-room for installing insulation because of sloped lower chord. • Baffles may be required to prevent settling of loose-fill insulation. • Limited roof pitches of 5:12 or more, depending on snow loads.

12.2.5 Parallel-chord truss

Parallel-chord trusses consist of parallel wood chords and steel or wood webs (Figures 12.10 and 12.11).

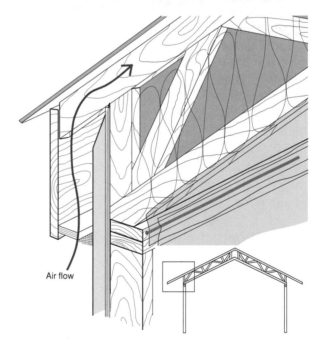

Figure 12.10 Top-bearing parallel-chord truss

Air flow

Firestop

1" x 3" backing board

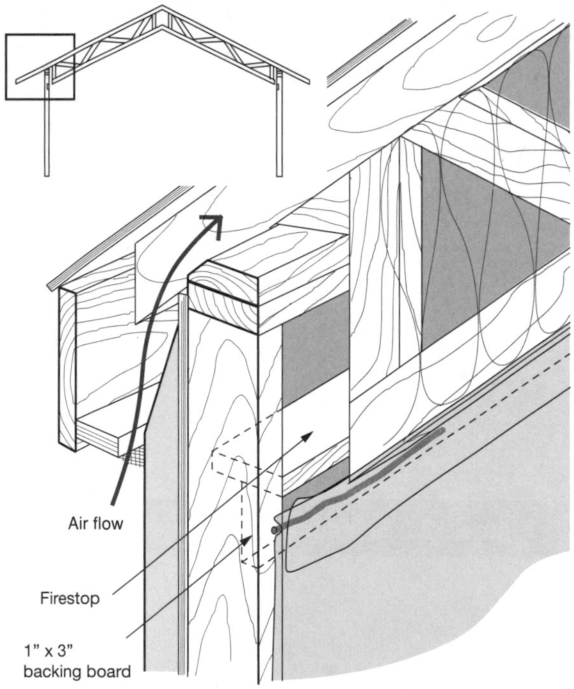

Figure 12.11 Bottom-bearing parallel-chord truss

Air flow

Parallel-chord trusses

Advantages	Disadvantages
• Installation of full-depth insulation in cathedral ceilings is enabled. • Ventilation can be provided without the use of purlins (transverse framing).	• Steel web parallel chord trusses have higher heat loss due to thermal bridging. • Restricted height between top and bottom chords may make it is difficult to insulate between chords.

12.3 Flat Roofs

Flat roofs are used frequently in commercial construction and occasionally in residential construction. Built-up and flexible membrane roofing can be used, as can garden roofs that employ vegetation to reduce interior heat uptake and reduce water runoff (the structure must have been designed for additional loads, and waterproofed to take into consideration that repairs are difficult to make once the topsoil layer has been placed). Insulation, ventilation and moisture vapour control are equally important for a flat roof as for pitched roofs. For cases where the use of a flat roof is desired, vinyl membranes are available that are suitable for this application (Figure 12.12).

12.4 Superinsulated Attics and Roofs

This section presents ways of building framed attics and roofs to incorporate high levels of insulation.

12.4.1 Superinsulated framed attic

A method of framing an attic space using standard dimension lumber is shown in Figure 12.13. Note that the ceiling joist extends beyond the top plate of the wall at the eaves to produce a triangular structure that can accommodate higher levels of insulation at the perimeter wall.

Figure 12.13 Superinsulated framed attic

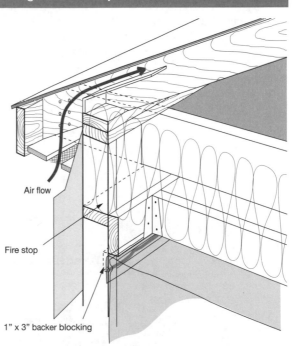

Air flow

Fire stop

1" x 3" backer blocking

Figure 12.12 Vinyl-covered flat roof

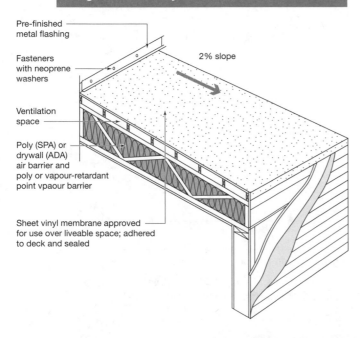

Pre-finished metal flashing

Fasteners with neoprene washers

2% slope

Ventilation space

Poly (SPA) or drywall (ADA) air barrier and poly or vapour-retardant point vpaour barrier

Sheet vinyl membrane approved for use over liveable space; adhered to deck and sealed

Flat roof	
Advantages	**Disadvantages**
• Enables auxiliary use of roof space.	• Has limited space for insulation, and therefore at least some rigid insulation is required to provide R values.
• Facilitates rainwater harvesting.	• Requires at least twice as much roof vent area as steeper roofs with attics.
• Allows for a variety of roof membranes to be used.	
• Permits the use of garden roofs.	• Bears risks of moisture problems or thermal bridging.
	• Garden roofs, if present, increase structural loads.

Superinsulated framed attic

Advantages	Disadvantages
• Allows for higher insulation levels above the top plate.	• Is more expensive to construct than a truss roof in most cases.

12.4.2 Framed cathedral ceiling

Figure 12.14 shows the framing of a cathedral ceiling using dimension lumber with 38 x 286 mm (2 x 12 in.) rafters and 38 x 38 mm (2 x 2 in.) purlins. Two layers of RSI 3.5 (R-20) batts between the joists allow for adequate ventilation of the attic space.

Where a cathedral ceiling is used to create living space in the attic, all attic spaces need to be ventilated (Figure 12.15).

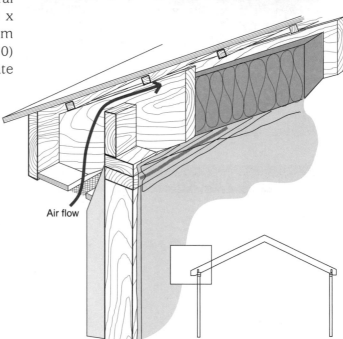

Figure 12.14 Cathedral ceiling

Air flow

Framed cathedral ceiling

Advantages	Disadvantages
• Costs can be lower than for parallel chord truss construction.	• Clear span is limited by the maximum size of dimensional lumber.
	• Insulation is limited to a maximum of RSI 7.0 (R-40), unless additional strapping and batt insulation or boardstock insulation is used.
	• Thermal bridging occurs through the rafter.
	• Material and labour costs may be increased.

Figure 12.15 Ventilation of cathedral ceiling attic spaces

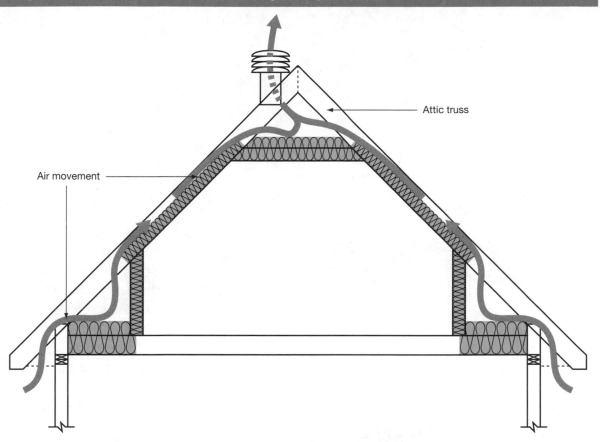

Attic truss

Air movement

12.5 Interior Partition/ Ceiling Joints

Interior partition construction can greatly affect the energy efficiency of a ceiling, because a considerable quantity of air can move through the ceiling/partition wall junction. Special care is required to keep the air barrier continuous.

12.5.1 Sealed polyethylene approach (SPA)

To ensure the continuity of a polyethylene air barrier, a 600-mm (24-in.) wide strip of 0.15 mm (6 mil) polyethylene is placed between the partition wall top plates (Figure 12.16). The polyethylene flange is sealed to the ceiling air barrier on either side of each partition before the ceiling drywall is installed.

Figure 12.16 Interior partition wall: membrane (SPA) air barrier

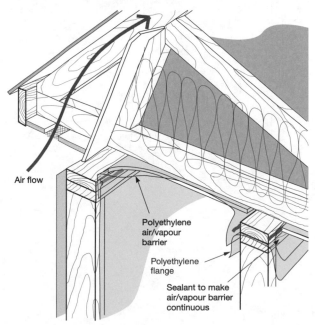

Air flow

Polyethylene air/vapour barrier

Polyethylene flange

Sealant to make air/vapour barrier continuous

12.5.2 Airtight drywall approach (ADA)

Standard pre-cut wood or steel studs can be used for interior partitions if a 19 x 89 mm (1 x 4 in.) plate is placed on top of the exterior wall top plate. This raises the trusses enough to accommodate 16 mm (5/8 in.) drywall and to allow the interior partition walls to be raised and moved into a vertical position. The drywall can be taped before the interior partitions are raised (see Figure 12.17). For this method, cove moldings may be required to conceal truss uplift. It may not be suited for all house designs, as it does involve coordinating trades.

Figure 12.17 Interior partition wall: rigid (ADA) air barrier

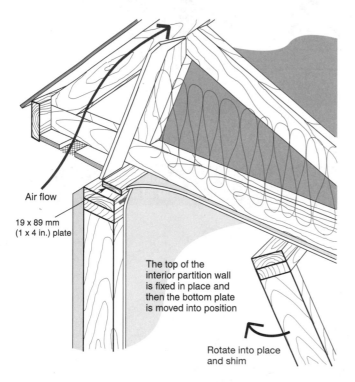

Air flow

19 x 89 mm (1 x 4 in.) plate

The top of the interior partition wall is fixed in place and then the bottom plate is moved into position

Rotate into place and shim

12.6 Ceiling Penetrations

Ceiling penetrations between the living space and the attic must be carefully sealed to minimize airflow into the attic space.

12.6.1 Plumbing stacks

The number of plumbing stacks that penetrate a ceiling should be minimized by bringing vents together inside the envelope. Use an air- and vapour-tight flexible seal, such as a rubber membrane, to prevent air leakage where plumbing stacks penetrate the ceiling at partition wall top plates. The seal assembly must be flexible, since plumbing stacks move as a result of expansion and contraction, and from shrinkage and settling of the house frame. Plumbing expansion joints are another way to minimize thermal expansion and contraction effects.

Figure 12.18 shows several methods for sealing plumbing stacks to the air barrier. One method is to pass the plumbing stack through a rubber gasket secured with a wood panel sheathing collar. The hole in the rubber is cut 40 mm (1-1/2 in.) smaller than the plumbing stack diameter and forms a tight friction fit when the stack is forced through it. Another approach is to cut an "X" in the gasket, keeping the cuts slightly shorter than the diameter of the pipe. The rubber gasket may also be secured by stapling into compressible foam tape, as shown for the rigid air barrier approach.

Figure 12.18 Sealing plumbing stacks

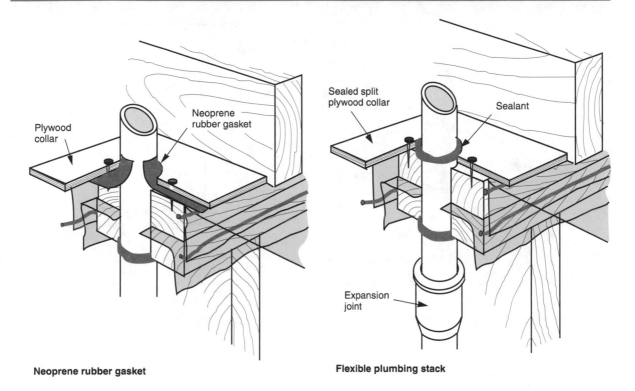

Neoprene rubber gasket

Flexible plumbing stack

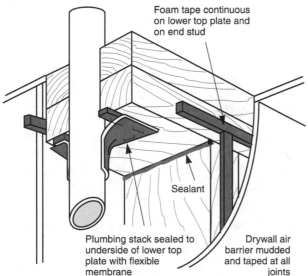

Rigid air barrier approach

An off-the-shelf neoprene rubber roof boot will also work well and may be less expensive. An equally effective approach, generally used with rigid air barriers, is to seal the stack permanently and rigidly to the air barrier and to use a more flexible plumbing system. This will require an expansion joint in the stack, or an offset and a horizontal run of pipe close to the vent in the attic.

Figure 12.19 Ceiling electrical box and pot light

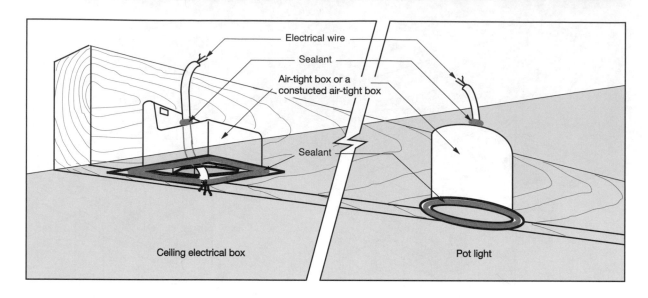

Electrical wire

Sealant

Air-tight box or a constucted air-tight box

Sealant

Ceiling electrical box

Pot light

12.6.2 Wiring and electrical boxes

Wiring can penetrate the ceiling through partition wall top plates. The penetration is sealed directly to the air barrier and top plate with expanding foam or acoustical sealant.

Electrical boxes for lighting fixtures can be sealed several ways by:

- Placing the electrical device in a prefabricated polyethylene envelope

- Placing the box in a site-built wood box wrapped in 0.15 mm (6 mil) polyethylene

- Using an airtight electrical box (Figure 12.19)

12.6.3 Recessed lighting

Recessed lights are very popular, particularly in bathrooms and kitchens, both high-moisture areas.

Where recessed lights are required in the top-storey ceiling, fixtures should be used that are approved to be in direct contact with insulation materials. To create a continuous air barrier, it may be necessary to seal the fixtures with aluminium duct tape.

12.6.4 Attic access hatch

Where the attic access hatch must pass through the ceiling, the frame should be sealed to the drywall and the access door should be weather stripped, insulated and latched (Figure 12.20). This air barrier penetration can be eliminated by relocating the attic access to the garage or exterior gable.

Figure 12.20 Attic access hatch

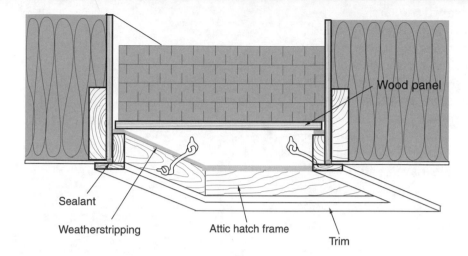

Wood panel

Sealant

Weatherstripping

Attic hatch frame

Trim

12.6.5 Ventilation and heating ducts

Poorly sealed ducts running through unheated space are a major cause of heat loss and potential condensation problems. All heating ducts need to be sealed and this is particularly important where their location in an attic space cannot be avoided.

Where ducts pass through a ceiling, they should be sealed to the air barrier with caulking (Figure 12.21). Insulation must be placed over the ductwork to an RSI (R) value equal to that found elsewhere in the attic space. If the duct passes through the top plate of a partition wall, it must be sealed in the same manner as a plumbing stack.

Figure 12.21 Sealing heating and ventilating ducts

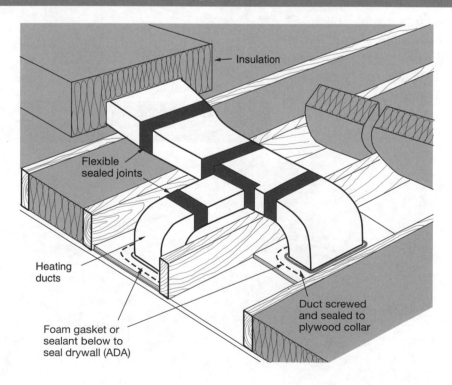

Insulation

Flexible
sealed joints

Heating
ducts

Foam gasket or
sealant below to
seal drywall (ADA)

Duct screwed
and sealed to
plywood collar

A bathroom is a high-humidity area and the air sealing of penetrations between it and the attic is very important. The fan housing needs to be airtight to prevent the leakage of humid air, and insulation should be installed over the fan housing. To avoid overheating of the fan motor, it is important to select a fan with a cool-running motor that is approved for use when the housing is insulated. The duct should have sealed joints, be insulated, and connect to a good quality metal roof exhaust hood extending at least 130 mm (5 in.) the roof surface.

Birds and rodents can damage roof and wall insulation, electrical wiring and plastic roof vents. For all penetrations of the roof deck and soffits, it is important to provide screening to keep rodents and birds out of the attic space, and to use vent caps that cannot be chewed.

12.6.6 Chimneys and vents

Figures 12.22 and 12.23 illustrate the procedure that should be used to seal around prefabricated metal chimneys. The same procedure should be used to seal the space around masonry chimneys. Figure 12.24 illustrates a method for sealing masonry chimneys when a rigid air barrier is used.

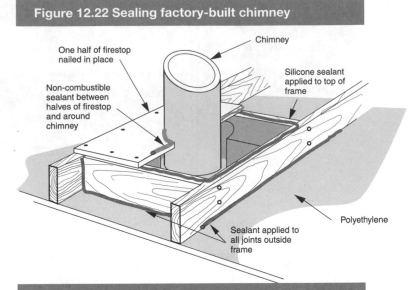

Figure 12.22 Sealing factory-built chimney

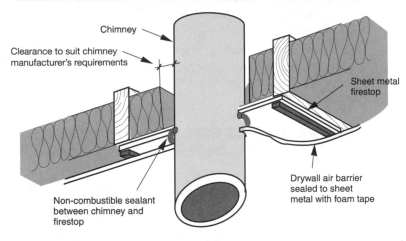

Figure 12.23 Sealing factory-built chimney-rigid air barrier approach

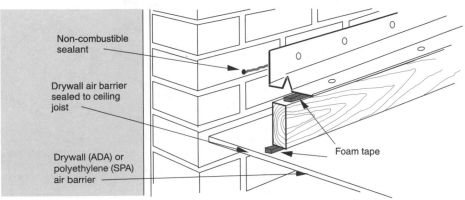

Figure 12.24 Sealing a masonry chimney to a rigid air barrier

12.7 Northern Considerations

Building codes require ventilation of the attic/roof space. Ventilation helps to exhaust any moisture or water vapour that may enter the space and keeps the attic/roof space cooler in summer. The most effective technique is to use a continuous soffit ventilation strip and continuous ridge vents at the roof edge and roof ventilators equally spaced near the ridge.

However, in northern regions, where fine blowing snow is common, local authorities may approve unvented attic/roof spaces.

12.7.1 Unvented roofs

An unvented (hot) roof has no ventilation in the roof or attic space. This type of roof assembly has been used successfully in the north, where it evolved out of necessity. In Arctic areas with fine blowing snow, roof ventilators have often not performed well. This type of roof should be used only if:

- The roof is tightly constructed to prevent the entry of fine, blowing snow.

- Heat loss and moisture transfer through the ceiling is minimized by using proper air leakage control practices and an adequate layer of insulation that extends over the top plates at the wall/ceiling intersection.

- Snow is not allowed to accumulate on the roof – either the wind must blow it off, requiring an average annual wind speed of 16 km/h (10 mph), or it must be removed by the occupants.

Figure 12.25 Unvented roof

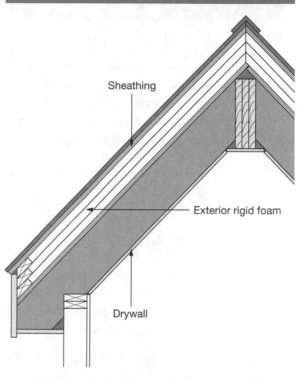

Sheathing

Exterior rigid foam

Drywall

Figure 12.26 Unvented roof with SIP panels

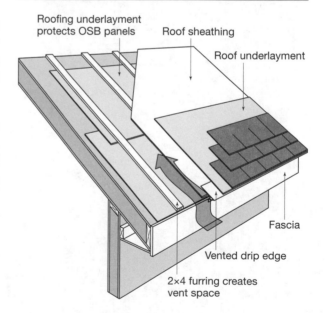

Roofing underlayment protects OSB panels

Roof sheathing

Roof underlayment

Fascia

Vented drip edge

2×4 furring creates vent space

An unvented roof is permitted by the NBC as a special exemption for use where it can be shown that venting is unnecessary. As a result, more unvented roofs are being constructed in more southern regions of Canada although they are not common. Careful construction is required to ensure satisfactory performance of an unvented roof, particularly with regard to the air and vapour barriers to ensure that moisture does not get into the attic space.

Figure 12.25 shows a typical unvented roof. Note that in this figure, the insulation is rigid foam insulation and it all located above the sheathing on the top cord of the truss or rafter top. With no insulation in the cavity between the rafters or trusses it will be difficult to achieve the insulation levels required for Net Zero levels of performance. An alternative is to also fill the cavity between the roof sheathing and the drywall inner surface with insulation.

Structural Insulated Panels (SIPs) (Figure 12.26) may be another solution which can provide the required insulation as well as the air barrier and vapour barrier qualities needed.

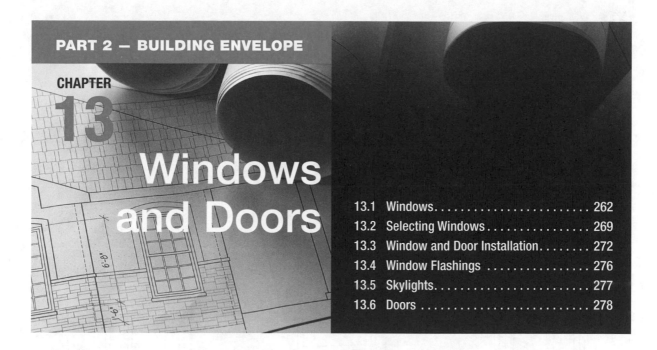

Windows and Doors

The style and placement of windows and doors is a major design and marketing consideration and can significantly affect heating load and occupant comfort. In typical housing using conventional technologies, windows can account for as much as 35% of the heat loss from a house. In an energy-efficient house, however, the windows may be an even higher proportion of total heat loss, since heat loss from other components of the house has been minimized.

Modern windows have higher-performance glazings with low emissivity coatings, gas fills and insulating spacers, and improved frames incorporating thermal breaks. If properly placed, energy-efficient windows can now be viewed as energy assets, rather than liabilities. For example, most fixed high-performance windows actually gain more heat over the heating season than they lose.

The keys to reducing heat loss from windows and doors (and in optimizing solar gains) are to carefully choose orientation (Chapter 3), select good quality, energy-efficient units, and ensure that installation minimizes air leakage around the frames.

13.1 Windows

13.1.1 Heat loss and gain

Heat can be lost through windows by:

- Conduction, convection and radiation through the insulating glazing units (IGUs)

- Conduction through the edge of the glazing unit and through the frame

- Airflow through operable components of the window (Figure 13.1)

- Conduction and airflow between the window frame and the wall framing

The first three sources of heat loss can be reduced by selecting appropriate units, while the last can be reduced through proper installation.

Figure 13.1 Types of operable windows

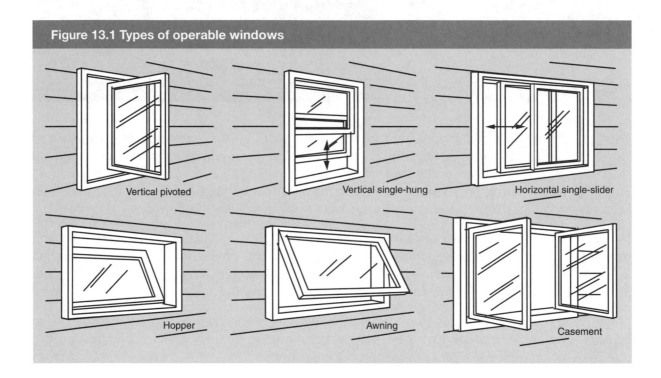

Vertical pivoted | Vertical single-hung | Horizontal single-slider

Hopper | Awning | Casement

Most window manufacturers rate the thermal performance of windows not by thermal resistance (RSI/R value), but by the heat loss coefficient (U-factor) – the rate at which heat transfers. The greater the U-factor, the greater the heat flow through a window.

The U-factors are commonly published on the basis of the conductance of only the centre of the glazing. When increased heat loss at the edges of the glass and frame is factored into an equation, published centre of glass values are almost always overstated in relation to the actual thermal performance of a given window. ENERGY STAR®-qualified windows,

which are discussed later in this chapter, do take into account the heat loss of the entire window assembly. Energy codes require the total product U-factor that takes into account the centre of glass, edge of glass and frame heat loss.

Windows can also serve as a major source of heat gain to a house, allowing solar energy into the occupied area. While in winter these gains are of major benefit – reducing heating requirements and providing respite from the cold outdoors – solar gains in the summer, and even at times in the spring and fall, can result in overheating.

Solar heat gains through a given window are a function of the amount of available solar energy, the window's orientation, external shading, and the solar heat gain coefficient (SHGC). It is expressed as the fraction of solar energy striking the window that passes through the window. SHGC is expressed as a number between 0 and 1. The lower the SHGC, the lower the amount of solar energy that will enter the living space. For example, a window with a SHGC of 0.87 transmits approximately 87 % of available sunlight, while one with a SHGC of 0.48 transmits 48 % of available sunlight.

The hours of available solar energy vary considerably throughout the country. Window orientation (Chapter 3) also affects the amount of solar gain and determines when those gains will occur – both over the course of the day and throughout the year. South-facing glazing provides the greatest gains in the winter, and can be shaded against the higher sun during the warmer months.

Several computer programs are available to assess the heat gain potential of windows at different orientations and slopes in various climatic zones of the country. As a general rule, precise computer modelling of passive solar gains is not warranted in the design of the average house. However, it is definitely recommended if the aim is to optimize the solar design and achieve more than 20 % solar heating.

13.1.2 Balancing heat losses and gains

A standard test procedure to measure or calculate the heat loss and solar gain performance of an entire window or door has been adopted. This method, defined in CSA Standard A440.2, provides a rating on window and door performance based on:

- Transmitted solar gains;

- Conductive, convective and radiant heat losses through the IG glazing;

- Conductive heat losses through the edge of glass and opaque framing; and

- Heat losses associated with air leakage through the assembly

Windows and sliding doors can now be compared using a single number based on a standard-sized unit in each of seven window categories. Opaque doors are compared on U-factor alone. As a general rule, the performance of fixed windows will be better than other window types for two reasons: the overall area of the frame is smaller in relation to the glazed area of a fixed unit; and air leakage (through the unit) is minimal. Standard sizes for measuring or calculating the energy performance of different window and door types include:

- 1200 x 1500 mm (4 x 5 ft.) vertical sliding /tilt turn

- 1500 x 1200 mm (5 x 4 ft.) horizontal sliding

- 1200 x 1500 mm (4 x 5 ft.) fixed

- 600 x 1500 mm (2 x 5 ft.) casement

- 1500 x 600 mm (5 x 2 ft.) projecting (awning)

- 2000 x 2000 mm (6.7 x 6.7 ft.) glass door

- 1000 x 2000 mm (3.3 x 6.7 ft.) hinged door

The measured or calculated performance of a specific window or sliding glass door is reported as the energy rating (ER). The ER is based on the average performance of the product at the four cardinal orientations, in a range of climates, as measured or calculated over the heating season. The ER calculations are derived from the equation:

ER = solar gains – conduction losses – air leakage losses + 40

Table 13.1 shows ER values for several glazing and frame options of a typical casement window with a standard air leakage rating. The ER is useful in comparing two similar windows to determine which is more energy-efficient, but cannot be used to estimate the actual heat loss (or gain) through the window.

Table 13.1 Energy rating (ER) of casement windows				
Window Category	Type of Spacer	Type of Glazing	Fixed Window	Operable Window
Common	Aluminum	Double	18	8
Moderate-cost, energy-efficient	Insulating	Double, low-e, argon	33	25
Most energy-efficient commercially available	Insulating	Triple, two low-e-coatings, argon	41	34

As stated, these ratings represent an average of performance of products at different orientations. CSA-A440.2 provides information for calculating specific ratings (ERS) for windows at a specific orientation, in a particular location and for different house types (insulation levels and mass levels). More sophisticated window choices can be assessed using HOT2000 modelling or other energy modelling software.

The ER has been formulated for residential buildings in a heating-dominated climate. Thus, it is appropriate for use as a comparative yardstick in Canadian housing, but should not be used to assess glazing options for commercial buildings or for cooling-dominated buildings. When all windows carry labels with their performance ratings under CSA-A440.2, builders will have a better means to compare windows of a similar type. In some jurisdictions, minimum ER levels or maximum U-factors have been specified to meet energy code requirements. It should be noted that many manufacturers use the United States NFRC (National Fenestration Rating Council) program to rate and label their products for U-value and SHGC. Energy Star® and provincial energy codes recognize the NFRC ratings and labelling as equivalent to the CSA ratings and labelling.

The ER is one of many considerations in the purchase of a window. Appearance, durability and price are also important factors.

ER Considerations for Net Zero Energy Housing

As noted above, ER should not be used for "cooling-dominated buildings". The levels of insulation being used by builders for achieving the Net Zero Energy or Net Zero Energy Ready energy targets is reducing the heat loss to such an extent that practically, Net Zero Energy houses are "cooling-dominated" rather than "heating-dominated". Picking windows with a high ER values means that the window provides a net energy gain over the heating season. Extend this heat gain into the summer and the windows are adding to the cooling load on the building. Field experience is showing this to be significant, and in some cases problematic in terms of cooling loads and occupant comfort. Characteristics of windows for Net Zero houses will include high performance in terms of U-factor (low U-factor) but designers should also be looking at the Solar Heat Gain Coefficient (SHGC).

Note that the concept of ER was was developed at a time when the building industry was looking to reduce purchased heating energy. ER is all about getting solar gains into the house and providing builders and designers with a simple way of comparing windows. Looking at the equation for ER, a manufacturer can improve their ER number by having a SHGC as close to 1.0 as possible. What we are learning, even at this early stage of Net Zero Energy Housing, is that we are driving the heating load down to the point where the cooling load is becoming very important. The high cooling load in some cases is now driving the sizing of the heat pump chosen, which results in more expensive mechanical systems.

Until some "rules of thumb" emerge regarding selecting windows and mechanical systems for Net Zero Energy houses, it will remain a trade-off during the design process to pick the combination of windows and mechanical systems that provide the best cost benefit. Early indications show that sacrificing a reduced solar heat gain which reduces winter time heat gain, also reduces summer time heat gain and therefore reduces cooling load. The characteristics of low U-factor (good insulating window) and low SHGC windows (reduced solar gains) provide the best compromise. These options are being evaluated at the design stage using HOT2000. This situation is very illustrative of the importance of considering the "house as a system" approach, as is presented in this Manual.

13.1.3 Reducing heat loss through glazing

Window manufacturers can minimize the heat loss of their products by:

- Optimizing the size of the air space between the panes to minimize convection and condensation;

- Increasing the number of air spaces between panes to reduce conduction (Table 13.2);

- Incorporating low-emissivity coatings on one or more of the layers of glazing to minimize radiant heat loss;

- Substituting inert gases for the air between panes to reduce heat loss by convection within the air spaces; and

- Using windows made with insulated glass units that have insulating spacer bars.

Energy-efficient windows combine all of these features. Using available technology, centre-of-glass U-factors can be reduced from around 2.85 W/m²C for a standard double-glazed unit to levels less than 1.0 W/m²C. Many energy-efficient windows have benefits that quickly surpass the initial increased capital outlay.

Energy-efficient windows also offer the advantages of maintaining a warmer interior surface temperature on the inside of the inner glazing – reducing the potential for condensation and enhancing occupant comfort through reduced radiation. The following sections look at the components of energy-efficient glazings.

Low-emissivity (low-E) coatings

Most of the heat lost through standard windows is radiant heat, whereby the inside panel of glass absorbs heat from the room and radiates it to the cooler outside panel. This type of heat flow can be reduced with low-emissivity (low-E) coatings – thin metallic coatings that decrease the rate at which glass radiates heat.

A low-E coating on one sheet of glass of a double-glazed window will give that window an insulating value approximately the same as a standard triple-glazed window (Table 13.2). Double-glazed windows equipped with these coatings weigh significantly less than standard triple-glazed windows with comparable U-values. The reduced weight of high-performance double-glazing makes them easier to install, and results in less wear-and-tear on window hardware.

Although low-emissivity coatings decrease the U-factor of a window by reducing radiant heat loss, they may also reduce the amount of solar heat gain. Table 13.2 also shows the solar heat gain coefficient (SHGC) for various configurations, which indicates how well a window blocks heat from sunlight. As noted earlier, this is important for Net Zero housing.

The selection of glazing type should take into account the orientation of the specific window. North-facing windows with little opportunity for solar gain in winter should be selected on the basis of minimum U-factor. The lower solar heat gain coefficients that accompany multiple low-e coatings will not represent a major disadvantage for north-facing windows. On the other hand, south-facing windows in Net Zero house will need to be analyzed using HOT2000 to ensure the most cost effective blend of U-factor and solar gains is used, taking into consideration both the heating and cooling loads as well as occupant comfort.

Occasionally, design and building orientation conditions are such that there may be large glass areas where passive controls cannot be incorporated. For example, large west-facing glass areas on a property with a view can contribute to conditions that will overheat the house, especially if there is body of water that can also reflect solar radiation. In these cases, the position and type of low-E coating in a window can be selected so that solar energy gains are rejected, thus reducing the potential for overheating and increased cooling loads.

Table 13.2 Thermal resistances and shading coefficients for typical casement windows		
Centre of Glass *SI (U) and RSI (R) through centre of glazing*	**U-Factor** **USI (U)**	**SHGC**
Single Glazing	5.90 (1.04)	0.87
Double Glazing: 12.7 mm (1 /2 in.) air space	2.72 (0.48)	0.70
12.7 mm (1/2 in) air space, hard-coat low-e coating (e = 0.2)	1.99 (0.35)	0.66
12.7 mm (1/2 in.) air space, argon fill, hard-coat low-e coating (e = 0.2)	1.70 (0.30)	0.66
12.7 mm (1/2 in.) air space, soft-coat low-e coating (e = 0.05)	1.70 (0.30)	0.37
12.7 mm (1/2 in.) air space, argon fill soft-coat low-e coating (e = 0.2)	1.42 (0.25)	0.37
Triple glazing – 12.7 mm (1/2 in.) air spaces	1.76 (0.31)	0.62
Triple glazing – 12.7 mm (1/2 in.) air spaces, argon fill hard-coat low-e coating (e = 0.2)	1.25 (0.22)	0.54
Window Type *Operable window (slider or casement). All units assume metal spacers. Insulating spacers can significantly improve performance.*	**U-Value** **USI (U)**	
Double Glazing – 12.7 mm (1/2 in.) air space wood or vinyl frame thermally broken metal frame insulated fiberglass frame	2.87 (0.51) 3.43 (0.60) 2.53 (0.44)	
Double Glazing – 12.7 mm (1/2 in.) air space, low-e coating (e = 0.2) wood or vinyl frame thermally broken metal frame insulated fiberglass frame	2.38 (0.42) 2.89 (0.51) 2.07 (0.36)	
Double Glazing – 12.7 mm (1/2 in.) air space, argon fill, low-e coating (e = 0.2) wood or vinyl frame insulated fiberglass frame	2.21 (0.39) 1.89 (0.33)	
Triple Glazing – 12.7 mm (1/2 in.) air space wood or vinyl frame insulated fiberglass frame	2.19 (0.39) 1.91 (0.34)	
Triple Glazing – 12.7 mm (1/2 in.) air space, argon fill, low-e coating (e = 0.2) wood or vinyl frame insulated fiberglass frame	1.87 (0.33) 1.59 (0.28)	

Gas-filled units

Replacing the air between glazing panes with an inert gas improves the glazing U-factor. Argon-filled windows have become commonplace for residential applications. Krypton gas is also used. These inert gases reduce convection within the space, thereby reducing heat flow through the window. While krypton is the better performing gas, it is also much more expensive and is effective for smaller air spaces of 8 mm (5/16"). In air spaces greater than 8 mm (5/16"), krypton loses its superior performance and there is no appreciable difference between the two gases. Krypton is more commonly used in triple-glazed IGUs.

As thermal performance is dependent on the glass selected, low-e coatings, spacers and framing materials, the percentage of gas fill may vary from one window product to another. Programs for insulating glass unit certification such as the Insulating Glass Manufacturers Alliance (IGMA) program require test samples to meet an initial average value of 90% and a final average value of 80% once cycling tests have been completed. These requirements are specified for test specimens only; the actual gas content values on production units may or may not be filled to 90%.

Some manufacturers quote only centre-glass U-factor when comparing their windows to other products, but whole-window U-factor is a more appropriate comparison. An even better comparison can be made using the ER value if one is only considering the net energy gains over the heating system.

13.1.4 Reducing conduction through the edge of the glazing

Considerable heat transfer occurs at the edge of the insulating glass unit, where a spacer is in contact with each layer of glazing. This is why even insulating glass will form condensation at the edges in cold weather. Manufacturers of energy-efficient windows reduce this heat loss by using insulating spacers in the sealed unit.

Spacers were traditionally made of aluminium. Most manufacturers now offer windows incorporating spacers that are less conductive. These help to reduce the heat loss at the edge of the glazing and condensation. The insulating spacers can be made of stainless steel, plastic, silicone foam, glass fibre, or composite materials.

Increasing the width of the air space in the sealed unit allows use of a wider spacer but also permits convection currents to form in the space between the panes. Manufacturers design glazing systems to provide optimal spacing of the panes, depending on the type of gas fill. For air, this spacing is 13 mm (slightly more than ½ in.), for argon it is 12 mm (slightly less than ½ in.) and for krypton, it is 8 mm (5/16 in.).

13.1.5 Reducing conduction and infiltration through the frame

Conduction

As noted, the ENERGY STAR® mark takes into account heat loss through the glazing and frames of windows, doors and skylights. Conduction heat loss through the window frame can be reduced by using a low-conductivity material such as wood, vinyl, or fibreglass for the frame. If a metal-frame window must be used, it must incorporate a thermal break (Figure 13.2). The wider the thermal break in a metal-frame window, the more effective it will be.

Extruded PVC frames with insulating reinforcing elements such as wood or glass fibre can also lower conduction. Large PVC windows usually incorporate reinforcing elements in their frames and sashes to reduce deflection. The metal reinforcement can substantially increase the U-value of a window, so these types should be avoided. Good quality PVC windows have minimal metal reinforcing, and are not subject to air leakage resulting from thermal expansion/contraction cycling.

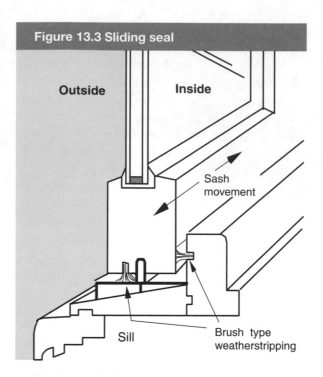

Figure 13.2 Thermal break in a metal frame

Rain deflectors

Drainage

Thermal break

Air seal

Figure 13.3 Sliding seal

Outside   Inside

Sash movement

Sill   Brush type weatherstripping

Some window manufacturers now produce a PVC or fibreglass frame with foam-filled frame cavities. The foam filling reduces convection within the extruded cavities of the frame, thus reducing the U-value of the window. Fibreglass frames are strong and have low-conductivity and a low profile, reducing the area over which heat loss can occur.

Infiltration

Infiltration through a window assembly is another source of heat loss. Air leakage is often associated with increased condensation on the inside of the window. Using fixed (non-operable) windows where appropriate will minimize this problem.

Operable windows should use durable, flexible gaskets to make an airtight seal between sashes and the frame. The airtightness of the joint depends on the type of weather-stripping used and the amount of pressure that can be applied by the closing system. Air leakage through sliding windows (Figure 13.3) tends to be higher than in casement, awning, or hopper windows, which can use compression seals (Figure 13.4). Warping of the frame or sashes and painting also affects the airtightness of a window, as do changes due to thermal expansion and compression of components.

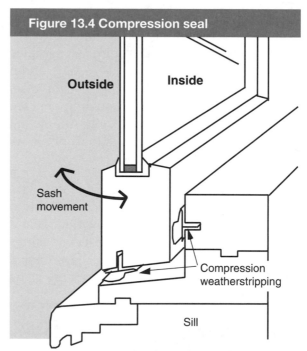

Figure 13.4 Compression seal

Outside   Inside

Sash movement

Compression weatherstripping

Sill

In general, a window can achieve high resistance to air, water, and wind leakage only by having tight-fitting corner joints, good seals and gaskets, and weatherstripping. Air leakage characteristics of a given window are factored into the energy rating (ER) calculation.

In northern areas, durability and operability in extreme conditions must be considered. Opening windows in very cold conditions can cause a heavy accumulation of ice from condensing interior air, making it difficult to close the windows again. Operable windows in northern houses need to be extremely sturdy.

13.1.6 Optimizing solar gain

The selection of windows should include consideration of useful solar gains. Many glazing technologies that reduce heat loss can also reduce the useful solar gain by decreasing the solar heat gain coefficient (SHGC). Therefore, window orientation should be a factor in selection.

Several factors should be considered to optimize solar gains for a conventional house and with a Net Zero Energy house consideration of both U-factor and SHGC are important:

- Choose units with the best SHGC for south-facing windows (simulation will be helpful)

- Consider that multiple glazing layers and certain types of coatings will reduce SHGC, but may offer better U-values required for north-facing windows.

- Choose windows with maximum clear opening – minimize mullions, dividers, etc.

- Minimize the size of the window frame and depth of profile to reduce shading.

- Design window placement and landscaping for the best year-round performance.

Even in well-insulated homes with energy-efficient windows, excessive heat loss and overheating are concerns, and window placement and sizing should be carefully reviewed. Where possible, adjustments should be made either to sizing or window specifications to minimize overheating and heat loss. Increased thermal mass within the heated space and strategic distribution methods to move heat to other areas of the house are options for reducing overheating in addition to selecting windows with lower

SHGC. Awnings can be used to restrict solar heat gain in the summer and allow solar heat gain in the winter, when the angle of the sun is lower.

13.2 Selecting Windows

As seen from previous sections, many factors affect the performance of windows. This section provides simplified guidelines for selecting windows as follows:

1. Windows, doors and skylights must meet the requirements of NAFS-11 (North American Fenestration Standard) that essentially ensures these products are structurally capable of handling climatic loads for a given location.

2. It is recommended that windows meet the energy-efficiency levels set out by the ENERGY STAR® program.

In addition, builders might also consider selecting different product specifications based on the orientation of the window. If high heat gain is the goal, windows with higher SHGC should be selected for southern exposures. Alternatively, if overheating in summer is a concern windows with lower SHGC will address this for southern windows, while windows on the north face of a house should be chosen on the basis of lowest U-factor. Installing triple-glazed windows in high-moisture areas such as bathrooms will decrease the likelihood of condensation.

It is important to remember that solar heat gain can also increase cooling loads in the summer, and a balanced approach needs to be considered.

13.2.1 NAFS-08

The 2015 NBC changed the reference standard for windows, doors and skylights to the NAFS-11 standard and the Canadian supplement to NAFS-11. NAFS and the Canadian supplement replace several window, door and skylight standards previously referenced in the code.

CANADIAN HOME BUILDERS' ASSOCIATION

The NBC requires windows, doors and skylights for Part 9 buildings to meet the minimum requirement in the NAFS and the supplement. NAFS uses performance grades, product classes and air infiltration values to rate products.

The Canadian supplement to NAFS defines the method to determine the minimum performance required by the geographic location and product exposure. As a minimum, a product must meet an air infiltration of A2 and a performance grade of R15 to meet the standard. Table 13.3 lists the air infiltration performance levels and Table 13.4 lists the performance grade levels

in NAFS. The Canadian supplement will need to be consulted to determine the appropriate performance grade for any given location and exposure condition.

Table 13.3 Air Infiltration Performance Levels (NAFS-08)

Window Ratings	Max. Air Infiltration Rate L/s/m²
A2	1.5
A3	0.5
Fixed	0.2

Table 13.4 Performance Grade Levels (NAFS-11)

Minimum Performance Grade (PG)[1]				Design Pressure (DP)		Water Test Pressure 15% x DP		Structural Test Pressure (150% x DP)	
R	LC	CW	AW	psf	Pa	psf	Pa	psf	Pa
15	–	–	–	15	720	2.8	140	22.5	1080
20	–	–	–	20	960	3.0	150	30.0	1440
25	25	–	–	25	1200	3.8	180	37.5	1800
30	30	30	–	30	1440	4.5	220	45.0	2160
35	35	35	–	35	1680	5.3	260	52.5	2520
40	40	40	40	40	1920	6.0	290	60.0	2880
45	45	45	45	45	2150	6.8	330	67.5	3240
50	50	50	50	50	2400	7.5	360	75.0	3600
55	55	55	55	55	2640	8.3	400	82.5	3960
60	60	60	60	60	2880	9.0	440	90.0	4320
65	65	65	65	65	3120	9.8	470	97.5	4680
70	70	70	70	70	3360	10.5	510	105.0	5040
75	75	75	75	75	3600	11.3	540	112.5	5400
80	80	80	80	80	3840	12.0	580	120.0	5760
85	85	85	85	85	4080	12.8	620	127.5	6120
90	90	90	90	90	4320	13.5	650	135.0	6480
95	95	95	95	95	4560	14.3	690	142.5	6840
100	100	100	100	100	4800	15.0	720	150.0	7200

[1] There are four performance classes listed in order of increasing performance: R, LC, HC, and AW.

13.2.2 ENERGY STAR® windows, doors and skylights

Canada's Office of Energy Efficiency (Natural Resources Canada) has introduced the ENERGY STAR® mark for fenestration products to help

in the selection of energy-efficient windows, doors and skylights. To qualify for the ENERGY STAR® mark, products must meet strict technical requirements for both thermal and structural performance. Products are qualified

Figure 13.5 Climate zones for ENERGY STAR® windows, doors and skylights

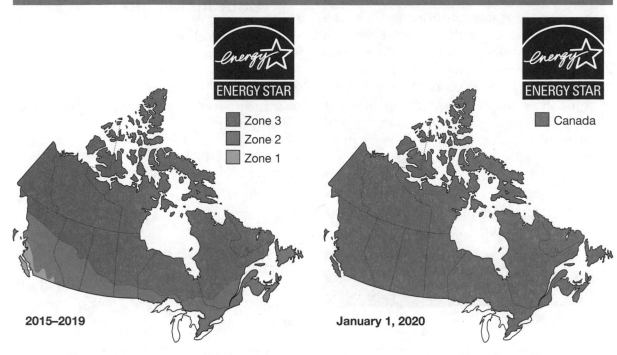

based on either their U-factor (rate of heat transfer from a warm area to a cold area) or their energy rating (ER), a scale that takes into account a product's U-factor, potential solar gain and airtightness. The colder the climate zone, the more stringent the requirements are. To ensure the integrity of the ENERGY STAR® mark, all product testing is done by accredited laboratories under standardized, quality-controlled conditions.

In the early days of Energy Star® (2004 to 2015) Canada was classified into 4 Climate Zones. That changed to 3 Climate Zones between 2015 and 2019. As of January 2020, Canada is classified as only 1 Climate Zone, (Figure 13.5). This makes it easier to pick Energy Star® products since it removes the two-step process. With the multiple zones approach, the user was required to verify that the product was Energy Star® Certified and verify that the product was certified in the specific Climate Zone where it was to be used. With the single zone approach, the product is either Energy Star® Certified, or it is not. The products that carry the Energy Star® Certification were rated for the coldest areas of the country.

The initial Canadian ENERGY STAR® criteria covered windows and sliding glass doors and came into effect 2004. Soon after, the ENERGY STAR® criteria for these products were strengthened.

The criteria in place during 2015 to 2019 was Energy Star® Version 4. This specified ER and U factors as follows for windows and doors:

	Minimum ER	Maximum U-Factor
Zone 1	25	1.60 W/m²·K (0.28 Btu/h·ft²·F)
Zone 2	29	1.40 W/m²·K (0.25 Btu/h·ft²·F)
Zone 3	34	1.20 W/m²·K (0.21 Btu/h·ft²·F)

For Energy Star® Version 5 (effective January 2020) the following applies for windows and doors:

	Minimum ER	Maximum U-Factor
All of Canada	34	1.22 W/m²·K (0.21 Btu/h·ft²·F)

A good starting point for those wanting more data is to go to the Energy Star website and look up the window specifications on the Energy Star site using the NRCan Reference Number and the Energy Efficiency Verification Reference number for each different model of window they are interested in. This information is valuable when choosing from different makes and models as all windows are different in terms of U-factors, ER Ratings, Solar Heat Gain Coefficients, and air Leakage. Using this reference will also verify that the window meets the new Version 5 requirements. http://oee.nrcan.gc.ca/pml-lmp/index.cfm?action = app.welcome-bienvenue

Table 13.5 Sample window listing from Energy Star Energy Efficiency Ratings

Model	C-FC-1-1/8-3,71/38(2)-3,71/38(4)-3,IS20(6)-0.375KR90F
Brand	Vinylguard
Product Name	Energyguard
Style	Fixed Casement
U-factor (W/m²-K)	0.65
Solar Heat Gain (SHGC)	0.23
Emergy Rating	39
ENERGY STAR Most Efficient 2020	Y
Frame Material	Vinyl
Layers of Glazing	3
NRCan Reference	NR6742-21663106-ES5
Energy Efficiency Verification Reference	W559
U-factor (Btu/h/ft² – °F)	0.11
Visible Transmittance	0.21
Air Leakage – Infiltration (L/s*m²)	0
Air Leakage – Exfiltration (L/s*m²)	0
Registration Date	2018-04-13
Last Submitted	2018-08-23
Delisting Date	2023-01-22

13.3 Window and Door Installation

In relatively thick walls, windows and doors can be located anywhere between outside and inside faces of a wall (Figure 13.6). Doors tend to be mounted close to the inside face for aesthetic reasons and for ease of operation of in-swing doors.

It is generally more energy-efficient to mount windows close to the inside because:

- The window surface is sheltered somewhat from the wind;

- Condensation on the inside surface of the glass is reduced because the flow of warm air over the surface is improved and the window is in the warmer part of the wall; and

- The small wall overhang above the window provides some protection from rain.

However, inside mounting requires extra care to construct the deep weatherproof sill. When windows are installed close to the exterior face of the wall, the frame can be extended to the face of the inside wall, or the recess can be faced with drywall. It is also possible to use wood panel sheathing jamb extensions that are sealed to the outside of the window frame.

Windows and doors are typically installed in a space that is 12 to 25 mm (1/2 to 1 in.) larger than the frame in both the horizontal and vertical directions. Heat is lost through this shim space by conduction through whatever material has been used to fill the space, and by airflow through the space.

To minimize this heat loss, the shim space must be insulated and sealed. The traditional way to fill the shim space has been to stuff scraps of batt-type insulation into the gap before applying the trim. This provides some insulation but does little to reduce airflow through the space. The space must also be sealed to cut airflow around the window frame.

Figure 13.6 Effects of window placement in the wall

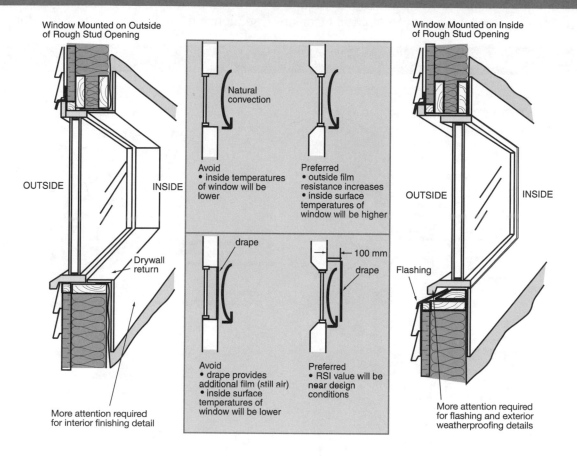

The recommended approach to air sealing involves filling the space with foam. Foam has a higher insulating value per unit of thickness than batt-type insulation and eliminates airflow far more effectively than insulation scraps and plastic. Low-expansion foam should be used so that less pressure is exerted on the window frame. Foam sealing is effective if it connects the window frame to the air barrier in the wall assembly.

Many modern windows have nailing flanges to facilitate installation. If the rough opening is a little oversized, there is a risk that the fasteners through the flange will not be securely embedded in the framing members around the window opening. This could cause the window to be poorly secured, particularly for large, operable windows where the open window puts additional load on the window connection. In these cases, additional fasteners should be added through the window framing, bearing on shims and secured by screws to the wall framing.

CSA-A440.4, *Installation of Windows, Doors and Skylights* describes methods for both new installation and replacement installation of factory assembled windows, exterior doors, and unit skylights that are intended for installation in low-rise buildings and buildings used primarily for residential occupancy. Some of the installation methods outlined in CSA-A440.4 are described in the following sections. Whichever method is used, it is essential to follow the proper sequence and provide:

- Vapour barrier;

- Air barrier;

- Exterior moisture barrier; and

- Water-shedding surface.

CSA A440.4 provides suggested installation details for low, medium and high exposures. Locations with a high exposure to wind-driven rain require a more comprehensive installation procedure. Figure 13.7 provides an example of the installation sequence for a low-exposure condition.

Figure 13.7 Example of window installation sequence

1. Prepare window opening

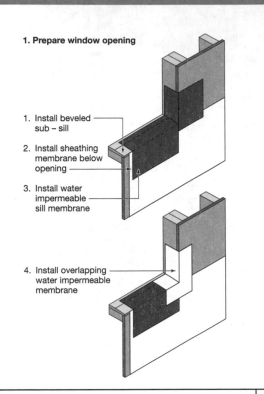

1. Install beveled sub – sill
2. Install sheathing membrane below opening
3. Install water impermeable sill membrane
4. Install overlapping water impermeable membrane

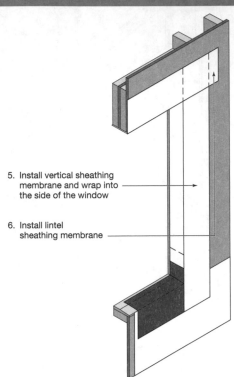

5. Install vertical sheathing membrane and wrap into the side of the window
6. Install lintel sheathing membrane

2. Install window

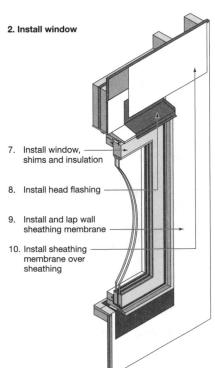

7. Install window, shims and insulation
8. Install head flashing
9. Install and lap wall sheathing membrane
10. Install sheathing membrane over sheathing

3. Finish around window

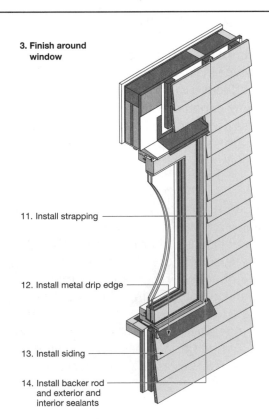

11. Install strapping
12. Install metal drip edge
13. Install siding
14. Install backer rod and exterior and interior sealants

13.3.1 Foam/tape method

This installation method can be employed on any window type. Complete filling of the void between the window frame and the rough stud opening is required, as the foam serves as the air barrier. A low-expansion foam must be used as follows to avoid placing excessive pressure on the window frame (Figure 13.8):

• Fill the gap between the stud and window frame, using two passes, allowing excess foam to "bleed" to the interior;

• Trim the foam to the inside face of the window jamb; and

• Tape or seal the air barrier to the inside face of the jamb prior to installation of trim.

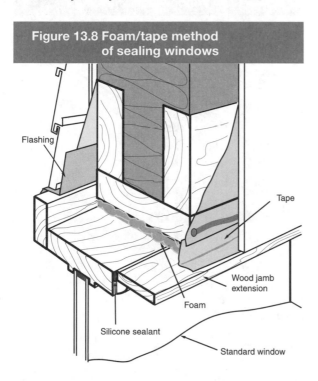

Figure 13.8 Foam/tape method of sealing windows

Flashing

Tape

Wood jamb extension

Foam

Silicone sealant

Standard window

13.3.2 Plywood wrap

This method can be used for metal and PVC windows and doors (Figure 13.9). The steps are as follows:

a) Frame the rough frame opening to accommodate a 12.7 mm (1/2 in.) wood panel sheathing liner covering the full depth of the opening on all four sides. This means an increase of about 25 mm (1 in.) in both the height and width of the opening.

b) Nail the liner into place flush with the interior finish and the exterior sheathing. The liner can be caulked to the rough frame opening on the interior.

c) Seal the wood panel sheathing liner at the interior edge to the wall with either polyethylene or drywall.

d) Install the window into the liner from inside or outside, depending on the intended location. If the window is to be mounted to the inside of the wall, slope and flash the sill properly prior to installation.

e) Insulate and seal the shim space between the wood panel sheathing liner and the window.

f) Install drywall over the liner with finish trim.

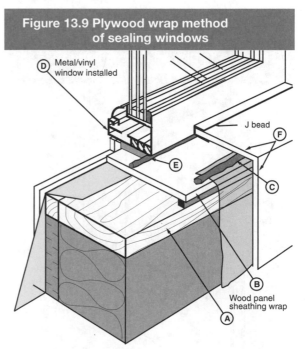

Figure 13.9 Plywood wrap method of sealing windows

Metal/vinyl window installed

J bead

Wood panel sheathing wrap

13.3.3 Drywall method

This method is commonly used with wood-frame windows. The window is installed in the opening and the opening is finished with drywall sealed to the window frame (Figure 13.10) as follows:

- Frame the rough stud opening.

- Install the window and insulate and seal the shim space.

- Butt and seal the drywall to the window frame.

- If the window is installed towards the outside of the wall assembly, install a drywall return in the recess. Caulk the joint between the face edge of the window frame and

- the drywall.

- If the window is installed towards the inside of the wall assembly, the face of the drywall should be flush with the face edge of the window frame. Tape the joint and cover it with trim.

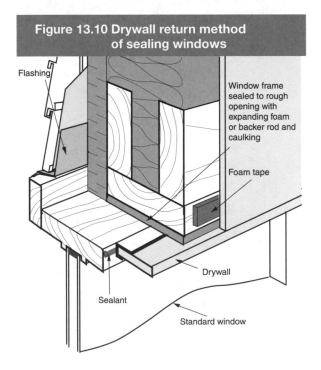

Figure 13.10 Drywall return method of sealing windows

Flashing

Window frame sealed to rough opening with expanding foam or backer rod and caulking

Foam tape

Drywall

Sealant

Standard window

13.4 Window Flashings

Window flashings help to protect windows and the walls in which they are mounted from water penetration. The key flashings that must be considered are at window heads and sills.

The head flashing helps to redirect and deflect water away from the top of the window frame. It should be well-sloped (a minimum of a 2 in 1 slope) and should extend a minimum of 25 mm (1 in.) past the outer edge of the window frame. The head flashing must be terminated at both ends in an end dam to direct any water that collects on the flashing to drain out and away from the wall (Figure 13.11).

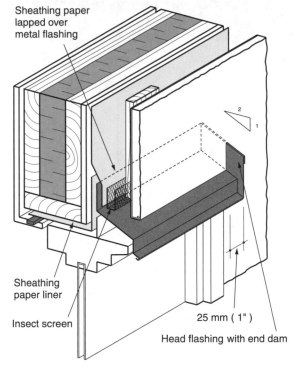

Figure 13.11 Window head flashing

Sheathing paper lapped over metal flashing

Sheathing paper liner

Insect screen

25 mm (1")

Head flashing with end dam

A jamb flashing is usually used only if the window must be adapted to a rainscreen wall. This type of flashing extends the window jamb to meet the exterior cladding.

Particularly in wet coastal climates, the detailing of the wall opening at the window sill is critical to prevent water penetration into the wall. This detail requires a sill flashing or pan flashing to divert and deflect rainwater out of the wall cavity or a sloped subsill covered with a membrane to direct away water that does penetrate a window frame (Figure 13.12).

Figure 13.12 Window sill flashing

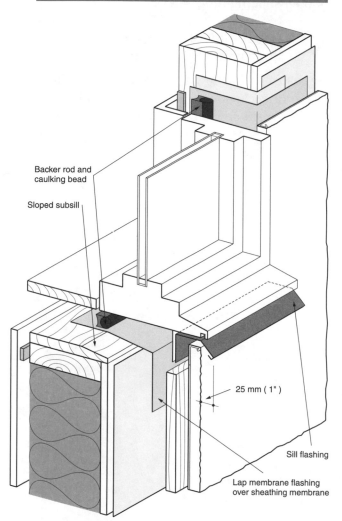

Backer rod and caulking bead

Sloped subsill

25 mm (1")

Sill flashing

Lap membrane flashing over sheathing membrane

To allow for drainage from behind the bottom nailing flange of a window, the flange can be removed or notched, or the window can be installed with spacers to allow for drainage from behind the flange. However, to ensure the warranty is not voided, modifications to the flange should only be done with the knowledge and approval of the window manufacturer. The sill flashing must extend 25 mm (1 in.) beyond the face of the wall cladding to ensure that water passing over the flashing is deflected away from the wall.

Specific flashing profiles will vary depending on window frame profile, type of cladding used, and building design and exposure.

13.5 Skylights

Skylights provide natural lighting and are available in a wide range of sizes and features, such as low-E coatings and gas fillings. A skylight is essentially a window in the ceiling/roof. As such, the selection criteria used by builders for windows should be applied to skylights. Even the most energy-efficient skylights have a much lower insulating value than the surrounding attic. This means that there is a high potential for the rising warm air to condense on the cool surface of the glass and drip. This can be reduced by selecting skylights with the best insulation value by referring to ENERGY STAR® ratings. Proper control of interior relative humidity through adequate ventilation can also help to reduce the condensation potential.

Skylights are directly exposed to driving rain and snow accumulation. The installation of a skylight and the construction of its housing should follow the skylight manufacturer's instructions and be capable of preventing water infiltration from the melting snow and rain, on and around the skylight and its housing.

CANADIAN HOME BUILDERS' ASSOCIATION

13.6 Doors

Heat is lost through doors by:

- Conduction through the door and frame, conduction through any door hardware (handles and deadbolt locks), and any door glass or sidelites;

- Airflow between the door, frame and sill; and

- Airflow between the door frame and the rough frame opening.

The first two sources of heat loss can be reduced by selecting good quality units; the last can be reduced through proper installation.

Other ways of reducing heat loss include:

- Limiting the number of doors;

- Placing doors out of the path of prevailing winds, either by locating them on the leeward side of the house or by providing windbreaks;

- Limiting the number of patio doors or selecting efficient units; and

- Using an air-lock vestibule.

- Better designs will situate doors under overhangs or roofs to provide protection from rain and snow.

13.6.1 Reducing conduction through doors

Doors are made from a variety of materials, some of which reduce conduction better than others. Solid wood doors will have U-factors ranging from 2.30 to 2.85 W/m²C. Metal-clad, insulated doors can have U-factors as low as 0.75 W/m²C, depending on the style of the door and the insulation material used to fill it. Any glazing in or around doors should have good insulating properties.

13.6.2 Reducing airflow between the frame and the door

Heat lost by airflow between the door and the frame can be reduced by providing an airtight seal between the door and the frame. The airtightness of the joint between the door and the frame depends on the type of weatherstripping used and the amount of pressure that can be applied on the joint. Doors with compression seals perform better than doors with sliding seals. Insulated, pre-hung entry door systems generally have good air seals. Some steel-clad doors use magnetic weatherproofing to improve the seal.

13.6.3 Insulated pre-hung entry doors

Insulated, pre-hung entry door systems provide better thermal performance than conventional wood doors. They consist of an entry door with a core of polyurethane or polystyrene foam insulation. The door is installed in the frame and sill system at the factory. Pre-hung insulated door systems are available with steel- or wood-faced doors. A variety of materials may be used for the door framing, the insulation in the core and the weatherstripping. Performance depends on:

- The thermal resistance of the door;

- How the manufacturer prevents thermal bridging at the edge of the door and at the frame and/or sill; and

- Tested air leakage rates for the door system in litres per second per square metre of door area (cubic feet per minute per square foot of door area).

Pre-hung insulated door systems have several advantages:

- Higher insulating values (U-values as low as 0.75 W/m2C) than conventional wooden doors;

- Air seals that are tight and durable;

- A thermally broken adjustable sill assembly to reduce conductive heat loss; and

- Shorter site installation time.

13.6.4 Selecting doors

For energy efficiency, doors should be selected that carry the ENERGY STAR® rating. Other desirable features include:

- High-quality weatherstripping;

- Low air leakage rates (for pre-hung door systems); and

- Maintenance-free framing materials.

13.6.5 Selecting patio doors

In terms of heat loss and heat gain, patio doors act like large, horizontally sliding or casement windows. Selection of patio doors should reflect an understanding of window selection procedures based on glazing performance. The energy rating (ER) system applies to sliding glass patio doors, as does the U-factor and SHGC, so selection can be based on a comparison of ER ratings for conventional housing and the most cost effective U-factor and SGHC trade-off in order to minimize the annual heating and cooling loads in Net Zero Energy houses.

Doors with good air seals should be selected. French doors and tilt-turn type patio doors provide a more positive seal against air leakage than sliding units. In locations or exposures where wind-driven rain is a problem, double-double glazed patio doors (an outside and inside set of thermal glazed doors) can be used to minimize rain infiltration.

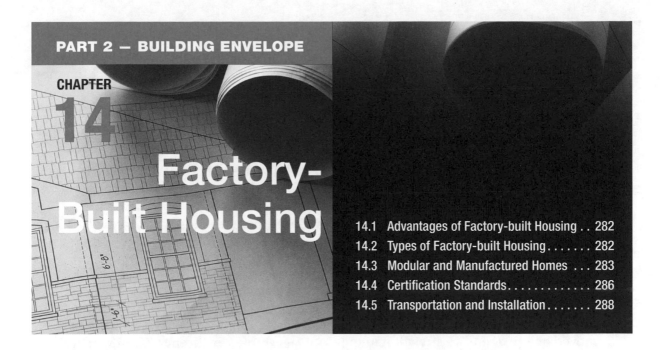

PART 2 — BUILDING ENVELOPE

CHAPTER

14

Factory-Built Housing

Over the last several decades, factory-based construction has played an ever-increasing role in the construction of housing. Roof trusses, manufactured stairs, cabinets, framing materials and panelized wall systems are widely used. Complete single-family homes and multi-unit residential buildings are installed on single lots and entire subdivisions. Factory-built modules and panels are also used in renovations and additions.

Making use of factory-built products is an approach that traditional builders can take to provide the quality and certainty of factory production, and to extend their product line to appeal to a broader clientele. It also allows traditional builders a high degree of control over costs and schedules, and more time to dedicate to projects at the site. This chapter describes the types of factory-built products being used.

14.1 Advantages of Factory-built Housing

The factory offers a number of advantages over on-site construction:

- Greater control over the building process and ready availability of skilled trades, resulting in predictable delivery schedules.

- Improved design flexibility and lower customization costs due to computer-assisted design equipment and processes.

- Systematic quality control resulting in consistent compliance with codes and regulations and reduced defects (e.g. improved ability to ensure straight framing and square and level window/door openings, faster drywall installation with fewer nail-pops).

- Weather-protected construction resulting in reduced moisture-related problems.

- Improved energy and resource efficiency through increased ability to ensure integrity of air and vapour barriers and insulation.

- Efficient material use and waste management.

- Reduced exposure to on-site theft.

The factory-based construction process results in homes that meet the highest levels of energy efficiency.

Historically, factory-built housing producers have been first out of the gate with ground-breaking projects such as Natural Resources Canada's R-2000 and Advanced Houses initiatives, Canada Mortgage and Housing Corporation's EQuilibrium™, and the Canadian Home Builders' Association's EnviroHome® and Net Zero Energy Housing initiatives, showing that factory-based homebuilding can provide improved energy efficiency, superior indoor air quality and increased environmental responsibility. For example, the first net-zero EQuilibrium™ demonstration home, the ÉcoTerra™ two-storey detached home in Eastman, Quebec, is a factory-built house.

14.2 Types of Factory-built Housing

There are several types of factory-built housing that vary depending on their degree of completion when they leave the factory.

Pre-engineered homes are packages that include all major building components prepared in the factory and shipped to the building site ready for assembly, including framing materials, doors, windows, roofing, siding, interior wall partitions and sub-flooring. The pre-engineered building system emphasizes precision design and pre-cutting, and can be used for virtually any home design. Once at the installation site, the same principles of good construction described in this Manual apply to the assembly of pre-engineered homes.

Panelized homes, including panelized multi-unit residential buildings, are built with prefabricated wall, floor and/or roof assemblies that have been custom-manufactured to suit the load and size requirements for a specific application. The use of panels can reduce on-site construction time significantly.

Most builders use prefabricated roof trusses. Wall and floor panels are also available that offer the advantages of factory-based construction, a controlled, weather-protected environment, precision cutting to match components to shop drawings, automated fabrication, and quality control. Wall panels may be partially or fully completed in the factory, with windows, doors and siding often factory-installed. The panels are shipped to the site where they are assembled, and the home is finished inside and out.

Modular homes and modular multi-unit residential buildings are built in a factory as three-dimensional modules that are combined on-site to make one, or multi-storey homes. A bungalow typically consists of one or two modules, while a two-storey home will use four or more modules. Most modular homes are set on full-perimeter foundations; smaller houses may be installed on surface foundations. Multi-unit buildings may be installed slab-on-grade or on full foundations.

Insulation, air and vapour barriers, plumbing, wiring, exterior siding and other construction details are largely completed in the factory. Interior work may also be completed in the factory including drywall, trim, flooring, cabinets and bathroom fixtures. Finishing the home on-site may take a few days or a few weeks depending on the size, style and features of the home. Some features are best done on-site, such as brick cladding and some types of flooring.

Manufactured homes are single-storey homes, built in one or two sections. They are virtually complete when they leave the factory, and are often ready for move-in the same day or a few days after arriving on the site. Manufactured homes are often installed on surface-mount foundations such as piers. They can also be relocated, although most are never moved from their original site.

14.3 Modular and Manufactured Homes

14.3.1 Planning

Modular and manufactured housing provide builders with another option for providing quality that meets market expectations. A key success factor is close collaboration between the factory and the builder installing the home at the site to ensure the final product meets schedule, quality, cost and homebuyer expectations. This team should consider all aspects of the project, and clearly determine who will be responsible for each aspect such as:

- Utilities;

- Lot inspection, access and home siting;

- Lot preparation (access, road, grading, etc.);

- Foundation;

- Foundation inspection;

- Pre-delivery inspection;

- Transportation;

- Inspection on delivery;

- Installation/set-up;

- HVAC system;

- Service hook-ups; and,

- Finishing and final adjustments.

14.3.2 Building in the factory

Constructing modular and manufactured homes combines leading-edge automation with traditional building practices and craftsmanship. The in-factory construction process is a series of steps, or activities, organized for assembly-line production.

The assembly line consists of a number of workstations where specific components are put together and/or added to the home, module or panel. The home is assembled as it moves along the line from one workstation to the next. It can be rolled, lifted by crane or pulled forward along the line. Time-consuming and specialized work such as the construction of door frames or kitchen cabinets is done away from the assembly line.

The assembly line and the sequence of activities may vary from one factory to another, depending on the equipment, preferred methods, and the type of factory-built housing being produced. The following describes a typical assembly process.

Sub-floor framing

Wood sub-floor framing is constructed with dry pre-cut lumber or pre-engineered floor trusses in a jig that ensures perfectly straight lines and square corners. A number of different products are used for sub-flooring, such as plywood, OSB (oriented strand board) or particleboard. The sub-flooring may be tongue and groove, nailed and glued for additional strength and to eliminate floor squeaks. Heating ducts, plumbing pipes and wiring are run through the spaces under the sub-floor. The main trunk duct may or may not be installed under the sub-floor framing.

If the home is to be installed over a heated basement or crawl space, perimeter header insulation is added. If the home is to be installed on a surface foundation, insulation is added to protect the entire floor area and the trunk duct (if installed). The underside of the sub-floor assembly is enclosed and plumbing connections for fixtures such as baths and toilets are attached, and sub-floor sheathing is fastened to the floor framing.

The floor assembly may be raised to provide easy access for the crew, allowing electricians, for example, to drill holes and string electrical wires conveniently and precisely. Openings in the sub-flooring for plumbing as well as HVAC (heating, ventilation and air conditioning) may be pre-cut before the sub-floor is installed on the floor framing. The floor assembly may be built upside down, and then flipped over. For single-module homes, the floor assembly may be installed on two beams that run the length of the unit beneath the assembly to provide support when surface-mount foundations are used.

Floor finishing

Floor coverings, such as vinyl or carpeting can be stretched properly over the entire sub-floor to eliminate bulges and bad seams. The flooring is covered with plastic for protection during the remainder of the finishing and installation. Some manufacturers prefer to install floor covering room-by-room, after the exterior and interior walls are up. This facilitates removal if the homeowner wants to change the floor covering in the future. Hardwood and ceramic floors are usually installed on-site to avoid possible damage during construction and transport.

Wall assemblies

Typically, both interior and exterior walls are assembled on jigs next to the line and then moved onto the line and fastened to the floor of the home or section. This ensures straight and plumb lines. Electrical wiring is usually threaded through the walls before they are moved on to the line. Insulation and inside wall panels may also be installed on the jig.

Alternately, insulation and an air barrier may be added after the exterior walls are up. The most commonly used insulation is fibreglass batt. Some manufacturers use extruded polystyrene panels or blown-in insulation.

For multi-section modular homes, careful attention must be paid to joined areas of the sections during installation at the site. Joined areas must be properly aligned and sealed at the site to ensure the integrity of the air barrier. If a blower-door test is to be conducted, it may be done in the factory or after the home is installed at the site, depending on the purpose of the test.

Windows and doors are installed on the line. If drywall is used, it is applied on the line as well. Taping, mudding and painting are done at the same time that other interior and exterior work takes place.

Roofing

Engineered roof trusses are used for roof framing. The entire roof structure, including trusses and sheathing, is assembled on a jig. It is then hoisted on top of the home and fastened with metal plates and/or straps. Hinged roof truss systems make it possible to build high-pitch roofs that can be shipped in the folded position and then raised into position at the site. Alternatively, some manufacturers use roof caps that are built and transported separately to the site and placed on top of the lower sections.

Exterior and interior finishing

Up to the point of finishing, the assembly process draws heavily on the automation process and equipment that is unique to in-factory construction. Exterior and interior finishing more closely resembles on-site construction. However, with an established process, trained people and built-in inspections, the factory setting makes it easy to attain high levels of quality and efficiency in the finishing stages.

Exterior finishing

Roofing can be installed when the roof assembly is manufactured, or it can be added after the roof assembly is placed on the walls. Exterior walls are covered with sheathing and siding on the outside (siding on walls to be joined on-site will be applied later). If brick or stone is specified, it is applied on-site after the home has been installed, due to the weight and lack of ductility of these materials during transportation.

Eaves finishing is installed. Eaves that project well over the sides of the home may be attached with hinges so they can be folded up on the roof during transportation.

Interior finishing

The remaining finishing details such as kitchen and bathroom cabinets and fixtures, light fixtures, trim, and moulding are completed.

14.3.3 Preparing for transport

A final quality inspection of the home is conducted inside and out. Any necessary touch-ups or corrections are done immediately or noted for completion once the home is installed. The home is prepared for transportation. Several different methods are used to protect the home during transportation.

14.4 Certification Standards

Regardless of how or where a home is constructed, the jurisdiction in which the home will be located has a mandate to confirm that the home is built to code requirements. As factory-built housing is for the most part completed in the factory, a label from an accredited certification and testing body is the building inspector's assurance that factory-completed and concealed areas meet applicable requirements.

In addition to provincial/territorial/municipal building code requirements, there are three Canadian Standards Association (CSA) standards that apply to factory-built housing in Canada:

• CAN/CSA A277, *Procedure for certification of prefabricated buildings, modules, and panels*;

• CAN/CSA Z240 MH Series, *Manufactured homes*; and

• CAN/CSA Z240.10.1, *Site preparation, foundation and installation of buildings*.

CAN/CSA Z240.10.1 applies to both factory- and site-built buildings. It is referenced in the National Building Code of Canada (NBC) and in all provincial/territorial/municipal codes that address housing.

CAN/CSA A277 is referenced for compliance in British Columbia, Alberta, Ontario, Quebec, Nova Scotia and Yukon. The CAN/CSA Z240 MH Series of Standards is referenced for compliance in British Columbia, Manitoba, Ontario, Nova Scotia and Yukon with limitations on its use in Manitoba and Ontario.

14.4.1 CAN/CSA A277, Procedure for certification of prefabricated buildings, modules, and panels

CAN/CSA A277 is a factory-certification procedure that defines the quality-control procedures and staff that a plant must have in place to ensure that the buildings or components it produces are built properly and in accordance with the relevant standards and codes. The A277 standard involves both the manufacturing plant and the homes. It addresses quality throughout the manufacturing process, not just in the final product. The A277 standard covers the procedure for certification of buildings, modules and panels, including the plant quality program and the product built, auditing of the plant quality program, and in-plant inspection.

14.4.2 CAN/CSA Z240 MH, Manufactured homes

The CAN/CSA Z240 MH Series of standards sets out requirements specifically for the construction of single-storey, manufactured homes. The requirements are related to structure, plumbing, and electrical and heating service, for example. In general, these requirements mirror the provisions of the NBC. Consistent with the NBC, CAN/CSA Z240 MH references the Canadian Electrical Code and the National Plumbing Code.

14.4.3 CAN/CSA Z240.10.1, Site preparation, foundation and installation of buildings

The CAN/CSA Z240.10.1 standard details the construction of a surface-mount foundation and the installation of the building. The standard is applicable to any building, factory- or site-built, where the structure provides sufficient rigidity to protect the home from damage due to minor movements in the foundation. For buildings constructed according to the NBC or provincial regulations based on the NBC, the standard is applicable to buildings not more than 4.3 m (14 ft. 1 in.) wide.

14.4.4 Labelling

CAN/CSA A277 requires all prefabricated buildings, modules, and panels to be labelled or marked before they leave the factory. The label plays a key role in the municipal inspection process; it clearly signifies to the inspector that the work completed in the factory is in accordance with the appropriate codes and standards, and that only work done on-site requires inspection.

For buildings, and every unit or suite in a multi-unit/suite building, a certification label is affixed permanently in a readily visible location, often on or near the electrical panel. Units built to the CAN/CSA Z240 MH Series standard carry a CSA Z240 MH label – all other factory constructed buildings use a CAN/CSA A277 label. The name or logo of the certification body appears on the label. Special labels have been developed for members of the CHBA Modular Construction Council that incorporate the CHBA name. The labels:

- identify the certifying body;

- provide the serial number;

- identify the applicable code(s) and/or standards with which the building complies; and

- reference the specification sheet(s) for the building.

Prefabricated structural modules and panels (other than those that are part of a certified prefabricated building that is already labelled), also carry a permanent, readily visible label or stamp in order to confirm compliance at the installation site. Labels or stamps for modules and panels:

- idenify the certifying body;

- identify the manufacturer

- provide a serial number, product code, and part number as applicable; and

- reference the specification sheet(s) for the module or panel.

The specification sheet also accompanies the building, module, or panel. The specification sheet includes information such as:

- Manufacturer's name and address;

- Model, serial number, product code, and part number as applicable;

- Date of manufacture;

- A statement indicating that construction was carried out in a factory;

- As applicable, the building code(s) and standards met by the building, module, or panel and whether the building, module, or panel is designed and constructed in compliance with the requirements that apply only to seasonal buildings; and

- As applicable, a list of components, assemblies and systems to be completed on site.

In addition, specification sheet information for buildings and structural modules and panels includes:

- the uniformly distributed live load floor load;

- the specified snow load, or the 1-in-50 year ground snow load and associated rain load;

- 1-in-50 year hourly wind pressure (for resistance to racking and up-lift);

- where the building is installed on piers, the allowable 1-in-50 wind pressure for resistance to overturning without anchorage (see CSA-Z240.10.1); and

- seismic spectral response acceleration Sa(0.2);

Where the building has been evaluated and in accordance with the deformation-resistance test in CSA Z240.2.1, a statement of compliance with the acceptance criteria for deformation resistance must also be provided.

Additional information is required for buildings, modules, or panels designed in accordance with Part 4 of the *National Building Code of Canada* or equivalent; for those designed for exposure to unconditioned space, ground or the exterior; and those delivered with appliances, with electrical sevice installed, or with limited-use running gear.

The construction specifications detailed on the specification sheet are helpful when the home is initially installed, and also in the event that a home is moved from one jurisdiction to another. The NBC clarifies that local jurisdictions need not apply the provisions of the current code when an existing home built to a previous code is relocated. However, a comparison of the as-built specifications to the current code requirements can help builders and renovators determine if upgrading is required to meet geographic requirements such as snow load.

14.5 Transportation and Installation

14.5.1 Transportation

Most builders contract with a professional transporter to deliver factory-built homes to the customer's site. Some factory-built housing producers have their own in-house transport vehicles.

Provincial/territorial/municipal regulations cover such things as maximum load weight and dimensions, licensing of transporters, and the process of applying for permits. Builders should contact the transportation departments in the jurisdictions through which the home will be transported to obtain local requirements, licences and permits.

14.5.2 Installation

For modular and manufactured home units, installation consists of setting the home on the foundation, joining sections as required, completing any outstanding work, and connecting services. Manufacturers provide an installation manual with every home that contains detailed instructions. The instructions provide directions for site preparation, foundations, joining sections, maintaining the integrity of fire separations, providing fire blocking (where required), levelling, anchoring (for some surface-mounted homes) and connecting utilities.

Just as on-site construction requires planning to establish how to construct the air and vapour barriers, coordination is required to ensure the attachment of sections to the foundation provides an airtight seal between the foundation and the sections.

Joining sections on-site requires the utmost care to ensure the structural integrity of the home is not compromised. The process begins in the factory with the precision construction of the sections and sometimes a trial mating to verify a perfect fit. At the site, the joining process consists of:

- Levelling the modules and aligning precisely the interior "mating" walls;

- Fastening the sub-floor framing;

- Securing the roof joint with strapping and gap protection;

- Ensuring the integrity of the building envelope; and,

- Anchoring to the foundation or the ground.

The amount of finishing work to be done on-site depends on the home or building. Typically, for a surface-mounted home, the outstanding work consists of installing skirting and exterior steps. For multi-section modular homes and buildings, all joined areas, inside and out, must be finished on-site. For all homes and buildings, some custom features such as brick cladding or ceramic tile work are best done after installation.

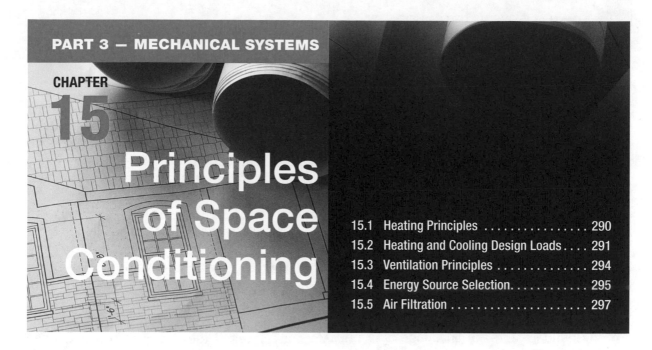

PART 3 — MECHANICAL SYSTEMS

CHAPTER

15

Principles of Space Conditioning

Space conditioning is a general term used to describe the processes by which the air and surfaces in a house are conditioned to make a comfortable living environment. Space conditioning includes:

- Heating in winter

- Cooling in summer

- Ventilation

- Management of indoor relative humidity levels

- Filtration of air to remove impurities

An efficient and effective space conditioning system is a major feature of a well-built home. A house operates as a system in which the space conditioning systems and the building envelope interact. This interaction has significant implications for the comfort and health of the occupants, the energy consumption of the home and the durability of the building envelope.

This chapter reviews principles that are critical to the design and installation of safe, efficient space conditioning systems. Equipment and systems considerations for the various space conditioning processes are provided in Chapters 16 to 20.

15.1 Heating Principles

All heating systems have four common components: the energy or fuel source, a heating device, a distribution system, and controls. The type of heating system selected will depend on the types of energy available. The sizing will depend to a large degree on how well the building envelope is insulated and made airtight. Net Zero Energy and Net Zero Energy Ready houses are pushing the insulation levels and airtightness levels further on more and more houses. In the past we had the occasional house that was insulated to this level and airtightness tested to below 1.0 ACH50. This is normal now for Net Zero Energy builders and the challenge is to find heating equipment that is small enough.

Understanding the conditions that affect comfort will help identify the type of heating system best suited for a given house.

15.1.1 Factors affecting comfort

Air temperature

The air temperature within a room usually varies between the floor and the ceiling, especially near windows. The optimum temperature required for comfort depends on air movement, the amount of thermal radiation to, or from room surfaces (especially windows), and the level of physical activity and the kind of clothing worn by occupants.

Mean radiant temperature

The amount of body heat lost by radiation depends on the surface temperatures in a room. Mean radiant temperature (MRT) is an average temperature of surfaces surrounding a person, and is one of the most important factors affecting comfort. It is a measure of the radiant heat exchange between a person and his or her surroundings, independent of air temperature.

Large, cold surfaces within a room, such as windows, lower the MRT, contributing to discomfort. For this reason, heating registers and radiators were always located against the outside wall under windows to heat the coolest part of the envelope and reduce radiant heat loss. With better-insulated walls, roofs, and foundations, and energy-efficient windows as being achieved in Net Zero Energy construction, the home has warmer and more even temperatures and a higher MRT, enhancing occupant comfort. In addition, the high performance envelope of Net Zero Energy buildings provides the builder with more options in terms of where the heating and cooling air can be introduced into the room, as well as the size of the ducts needed to move that air.

Relative humidity

Relative humidity is the amount of moisture in the air relative to the amount of water the air can hold at that temperature (see Chapter 2). When the relative humidity reaches 100 %, the air is saturated. Any additional water vapour will condense and in the form of liquid water, frost or ice, depending on the temperature of the condensing surface.

Cold air holds less water vapour than warm air. When cold outside air leaks into a house during the winter or is introduced as ventilation air and heated to room temperature, the relative humidity in the conditioned space decreases. Space cooling and dehumidification both reduce relative humidity. If the humidity falls too low, the air will draw moisture out of the furniture, carpets, walls and ceilings, and occupants may complain of dry throats and static electricity. On the other end of the spectrum, if indoor humidity becomes too high, mould and mildew can flourish.

Humidity level can also affect the performance of building components. For example, if the humidity is too low, gaps may occur between wood flooring planks. If it is too high, the flooring can swell and bow.

Air movement

Moving air generates convective and evaporative heat loss and a cooling sensation on exposed skin. Too much air movement leads to discomfort. However, because the heat capacity of air is small, it takes much air to move even small quantities of heat. Therefore, the design of the space conditioning system should manage air delivery velocities and consider the location of the air diffusers.

Effective temperature

Effective temperature is an index that represents the combination of temperature, humidity and air velocity at which people are most comfortable. It is defined as the temperature of saturated air (100% humidity) that provides a sense of physical comfort when the air velocity in the conditioned space is 7 to 12 m/sec. (15 to 25 mph). Various combinations of temperature and relative humidity can provide the same sense of comfort (Figure 15.1).

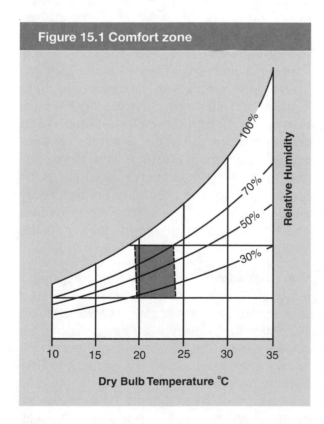

Figure 15.1 Comfort zone

15.2 Heating and Cooling Design Loads

Calculations are necessary for accurate sizing of heating equipment and distribution systems. If equipment is oversized, the capital cost is higher and operational efficiency is lost. If equipment is undersized, the house will not be comfortable and recalls are likely.

The most important factor for thermal comfort is the construction of the envelope – the amount of thermal insulation, the selection of windows and doors, and the control of air leakage. Heat loss calculations take into account the fact that heat is lost mainly by the building envelope and air leakage. The calculations consider the area of each component, the resistance to heat flow (the R-value) and the difference between the indoor and outdoor design temperatures. Heat loss by air leakage is calculated based on the amount of air leakage area and indoor-outdoor air pressure and temperature.

Outdoor design temperature is based on long-term local climatic data that has been established for every community and listed in the NBC. The outdoor design temperature typically used is the lowest temperature that may only be exceeded for 2.5% of the hours in January.

Heat loss and heat gain calculations are done for each component of the house: walls, ceilings, windows, doors, floors. There are several computer programs available that can be used to calculate heat gain and loss on a room-by-room basis. For central heating systems, a whole-house calculation is enough to size the system, but a room-by-room design is required for the distribution system, including ducts for the forced-air system, piping for baseboard heating, convector for radiant in-floor systems, and wiring size for electric baseboards. For zoned heating systems, calculations must be done per zone to ensure that the house will always be warm.

Heating system capacity requirements and sizing should be determined using CAN/CSA F280-12 (R2017) *Determining the Required Capacity of Residential Space Heating and Cooling Appliances.* For Net Zero Energy Housing, this is a mandatory requirement. This Standard was significantly updated in 2012. The original was done in 1990 and was no longer representative of how houses are built and operated. The 2012 Version removed the sizing limit restricting the designer from installing a unit with capacity more than 40% of the load. This means that the HVAC designer has more flexibility in responding to the reality of new homes and to meet the expectations of homeowners. For example, the designer may opt to install 2 small systems which operate independently and each serve a different part of the house. Another significant change is how ventilation and air leakage is handled. There are four important aspects of this:

- the calculation will allow the use of blower door airtightness test results. This allows real, on-site measured data to be used. As mentioned earlier, Net Zero Energy builders are striving to increase the airtightness of their houses. This is specifically to take advantage of this feature.

- the way the ventilation system (Chapter 18 Ventilation) chosen interacts with the home and how it affects the air leakage characteristics of the home is accounted for. Exhaust only systems depressurize the house and change leakage patterns. This Manual describes methods of building energy efficient houses to Net Zero Energy and Net Zero Energy Ready levels of insulation and airightness and therefore, balanced, mechanical ventilation is highly recommended for builders doing these houses.

- heat loss for each room considers the stack effect and that means that air leakage heat loss will be a function of floor level, i.e. first floor rooms will be assigned a higher portion of the air leakage component

- the impact of the heat recovery ventilator is considered.

Appendix 3 has an example of using F280-12. This is provided to assist HVAC contractors and builders to get familiar with the F280-12. Many have developed "rules of thumb" for sizing heating and air conditioning equipment. Unfortunately, these rules of thumb result in oversizing, especially in Net Zero Energy housing, and this ultimately leads to unhappy customers.

Example of the Oversizing Problem

As houses have become tighter and more energy efficient, heating systems have often been oversized. While on the surface this might not appear to be a problem because it ensured the house will always be warm. In reality, the "house is a system" and with an oversized furnace the effect is furnace cycling that results in short periods of operation that does not allow furnaces to reach their efficient operating mode. In the case of cooling the same is true, equipment oversizing results in high humidity levels due to short cycling, which can adversely affect occupant comfort. The reason short cycling is a problem for both heating and cooling is because the device turns on and quickly satisfies the thermostat setting and then turns off. Often the air does not get to the rooms furthest from the device and occupants complain the room is either too hot or too cold. The best option is a correctly sized system which runs for longer periods, and provides good mixing of the air in the entire home.

Using the traditional rules of thumb or the original F280 (1990), a typical practice was to select a space heating system based on the design load plus 40% and then choose the next highest capacity in a supplier's catalog. Figure 15.2 shows the distribution of furnace hourly outputs for an October 1 to May 30 heating season for the fully monitored, reference house at the Canadian Centre for Housing Technology (CCHT) on the campus of the National Research Council of Canada. Interestingly, this furnace was only "oversized" by 24%, (not as "oversized" as it would have been in the field) based on the calculated design load. The graph shows how often the hourly average space heating output exceeds a given level. In this house, the space heating system rarely needs to operate at its maximum output, even when "undersized" as in this example. This example illustrates the importance for builders to "right-size" their mechanical equipment by switching to F280-12 immediately. This is particularly important for anyone building to an advanced energy efficiency level, especially Net Zero Energy.

There are three solutions to furnace oversizing:

1. The first is to use a smaller furnace consistent with the lower heating requirements of more energy-efficient housing.

2. The second is to use a modulating furnace, which combines a modulating gas valve and a variable-speed fan. The furnace's gas valve operates between 40% and 100% of total capacity, in 5% increments, continuously regulating the amount of fuel burned according to the thermostat setting.

The thermostat and its remote temperature sensors provide feedback for the control board, which varies the furnace valve and fan settings. Heating mode starts with the gas at 100% and the fan at 0%, the valve reducing and the blower increasing until maximum efficiency is reached. The fan then runs continuously, ramping up or down depending upon air delivery requirements. Since the fan and burner almost never run at full capacity and energy-robbing on/off cycling is eliminated, the unit is very fuel-efficient.

3. The third option is to use a correctly sized, two-stage furnace, which, while running in the first stage, uses about 68% of its capacity and is sufficient to warm a house on milder winter days. When the heating demand increases on cold days, the furnace meets the extra demand by adjusting to the second stage in the heating cycle. Because the furnace operates most of the time in the lower-capacity stage, it burns less fuel than a traditional furnace that always runs at full capacity and then shuts off when heating demand is met.

Figure 15.2 Sample distribution of hourly furnace outputs

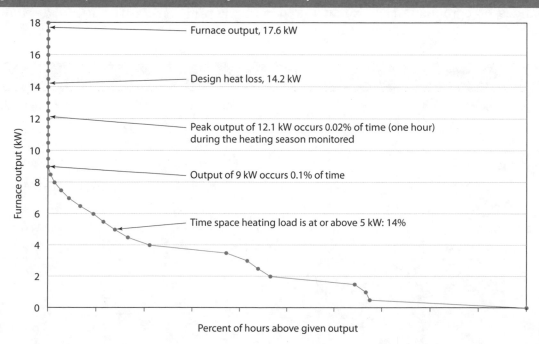

15.3 Ventilation Principles

Ventilation involves four main principles:

- Indoor-outdoor exchange: the process of removing stale indoor air and replacing it with fresh air from the outside;

- Treatment: air filtering, heating or cooling;

- Distribution: air delivery to each room; and,

- Circulation: air mixing within each room.

Ventilation is necessary to remove indoor pollutants and excess humidity, and to supply fresh air to maintain a healthy indoor environment.

As noted in Chapter 4, a wide range of contaminants can be present within the living space. As well, relative humidity levels can be high, especially when a house is new. Humidity can also become too high during periods of increased occupancy, while meals are being prepared or when occupants bathe or shower. To ensure good indoor air quality, the ventilation should operate continuously, balance supply and exhaust air, and distribute airflow.

Ventilation systems are not designed for the purpose of providing make-up air for exhaust appliances or combustion air for fuel-fired appliances. Therefore, additional air is also necessary to replace air removed by appliances such as clothes dryers, bathroom fans, downdraft cooktops, fireplaces and central vacuums. Table 15.1 provides air-flow rates for typical exhaust appliances.

In a house with a well-sealed envelope, a combination of these appliances operating together, or some even individually, such as a dryer or powerful downdraft cooktop fan, can exhaust enough air from the living space to cause a negative pressure. Such a negative pressure could cause a smouldering wood fire or other fuel-fired appliances to backdraft.

Backdrafting refers to a dangerous condition that occurs when a house is depressurized, resulting in combustion gases being drawn back into living spaces rather than being expelled via chimneys and flues. Backdrafting can be avoided in two ways:

1. Use appliances that are less likely to backdraft such as direct- or power-vented furnaces and hot-water tanks.

2. Provide make-up air for appliances that exhaust air such as shown in Table 15.1 so that depressurization does not occur. The air they exhaust needs to be replaced to balance interior and exterior air pressures. Experience has shown that make-up air systems are difficult to design and

Table 15.1 Air-flow rates for exhaust devices		
Exhaust device	litres per second L/s	cubic feet per minute cfm
Bathroom fan	20-50	40-100
Range hood	25-600	50-1,200
Indoor barbeque grill	60-600	120-1,200
Clothes dryer	40-55	80-110
Central vacuum	45-65	90-130
Fireplace (at full burn)	150+	300+

homeowners may have difficulty understanding their purpose and operation. Furthermore, make-up air systems can result in energy loss year-round.

Note that for combustion appliance efficiency, sealed combustion (direct vent) is the most efficient and is not subject to backdrafting, power-vented appliances are mid-efficiency and are less likely to backdraft because of the fan, but the possibility exists, and naturally aspirating appliances are the least efficient and are highly likely to backdraft if the house is depressurized. Net Zero Energy builders will use the highest efficiency, direct vent products, for the efficiency characteristics, which will also provide security from backdrafting.

15.4 Energy Source Selection

The choice of energy source depends on local availability, cost, convenience, supply security, environmental impact, safety, cleanliness, annual maintenance requirements, perception of risk, equipment preference, system efficiency and availability of service technicians. In addition, some utilities have pricing structures that vary with the time of day, time of year or quantity of energy purchased. Fuel type by itself does not define a heating system type, as the same fuel may be used in different heating systems.

A consideration resulting from Net Zero Energy construction is the ability for the electrical utility to accept electrical energy being put back on their grid. Since Net Zero Energy is defined as a house which produces as much energy as it consumes over the course of a year it is important that the electrical utility will accept the energy being produced by the home. Photovoltaic panels typically produce more energy than the house needs in the summer and less than the house needs in the winter. Being able to put this excess energy out on the grid represents a savings for builders because they do not have to add battery storage. In addition, many Net Zero Energy houses are being built with two energy sources; typically natural gas and electricity. Since the Net Zero Energy house is only producing electricity, it needs to generate an equivalent amount of electrical energy to represent the natural gas burned. This means that the house will be putting out onto the gird an amount of electrical energy equal to what it pulled from the grid in winter + the electrical equivalent of the natural gas consumed.

15.4.1 Combustion air

Natural- and forced-draft fuel-fired furnaces and boilers require combustion air for two purposes. They need air to support the burning process and air to dilute and exhaust the products of combustion. In a typical house with this type of heating equipment, the provision of air for burning accounts for about 1.5% of the heating load over the heating season. Dilution air can account for 10-15% of the heating load. While this equipment is commonly found in the existing housing stock, for Net Zero Energy building, this equipment is unlikely to be used, since builders and designers are opting for the highest efficiency, sealed-combustion products.

When house envelopes were less airtight than they are today, air for combustion and dilution came from random cracks and openings in the house envelope, which wasted energy. The modern, well-sealed envelope homes require dedicated sources for combustion air and dilution air if this equipment was to be used.

Most of the new higher-efficiency furnaces and boilers are sealed-combustion, direct-venting appliances, so they effectively eliminate the need for dilution air, as do the new, sealed-combustion, high-technology space heaters, such as the advanced combustion wood stoves and fireplaces.

A dedicated combustion air supply is usually not required if an appliance is power-vented. The combustion air supply for many higher-efficiency appliances is integrated into the equipment design. If it is not, the source of combustion air should be sized and located according to whichever of the following codes is appropriate:

- CAN/CGA-B149.1-15, *Natural Gas and Propane Installation Code*;

- CAN/CGA-B149.2-15, *Propane Storage and Handling Code*;

- CSA B139 Series-15, *Installation Code for Oil Burning Equipment*; and/or

- AN/CSA B365-10 (R2015) *Installation Code for Solid-Fuel-Burning Appliances and Equipment*.

Code provisions for wood appliances are starting to avoid explicit combustion air requirements, and depend on user interaction and alarms (smoke and CO) to reduce woodsmoke spillage.

Combustion air ducts should be insulated and provided with an external vapour barrier to avoid condensation on the outside duct surface during winter months, when it will be directing very cold outdoor air to an appliance. Condensation can also occur inside the duct if indoor air flows back into the duct when the appliance is not demanding combustion air. Some designers specify a damper in the duct to stop this backflow.

Details of wall penetrations are important. Unless a duct is sealed to the wall air barrier where it penetrates a wall, the air leakage around the cold duct can create condensation problems in the wall.

Where a separate combustion air supply must be provided, the same combustion air supply may be able to serve two gas- or oil-fired appliances. The single combustion air inlet may be acceptable as long as the appliances are located in close proximity to each other and the combustion air supply is sized to handle the combined requirements of both appliances.

15.4.2 Make-up air

Make-up air is required in houses where exhaust appliances induce a negative pressure that might lead to the backdrafting and spillage of combustion products from fuel-fired appliances. Upgraded standards and code changes have resulted in a phasing out of naturally aspirating heating equipment in favour of induced-draft and direct-vent appliances. Spillage can still be a concern where homes are equipped with wood-burning fireplaces, oil-fired appliances, wood stoves and similar appliances.

If there are no spillage-susceptible appliances, no make-up air is required – unless soil gas is a concern. For this reason, builders are encouraged to consider sealed-combustion water and space heating appliances. When make-up air is needed, it can be supplied through a single intake or through individual inlets in each room. It should be provided in a manner that does not create discomfort for occupants. Powered make-up air is more reliable at balancing pressures than a passive opening.

In houses that have a high level of airtightness, (such as Net Zero Energy Homes), kitchen, bath and dryer exhausts may not work properly unless there is a source of make-up air.

15.4.3 Wood-burning appliances

Natural draft appliances are not appropriate for use in energy-efficient, airtight construction. For this reason, open fireplaces and conventional wood stoves are not acceptable as they can have adverse effects on both energy consumption and air quality. However, many homeowners want the ambiance of a wood fire or an emergency heat source. Builders can meet customer needs by using wood-burning equipment that is appropriate for use in homes built in accordance with the recommendations of this Manual.

Wood-burning appliances have improved greatly in the past several years, both in their efficiencies and in their pollution control mechanisms. New appliances generally consume considerably less air for the combustion process. However, the potential for backdrafting remains. A supply of outside air for combustion to the appliance should be provided. Locating chimneys on the interior of the heated envelope rather than running them up the outside of the house makes them more effective and reduces the potential for combustion gas spillage. Chapter 16 provides more detail on the design and installation of both fireplaces and wood-burning appliances.

Smoke and carbon monoxide detectors are now required where solid fuel-fired appliances are used. These are also beneficial in homes with any combustion appliances susceptible to combustion gas spillage.

Unseasoned wood should not be stored indoors because of the moisture load it can add to the house as it dries.

15.4.4 Unvented gas fireplaces

Unvented gas fireplaces have been actively sold in Europe for 20 years but are relatively new products being actively marketed in the United States. These have a gas burner and ceramic log but no chimney. All exhaust products, heat and moisture are exhausted into the room where the appliance is located. This potentially creates a dangerous condition; therefore, unvented gas appliances are not approved for use in Canada.

15.5 Air Filtration

Dust control by air filtration has both health and maintenance benefits. Homes with excellent air filtration are better for people with allergies and other respiratory conditions, are easier to keep clean, and protect furnaces better.

House dust is made up of small particles generated indoors and outdoors. Generally, dust entry from outside will be less in an airtight home. However, air filtration may be necessary to meet the needs of a particular client or market segment such as an individual or family with severe allergies. Filtration devices can be installed to remove particulate matter such as lint, dust, pollen, smoke and other fine particles from the air. Air filters are most effective when they are in a recirculated air stream, such as the filter in a forced-air furnace or a portable room air cleaner, because trapping particles or gases in a filter is largely a matter of chance. Therefore, the more times contaminated air is passed through a filter, the higher the rate of contaminant capture.

Air filtration is straight-forward to provide for houses with forced-air heating systems, as good filters can be added easily to the ductwork. In houses with non-forced-air heating systems, a dedicated air handling system for air filtration must be added, or portable air filters can be used.

15.5.1 Filter performance rating

ASHRAE has developed a filter performance rating based on the composition of test dust and size called a MERV rating (minimum efficiency reporting value). MERV ratings are on a scale of 0 to 20, with 20 being the best rating. MERV replaces "percent efficiency," which did not relate particle size to the rating. MERV 1 to 8 filters account for about 75% of the filters used in most homes. The ratings and their capabilities are as follows:

- MERV 1 to 4 (throw-away or electrostatic filter): captures particles 10.0 microns or larger such as pollen, dust mites, and carpet fibres.

- MERV 5 to 8 (good residential filter): captures particles from 3.0 to 10.0 microns such as mould, hairspray, and cement dust.

- MERV 9 to 12 (superior residential filter): captures particles from 1.0 to 3.0 microns such as lead dust and milled flour. Typically, a MERV rating of 12 or higher is a filter suitable for people with sensitivities to dust and particles.

- MERV 13 to 16 (hospital-quality filter): captures particles from .3 to 1.0 microns such as all bacteria, copier toner, and most tobacco smoke. MERV 13 and over will require modifications to the HVAC system due to air flow resistance.

- MERV 17 to 20 (cleanroom filter): captures particles smaller than .3 microns such as viruses, carbon dust, and all combustible smoke.

A pleated paper filter has adequate filtering capability for the majority of homes and can replace typical throwaway furnace filters with no required modifications to the ducting. A HEPA (high-efficiency particulate air) filter can more effectively trap finer particles than a medium-efficiency filter, but it is more than what is needed in most homes. A HEPA filter requires configuration of the cold air plenum to accommodate the thickness of the HEPA filter and because of the increased resistance to airflow, a heavier-duty blower motor is also required. A HEPA filter captures particles in the 0.3 micron range, placing it in the MERV 13-16 range.

15.5.2 Forced warm-air heating system filtration

Furnace filters only work when the furnace fan is on; therefore, it is not worthwhile to invest in a high quality, expensive filtration system unless the fan will operate continuously (or at least a large amount of the time). If continuous circulation is used, the furnace should be equipped with a high-efficiency, brushless, direct-current motor or electronically commutated motor (ECM) to keep energy costs low. Note that for Net Zero Energy and other low energy housing, it is desirable to mix the air in the house, so operating the furnace fan full time when the furnace is on, or alternatively when the air conditioner is on will be common. The choice of a good quality, efficient motor will pay off quickly.

Most furnace filters reduce the amount of dust particles in the air of the ducts. However, there may still be a significant quantity of particles or dust in the air. This is because there are always particle sources in houses (people, pets, cooking, cleaning activities, outdoor air, etc.). The cleaning effect of a good furnace filter will reduce, but never eliminate, house particle concentrations. A more efficient furnace filter may have little effect reducing visible dust, which is too heavy to travel far from its source, and therefore is not filtered.

Basic filter

A basic furnace filter is only capable of catching large fibres and clumps of dust, which helps to keep the heat exchanger clean, but does not prevent smaller particles from circulating with the air stream. A better option is a pleated medium-efficiency filter. All furnaces allow space for a 25 mm (1 in.)-thick pleated fabric filter (usually made from polyester blends), which is several times more efficient than a standard filter. The fabric is more restrictive to airflow than a standard filter, so the larger the surface area of the pleated filter, the better. Usually, with some small modifications to the sheet metal work of the return air plenum, thicker filters (up to 100 mm (4 in.) thick) can be accommodated in the return plenum. Pleated filters are available in various MERV ratings, but a heating contractor should verify that the airflow through them is sufficient for a furnace to operate normally.

Medium-efficiency filters

Medium-efficiency filters are efficient at removing larger particles, such as lint, pollen and mould spores. They are pleated panel-type filters (Figure 15.3) typically 50 to 100 mm (2 to 4 in.) deep and made of fine non-woven synthetic or natural fibres. Medium-efficiency filters are not reusable, but must be replaced two or three times per year, depending on the environment. They are reasonably priced and perhaps the most cost-effective filter.

Pleated fabric filter

Another option is the pleated fabric bag filter (Figure 15.4). These are available in higher efficiencies than panel filters. Bag filters are similar to pleated filters, but they have larger surface area – 600 mm (24 in.) or more in depth. They are made with a finer fabric, so they are more effective than pleated panel filters. Bag filters are disposable and more expensive, but they may last as long as two years. A large plenum space is required to suspend the bag, and the heating contractor needs to verify that the furnace can handle this type of filter.

Electronic filters (Figure 15.5) are another option. They use electrical charges to trap fine dust on a screen that must be washed periodically. They have the advantage of lasting for many years. They are available in only a few sizes and installation usually requires some sheet metal and electrical work, though some furnaces are offered with them as a factory option. These are very effective for fine particles, and fungus and pollens. However, they do produce small amounts of irritating ozone gas and sometimes will make popping and crackling noises. Electronic filters require regular maintenance and must be kept continuously charged with an electrical supply.

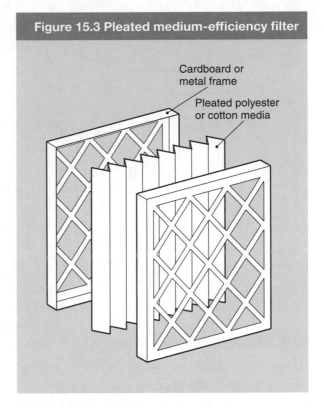

Figure 15.3 Pleated medium-efficiency filter

Cardboard or metal frame

Pleated polyester or cotton media

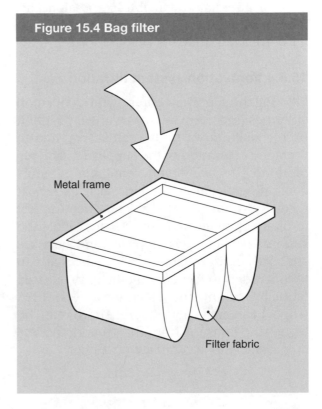

Figure 15.4 Bag filter

Metal frame

Filter fabric

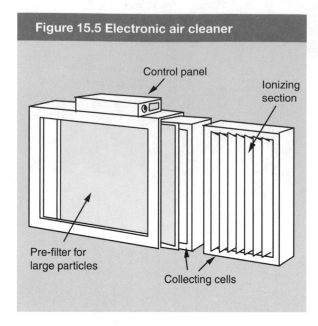

Figure 15.5 Electronic air cleaner

Control panel

Ionizing section

Pre-filter for large particles

Collecting cells

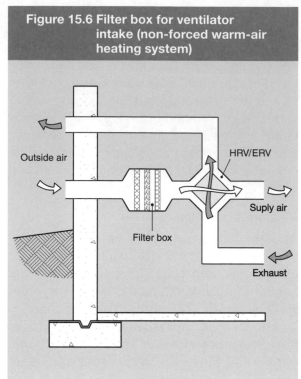

Figure 15.6 Filter box for ventilator intake (non-forced warm-air heating system)

Outside air

HRV/ERV

Supply air

Filter box

Exhaust

15.5.3 Stand-alone air filtration

Unlike homes with forced-air heating systems, homes with radiant or convector heating do not have a central system for moving and filtering air. Commercially available stand-alone air filters can be installed in a room to capture air-borne contaminants in that room.

15.5.4 Ventilation system filtration

Filtering the supply air entering the ventilation system is important in areas with air pollution or for occupants with respiratory health problems. Filtration of the supply air can only be done effectively with ventilation systems containing a supply air fan, such as a heat recovery ventilator. There is no effective way to filter supply air in exhaust-only ventilation systems (Chapter 18). Typical ventilators are supplied with a coarse intake filter that can be upgraded to a medium-efficiency, pleated fabric filter. Some manufacturers offer a HEPA (High Efficiency Particulate Air) filter. The higher the intake is from the ground, the less dust is likely to accumulate on a filter.

If more intake filtration is required, a special filter box can be fitted to the intake of the ventilator (Figure 15.6). It should be large enough to accommodate two or three panel filters. If a forced-air system is used with outside air mixed with return air, a similar filter box can also be used to treat the supply air, but an auxiliary fan may be needed so that the amount of air delivered is not restricted (Figure 15.7).

The installation of additional filtration or more-efficient filters in a ventilation system will affect air flow capacity of the system and should be considered at the design stage.

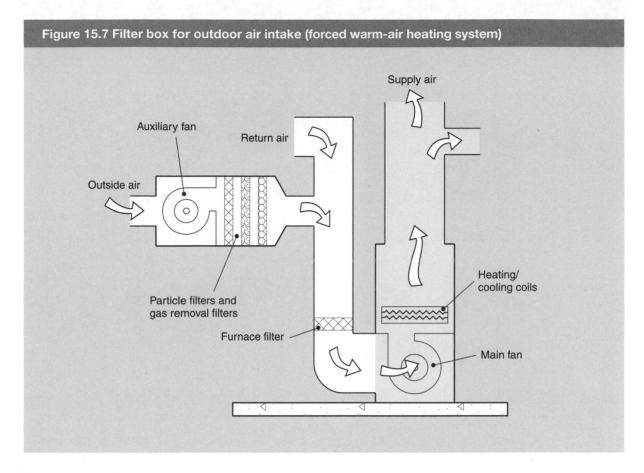

Figure 15.7 Filter box for outdoor air intake (forced warm-air heating system)

Supply air

Auxiliary fan

Return air

Outside air

Particle filters and gas removal filters

Furnace filter

Heating/cooling coils

Main fan

15.5.5 Odour removal filters

Occasionally, circumstances require the control of odours, which are gases. Special media are used to absorb contaminant gases. Odour removal filters should always be protected from clogging by a particle filter installed upstream.

Activated carbon filters are often used to trap odours. A large amount of carbon is needed for long-term performance, and carbon presents more restriction to airflow than fabric filters. The most effective option is a metal screen container with a large surface area that can be installed in the recirculated air stream. This unit is then filled periodically with fresh pellets of activated carbon, available from filter suppliers. This type of filter restricts airflow, so it must be matched to the furnace equipment. Generally, these are only used with fan-coil type furnaces, and are installed in a bypass configuration so that airflow is not excessively restricted.

A carbon-treated fabric filter is a less restrictive option. This type is less effective than carbon pellets, but can be helpful for moderate odour removal. However, the effective life of the carbon treatment can be limited.

One application for these types of filters would be in areas subject to atmospheric inversions where wood burning is common. An activated charcoal filter in the ventilation fresh air inlet can effectively remove smoke that would otherwise be drawn into indoor air.

Some chemically sensitive people find odour control filters beneficial. These filters are not effective for very moist air typical of a pool or tub room. If it is necessary to remove odours from very humid air, the air should first be dried by a cooling coil or desiccant. Other types of specialized odour removal filters are available for specific problems such as formaldehyde or hydrogen sulphide; advice can be obtained from a filter specialist.

PART 3 — MECHANICAL SYSTEMS

CHAPTER 16

Heating Systems

This chapter discusses the types of heating systems suitable for energy-efficient housing. The more energy-efficient a home is, the smaller the heating system can be. In houses built according to the techniques described in this Manual, it may be possible to use simple, innovative, low-cost heating options that might not be practical in less-efficient houses.

Several sections in this Chapter deal with gas-fired appliances. Much of this information also applies to propane-fired appliances.

16.1 Equipment Efficiencies

Equipment efficiencies and system efficiencies

While this section focuses on the efficiency of residential heating equipment, operating efficiency is also greatly affected by system factors. Choosing an appropriate distribution system will reduce noise, minimize the electricity required to distribute conditioned air, and for hydronic systems, have a significant impact on equipment operating efficiency. See Chapter 17 for information about distribution systems. Proper equipment sizing and/or using staged or modulating equipment can help match loads to need.

Typical equipment efficiency ranges

Home heating product efficiencies are based on the conversion efficiency of the fuel source. They do not include any upstream inefficiencies in generating the energy source that arrives at the home. Table 16.1 shows typical efficiency ranges for heating equipment based on the energy source and the approach taken to using each source. Efficiencies for specific product classes are presented later in this chapter.

Table 16.1 Common heating approaches and their effective efficiency ranges

Energy Source	Approach	Approximate Efficiency Range (%)
Natural Gas and Propane	Condensing	90–98
	Non-condensing	60–84
Oil	Condensing	76–96
	Non-condensing	60–86
Electricity	Resistance	100
	Heat pumps	170–260*
Wood	Various	45–80
Pellet	Various	55–80

* Heat Pump performance is typically stated as a Coefficient of Performance (COP) and would be given
as a COP range of 2.3 to 3.3 for the example in the table.

Regulated minimum performance levels

Minimum performance levels are typically set by federal energy efficiency legislation. These minimum performance levels are set for individual classes of heating equipment based on ratings to a performance standard, such as those developed by CSA. These standards exist for most common types of heating equipment. For example, in 2012 the required annual fuel utilization efficiency (AFUE) ratings for residential gas furnaces and boilers were 90 or higher for the majority of gas furnace applications and 80 or higher for gas boilers. Minimum efficiency levels can change and builders need to stay informed. The AFUE is calculated by dividing the amount of fuel supplied to the heater by the amount of heat produced (usually in Btu).

For field assembled systems such as combination systems, the minimum performance levels are set for the class of heat generator. Water heaters are tested and rated in water heating mode and approved on that basis. A 50-gallon tank-type water heater must have a minimum Energy Factor rating of 0.565. The energy factor (EF) is the amount of energy supplied as hot water divided by the total amount of energy used by the water heater over a 24 hour period. New standards have been developed to test and rate water heaters with air handlers in space heating mode so that space heating efficiencies can be determined and more easily compared to those of traditional appliances.

Recognizing premium performance

For individual heating appliances, the ENERGY STAR® rating identifies units that provide superior energy-efficiency. These ratings are often based on both the efficiency of utilizing the space heating energy source and the additional electrical power required for auxiliary electrical equipment such as fans and pumps. ENERGY STAR® categories have been established for most common types of space heating equipment.

Combustion-based systems

As envelopes have become tighter and higher-powered exhaust equipment is being installed, the potential for depressurizing homes has greatly increased. This in turn results in an increased potential for backdrafting the combustion products from spillage-susceptible heating appliances. The NBC requires that indoor air quality not be contaminated by combustion exhaust by either:

- Selecting heating appliances that are all direct- or mechanically-vented units so that exhaust cannot be drawn into the house, even when the house is experiencing negative pressure due to the operation of the principle ventilation and other kitchen and bathroom fans; or,

- Designing and installing an array of dampers, heat exchangers, and controls to admit conditioned air to a house to replace the air lost to combustion, exhaust and ventilation so that there is never negative pressure induced on spillage-susceptible heating appliances.

Cost analysis indicates that installing direct-vented appliances is often the lower-cost option.

16.1.1 Gas-fired space heating appliances

Natural gas is an economical energy source and is the fuel choice to heat most homes in areas where it is available. In areas where natural gas is not available, propane can be used to fuel gas-fired heating appliances, subject to modification of the burner by a qualified technician. For Net Zero Energy and Net Zero Energy Ready houses the amount of gas (or propane) needed to heat the home is significantly reduced compared to Code-built housing. While this is good for the consumer operating the house, the gas company will need to evaluate their product sales and the cost of providing piping to serve a subdivision. In the past, the gas company may install the gas line at the street because they knew that they would recover the costs of doing so in a reasonable period of time. When the consumption drops, the payback on installing the gas line becomes unreasonable. As a result, a fee must be charged to cover the cost of the gas line.

There is a wide range of gas heating options. All new residential furnaces and most other new space heating products deploy condensing technology. They include heat exchangers designed to cool the combustion products below their dew point, condense the water vapour in the flue gas and use the latent heat to help heat the home. Usually, the temperature of the exhaust is so low (35°C to 50°C) that a sidewall vent can be used to exhaust the gases, eliminating the need for a chimney. Many products also modulate or stage the gas supply to the burner so they can reduce their heating output to more closely match heating loads as they vary throughout the year.

16.1.2 Oil-fired space heating appliances

Oil heating is still a common choice in many regions where natural gas is not available. It has the advantage of being a compact, storable fuel that can be less expensive than electricity and propane.

Burners in new furnaces mix the air and oil better to create more efficient combustion and higher efficiency. This type of burner is called a flame retention head burner, named after the more compact shape of the flame that ejects from the burner. Some flame-retention head burners operate at a high static pressure, enabling them to run at lower excess air levels (with commensurate efficiency gains) while overcoming pressure fluctuations generated at the vent termination. The pressure drop across the burner head also precludes the loss of heated house air through the burner and furnace and out the vent during the off-cycle. Oil furnace and oil boiler AFUE performance typically ranges from 78% to 86%. Minimum efficiency performance levels change over time and need to be checked.

In comparison to gas, oil has about half the hydrogen content, resulting in a much lower potential latent heat gain with condensing technology (i.e. lower hydrogen content means less water vapour is created during combustion, therefore, there is less latent heat to be extracted by condensing the water vapour).

16.1.3 Electric space heating appliances

Electric resistance heating systems with central furnaces/boilers or electric baseboards are used by many builders. They are relatively easy to size and control, and require neither combustion air for operation nor a venting system for combustion products. They are inexpensive to install, are easily sized and controlled, and have a long life span. Electric resistance heating systems are considered to be 100% efficient at converting purchased electricity to heat.

The use of electric heating is discouraged in many areas – especially those with limited electrical-generating capacity or where electricity is provided by fuel-fired generation stations. Builders wishing to use electric heat should increase insulation levels to the Net Zero Energy level or beyond, use heat recovery ventilators and take other energy-conserving measures.

In most areas, the operating cost of electric resistance heating will be significantly higher than for natural gas fuelled heating, rapidly outstripping any first-cost savings of the resistance heating system, except in houses with especially low requirements for space heating, such as Net Zero Energy Homes. Building to Net Zero Energy is resulting in builders re-thinking their fuel mix. For example, if builders are going to Net Zero Energy levels they will need to be generating energy from renewable sources. The energy being generated is likely to be electricity from PV panels. There will be excess electricity generated in the summer months and a shortage in the winter months. Unless battery storage is planned, using the electrical grid as a storage will be the most cost-effective solution.

Once this decision regarding electricity has been made, the builder/designers need to consider the costs of the second fuel source. Paying to install the gas-line at the road may now become a significant cost, even though the cost of the gas is low.

16.1.4 Heat pumps

Heat pumps can provide space heating, air conditioning, and in some cases, hot water. A heat pump has a heat exchange coil containing a refrigerant that extracts heat from an air or ground source. The ratio of home heating energy supplied to the electrical energy consumed is defined as the coefficient of performance (COP). In general, the higher the COP, the more efficient the heat pump.

COP is not constant. It goes down as the difference increases between indoor temperature and the temperature of the ground or air from which heat is being extracted. Appropriately designed ground source heat pump systems extract heat from the ground where the temperature remains above 0°C and operate effectively throughout the year.

The COP of traditional air source heat pump systems drops to 1 when the outdoor temperature falls into the 0°C to -10°C range. These systems typically switch over to back-up electric resistance duct heating coils when outdoor temperatures get colder.

Cold climate air source heat pumps specifically address this issue. They are designed to keep operating at much colder temperatures at high COPs. Traditionally air source heat pumps have been tested and rated at -8.3°C. A new test point has been added to the standard to evaluate the performance of cold climate air source heat pumps at -17.8°C (January 1, 2014). The graph below (Figure 16.1) is illustrative of the performance of various systems. Points to note:

- the GSHP (Ground Source Heat Pump) operates at a high COP to well below zero, illustrating the thermal inertia of the ground

Figure 16.1 Typical performance of heat pump systems

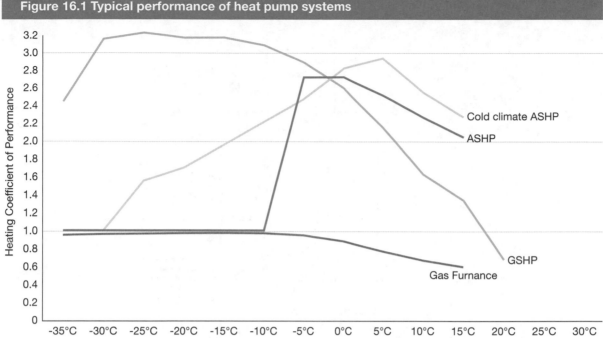

- the COP of the ASHP (Air Source Heat Pump) drops off very quickly at -5

- The Cold Climate ASHP continues to operate with a COP above 1.0 to nearly -30

- The Gas Furnace will always have an efficiency less than 1.0

16.2 Gas-fired Furnaces

Gas furnaces are broadly used to provide space heating with forced air distribution systems. The related distribution system is typically used for distributing air conditioned and ventilation air too. The most commonly used types of residential gas furnaces are currently required to be condensing with an AFUE rating of 90% or more. A directory of gas furnace capacities and efficiencies is available from the Air Conditioning, Heating and Refrigeration Institute.

A wide range of furnaces are now available with high efficiency motors and varying heating capacities. Electronically commutated (ECM) motors are a common option that can drastically reduce fan energy consumption.

They can also enable air flows to be more precisely set by the manufacturer to ensure adequate distribution in both heating and air conditioning modes. Multi-staged and modulating furnaces are common with a higher stage set to meet design outdoor conditions, and lower operating ranges set to meet a range of typical operating demands throughout the year.

Condensing furnaces (Figure 16.2) have high quality heat exchangers to cool the combustion products below their dew point, condensing the water vapour in the flue gas and regaining the latent heat. The resulting low exhaust air temperature typically enables the use of sidewall venting. For most residential applications, non-condensing gas-fired furnaces are no longer permitted.

The condensate is slightly acidic and therefore the heat exchanger needs to be made of non-corrosive material such as high-grade stainless steel. The exhaust piping must also resist corrosion and is usually plastic pipe approved for this application. The condensate is collected and discharged directly to a drain.

Figure 16.2 Condensing gas furnace

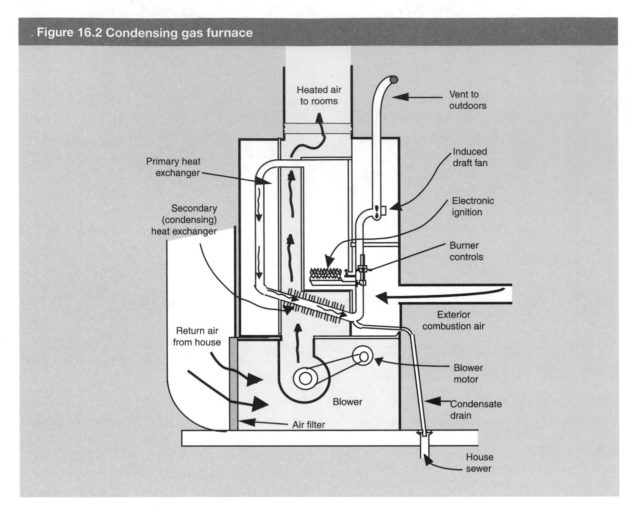

Condensing furnaces work well with a shorter use cycle length because more water is condensed due to cold furnace walls, and higher efficiency is achieved. Most units use a sealed combustion system, with air drawn directly from outside to the burner and exhausted through a different pipe. The sizing and configuration of the intake and exhaust pipes is important, and installation must be done by a qualified technician.

16.3 Gas-fired Boilers (with hydronic or radiant distribution)

Gas-fired boilers are commonly used to heat homes with in-floor radiant systems or other forms of hydronic distribution. (Combination systems that distribute heat using an air handler are discussed in the next Section.)

Gas-fired boiler based systems heat a fluid (typically water) in a closed loop that provides space heating. They may also provide domestic water heating with the use of a heat exchanger. A wide range of wall-hung, low-mass gas boilers has made both condensing and modulating equipment commonplace. Condensing and non-condensing gas boilers share this market. Modulating the boiler input can help match capacity to demand. Boilers have recently been required to use outdoor resets to monitor outdoor temperature and reduce boiler set point temperatures when space heating loads are lower. An outdoor reset is a device that automatically adjusts boiler output according to the outdoor ambient air temperature. It makes it easier for condensing equipment to operate more efficiently throughout the year.

Condensing systems are designed to reduce the return water temperature sufficiently for the flue gases to condense in the heat exchanger when reheating the circulating boiler loop water. The boiler is selected and the distribution system is designed so that the boiler will condense throughout most of the year. Only during the coldest days when the boiler set point temperature has to be raised to its maximum will it become less efficient and potentially not condense.

The most commonly used types of residential gas boilers are currently required to be condensing with minimum AFUE ratings of 82% or more. A directory of gas boiler capacities and efficiencies is available from the Air Conditioning, Heating and Refrigeration Institute.

To maximize efficiency, a boiler system that serves multiple purposes will have separate loops and controls for each one. This enables the control system to minimize the supply temperature setting individually for different needs such as hydronic baseboards, radiant in floor, and domestic hot water heating. Figure 16.3 The set point temperature for domestic hot water heating must stay constant while varying the set point temperature for space heating is essential for efficient operation.

Each hydronic zone requires a thermostat (or temperature sensor), and either a zone valve or zone circulator. The preferred approach for controlling multiple hydronic zones is to add a zone controller. Zone controllers are available that simplify the field wiring of multiple hydronic zones and interconnection to the boiler.

It is best to arrange the thermal zones in such a fashion as to achieve the lowest possible return temperature. For example, if one zone will be serving a portion of radiant floor heating (a low temperature load), and another zone will be serving some convectors or radiators (high temperature loads), the designer should carefully consider the arrangement of the heating circuits to produce the lowest possible return water temperature.

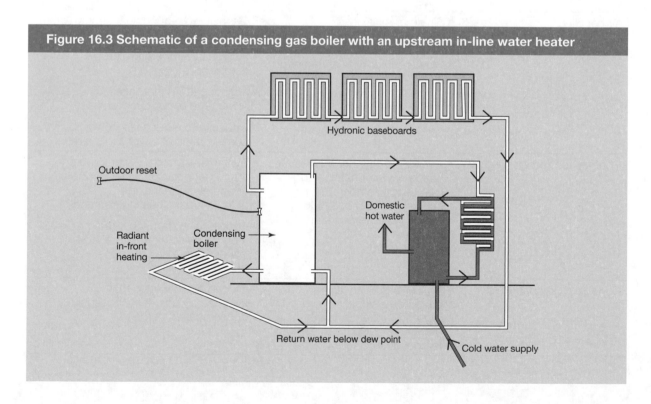

Figure 16.3 Schematic of a condensing gas boiler with an upstream in-line water heater

Hydronic baseboards

Outdoor reset

Domestic hot water

Radiant in-front heating

Condensing boiler

Return water below dew point

Cold water supply

16.4 Gas-fired Combination Systems (for air handler applications)

A combination system provides space heating and domestic hot water heating. This Section focuses on combination systems with forced air distribution. For combination systems that use hydronic or radiant heat distribution, see the previous Section on boiler-based systems or the Section on ground source heat pumps.

Combination systems are most commonly used in homes with low space heating design and operating loads as they can be readily adapted to low capacity needs. The small footprint required for some combination systems can also be useful in smaller homes where space is at a premium. Different combination systems are used for large homes where they can provide both forced air and radiant heating zones.

Combination systems can come as factory engineered packages or be built on site. (Because of their potential complexity – in calculating loads, having multiple trades working together, and determining a control strategy – on-site combination systems are not recommended) Table 16.2 shows the wide range of technologies and potential features that can be part of a combination system. Understanding these options is important for selecting an appropriate combination system for a specific application.

Table 16.2 Options for gas-fired combination systems		
Function	**Component options**	**Factors increasing efficiency**
Heat generation	• On-demand water heater • Tank-type water heater • Boiler	• Capacity to condense flue gases • Minimized burner cycling • Minimized hot water storage losses
Air handling	• Single or multiple zones • Coil type and size • Blower motor type and control (ECM, PSC etc.)	• Capacity to reduce heat supply where it is not required • Increased temperature drop across coils • Airflow pattern that takes full advantage of coil dimensions • Capacity to reduce fan power consumption at lower air flow rates
Controls for heat generator	• Recognize whether a call is for space or water heating and vary supply temperature in space heating mode or keep supply water temperature constant	• Systems without hot water storage that reduce supply water temperature to enable condensing at lower space heating demands • Tank-type systems that reduce water loop pump flow rates to enable condensing at lower space heating demands
Controls for air handling	• Vary or don't vary air flow rates based on a signal such as incoming water temperature, demand time span, or outdoor temperature	• Staged air flow rates that increase air flow at increased space heating demands

16.4.1 Space and Water Heating Capacities and Efficiencies

Both condensing and non-condensing gas water heaters and boilers can be used in a combination system. However, by definition, a system with a non-condensing heat generator will be a less efficient space heater than even the code minimum allowable gas furnace.

Unlike the standardized performance ratings that can readily be found for furnaces, no comparative ratings are available for combination systems. As a result, builders need to spend more time investigating capacity and efficiency claims in order to have confidence that they will satisfy customer needs.

The CSA P.9 Standard, *Test method for determining the performance of combined space and water heating systems (combos)* was first published in 2011 (current version is CAN/CSA-P.9-11 (R2015)). Systems tested to CSA P.9 will have a wide range of standardized performance ratings including those for:

- Space heating capacity;

- Water heating one-hour draw and concurrent space and water heating draws; and,

- Efficiency ratings in each operating mode and as an overall combined space and water heating system.

Manufacturers of packaged combination systems are testing their products to this standard. Builders can reduce risks related to efficiency and capacity by selecting systems that have been rated. Where one manufacturer provides the full combination system, they can provide greater certainty of performance and warranty on the full system.

It can be challenging to determine the efficiency of site-built systems that have not been rated as a system. From an efficiency perspective, the combustion efficiency must be deduced from the rating of the heat generator.

For instance, water heaters are rated with cold mains water entering into the unit and the much warmer return water from a space heating loop typically reduces efficiency significantly. The fan coil and its control can have a large impact on efficiency and these interactions are unknown from standardized water heater or boiler testing.

It can also be difficult to determine the space and water heating capacities of site-built systems that have not been rated as a system. While the heat generator may have a capacity that is many times that required for space heating, the space heating system capacity is typically limited by air handling factors related to pump capacity, coil size, water loop set point temperature, and the evenness of the air flow across the coils. The Heating Refrigeration and Air Conditioning Institute has sizing guidelines for tank-based combination systems to evaluate space heating capacities. Site-built combination systems need to be designed as a system to meet pre-defined home space and water heating needs.

16.4.2 Water Heater-based Combination Systems

Water heater-based combination systems are common, particularly in small homes where loads are low. Air handlers can provide low and varying outputs to match space heating needs. With no minimum air flow requirements for combustion, air handlers enable builders to choose between traditional and alternative duct distribution systems (see Section 17.1). Water heater-based combination systems can also be compact, using little floor space. The use of a single combustion venting system can minimize the impact on exterior walls in townhouse applications.

Water heater-based systems typically flush hot water through the space heating coils in the air handler once a day throughout the year to comply with regulations.

On-demand (tankless) water heaters and air handlers

On-demand water heater systems can be particularly compact and have the potential to provide very efficient space heating. On-demand water heaters modulate the gas firing rate to match the wide range of tap water heating demands. While the high firing rate for tap water heating may produce an output many times that required for space heating, the space heating capacity of the system is set by the air handler capacity, the pump flow rate, and the operating temperature settings. Typically these systems have high output capacities and are designed to meet both water and space heating loads without prioritization.

Before choosing to use a tankless water heater-based combination system, water quality needs to be considered. In areas where water hardness or solutes cause water heater liming or corrosion issues, they will occur faster when a tankless system is also used for space heating. Choosing a different combination heating system may be advantageous.

Combination systems using condensing on-demand water heaters may have the potential to provide very efficient space heating if controlled correctly. Minimizing the return water temperature to the water heater is crucial for high efficiency space heating. Systems could be made to condense most of the time by varying the temperature of the water supplied to the air handler so that it is cooler when the space heating loads are lower (most of the time). See Section 15.2 for more information on design and operating loads.

For performance in water heating mode, see the related technology information in Section 20.2.4. Note that where high-flow taps are used such as with a soaker or jet bathtub, an additional tankless heater may be needed in place of a storage tank. Adding storage will dramatically impact the standby loss and thus the overall efficiency of the system.

The tankless heaters in combo systems are used to heat domestic hot water using burners at high-fire and to provide hot water for space heating, often with burners at a less-efficient, low-fire mode. The combined operating time could affect service life longevity.

Fired tank water heaters and air handlers

Tank-based systems that heat water have a constant set point temperature. Water is typically drawn from the top of the tank, circulated through the air handler, and returned to the bottom of the tank. To enable a condensing tank to condense in space heating mode again requires minimizing the return water temperature. This will require selecting an appropriate fan coil and ideally varying the pump flow rate and air handler air flow rates to reduce return water temperatures in all but the most severe design conditions. Figure 16.4 shows the use of a hot water tank or instantaneous water heater to provide both domestic hot water and space heating.

Figure 16.4 Hot water tank or instantaneous water heater providing water and space heating

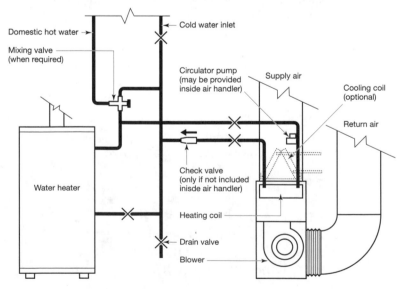

The Heating, Refrigeration and Air Conditioning Institute provides sizing guidelines and related training for tank-based combination systems. For performance in water heating mode, see the related technology information in Chapter 20.

16.4.3 Boiler-based Combination Systems

Boiler-based combination systems are more common in larger homes where they can provide both radiant floor heating in tiled areas and basements, and forced air heating using an air handler on upper floors where cooling is also required.

There is a clear distinction between boilers and water heaters. Water heaters heat domestic water directly. Boilers heat a fluid in a closed loop that includes a liquid-to-liquid heat exchanger to provide domestic water heating. Each technology is governed by different safety and performance standards. However, modern boiler and on-demand water heaters share some of the same base technologies and features. For both boilers and on-demand water heaters, there are now many models of wall-hung condensing modulating units that can turn down their outputs to a small fraction of their maximum firing rates. As a result, boiler-based combination systems are also gaining market share in the smaller home market. Some boilers are now also being certified as water heaters so that they can be installed in either application.

In space heating mode, heat is passed from the boiler to the air via a heat exchanger. Because the boiler water is in a closed loop, this arrangement is useful where the water supply is hard or corrosive. For boilers, hot water is typically heated using a plate-to-plate heat exchanger or an indirect tank. In either case, the system may still be subject to fouling and these components need to be accessible for maintenance. Some boiler based systems may provide priority to calls for domestic hot water over calls for space heating. This is because house heat loss is a slow process with long on-duty cycle times, whereas domestic hot-water usage (showers, dishwashing, hand-washing) requires a fast response and is characterized by comparatively short duty cycles.

Boilers differ from instantaneous water heaters in other ways. Using a boiler with an air handler for space heating does not require a short, daily, hot-water circulation cycle during the summer. Many boilers have lower maximum energy outputs than instantaneous water heaters. Boilers require a heat exchanger to heat water. These factors make it more likely that a boiler-based system will also include a form of hot water storage.

Modulating condensing gas boilers can provide very efficient space heating using an air handler. They already require the use of outdoor reset, and this temperature gauge or a duty cycle timer based approach can be used to vary boiler temperature for space heating, keeping it cooler under the part-load conditions that exist almost all the time.

Using non-condensing boilers with an air handler provides a system that works much like a furnace but will be less efficient in space heating mode than a minimum efficiency furnace. Systems that require the boiler to stay hot continuously to provide water heating are less efficient.

16.5 Gas-fired Integrated Mechanical Systems

Integrated mechanical systems can be efficient, require little floor space, be used to provide both forced air and radiant heating within the same home, use only a single vent, and reduce coordination issues between the space heating and ventilation system.

An integrated mechanical system (IMS) is a factory engineered system that provides forced air space heating, domestic hot water, ventilation with heat recovery, and air distribution. Essentially, an IMS is a combination system that also includes a heat or energy recovery ventilator, and is engineered to function as a complete system (Figure 16.5). It may be built entirely within one casing or may come in components designed to be installed together in the field. The heat generator for it may be an on-demand water heater, tank-type water heater, or boiler.

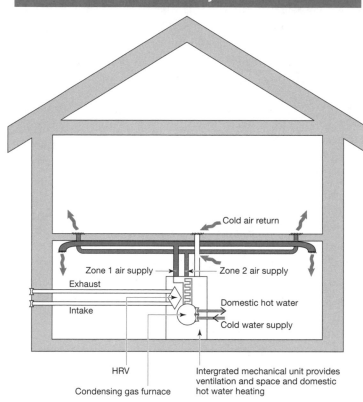

Figure 16.5 Sample layout of an integrated mechanical unit system

Cold air return

Zone 1 air supply → ← Zone 2 air supply

Exhaust

Intake

Domestic hot water

Cold water supply

HRV

Condensing gas furnace

Intergrated mechanical unit provides ventilation and space and domestic hot water heating

Air conditioning and radiant floor heating are optional extras. Air conditioning is added in the same way as it would be with any other forced air heat and distribution system. Where a home is to include radiant as well as forced air heating, a boiler-based IMS would require a similar manifold and controls that a typical boiler based system would use.

The CAN/CSA P.10-07 (R2017) Standard, *Performance of Integrated Mechanical Systems for Residential Heating and Ventilation* was published in 2007. Systems tested to it will have a wide range of standardized performance ratings including those for:

- Space heating capacity;

- Water heating capacity;

- Ventilation system capacity;

- Efficiency ratings in each operating mode; and,

- Overall thermal and electric efficiency ratings.

Like other product classes, IMS systems vary in efficiency and capacity. As with combination systems, capacity and efficiency are challenging to approximate without the use of standardized test results. Builders are encouraged to seek standardized product test results from suppliers.

An IMS product meeting the premium performance levels set within the P.10 standard integrates a modulating, low-mass condensing boiler, a water-to-air heat exchanger with a fan that uses a variable speed brushless permanent magnet motor, a segregated hot-water heater using a brazed plate heat exchanger, and a heat recovery ventilator. It uses advanced controls to continuously monitor performance and automatically adjust its firing rate, blower circulation speed, and load priority.

16.6 Gas Fireplaces and Space Heaters

Gas fireplaces and space heaters can be an effective way of heating a portion of a house. Some gas-fired appliances develop an attractive visual flame and have a special ceramic glass panel to allow viewing while transmitting radiant heat to the room. Other gas fireplaces have convection fans that extract more heat from the appliance and move it into the room. Controls for these units can either be a wall-mounted thermostat or a hand-held remote control. These fireplaces often have direct-vent or induced-draft fan exhaust.

New, efficient gas fireplaces offer the attraction of visual flame and high energy efficiency compared to older versions, but are still less efficient than modern gas furnaces. They may be side- or chimney-vented, depending on the particular appliance. CAN/CSA-P.4.1-15 *Testing Method for Measuring Annual Fireplace Efficiency* provides guidance for selecting a suitable gas fireplace.

Pilot lights in gas fireplaces can consume a significant amount of natural gas over the course of a year. Electronic ignition systems should be chosen for natural gas/propane fireplaces. Although the initial cost is higher than an appliance with a pilot light, the simple payback period is 1 to 2 years. If it is intended that the gas fireplace be used as a back-up heater during power outages, the fireplace needs a non-electric activator for the flame.

16.7 Oil Furnaces (forced- or induced-draft)

Oil furnaces are common in areas where natural gas is not available. The mid-efficiency oil furnace effectively eliminates the barometric damper, with its large air requirement. It may have an induced-draft fan, located downstream of the furnace proper (often at the side wall of the house), which pulls the gases through the furnace and expels them up the stack or out the side wall of a house (Figure 16.6).

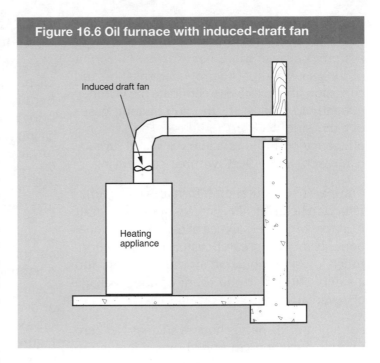

Figure 16.6 Oil furnace with induced-draft fan

An alternative is forced-draft, where a high static pressure drop burner is coupled with a properly baffled furnace, allowing the burner to withstand any pressure fluctuations transmitted from the top of the stack (Figure 16.7).

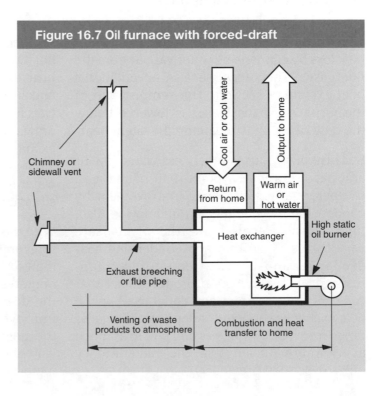

Figure 16.7 Oil furnace with forced-draft

Knowing the exact characteristics of the flue gas allows closer tolerance of the venting system, because more heat can be taken out of the gases without fear of condensation and corrosion. It is possible to eliminate the chimney altogether, exhausting the combustion gases out the side wall of the house. The seasonal efficiency of a mid-efficiency oil-fired furnace can reach nearly 90% without condensing.

Compared to natural-draft furnaces with flame-retention head burners, forced- or induced-draft furnaces offer fuel savings of 5-10%. Additional benefits include greater customer satisfaction, much lower combustion air requirements and a safety shut-off in the event of flue blockage or reversal.

For high performance houses such as Net Zero Energy, designers and builders are looking to get every bit of energy efficiency out of the installed equipment. Natural-draft furnaces are unlikely to be the first choice of these builders, regardless of whether they are oil, gas, or propane.

16.7.1 Condensing oil furnace

A further possibility is a condensing oil furnace, which is designed to recover some of the latent heat loss by condensing water vapour from the flue gases. This takes place in an additional heat-exchange section. The temperature of the furnace exhaust gases is lowered below the dew point, thus regaining the latent heat.

Because oil produces much less water vapour and has a lower dew point than natural gas, the potential for efficiency improvement by condensing the flue gas is much lower. Also, high sulphur levels make the condensate very corrosive, so that any condensing heat exchanger must be extremely corrosion-resistant. Oil combustion produces soot that can concentrate as an acidic condensate on the heat exchange surface. Condensing oil furnaces range from somewhat less efficient to as much as 8% more efficient than the mid-efficiency types described previously.

16.7.2 Use of oil-fired appliances in low-energy houses

A significant problem appears to exist with oil heating systems in low-energy housing. Because of the limitations in burner technology, firing rates cannot be reduced much below 0.4 gallons per hour (70,000 Btu/hr) and minimum furnace outputs of about 60,000 Btu/h. Net Zero Energy and Net Zero Energy Ready houses can have a design heat load between one-third and two-thirds this level.

Combining space and water heating in an integrated system may allow efficient operation of the furnace/boiler without short cycling and the attendant losses in efficiency and comfort, improving the suitability of oil as an energy source for new housing. Figure 16.8 shows a basic system, with the energy generator (usually a low-mass boiler) coupled to a well-insulated storage tank by a water-to-water heat exchanger. Advanced systems include intelligent microprocessor controls and a reversible pumping system. When the thermostat calls for heat, the boiler runs normally.

When the heat level or thermostat set point is reached, the burner continues to run, but the hot water it generates is passed through the heat exchanger, sending heat to the storage tank instead of the house. When the thermostat calls for heat, the process reverses, and heat is drawn out of the storage tank, across the heat exchanger, and distributed around the house, without the boiler operating. If domestic hot water is required, it is taken directly out of the storage tank.

With this type of system, the boiler operational time and the number of cycles are much less than for a conventional system. As the boiler operates more efficiently in heating mode, the domestic hot-water heating efficiency is improved dramatically. This can eliminate the need for a separate electric or oil-fired water heater, and eliminates short-cycling and inefficiency typical of hot-water heating.

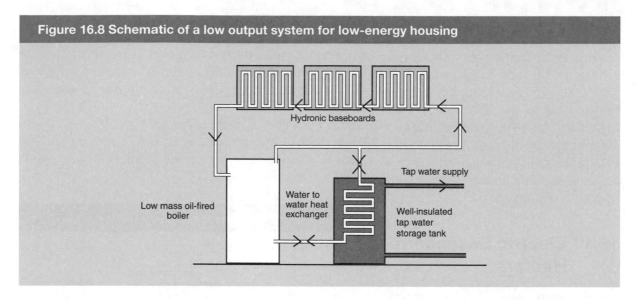

Figure 16.8 Schematic of a low output system for low-energy housing

16.8 Oil-fired Boilers (for hydronic or radiant applications)

An oil-fired boiler is intended for application in a low-pressure steam or hot water central heating system to provide heating via hydronic or radiant heat distribution systems. Unlike gas-fired equipment, installers can configure oil-fired furnaces and boilers on-site to meet the heating requirements of the home.

The nozzle size, which affects the heating capacity, venting arrangement (side wall or chimney) and burner model are three important components that can change the AFUE efficiency and ENERGY STAR® qualification.

16.9 Oil-fired Combination Systems

Combined units that provide space heating and domestic hot-water heating are available with oil-fired heating devices and operate in a similar fashion to the gas units described in Section 16.4.

The combining of space and water heating systems (combos) was first introduced in Canada in the 1980s. Unfortunately, there were problems with the early combo systems – some simply did not provide enough heat. The development of CAN/CSA-P.9-11(R2015), *Test method for determining the performance of combined space and water heating systems (combos)* was intended to ensure combination systems meet basic requirements. The Standard describes the test procedures required to determine the performance, capacities, energy consumption, and overall efficiency of gas-fired and oil-fired combined space and water heating systems (combos).

There are two basic types of oil-fired combination systems:

• Water-heater-based combination systems; and

• Boiler-based combination systems.

Combination systems allow oil-fired systems to be decoupled from space heating demand so that the furnace operates less frequently and for a longer period of time.

16.10 Electric Furnaces and Boilers

Electric furnaces use a forced-air distribution system and a centrally located thermostat. An electric furnace consists of a number of resistance coils and a circulating fan. The coils are capable of being operated with staging controls to limit swings in temperature. In a house with a very low heat load, it may even be possible to use a simple in-duct heater and fan to provide heating and air circulation. Electric boilers, with resistance coils immersed in water, are available for homes heated with hydronic systems.

16.11 Electric Baseboard Heaters

Electric baseboards and other room-by-room systems allow each room to be individually thermostatically controlled, either with a low voltage thermostat or a CSA-certified line voltage wall-mounted thermostat. This type of system has been popular because of its very low initial costs, ease of installation and the extremely long life of the equipment. Lower-temperature heating element units such as liquid-filled electric baseboard heaters may reduce the problem of dust charring, and may have some comfort and air quality benefits.

The advantages of individual room control and low initial costs have to be weighed against the cost of operation for the homeowner, unless heat losses can be minimized. A separate distribution system must be installed for ventilation air. In addition, for energy-efficient building envelopes, it makes less sense to control the temperature of each room; it is more practical to mix the air to take advantage of passive solar heat gains. For these reasons, electric baseboard heating is not considered a best choice as a primary source of heating for Net Zero Energy Homes.

16.12 Air Source Heat Pumps

Air source heat pumps (Figure 16.9) extract heat from the outside air. The colder it is outside, the less heat is available from the heat pump due to the wide temperature difference between the source and the delivery. Air source heat pumps are most efficient when the outside temperature is about 7°C (45°F), but at that outside temperature, an energy-efficient house needs very little heat.

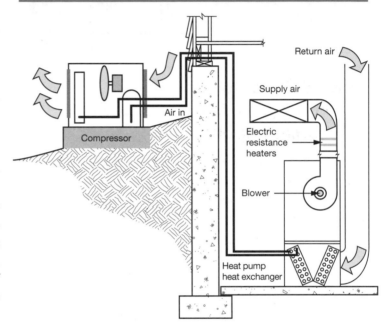

Figure 16.9 Electric heat pump

Air source heat pumps require integrated supplemental heat when the outdoor air temperature is too low. Most heat pumps are manufactured with an electric resistance heat coil to provide supplemental heat. However, air source heat pumps can also be coupled to fossil-fuel-fired furnaces. In either case, the heat pump shuts off when the outside temperature falls below a certain point, and the house heating is supplied by the supplemental heating. The heat pump should be controlled by the outside temperature to prevent short cycling of the fossil-fuel furnace, an inefficient and potentially corrosive mode of operation.

Cold Climate Air Sourced Heat Pumps (CCASHP)

Whereas the performance of older air source heat pumps drops dramatically at 0 to -10°C, cold-climate air-source heat pumps are available to supply up to 100% of a home's heating needs without back-up for weather conditions as cold as -25°C, and are available and being used in Net Zero Energy housing today.

CCASHP come in two forms; ducted and non-ducted. Ducted systems have the indoor coil installed in the ductwork of the furnace and use the existing ducts to each room for delivering space heating and space cooling. Non-ducted systems use an indoor coil mounted in an indoor unit in each room. The indoor unit is usually attached to a wall or ceiling and it provides heat or cooling to that space. Up to 8 indoor units can be run from one outdoor unit, thereby creating 8 zones with a house.

Whereas the conventional ASHP has difficulty providing sufficient heating capacity at low outdoor temperatures, the CCASHP uses variable capacity technologies which can efficiently meet space heating loads at low ambient temperatures. CCASHP are relatively new and designers and builders are learning about their capabilities. Better simulation tools will help with their adoption, but so will shared field experiences with the technology.

For Net Zero Energy builders, the technology offers the potential for single fuel houses. Conventional ASHP systems are often combined with a natural gas furnace to take advantage of the high performance (greater than 100%) of the heat pump down to 0°C, and then switching to a lower cost fuel to provide the heat below that temperature. The CCASHP offers the improved performance to -35°C. In much of Canada the temperature will dip to -35°C but it does not remain there for long amounts of time. It may be an acceptable trade-off to use electric resistance heaters for these times rather than bringing in a second fuel type. Keeping the house as "all-electric" also allows energy generated by the PV system to be directly used by all of the equipment in the house.

16.13 Earth Energy Heat Pumps

Earth energy systems, also known as geothermal or ground-source heat pump systems, use the earth or groundwater as a source of heat in the winter and as a heat sink in the summer for air conditioning (Chapter 22). Because the ground or groundwater below the frost line is at a relatively constant temperature throughout the year (well above outdoor temperatures in winter and below them in summer), it provides a constant heat source for a heat pump to heat both the house and the hot water.

The initial cost of an earth energy system is high compared to air source heat pumps because of the need for trenches or a borehole, but the efficiency in terms of COP is very high (3.0-3.5), so operating costs are much lower than for other electric systems. In areas where electricity is the only fuel source, (either due to location or by choice of the designers), ground source heat pumps may be cost-effective over the long term.

Due to the complexity of earth energy systems, they should be designed and installed by qualified, experienced contractors, and local maintenance providers should be available to assist the homeowner.

16.14 Wood-fired Space Heating Appliances

Wood-fired space heating appliances are available in a variety of forms: stoves, furnaces, boilers, and fireplaces, for both heating and recreational uses. In many locations, wood heating is an economical way of providing primary or secondary heat. Wood is also a renewable source of energy. The challenge is to burn it as efficiently and cleanly as possible.

For some consumers, wood heat is the fuel of choice, providing self-sufficiency, security of supply, greater comfort, utilization of a renewable resource, and a low-cost source of energy. However, wood heating requires more work than some owners wish to do, and therefore the resale value of a house with only wood heating needs to be considered. Some homeowners may wish to have a wood heater as a back-up to a conventional heating system for use in emergencies, especially in locations subject to frequent electric service interruptions.

- Like any combustion system, wood-burning equipment needs to be designed and installed carefully to ensure safe operation. Chimney types, flue connections, clearance to combustible surfaces, spark arrestors and all other installation factors must comply with codes and insurance requirements. Other considerations are:

- Wood fuel requires considerable storage space and protection from snow and rain.

- If wood is stored indoors and not dry, it will add a significant amount of humidity to the indoor environment as it dries. It can also be a habitat for insects. Indoor storage and/ or drying of wood is not a recommended practice for any house.

- For consistent heat, the fire must be fuelled at regular intervals. The exception is for masonry heaters (Section 16.14.5) or boilers that are integrated with heat storage.

- A back-up heating system should be provided to ensure the home's temperature doesn't fall too low during extended absences.

- Conventional wood stoves can have very poor combustion efficiency during low burn, resulting in smoke and flammable tar deposits.

- The user must become knowledgeable about the heating system's operation and maintenance requirements to optimize efficiencies and avoid hazardous situations.

Table 16.3 Emission characteristics of wood-burning appliances				
Type of wood-heating appliance	Emissions			
	Particulates less than or equal to 2.5 microns (dia.) (PM$_{2.5}$) g/kg	Carbon monoxide (CO) g/kg	Volatile organic compounds (VOCs) g/kg	Polycyclic aromatic hydrocarbons (PAHs) g/kg
Wood-burning fireplace				
Fireplace without glass doors	18.4	77.7	6.5	0.0375
with glass doors	12.9	98.6	21	0.0375
Fireplace with insert conventional	13.6	115.4	21.3	0.215
advanced (catalytic)	4.8	70.4	7	0.064
Wood-burning stove				
Conventional stove non airtight	23.2	100	35.5	0.215
airtight	13.6	115.4	21.3	0.276
Advanced technology stove	4.8	70.4	7	0.064
Central furnace/boiler	13.3	68.5	21.3	0.288
Pellet stove	1.1	8.8	1.5	0.0015
Masonry heater	1.5	25	3.0 (est.)	0.01 (est.)

- Regular cleaning of the wood-burning appliance and chimney is required.

Emissions from some types of wood-fired appliances can cause indoor and outdoor air quality problems that can impact occupants and neighbours. On the other hand, some types offer superior environmental performance (Table 16.3).

16.14.1 Conventional fireplaces

Conventional decorative fireplaces are between -5% and +20% efficient. In other words, they supply little if any energy to the house, particularly when it is cold outside. One of the main reasons for the extremely low efficiency of a conventional fireplace is its large air requirement (about 1.5 air changes per hour in a typical house) that draws large quantities of heated air out of the house and out the chimney.

In some conditions, fireplaces can release hazardous pollutants indoors. For example, if a fireplace is smouldering and an occupant turns on a device with an exhaust fan such as a clothes dryer, the suction from the dryer can overpower the chimney draft and draw smoke back into the house. Furthermore, depressurization caused by the fireplace can also affect the performance of other combustion appliances, causing them to spill combustion products into the house. Finally, conventional fireplaces emit large quantities of outdoor air pollutants in the form of suspended particulates. Devices such as glass doors, heat exchangers and the provision of dedicated makeup air improve the efficiency marginally (up to a maximum of perhaps 20%), but have only a limited effect on the indoor and outdoor pollution problems. For these reasons, conventional fireplaces are not recommended for energy-efficient homes.

16.14.2 Advanced combustion wood fireplaces

Advanced wood combustion designs are now being utilized by Canadian manufacturers to produce advanced combustion wood-burning fireplaces. These have: airtight doors to allow clear viewing of the flame and good infrared heat transmission; an insulated outer casing; good heat exchange; and an effective circulating fan to supply heat to the house. Most importantly, the emissions of incomplete combustion products are greatly reduced compared with to a conventional fireplace. Advanced combustion wood-burning fireplaces can supply energy to the house at about 70% efficiency; however, in order to achieve this performance, units meeting the emissions criteria of either EPA 2016 or CSA B-415.1 must be used. Only wood-burning fireplaces that satisfy these criteria meet the requirements of the R-2000 Program and therefore the Net Zero Energy Program Technical Requirements. In all cases, advanced combustion wood fireplaces must be operated competently, using good quality fuel that is well seasoned.

16.14.3 Space heating wood stoves

Wood can be a useful energy source when burned in a well-designed, airtight wood stove, properly located in a major living area and vented directly into its own chimney, or into the fireplace chimney, if it has been fitted with a stainless steel liner.

Unlike other fuels, wood does not burn evenly. This means varying amount of waste products (CO, hydrocarbons, ash, particulates and creosote condensate) are emitted as the wood burns. The slower the rate of combustion, the higher the release of products of incomplete combustion. In conventional airtight stoves, a large quantity of these incomplete combustion products escape the burning process and are deposited in the chimney as creosote or are emitted to the environment as air pollutants. Creosote deposit poses a risk of chimney fire; regular cleaning is essential for safe operation.

Chimney location

Chimneys should be located inside the house so that most of their length is contained within the heated envelope of the house, only penetrating to the outside near their termination. This placement will keep the mass of the chimney warmer, reducing build-up of creosote in the chimney, allowing additional heat transfer to the indoor environment, and maintaining the draft once it has been established.

Traditional house designs with exterior flue installations are not safe because they permit the flue to cool down too quickly as a fire dies down. If the draft in the flue is lost before the fire has been extinguished (as can happen in cool weather), toxic gases can spill into the house rather than be vented to the exterior.

16.14.4 Advanced combustion wood stoves

Advanced combustion wood stoves give better combustion and are able to burn cleaner at lower heat outputs. There are a number of designs, employing advanced combustion techniques and/or catalytic converters, to reduce the amount of incomplete combustion products and to increase efficiency.

Advanced combustion wood stoves (Figure 16.10) significantly reduce emissions of incomplete combustion products and increase efficiency 10-20% relative to conventional wood stoves. They can be effective complements to conventional heating systems in many regions of the country. They offer the potential to displace 60-70% of the fossil fuel used for central heating in these regions, with some reduction in overall CO2 emissions. They are also ideally suited for use in electrically heated homes, easily displacing 70% of the electricity used for space heating.

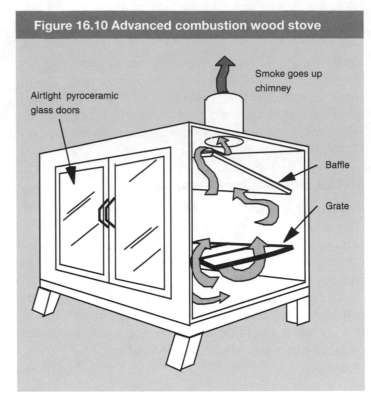

Figure 16.10 Advanced combustion wood stove

Airtight pyroceramic glass doors

Smoke goes up chimney

Baffle

Grate

16.14.5 Masonry heaters

A masonry heater is a site-built or site-assembled, solid-fueled heating device constructed mainly of masonry materials. It burns wood fuel rapidly at high temperatures. Heat is stored in the mass of the appliance and is then gradually released over 8 to 10 hours as radiant heat. The combination of rapid combustion and heat storage results in high efficiency and excellent resistance to spillage. The heater has an interior construction consisting of a firebox and heat exchange channels built from refractory components, and has the following characteristics:

- A mass of at least 800 kg. (1760 lbs.);

- Tight-fitting doors that are closed during the burn cycle;

- An overall average wall thickness not exceeding 250 mm (10 in.);

- Under normal operating conditions, the external surface of the masonry heater, except immediately surrounding the fuel loading door(s), does not exceed 110°C (230°F);

- The exhaust gas path through the internal heat exchange channels downstream of the firebox includes at least one 180-degree change in flow direction, usually downward, before entering the chimney; and,

- The length of the shortest single path from the firebox exit to the chimney entrance is at least twice the largest firebox dimension.

Masonry heaters can be a very good match for low energy houses because they are capable of delivering low heat outputs without compromising performance. Heat storage provided by the thermal mass allows an optimum burn rate to be used for combustion without overheating the house.

Masonry heaters work best in houses with open floor plans. Because of their mass, structural supports for them need to be considered at the design stage. They are available in kits that are installed by a mason, or as factory-made units that can be directly installed. Some jurisdictions do not yet permit masonry heaters because, despite their good performance record, standards governing their design and installation do not yet exist. However, standards development is in progress in Canada.

Masonry heaters are now recognized in the USA in the International Building Code (IBC) and International Residential Code (IRC) as an extension of the masonry fireplace provisions, and which reference ASTM 1602-03 (2010). In Canada they meet all of the requirements of the masonry fireplaces section of the NBC if the "function statement" version is used for the smoke chamber angle requirement.

16.14.6 Central wood-fired systems

Outdoor wood furnaces offer a good level of combustion and the fuel never comes inside the house. They can be considered a primary heat supply for properties that have room for the proper siting of the furnace and fuel. However, conventional outdoor furnaces are extremely dirty and are now illegal to sell in the USA. They are now included in the New Source Performance Standard (NSPS) (EPA regulated) as of 2016. It is recommended that only EPA certified outdoor furnaces should be installed in order to ensure higher levels of environmental protection and improved efficiency.

Indoor central wood-burning furnaces and boilers distribute heat to the house via a central system controlled by a thermostat, which regulates the heat output by cycling the furnace. Many central systems are oversized for the house. In addition, contrary to the practice of on/off cycling with oil or gas furnaces, wood-burning furnaces/boilers cycle between high and low fire. This can produce incomplete combustion products on each cycle change. To address this, new generation boilers incorporate thermal storage tanks to allow intermittent firing at optimized burn rates.

16.14.7 Wood pellet appliances

Wood pellet appliances provide several advantages. The pellet fuel is produced from dried, finely ground wood waste that is compressed into hard pellets about the diameter of a pencil and up to 2 cm (1 in.) in length, and is clean to store and handle. Once an 18.1 kg (40 lb.) bag of pellets is loaded into its hopper, a stove can run automatically for up to 24 hours, as pellets are metered gradually into a small combustion chamber.

Efficiency varies widely from fair to excellent, so a careful review of manufacturers' literature is important. Emissions are generally low to very low (Table 16.3). *Performance is based on CSA B415.1-10, Performance testing of solid-fuel-burning heating appliances.*

The stove's fans and pellet delivery augers need electricity to operate, so an electrical power failure causes them to shut down. A small battery back-up system is a good extra feature that will provide electricity to keep the stove's exhaust fans running long enough to burn the fuel left in the combustion chamber and expel the remaining exhaust to the outside.

The amount of air needed for optimum combustion efficiency is delivered automatically or with minor manual adjustments. In most designs, a fan delivers air to the fire and blows exhaust by-products out of a vent pipe that is smaller and typically less expensive than a chimney. A fan then delivers heat to the home by blowing air through heat exchangers in the stove and out into the home.

Advanced pellet stoves include automatic ignition and temperature output accurately regulated by a wall thermostat. Some stoves are capable of running via a remote thermostat. Proper venting is essential for ideal appliance performance, dwelling safety, maintenance frequency, and indoor environment conditions. Pellet stoves produce little or no visible smoke after start-up, but exhaust gases, fine ash, and water vapour must be removed safely from the appliance to the outdoors.

For most designs, the exhaust is mechanical: a fan blows the combustion by-products out and pulls air needed for combustion into the fire. A few types operate without a combustion air fan and use natural draft both for exhaust and combustion air intake.

Sidewall horizontal venting is the least expensive venting system but increases the risk of smoke spilling into the house in the event of a power outage, component failure, or house depressurization. Vents for appliances designed without mechanical exhaust fans must meet stove manufacturer's requirements for minimum draft and must terminate above the roof.

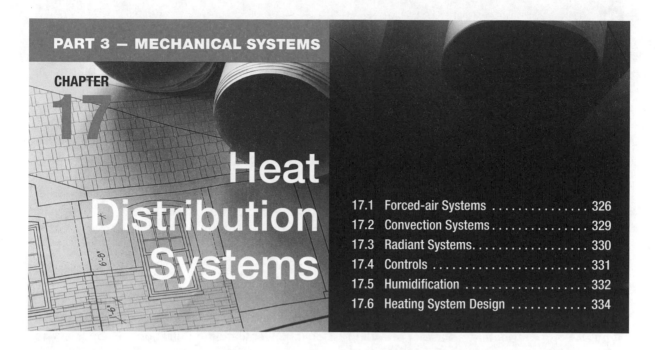

PART 3 — MECHANICAL SYSTEMS

CHAPTER

17

Heat Distribution Systems

House space conditioning requires a means of supplying and distributing heating and/or cooling efficiently to maintain comfort conditions. In addition, ventilation systems are required to supply fresh air and exhaust stale air. There may also be requirements for filtration and/or humidity control of indoor air.

In Canada, heating and ventilation are regarded as essential elements of a home's mechanical system. Other space conditioning systems, such as cooling systems, humidification and air filtration, may also be added, depending on the needs of a particular market or the preferences of a particular client.

This Chapter presents various heat distribution systems that can be used to meet the space conditioning requirements of a house.

17.1 Forced-air Systems

A forced-air system is the one heating system that can easily provide the space conditioning requirements of a house (Table 17.1). When properly designed, a forced warm-air distribution system can be used to distribute heating, cooling and ventilation air, and the air can be easily humidified, dehumidified or filtered. This is advantageous, as it is generally less costly to use a single duct system to distribute heating, ventilating and/or cooling air than it is to install separate distribution systems.

A typical central forced-air system is shown in Figure 17.1. In winter, the circulating air can help distribute heat gain from point sources such as the sun or a wood stove through the house. This reduces temperature variations in the house and overall heating requirements. However, individual room or zone temperature control can be more complicated. Thermostatically controlled dampers can be used, as can branch duct heaters with room thermostat controls (Section 17.4), to provide zone control.

Table 17.1 Comparison of space conditioning distribution systems						
Type	**Heating**	**Ease of providing zoning**	**Cooling**	**Ventilation**	**Filtration**	**Humidification**
Forced-air	√	Complex	√	√	√	√
Convection Electric Hydronic	√ √	Easy Moderate	* *	* *	* *	* *
In-floor radiant	√	Moderate	*	*	*	*

*Separate system required

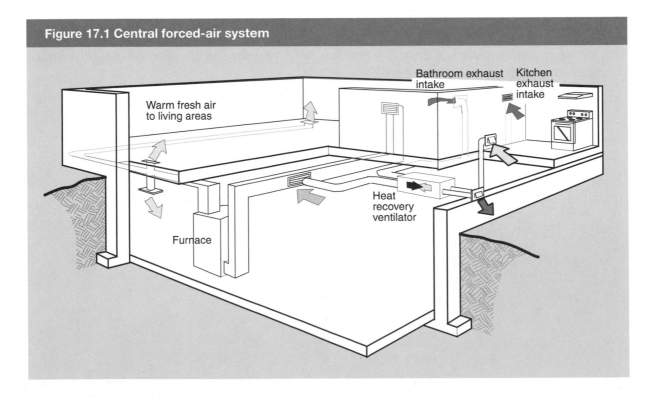

Figure 17.1 Central forced-air system

Warm fresh air to living areas

Bathroom exhaust intake

Kitchen exhaust intake

Heat recovery ventilator

Furnace

17.1.1 Design considerations

The sizing and design of the duct system should be based on the *Residential Air System Design Manual* and the *Residential Mechanical Ventilation Systems Manual* from the Heating, Refrigerating and Air-conditioning Institute of Canada (HRAI). The volume of air required for heating is generally much larger than the volume of air required for ventilation in houses build to current Code requirements. (Building to Net Zero levels of performance are challenging this rule.) Consequently, if a duct system is required to serve both heating and ventilation, its sizing is governed by heating, but the outlet and return locations are based on ventilation requirements. The sizing of the branch ducts is based on a standard room heat loss and/or heat gain analysis.

If the ducting is used to supply ventilation air as well as heating and cooling air, the circulating fan must be operated continuously. This can add significantly to the energy budget of a home. For example, the energy consumption for an older single-speed fan operated continuously can be as high as 4,000 kWh per year. In winter, heat generated by fans can contribute heat to the house (an electrical cost, rather than a fossil fuel cost) but during the rest of the year, it is an unwanted heat gain.

If the ducting is used to supply ventilation air as well as heating and cooling air, an electronically commutated motor (ECM) should be used. Such furnace motors use as little as 1,000 kWh per year, with the fan running continuously. A two-speed fan runs most of the time at the lower speed to provide circulation and ventilation, and at the higher speed when there is a demand for heating, but is not as energy-efficient as an ECM.

Another alternative is to provide a separate distribution system for ventilation air and the heat recovery ventilator (HRV) rather than use the furnace motor to move air continuously. The smaller motor can save energy that can make the payback period for the dedicated duct system reasonable.

If the system is designed to carry cooling air as well, larger ducts may be needed because of the increased volumes of air that cooling systems must carry, relative to heating systems. Most forced-air heating systems introduce warm air into a room at a low level, since warm air naturally rises. Conversely, because cool air falls, it seems logical to provide cool air at a higher level. For distribution systems performing both functions, a good compromise is a floor system that can direct the cold air upwards with sufficient velocity to reach the ceiling.

In well-insulated, airtight houses such as Net Zero Energy, the location of outlets becomes less important for heat distribution, but it is always important to design outlet locations so that they do not cause comfort complaints due to excessive air movement. Certain register locations such as ceilings or high on walls work well when a distribution system is used for both ventilation and cooling.

Other forced-air system design considerations are as follows:

- To maximize efficiency and to avoid possible moisture damage, ducts should not penetrate the outside walls or attic space.

- Duct runs through unheated areas should be avoided. Where this cannot be avoided, the ducts must be insulated and all joints must be sealed to reduce heat loss.

- To avoid condensation in ducts, cold air ducting for central air conditioning or outside air intakes must be insulated and provided with a sealed, external vapour diffusion retarder.

- To minimize friction losses and to reduce fan power requirements, the ductwork should be adequately sized, have smooth junctions, the lowest possible number of elbows and transitions, short runs and turning vanes for tight corners.

- Adequate cold air returns must be installed in areas that are not likely to be blocked by furniture.

- All joints in return and supply air ducts, especially those that will be hidden and inaccessible after construction is completed, should be sealed with a special duct sealing compound (mastic) that is available from heating wholesalers. Some types of metal foil duct tape may also have the required adhesion and durability at elevated temperatures. Liquid sealants that are atomized and sprayed into ducts to seal them are now available.

- High-efficiency furnaces have higher airflow requirements than older, less efficient furnaces; therefore, ductwork may have to be larger than for older furnaces.

- If the heating/cooling system is to be used to distribute ventilation air as well, the ventilation air will need to be tempered to ensure that the temperature of the air being discharged from the supply air outlets is above 18°C (65°F). Alternatively, high inside-wall supply outlets can be provided to prevent cold drafts from causing occupant discomfort.

- Any duct carrying air cooler than 13°C (55°F) must be insulated and the insulation covered with a vapour barrier to prevent condensation.

It has been standard practice to locate heating vents under windows, which are the coldest surfaces in a room and keeping them relatively warm reduces condensation. As window insulating values increase (the use of triple glazing, for example), using heating ducts to warm window surfaces is less of a concern. Experience with highly insulated and air-tight construction is that heat outlets can be moved high onto interior walls without affecting window condensation. The placement of heating outlets high on walls can reduce the amount of ductwork required and leave floors uncluttered by registers. Experience has also shown that Net Zero Energy buildings can use

small diameter ducts (2") with high velocity air to satisfy the heating, cooling and ventilation needs. For selection of the distribution system it is useful to know the heat load of each room using F280 in order to determine the amount of air to move into each room. (See Appendix 3 for an example of using F280.)

17.1.2 Zoning

Zoning is one way of providing more even and more controlled comfort to homes that may have localized overheating issues or zones that cool faster than others. Warm air rising and cool air falling can stratify the air in a home, making upper floors warmer than lower floors. Homes with a single thermostat on the main floor may have basements that are too cold and upper floors that are too warm. Distinct heating and cooling needs can also result where one face of the home has a vaulted ceiling or there is a large expanse of glass. Deep single homes on narrow lots and deep town-homes can have different heating and cooling needs at the front and back depending on exposure to solar heating. Rooms over garages may cool and heat up more quickly than the rest of the house.

Zoning can be used to reduce these issues. Local thermostats that trigger a call for heating or cooling and open a motorized damper to the zone that has the demand can be used to maintain the temperature balance in each area of the house.

Many different types of forced air zoning are available. Some systems install a damper within each register or branch duct and have a thermostat in each room to control comfort.

Centrally zoned systems typically split the furnace plenum into two or more primary trunks that service different zones (such as different floors) within the house. Some furnace manufacturers now offer add-on zone control packages with a centralized controller. Some air handler manufacturers have physically built the zones and controls into the air handlers so that there is a direct supply take-off for the plenum to each zone.

Some centrally zoned systems function independently from the heating system. The same rate of air flow goes through the heating device whether one or more zones have a heating or cooling demand. These systems often use a dump zone to control static pressure and sound when only one zone is calling for conditioning. Where the controls for the zoned system are integrated with the controls for the space conditioning system, air flow is typically reduced when less zones have a demand.

17.2 Convection Systems

Convection systems distribute heat by warm air buoyancy, such as: hydronic (hot water) central heating systems; space heaters such as electric baseboard heaters; balanced flue, gas-fired baseboard heaters; or wall-mounted heaters. If a convection heating system is installed, there must be a separate duct system for the distribution of ventilation air.

Convection heating systems rely on natural convection currents (warm air rises, cool air falls), sometimes with a fan assist, to distribute heat throughout a room (Figure 17.2). Such units may be independent, as in room-by-room convector systems, or they may be connected, as in hydronic systems. In either case, air heated by convectors rises and is replaced by cooler air flowing in from the rest of the room, resulting in a convective loop with heat being distributed throughout the room.

A room-by-room heat loss analysis is required to size the individual room convectors. These can be controlled individually (as required by the electrical code for electric heaters) or in zones by using one central control. If more than one room is serviced by a central control, sizing of the convectors is especially critical. All spaces within a zone must have similar thermal responses and heating requirements. This usually leads to floor-by-floor control or north/south zoning. Smaller zones cost more to install but improve space-use flexibility and save energy.

Convectors have traditionally been placed at the floor level of perimeter walls, usually under sources of high heat loss such as windows. In locating convectors, the anticipated placement of furniture and drapes should be considered so that, as the heat rises, it can enter the space without interference.

Convection systems require a separate ventilation system. Because convective heating systems do not move air through the entire house, other measures need to be provided for cooling, humidifying, dehumidifying or filtering the air, as well as for making optimal use of point heat sources such as solar gains or heat from an advanced combustion fireplace or stove.

Individual room convectors make room temperature and zoning (see Section 17.4) particularly easy. The units can be housed in baseboards or in recesses in floors, walls or cabinets. Electric baseboard heaters are the most common room convectors. They have a low capital cost and no need for exhaust ventilation, but they can be

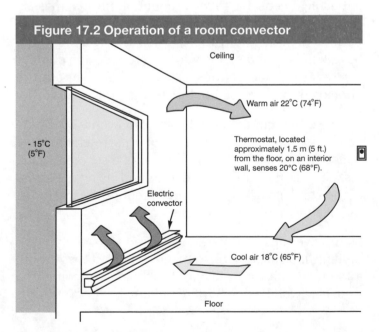

Figure 17.2 Operation of a room convector

Ceiling

Warm air 22°C (74°F)

-15°C (5°F)

Thermostat, located approximately 1.5 m (5 ft.) from the floor, on an interior wall, senses 20°C (68°F).

Electric convector

Cool air 18°C (65°F)

Floor

costly to operate. Direct-vent natural gas-fired convectors, space heaters and efficient fireplaces, oil-fired space heaters, and advanced combustion wood-burning stoves and fireplaces can be cost-effective alternatives. Some of these units, particularly advanced wood stoves and fireplaces and some gas fireplaces, can also function as radiant heaters.

17.3 Radiant Systems

Radiant systems function by transferring heat from one surface to another, largely independent of moving air. Fuel-fired appliances can effectively provide both radiant and convective heat. However, the term radiant is usually applied to systems that use hydronic or electric resistance elements to heat floor areas.

Radiant systems work by heating surfaces, usually the ceiling or floor, so the heat radiates into the room, increasing the room's surface temperatures. Air temperatures may be kept lower for equivalent comfort than with other systems. Radiant heat has a particular advantage for areas where occupants may be susceptible to cold (such as bathrooms), or areas of high heat loss (such as entranceways and rooms over concrete floor slabs), or in major living areas, where occupants spend a majority of their time.

Hydronic radiant in-floor systems

Hydronic radiant in-floor systems (Figure 17.3) require special design expertise to ensure the system meets all current regulations, and must be designed in accordance with CSA B214-16 *Installation Code for Hydronic Heating Systems*. Because

heat distribution is by radiation alone, only the area above or below the radiant heating is directly heated.

Radiant heating is a good way to heat ceramic tile or terrazzo floors that may otherwise feel cool. The floor is heated by means of hot water or a glycol mixture flowing through plastic pipes embedded in a concrete topping. This type of system should be installed with a thermostat connected to a sensor in the floor to keep the floor warm but slightly below room temperature. Floor heating systems operate at low temperatures – the surface should not be more than 29°C (85°F), the upper comfort limit for bare feet.

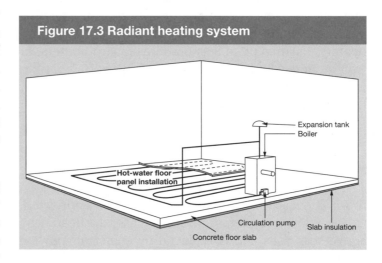

Figure 17.3 Radiant heating system

Expansion tank
Boiler
Hot-water floor panel installation
Circulation pump
Slab insulation
Concrete floor slab

Radiant floor systems respond slowly to rapid changes in heating needs due to the amount of thermal mass in the system, especially concrete floors. This can mean periods of time when there is too much or too little heat in the fall and spring when there are large outdoor temperature fluctuations. An external temperature anticipator can be used to foresee heating needs.

On the other hand, thermal mass can evenly distribute heat over a period of time. For this reason, some builders are treating the basement as a separate zone, installing in-floor radiant heating and using the mass of the concrete basement floor to reduce the cycling of the heating appliance.

Floor coverings can dramatically reduce the ability of radiant floor heating to transfer heat. For this reason, a tile floor will warm faster and cool faster compared to a hardwood floor. When radiant heating systems are installed in basement slabs, insulation is required below the slab to direct the heat up into the liveable space. Radiant floor systems are also used for suspended floors. Insulation may be required in the floor assembly below the heating coils to ensure the heat is directed up into the room above.

Radiant heating systems located in ceilings below roof spaces are subject to losing heat to the outside. Therefore, a high level of insulation and prevention of convective heat loss in the insulation are essential. Ceiling radiant heating systems usually respond faster to demand for heat than heated concrete slab systems, because there is less mass to heat.

Electric radiant floor systems

Electric radiant floor heating uses electric resistance elements embedded in a concrete topping to provide warm floors in selected areas.

Radiant space heaters

A radiant space heater, such as a gas fireplace or a wood stove, can be an effective way of supplying heat to the room where it is situated. Some of the new efficient, direct-vent gas fireplaces, with ceramic glass windows function as effective radiant space heaters.

Advanced combustion wood-burning fireplaces, meeting CSA B-415.1 (R2015) or EPA requirements, are very effective radiant heaters. The flame developed in these units is a radiant heat source, and the ceramic glass which allows viewing of the flame is effectively transparent to infrared radiation, allowing nearly all the infrared energy from the flame into the room. These wood fireplaces can cleanly and efficiently supply a major portion of a home's heating requirements, while using a renewable energy source.

17.4 Controls

Controls are an important part of a good heating system, and are essential for providing comfort.

17.4.1 Thermostats

Temperature can be controlled by a central thermostat, a zone thermostat, or by individual room thermostats. The location of a central thermostat is critical. It should be mounted on an interior wall, away from sources of thermal effects – including direct solar radiation, chimneys, plumbing vents, water pipes, fireplaces, wall ducts for heating and ventilating – and away from sources of drafts, such as stairwells.

Built-in thermostats on electric baseboard convectors are inexpensive, but generally provide poor comfort control because they are located on and influenced by the heat source itself. Therefore, they are best suited for areas not frequently occupied. Wall mounted thermostats are much better for providing comfort. Electronic pulse thermostats that can sense temperature differences as small as 0.5°C are now available and provide excellent service for electric baseboard heating. To avoid short cycling of equipment, care is needed when using pulse thermostats with gas-fired equipment, heat pump systems or radiant floor systems that require a longer run time.

Set-back and programmable thermostats schedule indoor temperatures to automatically reduce room temperature at night or during the day if the house is not occupied.

Controls can be used to smooth out temperature shifts for some heating equipment and systems by varying or staging the heat output according to indoor heat gain/loss, and outdoor temperature changes. This helps to maintain even temperatures and improve comfort.

Outdoor sensors can be used to turn on additional heating capacity as the outdoor temperature drops. They can also start a precisely sized heating plant before the indoor temperature falls, to compensate for sudden changes in outdoor temperature. These can be used to help improve the response of radiant systems to anticipated heating needs.

If advanced control systems are installed, it is important that the homeowner understands how to operate and maintain them. There are several types:

- Programmable set-back thermostats: Recent research has shown that even in energy-efficient homes, set-back strategies save considerable energy. Set-forward (during the cooling season) also saves energy, but the benefit is somewhat diminished. However, in most jurisdictions there is a considerable environmental benefit to widespread set-forward thermostats that results from reduced peak electrical demand. To gain the benefits of programmable thermostats, it is important to select a model that is easy for the homeowner to program and operate. Using programmable thermostats with zoned systems can enable homeowners to increase both winter and summer savings while maintaining more precise comfort conditions in the areas that are occupied.

- Two-stage thermostats: Although not normally required for two-stage furnaces, two-stage thermostats may improve the comfort and energy performance of this type of furnace. They may also be a good choice in heating systems that use multiple stages of heating capacity, in systems using multiple fuel sources, or where one system supplements another.

- Internet-enabled thermostats: Thermostats that can be remotely commanded by the user, either through the Internet or via telephone, offer a powerful enhancement to the set-back or set-forward strategy for

energy conservation. The home can cool to unoccupied mode and be warmed in time for the return of the occupants (see Chapter 23, Home Automation).

- Utility-controlled thermostats: Many utilities offer time-of-use rate structures that discourage electrical consumption during peak hours. These rate structures require 'smart' meters that communicate with the utility electronically to adjust the homeowner's thermostat (rebates and beneficial rates are offered to those who participate). Thermostats that are smart-meter enabled can be set-forward remotely (resulting, for example, in the air conditioning system turning off) as required by the utility in order to avoid power-delivery problems.

17.4.2 Other control devices

Space conditioning equipment can also include humidification and dehumidification devices to adjust the relative humidity of conditioned air in the house. Dehumidification devices are controlled by dehumidistats, which can also be used to control the operation of the mechanical ventilation equipment. Once the relative humidity of conditioned air rises above a certain preset level, the dehumidistat switches the ventilation system into high-speed operation. However, most available humidity controls are not very sensitive, and are difficult for the homeowner to understand.

17.5 Humidification

A humidifier is a device used to raise the relative humidity of a house to a comfortable level. The operation of a central humidifier can be controlled by a room or furnace-mounted humidistat that starts the unit when humidity drops below the set point. In drafty houses, humidifiers were a common addition to many oil and gas furnaces. Modern, more airtight houses have a lower need for humidification.

If a humidifier is to be provided, then the controller and humidifier will operate independently of the furnace or air handling unit, but should be wired so the humidifier controller is powered from the furnace's low voltage power source provided for controls. An interlock should also be provided so that the humidifier can only operate when both a demand for humidity is present and when the main circulation blower is operating.

17.5.1 Evaporative humidifiers

There are three main types of central evaporative humidifiers:

- *By-pass (rotating drum)* humidifiers (Figure 17.4) consist of a drum wrapped with a water-absorbent evaporator pad that rotates and picks up water from a reservoir. As air passes through the pad, it acquires moisture. This type of humidifier is installed on the return air plenum and connected to the supply air plenum with a flexible duct. Water is supplied through a 6 mm (1/4 in.) flexible tube connected to the nearest cold-water pipe.

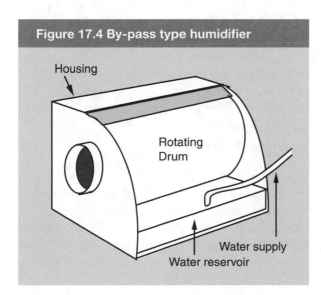

Figure 17.4 By-pass type humidifier

Housing

Rotating Drum

Water supply

Water reservoir

- *Pan type* humidifiers consist of a water pan, heating coils, and a fan with a motor. The heating coils, located in the pan, are warmed by low-pressure steam or forced hot water. Warm air is blown over the pan when the humidistat indicates that the air in the house is too dry. The fan shuts off when the relative humidity rises above the humidistat set point.

- *Stationary pan type* humidifiers consist of a pan and an evaporative pad. Warm air from the supply duct is passed over the pad by a blower or fan when the control system indicates that the relative humidity in the conditioned space is too low.

Minerals in the water can be a problem with evaporative humidifiers. Lime or other mineral deposits can build up on the water reservoir and on the evaporator pad, and when dry, can be circulated through the house as a fine dust. Some humidifiers are equipped with automatic flushing systems to clean out mineral deposits, while others must be cleaned manually.

Mould and bacteria can also build up in the humidifiers if they are not cleaned regularly. These can contribute to poor indoor air quality and health problems for occupants. In addition, humidifiers on central furnaces may leak over time, which could rust the furnace heat exchanger.

17.5.2 Spray-type humidifiers

Spray-type humidifiers convert water into fine mist, which is then converted to a vapour that is absorbed by the drier room air. They consist of a chamber that contains a spray nozzle system, a re-circulating water pump, and a collection tank. As the air passes through the chamber, it comes into contact with the water spray from the nozzles. These humidifiers can be installed on either the supply or the return air plenum, with or without a controlling device.

Any minerals contained in water used in a spray type humidifier will remain in the mist. When the water in the mist evaporates, the minerals are left as a fine dust, which can be blown around the house through the distribution system. Some spray-type humidifiers have filters to avoid this problem.

17.6 Heating System Design

The heating equipment and distribution systems need to be considered early in the design stage, and should consider the following:

- Design trade-offs between heating options and the construction of the house envelope.

- Types of heating equipment currently on the market, and their relative efficiency, cost and performance, especially in terms of comfort.

- Cost, availability and local market preference for heating energy source, including hook-up connection charges for low-volume systems.

- Capital costs.

- Maintenance requirements, parts and servicing availability.

- Implications of heat distribution options including customer preferences, space and locations available in the house, and the possible integration of the heat distribution and ventilation systems.

- Possible integration of space and domestic hot-water heating.

The Annual Fuel Utilization Efficiency rating (AFUE) for heating equipment is a better measure of relative annual fuel consumption than steady-state or peak combustion efficiency. Gas-fired equipment should be referenced in the Canadian Gas Association's *Directory of Certified Equipment*. Oil-fired equipment may have U.S. AFUE figures. Wood-burning equipment should meet CSA B-415.1 or the U.S. EPA 1990 standard.

Natural Resources Canada's ENERGY STAR® lists a wide range of heating, cooling and ventilation equipment that reduce energy consumption.

17.6.1 Energy sources for heating

The choice of heating fuel is influenced by:

- Personal preference of the homeowner;

- Capital costs of associated heating systems;

- Base and projected costs of the energy;

- Efficiency in converting fuel to useful heat;

- Regional or time-of-use fuel price differences; and

- Availability.

Remote regions have special considerations. In northern areas above the tree line, oil is often the best available energy source, as electricity is generated by oil-fired diesel generators and is often far too expensive for space heating. In northern areas below the tree line and in certain other regions where natural gas or fuel oil is not available, wood is often the main fuel for space heating. In other areas, wood can be an effective supplementary heating source.

For homes with low space heating requirements, the difference in operating costs between alternate energy sources may appear to be relatively small. For example, a 20% difference in energy costs may translate to a $50-$60 saving on an annual fuel bill; a 50% difference would save $125-$150 per year.

Many utilities have minimum prices or service charges, such as monthly billings, which can significantly affect the cost per unit of energy at low usage rates. In some cases, a utility may even impose a premium to hook up a system for a house with low projected fuel consumption.

Table 17.2 presents unit energy values for most common sources in Canada. Operating costs for various heating systems can be estimated as follows:

$$\frac{\text{Estimated annual}}{\text{heating energy cost}} = \frac{\text{Estimated annual energy demand x Cost per unit of energy}}{\text{Energy content}}$$

Table 17.2 Energy contents of fuels	
Fuel	**Energy content**
Fuel oil	38.2 MJ/l
Natural gas	37.5 MJ/m³
Propane	91.5 MJ/m³ (25.3 MJ/l)
Electricity	3.6 MJ/kWh
Hardwood (dry)	25,000 MJ/cord
Softwood (dry)	18,700 MJ/cord
Wood pellets	19,800 MJ/tonne

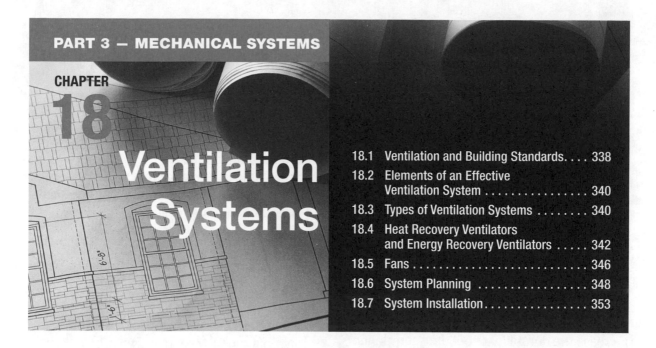

PART 3 — MECHANICAL SYSTEMS

CHAPTER

18

Ventilation Systems

Through the R-2000 Program, it has been demonstrated that more energy can be saved by constructing an airtight building envelope and providing heat recovery ventilation than simply by adding insulation to a leaky building. As builders strive to reach higher levels of energy efficiency by making houses more airtight and adding further insulation, the need to ventilate increases to ensure not only the health of the occupants, but also the durability of the building.

In terms of regulation for ventilation systems, there are two applicable standards: the National Building Code of Canada (NBC) Section 9.32; and CAN/CSA-F326-M91(R2014), *Residential Mechanical Ventilation Systems*. Since the NBC is used as a model code, provincial governments may have modified this section, so local provincial codes should be consulted.

This chapter reviews the two compliance paths, provides a review of ventilation strategies, and presents other information about ventilation system components.

18.1 Ventilation and Building Standards

Houses are increasingly built more airtight. This is due to the development of tools and materials that make it easier for builders to achieve higher levels of airtightness and because some builders are actively striving to achieve higher levels of airtightness. Net Zero Energy and Net Zero Energy Ready builders and designers see the important role airtightness plays in achieving the energy target for the house. As a result of these airtightness accomplishments, mechanical ventilation must be provided to meet occupant needs for good indoor air quality and to control humidity in order to increase the durability of building components. The need for mechanical ventilation has been recognized in Canadian building codes.

This Manual focuses on the benefits of airtight construction; for this reason, only balanced ventilation systems are described in detail. Systems that rely on infiltration or exfiltration of air through unintentional cracks and holes in the building envelope are not consistent with the goals of energy-efficient construction. They are mentioned only for information purposes, but their use is not encouraged.

18.1.1 National Building Code of Canada

The National Building Code of Canada (NBC) requires mechanical ventilation systems in all residential buildings. Every dwelling unit supplied with electrical power must be provided with a mechanical ventilation system complying with either:

1. CAN/CSA-F326 *Residential Mechanical Ventilation Systems*; or

2. Prescriptive systems as described in NBC Subsection 9.32.3., which provides a prescriptive compliance method that is loosely based on the F326 standard.

All mechanical ventilation systems complying with NBC Section 9.32 must include:

- A principal ventilation system capable of continuously ventilating at a rate governed by the number of bedrooms: The system must include an exhaust fan and a means for introducing, tempering, and distributing outdoor replacement air (exhaust-only systems introduce air by infiltration, and acceptable levels of tempering are assumed to occur as infiltration air mixes with conditioned house air).

- Exhaust from all bathrooms and kitchens: This can be provided in whole or in part by the principal ventilation system exhaust fan, or by supplemental exhaust fans.

- Protection against depressurization and air pollutants: Measures must be taken to minimize exposure to soil gas, combustion products and contaminated air from attached garages. Where soil gas is a significant risk, a) an active soil gas mitigation system must be installed, or b) a make-up air system is required to offset house depressurization caused by the operation of any exhaust device other than the principal ventilation fan operating at normal operating exhaust capacity. For b), this means make-up air is required for exhaust fans, HRVs and ERVs that have exhaust-only defrost, clothes dryers, central vacuums, range hoods and other cooktop and oven exhaust devices.

- Make-up air systems for exhaust devices if fuel-fired space and/or water heating devices are not direct-vented or mechanically vented.

- Carbon monoxide detectors in specific locations: This is a requirement in all dwellings that contain fuel-burning appliances or have attached garages.

- Fans that comply with airflow and sone (noise) ratings: Fans that are less than 1 m (3.3 ft.) from adjacent living spaces must meet the following sound rating requirements:

◇ 2.0 sones or less for principal ventilation fans

◇ 2.5 sones or less for supplemental fans installed in bathrooms

The normal operating exhaust capacity of the principal ventilation fan is calculated based on the number of bedrooms in the home. The principal exhaust fan must be sized to provide this ventilation capacity. Requirements for the principal exhaust fan can be met by one fan or a group of fans, provided that a controller manages all fans simultaneously. The principal exhaust fan should also be linked to a supply fan system so that ventilation air is supplied to the home; however, the NBC permits exhaust-only systems in some types of houses.

If the principal ventilation fan does not exhaust the kitchen and bathrooms, supplemental fans (rated at 50 L/s and 25 L/s respectively) are required in these rooms. If the principal ventilation fan does exhaust the kitchen, it must have a high exhaust rate equal to or exceeding 2.5 times its normal operating capacity.

Whenever the principal exhaust fan is operating, the ventilation air must be ducted to the main living area and to each bedroom, as well as to every storey of the house.

18.1.2 Canadian Standards Association F326

CAN/CSA-F326-M91 (R 2014) *Residential Mechanical Ventilation Systems* is a guide for effective ventilation systems. The R-2000 Program requires compliance with CSA-F326, as does Net Zero Energy and Net Zero Energy Ready. It is a performance standard that requires a continuous level of ventilation based on the number and types of rooms in a house. Two essential requirements are:

• The ventilation system must be capable of distributing air at a rate calculated by factoring in the main living rooms of the house. This rate is called the total ventilation capacity (TVC). The TVC is based on 5 L/second (10 cfm) for each room, and 10 L/second (20 cfm) for the master bedroom and the basement (Table 18.1). For continuous operation, the system must have controls capable of operating the system at 40% to 60% of the TVC. Exhaust capacity must be supplied in the kitchen and bathrooms, and a higher value of exhaust is necessary if continuous exhaust is not supplied to these rooms.

• Make-up air must be supplied to the house to offset pressure imbalances where an air-exhausting device, or group of devices operated by a single control, has a net exhaust capacity greater than 75 L/s (150 cfm). This requirement applies if there are combustion appliances susceptible to combustion gas spillage in the house.

Table 18.1 Calculation of total ventilation requirements for a typical 3-bedroom home	
Room	**Ventilation requirement**
Master bedroom	10 L/s (20 cfm)
Bedroom #2	5 L/s (10 cfm)
Bedroom #3	5 L/s (10 cfm)
Bathroom	5 L/s (10 cfm)
Kitchen	5 L/s (10 cfm)
Living room	5 L/s (10 cfm)
Dining room	5 L/s (10 cfm)
Family room	5 L/s (10 cfm)
Laundry room	5 L/s (10 cfm)
Bathroom	5 L/s (10 cfm)
Basement	10 L/s (20 cfm)
Total ventilation requirement (TVC)	**65 L/s (130 cfm)**

18.2 Elements of an Effective Ventilation System

An effective ventilation system has a number of important characteristics:

- It must provide a continuous base level of ventilation.

- Ventilation air should be supplied to all habitable rooms.

- The system should have additional capacity above the base level that can be turned on either manually or automatically, when needed.

- In houses with naturally aspirated, spillage-susceptible, fuel-fired equipment, the ventilation system must not impose a negative pressure on the house which might result in the spillage (backdrafting) of combustion gases into the house.

- Air exhausted from the building should be taken from those areas where the highest level of water vapour and pollutants are likely (e.g., kitchens, bathrooms, workshops, etc.).

- The fresh air supply should be the cleanest possible.

- The system must be acceptable to the homeowner in terms of comfort and noise levels.

- The ventilation system should be cost-effective to install and operate.

- It should include heat recovery capability.

18.3 Types of Ventilation Systems

There are three basic configurations of mechanical ventilation systems:

- Balanced supply and exhaust;

- Exhaust-only; and

- Supply-only.

18.3.1 Balanced supply and exhaust systems

The recommended ventilation method combines balanced exhaust and supply in a single ventilation system (Figure 18.1). This makes it possible to control both the quantity of air exhausted from the space and the quality and quantity of air supplied to the occupants.

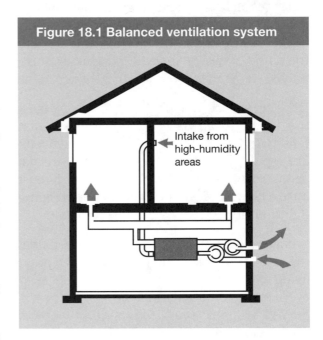

Figure 18.1 Balanced ventilation system

Intake from high-humidity areas

A balanced system is typically designed to maintain a neutral pressure inside the house, so that there is little pressure difference across the envelope caused by the operation of the equipment. Most rooms and all storeys have a fresh air supply and stale air exhaust either directly in each room or indirectly from an adjoining space, usually by way of an undercut door. The fresh air is normally distributed to all living areas of the house through the ductwork of a forced-air heating system or through an independent system of ducts. Stale air is generally exhausted from kitchens, bathrooms and workshops (the main humidity, odour or contaminant-generating areas).

With a balanced system it is possible (and may be necessary) to heat the incoming air for comfort reasons. However, a balanced system affords the opportunity for exchanging heat from the exhaust air stream to the incoming air stream through a heat recovery ventilator (HRV) or energy recovery ventilator (ERV) (see Section 18.4).

18.3.2 Exhaust-only systems

This system exhausts air from the house by means of one or more fans (Figure 18.2), and is not permitted in some jurisdictions. Fresh air enters the house through fresh air inlets and/or through random and uncontrolled cracks and holes in the building envelope when a negative pressure is exerted in the building from the operation of exhaust fans or appliances. Most commonly, outside air is distributed through an intake connected to the duct-work of a forced-air heating system, but this type of system has several potential disadvantages.

Colder air drawn into the house to replace the exhaust air may cause drafts and discomfort unless it is adequately preheated and mixed with house distribution air prior to delivery to the occupied areas of the home. Some furnace manufacturers void heat exchanger warranties because cold air from the furnace return can cause cracking and condensation.

The negative pressure created by the exhaust fan(s) could cause outside air to be drawn into the building through the chimneys of fireplaces, wood stoves, water heaters and other vented combustion appliances. This could produce spillage or backdrafting.

In areas where soil gas is a concern, exhaust-only systems may also increase the possibility that radon and other gases will be drawn into the house.

18.3.3 Supply-only systems

A supply-only system mechanically pushes fresh air into the house and forces stale air out through chimneys and random, uncontrolled cracks and openings in the building envelope (Figure 18.3). Supply-only systems are not recommended, and are not permitted in most jurisdictions.

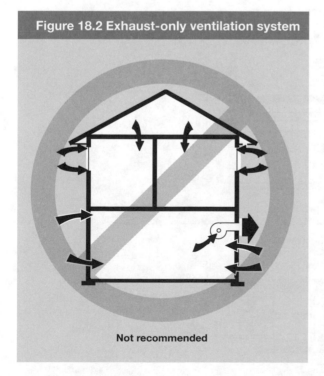

Figure 18.2 Exhaust-only ventilation system

Not recommended

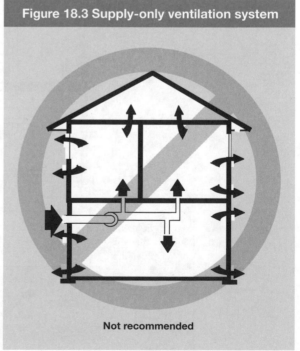

Figure 18.3 Supply-only ventilation system

Not recommended

The positive pressure created inside the house will minimize the likelihood of backdrafting and ensure that contaminants like radon are kept out of the living space. However, it also forces moist indoor air out of the house through any cracks and holes in the envelope. Experience indicates that this approach leads to concealed condensation in the walls and attic. As well, the cold fresh air forced into the house during the winter causes discomfort for the occupants unless it is preheated and properly distributed in small quantities to many locations.

18.4 Heat Recovery Ventilators and Energy Recovery Ventilators

Ventilation is required to ensure good indoor air quality. During cold weather, ventilation requires that warm indoor air be replaced with cold outdoor air, which must be heated. One way to reduce the cost of heating the fresh air is to extract heat from the outgoing stale air and use it to pre-heat the incoming fresh air. Heat recovery ventilators (HRVs) and energy recovery ventilators (ERVs) are devices that perform this task (Figure 18.4). HRVs typically have heat recovery efficiencies of 60 % to 80 % and are standard equipment.

HRVs transfer sensible heat (i.e. changes in air temperature without regard to the latent heat contained in water vapour in the air) while ERVs transfer both sensible heat and moisture to maintain humidity levels. HRVs are best suited to heating climates while ERVs, depending on their design, can be suitable for both heating and cooling climates. Because ERVs exchange moisture between incoming and outgoing air streams, they tend to enhance comfort by maintaining higher indoor humidity levels

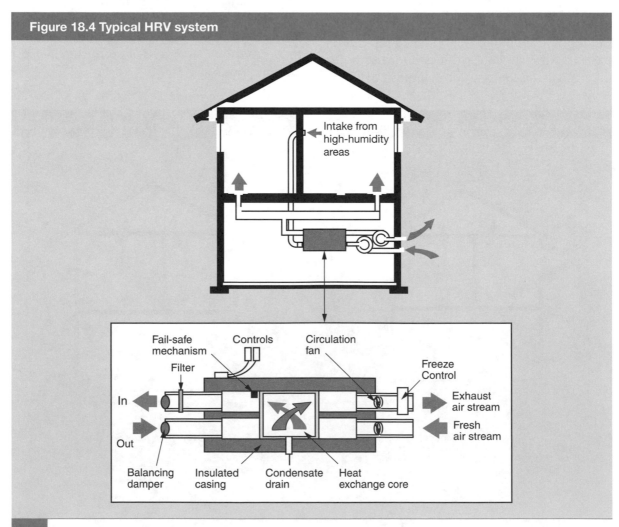

Figure 18.4 Typical HRV system

Intake from high-humidity areas

Fail-safe mechanism
Controls
Circulation fan
Filter
Freeze Control
In
Out
Exhaust air stream
Fresh air stream
Balancing damper
Insulated casing
Condensate drain
Heat exchange core

in winter. If operated in conjunction with air conditioning, ERVs reject 50% to 70% of the moisture difference between the incoming humid air an the cooler, drier indoor air . This helps reduce humidity loads in the summer. Not all ERVs are suited to every heating climate, so it is important to verify that equipment is certified for use for the temperatures in a given location.

The cost-effectiveness of installing an HRV or ERV depends on the cost of energy and weather severity in a particular location. HRVs or ERVs can reduce the amount of energy needed to preheat ventilation air, but have higher capital costs than ventilation systems without heat recovery. Experience has demonstrated that the energy savings over the life of an HRV or ERV will exceed the higher initial cost compared to a ventilation system with no heat recovery.

In addition to the capital cost of the unit itself, a heat recovery ventilation system requires ductwork to bring the exhaust and supply air to one location for the heat exchange process. Since moist, stale indoor air is being cooled through the HRV, the HRV system must also be able to drain water that condenses out of the exhaust air and provide defrosting if necessary. Drains are not required for ERVs, as ERVs pass the majority of moisture over to the opposite air stream.

18.4.1 Types of heat recovery ventilators

The heart of an HRV is the heat exchange core, which has the function of transferring heat from the exhaust air to the supply air. Most HRVs are built around "passive" heat exchangers. Residential ventilating systems typically use plate-type core HRVs (Figure 18.5). The core is constructed of thin sheets or plates of metal or plastic that form a series of channels. The supply air and exhaust air pass each other in alternate channels. The plates between the air streams prevent the supply and exhaust air from mixing, while allowing heat to be transferred from the warm side to the cold side. Canadian-made HRVs usually use what is known as a "cross flow" heat exchange strategy.

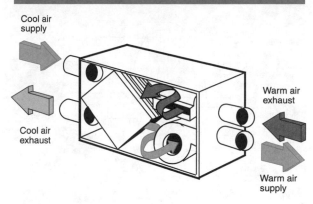

Figure 18.5 Plate-type HRV

Cool air supply

Warm air exhaust

Cool air exhaust

Warm air supply

Increasingly, units manufactured in Europe are being imported. Often, these units use a "counter flow" heat exchange strategy (which increases the opportunity to transfer heat from one air stream to another) to increase sensible heat recovery ratings. Counter flow systems can cause core icing problems in some climates in Canada, and therefore should have a good core defrosting strategy.

Energy recovery ventilators (ERVs)

Like HRVs, ERVs can have plate-type cores. However, this type of core uses a material that is water vapour permeable so that as the air streams pass by each other, both heat and water vapour are transferred (this is known as enthalpic heat exchange since both sensible heat and latent heat in the water vapour are exchanged). The plate ERV is most commonly used in climates that have mild winters and high summer cooling requirements; it must be verified with the manufacturer whether a given ERV is suited for a particular climate.

Builders and their HVAC subcontractor should verify that the ERV has been rated by HVI (Home Ventilating Institute) at a temperature of -25 C, or to a temperature at least as cold as the design temperature where the house is being built.

Another type of ERV core consists of a rotating wheel or drum (Figure 18.6) that contains numerous perforations or channels. As the wheel rotates, it passes through both the exhaust and supply air streams, picking up and releasing heat and moisture. The performance

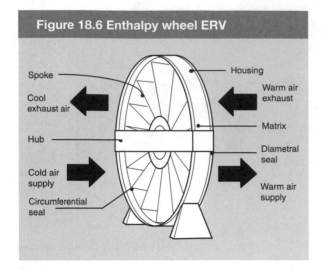

Figure 18.6 Enthalpy wheel ERV

Spoke

Cool exhaust air

Hub

Cold air supply

Circumferential seal

Housing

Warm air exhaust

Matrix

Diametral seal

Warm air supply

Electrically commutated motors (ECMs) offer advantages compared to common alternating current (AC) motors, running up to 50 % more efficiently and much cooler than comparable AC motors. Although more expensive, ECMs offer good payback in energy savings and are being used more commonly in heat recovery ventilators.

ENERGY STAR® has established qualifying criteria for HRVs and ERVs. The Home Ventilating Institute (HVI) provides a directory of certified ventilation products (www.hvi.org). The HVI-Certified label on residential ventilating products assures that the air flow, sound emission, and energy use claimed are the results of tests performed by an independent laboratory and verified by HVI.

The results of these tests are reported on an HRV/ERV design specification sheet that builders should request from the equipment supplier. These sheets are published in the Home Ventilating Institute's *Certified Home Ventilating Products Directory*. A sample specification sheet is shown in Figure 18.7. The specification sheet is a useful tool, but should not be the sole basis for selecting an HRV/ERV. Cost, warranty provisions, reliability, servicing and suitability of the unit for the climatic zone are some of the other issues that must be considered.

HRV/ERV design specification sheets can be used to compare the performance and efficiencies of different HRV/ERVs and to identify units that can satisfy the base ventilation requirements of a given house. From the heat recovery efficiency, the anticipated energy savings from a properly installed and operated unit can be estimated relative to a system providing the same air change without heat recovery. It should be remembered that the airflow performance of an HRV/ERV is more important than the heat recovery efficiency – a high heat recovery efficiency is of little value if the HRV/ERV cannot satisfy the base ventilation requirements.

of some ERV units is further enhanced through use of a desiccant coating on the wheel that increases its ability to absorb and release moisture, which increases the ERV's total energy recovery efficiency.

During the winter, as the wheel passes through the exhaust air stream, it is warmed and humidity is deposited on the core. As the core then moves into the supply air stream, heat and moisture are transferred to that air stream. This allows indoor humidity levels to be maintained in the comfort range. In the summer, if the home is air conditioned, the reverse happens.

18.4.2 Performance testing and rating

The performance of an HRV/ERV is determined by its air-handling capabilities and the percentage of heat it can transfer from the exhaust air to the supply air. HRV/ERVs must be rated in accordance with CSA-C439-18 *Standard Methods of Test for Rating the Performance of Heat/Energy Recovery Ventilators*. The standard describes the test equipment, instrumentation, procedures and calculations needed to determine airflows and heat recovery efficiency. These tests are carried out at a variety of airflows at three temperatures: 35°C (95°F), 0°C (32°F) and -25°C (-13°F). Some manufacturers also test their units at -40°C (-40°F) to determine their effectiveness for northern applications.

Figure 18.7 HRV specification sheet

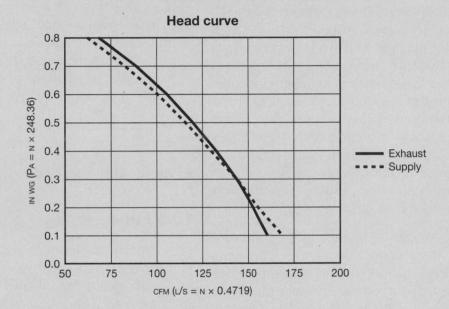

MECHANICAL LUNGS
Model: Blowhard Recovery **Options Installed:** Defrost Speed Control
Electrical Requirements: Volts: 115 **Amps:** 1.2

Head curve

Ventilation performance

EXT. STATIC PRESSURE		NET SUPPLY AIR FLOW		GROSS AIR FLOW SUPPLY		EXHAUST	
Pa	in. w.g.	L/S	CFM	L/S	CFM	L/S	CFM
25	0.1	79	167	79	167	76	161
50	0.2	73	155	73	155	72	153
75	0.3	67	142	47	142	67	142
100	0.4	61	129	61	129	62	131
125	0.5	54	114	54	114	56	119
150	0.6	47	100	47	100	49	104
175	0.7	39	83	39	83	41	87
200	0.8	29	61	29	61	32	68

Energy performance

	Supply Temperature °C	°F	Net Air Flow L/S	CFM	Power Consumed Watts	Sensible Recovery Efficiency	Adjusted Sensible Recovery	Apparent Sensible Effective- ness*	Latent Recovery/ Moisture Transfer
Heating	0	32	30	64	62	75	81	82	0.67
	0	32	55	117	120	70	78	78	0.60
	-10	14	30	64	62	75	79	82	0.70
	-25	-13	30	64	57	60	61	81	0.51

						Total Recovery Efficiency		Adjusted Total Recovery Efficiency	
Cooling	35	95	30	64	60	60		64	

To determine whether a particular unit will satisfy the ventilation requirements of a given house, the efficiency and installation details should be compared to other HRV/ERVs as follows:

- Determine the maximum airflow needed through the unit at high speed to meet ventilation requirements. Find this number in the "Net Supply Airflow" column, then look to the left and find the "External Static Pressure" available at this flow. This is a measure of how much duct-resistance the unit can overcome at a set flow. If the external static pressure available at the required flow is greater than 100 Pa (0.4 in. of water), or if it is thought the duct resistance (static pressure) will be higher than normal, select a more powerful unit or consult a duct designer.

- When comparing the energy performance of different units, look at their "Sensible Recovery Efficiency." This figure provides the basis for a comparison that integrates fan power, defrost and other factors. Efficiencies are given at various flows and at two or three test temperatures. Find the airflows that match the continuous flow rate required by the house, then determine the Sensible Recovery Efficiency. The higher the number, the better.

When building in a climate where cooling is a consideration, the "total recovery efficiency" measured at 35°C (95°F) should also be compared. This is a measure of how effective the unit is at pre-cooling and dehumidifying the incoming air when the home is air conditioned. The higher the total recovery efficiency, the better.

18.4.3 Selecting an HRV/ERV

The selection of an HRV/ERV should be based on the following:

- The ability of the equipment to meet the ventilation requirements for the dwelling;

- The heat recovery efficiency of the HRV/ERV during cold weather operation;

- The defrost mechanism (defrost strategies alter the flow of air through the unit, or can involve electrically heating air and can interrupt ventilation air flow) of the equipment-specifically whether it will depressurize the building and affect make-up air requirements;

- The availability of the equipment and trained installers and service people; and,

- The installed cost of the equipment.

18.5 Fans

Fans are the components of the ventilation system that move air. An HRV or ERV is provided with a fan. If an HRV/ERV is not used, a fan must be selected for the ventilation system. Fans consist of a motor and a blade or wheel, and are classified according to their method of operation (Figure 18.8) as follows:

- *Centrifugal fans*, or blowers, have impeller wheels that rotate inside a housing. The air is spun out as the impeller turns. They move air more efficiently at higher static pressures and are most commonly used in ducted applications. They are generally much quieter than axial fans.

- *Axial fans* move air perpendicular to the impeller or blade. They are efficient at low static pressure, and are normally used in non-ducted applications. Axial fans tend to be noisier than other types but are simple, inexpensive and can move large air volumes at low pressure.

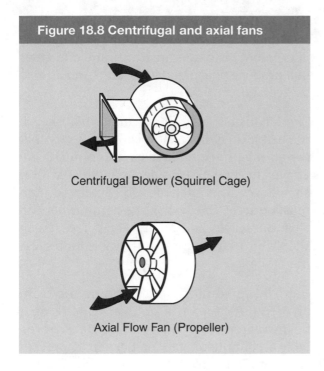

Figure 18.8 Centrifugal and axial fans

Centrifugal Blower (Squirrel Cage)

Axial Flow Fan (Propeller)

The fan performance curve (Figure 18.9) reveals the relationship between the static pressure across the fan and the airflow it will deliver. Airflow will increase as the external static pressure (the pressure difference between intake and discharge) decreases. Every fan has a characteristic performance curve for each rotational speed.

Figure 18.9 also shows a typical external static pressure curve for a duct system. The operating point is defined as the point where the fan performance curve intersects the external static pressure curve. The fan should be selected to match the operating point. A larger fan will provide more airflow, but will also use more energy.

In-line fans are installed within the ducting or within manufactured ventilation equipment. Their ease of installation represents a major benefit. Several manufacturers produce in-line fans capable of dealing with colder air temperatures. Most quality in-line fans are centrifugal types.

Surface-mounted fans (i.e., bath fans and range hoods) are rated according to airflow capacity and sound level. Airflow capacity is measured in litres per second (L/s) or cubic feet per minute (cfm) at a certain static pressure. Airflow should be determined based on the rating of the fan at 50 Pa static pressure. Sound level is measured in sones or decibels, depending on the manufacturer (a quiet refrigerator produces about one sone). A bathroom fan with a sound level of less than 2 sones should be acceptably quiet for most occupants. However, it is best to use a fan with a 1-sone or less rating for quiet areas where low sound levels are desired. (See Chapter 3; Units of Sound) To ensure quiet operation, fans must be installed in accordance with manufacturer's specifications.

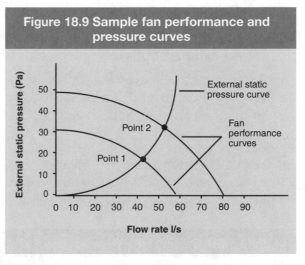

Figure 18.9 Sample fan performance and pressure curves

Fans that handle untempered outside air may be prone to the formation of condensation and frost. Therefore, it is important to select a fan approved by the manufacturer for the intended application. Fans intended for use in the primary ventilation system must be capable of continuous operation.

18.6 System Planning

Careful planning and system design are necessary for successful installation. Before subcontracting the detailed design and installation of the ventilating system to a certified installer, several important design decisions must be made.

18.6.1 Equipment selecting

Before selecting an HRV/ERV or fan unit, the amount of ventilation air needed to meet the requirements for the house design should be determined to ensure a particular system can meet the airflow requirements. Cost, warranty provisions, reliability, servicing and suitability of the unit for the climatic zone also need to be considered.

18.6.2 Locating the exterior supply inlet and exhaust outlet

Supply air inlets and exhaust air outlets must be carefully located and installed to avoid contamination and prevent blockage.

Supply inlet

All fresh air inlets must be located well away from areas of possible contamination. Problem areas include garages and driveways,

fan exhaust outlets, vents from combustion appliances, gas meters, oil fill pipes, dog runs and garbage storage areas. Shrubs and trees that produce pollen and leaf debris should also be avoided.

The air inlet should be located where it will not be blocked. Installation codes specify that the air inlet must be at least 450 mm (18 in.) above the finished grade or highest winter snow level. The inlet must be screened, and must be accessible so that the homeowner can clear out leaves and other debris. The screen should be accessible and removable for regular maintenance.

Both the incoming and outgoing air from an HRV/ERV and the cold air ducts must be insulated. The ducts must be covered with a continuous vapour barrier to prevent condensation from forming. The vapour barrier on the cold-side ducts must be effectively sealed to the house vapour barrier (Figure 18.10). Ducts must also be carefully sealed where they penetrate the air barrier.

Exhaust outlet

The exhaust outlet should not be located where it could contaminate fresh incoming air, nor in attics, garages or on walkways where

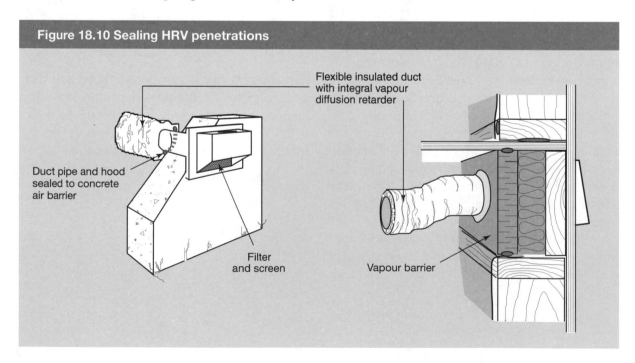

Figure 18.10 Sealing HRV penetrations

Flexible insulated duct with integral vapour diffusion retarder

Duct pipe and hood sealed to concrete air barrier

Filter and screen

Vapour barrier

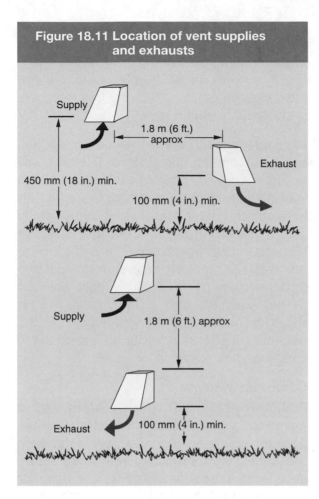

Figure 18.11 Location of vent supplies and exhausts

Supply

1.8 m (6 ft.) approx

Exhaust

450 mm (18 in.) min.

100 mm (4 in.) min.

Supply

1.8 m (6 ft.) approx

Exhaust

100 mm (4 in.) min.

condensation, moisture or ice could create problems. According to the CSA installation standard, the inlet and the exhaust shall be located so as to avoid cross contamination. The HRAI (Heating Refrigeration and Air Conditioning Institute) training course and several manufacturers recommend that an exhaust should be at least 1.8 m (72 in.) to the side of, above, or below the supply inlet (Figure 18.11), in order to avoid cross contamination. Builders are encouraged to check with with the local Codes because some do specify minimum distances from contaminated exhausts.

The separation and avoidance of cross contamination is an important aspect of a well installed ventilation system. It can be a challenge when constructing small townhouse projects to achieve adequate separation of the inlet and exhaust.

Tandem hoods with both supply and exhaust openings have been designed to minimize cross-contamination are also available. The bottom of the hood must be a minimum of 100 mm (4 in.) above grade or other horizontal surfaces or highest snow level. The exhaust duct must be carefully sealed where it penetrates the air barrier.

18.6.3 Locating the ventilator

In determining the location of the ventilating unit itself, such things as the inlet and outlet locations, noise levels, drainage and power supply should be considered. The unit should be located in the heated interior, away from noise-sensitive living areas (dining room, living room, bedroom, etc.). Vibration isolation of the fans should be provided to minimize transfer of noise to the structure. It should also be: close to an outside wall to minimize insulated duct runs; centrally located to optimize the distribution system; close to an electrical supply; and if an HRV, near a drain for condensate disposal.

The unit should also be easily accessible for maintenance purposes, and should be located well away from hot chimneys, electrical panels and other possible fire sources. The length of distribution ducting required, particularly for HRV/ERVs, should be minimized because duct length adds resistance and reduces airflow.

18.6.4 Air distribution

Fresh air must be distributed to all living areas in the house. Supply air can either be distributed through an independent duct system or integrated with, and distributed through, the ductwork of a forced-air heating system.

Independent systems

An independent system must be used in houses that do not have a forced-air distribution system. Some builders choose to use independent systems in homes that have forced-air heating because it eliminates the need for running the furnace fan continuously, and it allows the ventilation supply grills to be located in high

Figure 18.12 Ventilation grille location

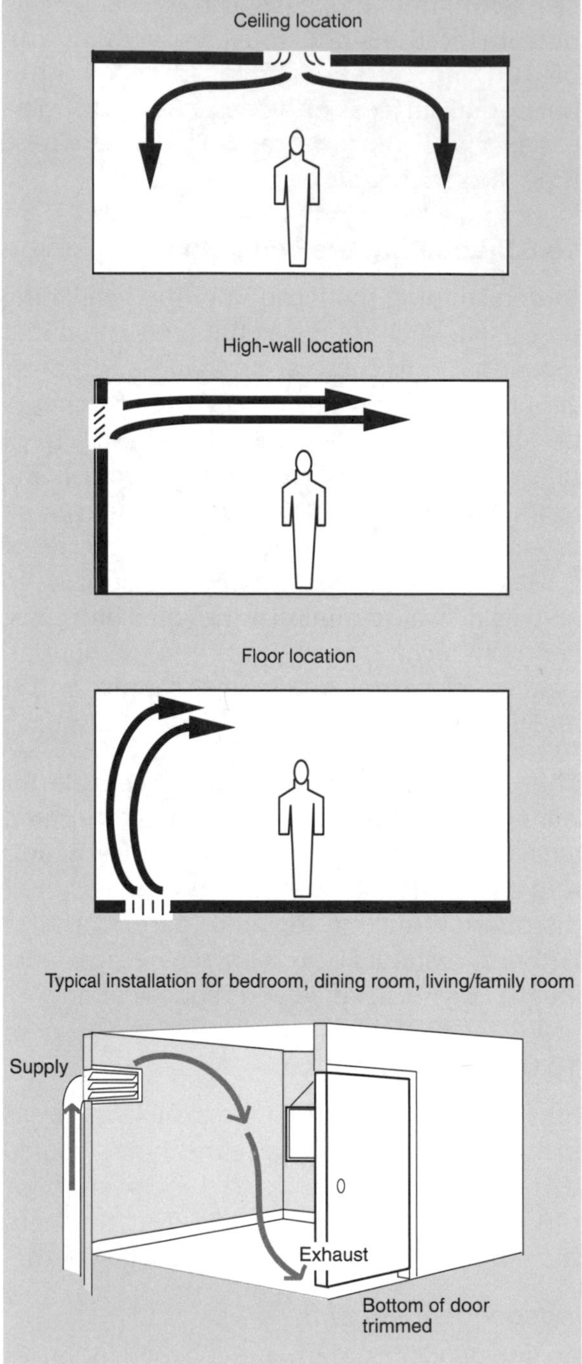

Ceiling location

High-wall location

Floor location

Typical installation for bedroom, dining room, living/family room

Supply

Exhaust

Bottom of door trimmed

Using independent ducts, the temperature of the air supplied to each room may be below room temperature. For example, if it is -10°C (14°F) outside, an HRV/ERV may only warm the supply air up to 10°C (50°F), unless there is an auxiliary duct heater.

The supply air will behave like cool air supplied by an air conditioning system. The best way to supply cool air to a room is through a high wall or ceiling outlet which discharges air horizontally along the ceiling using supply grills made specifically for use with ventilation systems. Incoming air has time and space to mix with the room air before dropping down to the occupied zone. If the supply air must be delivered through a floor grille, the air should be directed up the wall (Figure 18.12). Undersizing grills may result in restrictions to airflow and increases in air noise.

Combined systems

Combining the ventilation system with a forced-air heating system can eliminate the need for separate supply ductwork. However, the furnace blower must operate continuously (at a lower speed) to distribute the fresh air throughout the home and mix it with house air. This can lead to high electrical consumption and cause higher cooling loads in the summer due to waste heat from the furnace fan. The presence of constantly moving air at all supply register locations may also increase occupant discomfort due to drafts.

The outdoor air supply must be located at least 3 m (10 ft.) upstream of the plenum connection to the furnace (Figure 18.13) to protect against the contact of very cold air on the furnace heat exchanger.

Exhaust air

Exhaust air grills should be located in the rooms where the most water vapour, odours and contaminants are produced (kitchens, bathrooms, laundry rooms and workshop areas). Rooms with only exhaust grills will receive fresh air indirectly from other areas of the house. Undercut doors or transfer grills

wall or ceiling locations for maximum comfort (Figure 18.12, bottom). Although the initial installation cost for an independent system is higher, the energy saved by not having to operate a furnace fan continuously can result in long-term cost savings.

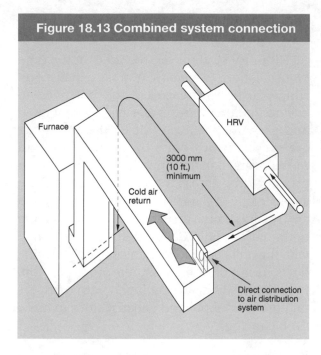

Figure 18.13 Combined system connection

and have too many bends will lead to low airflows and potentially cause indoor air quality problems. Trained and experienced HVAC contractors who have taken the Heating Refrigeration Air Conditioning Institute (HRAI) *Residential Mechanical Ventilation Installation* course will be familiar with ductwork sizing and layout that minimizes the length and the number of fittings. It is also important that all ductwork be sealed at all joints, seams and connections in both the fittings and the straight ducts for the following reasons:

- Air leakage in the supply air ductwork means less fresh pre-heated or pre-cooled air reaches the supply grills, reducing the ventilation efficiency of the system.

- Air leakage in the exhaust ductwork reduces the amount of air drawn through the exhaust grills. Drawing hot or cold air through leaks in the duct from unconditioned spaces such as attics and crawl spaces will significantly reduce the efficiency of the system.

are used to provide adequate airflow to these rooms (Figure 18.14). Exhaust grills in kitchens must be located in the ceiling or on the wall within 300 mm (12 in.) of the ceiling. If a grill is located within 1 m (3.3 ft.) of a cooktop, it must be fitted with a removable, washable, grease-resistant filter.

Ductwork can only be effectively air sealed with liquid duct sealers (also known as mastic) or aluminium foil tape. There is also an aerosol – based duct sealant which is highly-effective at sealing existing ductwork. Common duct tape is not durable enough for this application. All ductwork located in unconditioned spaces must be insulated to a minimum level as prescribed by the code.

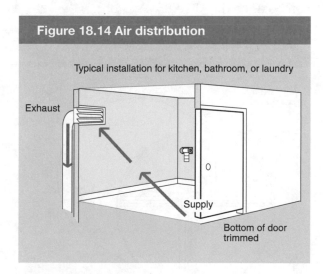

Figure 18.14 Air distribution

Typical installation for kitchen, bathroom, or laundry

Exhaust

Supply

Bottom of door trimmed

18.6.5 Dampers

Dampers can be adjusted to regulate airflow. Balancing dampers are required in HRV/ERV systems to even out the gross supply and exhaust airflows, thereby ensuring that the house is not placed under a negative nor positive pressure. Balancing dampers are either included as part of the HRV/ERV unit or installed separately in the warm-side main supply and exhaust ducts near the unit. In exhaust-only systems, mechanical dampers can regulate the entry of outside air into the building, as determined by the operation of exhaust appliances.

Ductwork installation

Correct sizing, layout and installation of ductwork is critical to the performance of a ventilation system. The use of undersized ductwork and or duct runs that are too long

Similarly, mechanical dampers can be electrically controlled to open upon operation of any single large-capacity exhaust appliance, such as a downdraft cooktop fan. This can help ensure make-up air is drawn in to reduce potential pressure imbalances.

Backdraft dampers should be provided on all exhaust hoods to prevent air leakage when the fans are not in operation. Poorly designed dampers can freeze open or closed in cold weather. Dampers must be capable of free operation at all times.

18.6.6 Controls

HRV/ERV systems are typically managed by a wall controller placed in a central location such as a main hallway, with additional timer controls placed in the bathrooms and kitchen. The central wall controller usually consists of a high- and low-speed switch, an on/off switch and a dehumidistat. Some controllers have a setting that allows the HRV/ERV to operate intermittently, such as for 20 minutes every hour. The HRV/ERV will typically operate continuously at low speed, and will only go to high speed when timer switches are operated in the bathrooms or kitchen, or when the indoor relative humidity rises above the set point of the dehumidistat. In regions of high summer humidity, a dehumidistat providing automatic control of the ventilation system could lead to problems of excessive humidity and condensation in the home. Solutions to this have been achieved in new equipment and builders should look for units with advanced controls that automatically adjust humidity settings summer and winter.

Central-ducted ventilation systems are designed to run continuously, or at least frequently on an intermittent basis (i.e., at least once an hour). If they are not operated this way, condensation may form in ductwork located in unheated spaces.

18.6.7 Measuring airflows in ventilation systems

All HRV/ERV systems are required, at the time of installation, to have their gross exhaust and supply airflows measured and balanced to ensure that the home is adequately ventilated and pressure-balanced. Most HRV/ERV units are supplied with ports that can be used to measure and balance flows by determining the pressure drop across the fresh air side and the stale air side of the HRV/ERV core. These ports are usually located on either the front or on the bottom of the unit. Calibration tables provided with the units permit a technician to determine flows based on the measured pressure drop. In addition, units are equipped with dampers on both the supply and exhaust sides to allow for balancing.

For HRV/ERV units without this feature, flow measuring stations (Figure 18.15) are installed on the warm-side main duct run and on the cold-side supply run, and a pressure gauge is then connected to the flow measuring station to provide a reading. With the airflow measurements and dampers located in the ventilator or in the main ducts, the installer can balance the HRV/ERV system.

Figure 18.15 Airflow measuring station

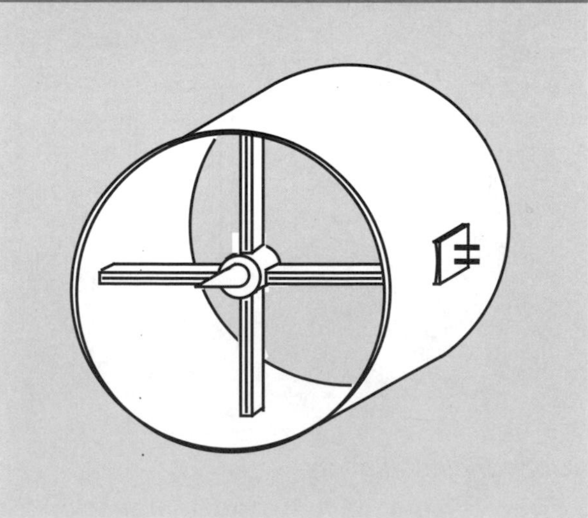

The correct location of airflow measuring stations and balancing dampers is shown in Figure 18.16.

Advancements in equipment technology allow some units to be self-balancing, or adjust their flows automatically based on the duct system. However, it is still important for the HVAC contractor to measure and record the flows to verify that the system is meeting the code required ventilation rate-flow verification.

18.7 System Installation

It is recommended that a mechanical subcontractor who has passed the Heating, Refrigerating and Air Conditioning Institute of Canada (HRAI) *Residential Mechanical Ventilation Design and Installation Course* be engaged. This will help ensure that the subcontractor complies with all design and installation requirements, balances the system and fills out any required installation reports. The checklist shown in Appendix 5 can be used to help ensure system installation is proceeding in a way that will lead to a quality installation.

The subcontractor should measure airflows, and balance the ventilation and exhaust air systems. Balancing air distribution systems involves adjusting fans, dampers and adjustable grills to ensure that the desired quantities of air are delivered to, and exhausted from, each area of the house. The ventilation supply fans must bring the same amount of fresh air into the house as the exhaust fans remove. To make it easier for the installer to balance the system, dampers should be located in an accessible location near the main supply/exhaust grills, or in an unfinished basement or utility room.

For HRV/ERVs, the installing contractor should complete CSA Standard F326 Form A, which describes the installation, provides airflow measurement results, and ensures that the HRV/ERV system meets industry standards. The installer should provide a written report on the measured airflows of the ventilation system.

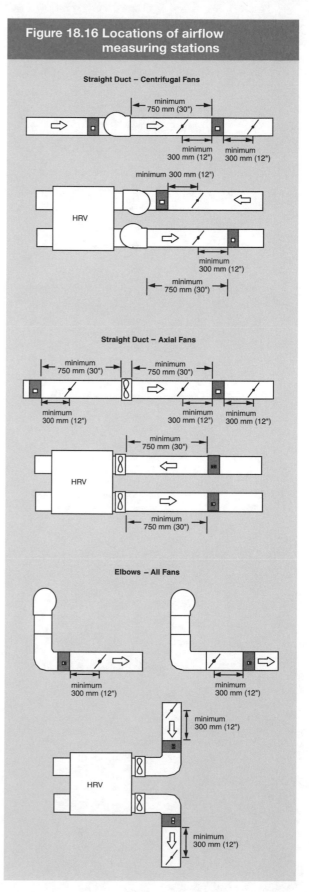

Figure 18.16 Locations of airflow measuring stations

Straight Duct – Centrifugal Fans

Straight Duct – Axial Fans

Elbows – All Fans

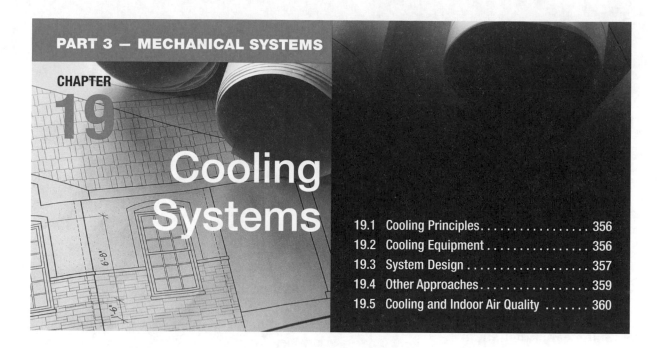

PART 3 — MECHANICAL SYSTEMS

CHAPTER

19

Cooling Systems

Cooling requirements are generally lower in well-insulated houses than in conventional houses. Nevertheless, in many parts of Canada, cooling systems are often demanded by buyers, and are becoming more common.

Central air conditioning can be an attractive marketing feature in many areas. It cools indoor air and increases comfort by reducing indoor humidity. Most residential air conditioning equipment uses a compressor cycle to alternately compress and expand a refrigerant. The cycle works on the same principle as a heat pump, only in reverse.

This chapter examines the different options for central air conditioning.

19.1 Cooling Principles

Space cooling or air conditioning is often desirable during warmer months in areas where hot, humid weather prevails. It should not be needed in more moderate climates. Excess heat results from:

- Window selection. Heat gain is often a function of the passive solar heat gain through windows. The Solar Heat Gain Coefficient is a large factor in selecting windows to reduce air conditioning loads;

- Heat gain through all components of the building envelope;

- Summer air infiltration;

- Summer air brought into the house for ventilation;

- Appliances and lights that produce heat;

- Activities of the occupants, such as cooking; and,

- Occupants (an adult at rest gives off 75W of heat).

Cooling equipment also provides dehumidification by condensing water vapour out of the air as it is chilled. Cooling load is calculated in the same way as heating load, but in reverse. Heat gain in a house is a function of the:

- Size, orientation and shading of windows and patio doors;

- Envelope insulation levels and the reflectivity of exterior surfaces;

- Air leakage rate of the structure;

- Ventilation rate and efficiency of a heat recovery ventilator (HRV);

- Impact on the micro-climate of shade trees and other landscape features; and,

- Adequacy of attic venting (summer attic temperatures can reach 65°C (150°F).

As with heating equipment, the cooling unit must be carefully sized. Undersized systems will not provide adequate comfort under design conditions. Oversized systems will be unnecessarily expensive and will not provide adequate humidity control, resulting in cool but damp indoor conditions. The design of distribution systems for cool air is also very important; larger ducts may be needed than for heating alone, because cooling systems usually need to move more air.

19.2 Cooling Equipment

Most air conditioning equipment is compression equipment that alternately compresses and expands a refrigerant (Figure 19.1). This equipment works in the same manner as a refrigerator:

- Liquid refrigerant is forced under high pressure to an expansion device. As the high-pressure liquid passes through the expansion device into the evaporator, it absorbs heat from the warm air flowing across the outside of the evaporator, expands into a larger volume, and vaporizes.

- The vaporized refrigerant is then pumped to the compressor where it is compressed and forced into the condenser. Cooled by air or water passing over the condenser coils, the hot vapour liquefies. It is then ready to start the cycle again.

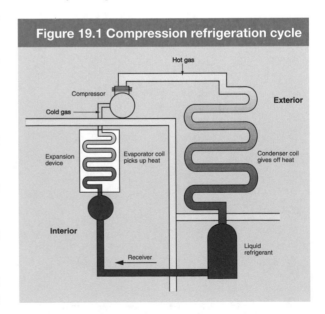

Figure 19.1 Compression refrigeration cycle

19.3 System Design

It is important to choose efficient equipment. Manufacturers rate equipment in terms of its seasonal energy efficiency ratio (SEER). SEER is a measurement of efficiency for cooling devices such as heat pumps and air conditioners. A unit's SEER is calculated by dividing the total amount of heat removed from the air by the total amount of energy required by the unit. The higher the ratio, the more efficient the unit. SEERs for new central air conditioners and air source heat pumps currently range from 13 to 21; the minimum requirement in most jurisdictions is 13.

HSPF (heating seasonal performance factor) is a term used to measure the efficiency of air source heat pumps. The higher the HSPF rating of a unit, the more energy efficient it is. The HSPF is related to the non-dimensional coefficient of performance (COP) for a heat pump, which measures the ratio of heat energy delivered to electrical energy supplied, independently of the units used to measure energy.

The capacity of air conditioning units is measured in Tons. A ton of refrigeration is the amount of heat transfer required to melt one short ton (2,000 lbs, 907 kg.) of ice in 24 hours. It is approximately equal to 12,000 BTU or 3.5 kW.

The compression/condenser unit is located outdoors, but the expansion/evaporator unit may be located indoors. The cooling equipment can be linked to the heating system or installed independently.

In one option, furnace-mounted cooling coils are connected to a remote outdoor condenser unit. The evaporator coils are mounted in the plenum and the system uses the furnace blower to provide air circulation. The refrigerant is carried in piping that connects the indoor coils to the outdoor condenser unit (Figure 19.2).

In a self-contained system, the entire cooling system, excluding the duct system, is contained in one enclosure located outside the house. Openings must be provided in the building envelope to allow the insulated supply and return air ducts to be connected to the indoor duct system. These openings should be sealed to the air barrier.

Most central air conditioning systems circulate cooled air through the house distribution system. However, systems adaptable to hydronic distribution systems are also available. These chill the water flowing through the heating loops.

Figure 19.2 Evaporator coil installed in the ductwork of a forced-air heating system

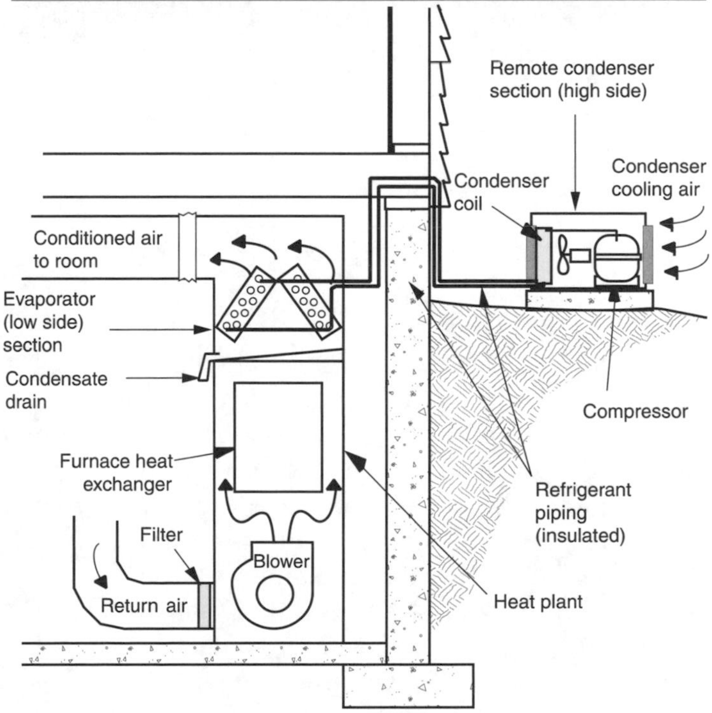

19.3.1 Ducted air systems

Most air conditioning systems use the heating distribution system to circulate cooled air during the warm months. While more expensive, it is possible to provide a separate duct system for cooling. The design of the duct system and the position of air supply vents is different for combined versus separate systems.

Combined duct systems

Combined duct systems are less expensive, easier to install, and take up less space than two separate systems. However, the homeowner may have to adjust duct dampers and blower speeds seasonally, or install more sophisticated controls to ensure that each room is conditioned appropriately. Cooling systems tend to require a greater volume of airflow than heating systems, so larger ducts may be necessary.

Since warm air rises, most heating systems introduce warm air into a room at a low level. However, cool air falls, and thus should be provided at a high level. For combined systems, a good compromise is a floor unit that directs the airflow upward with sufficient velocity to reach the ceiling.

Zoned combined duct systems

Separate cooling is provided for each zone controlled by dedicated thermostats. With a thermostat on each floor, most of the calls for cooling will come from the upper floors, and rarely from the basement. Lower-floor zones can have floor level outlets where heating is dominant. The upper floor zone can have horizontal, ceiling outlets to support cooling. During peak electricity demand times, typically on hot summer days, some utility energy-saving programs send a message to reduce the electricity demand of a central air conditioning to reduce provincial peak loads. A field trial showed over 50 % cooling energy saving when combining this approach with a three zone system for cooling delivery.

Separate systems

If a cooling system has separate ducts and return air intakes, they should be located in the ceiling or high on the walls. This type of system is simpler to design, and since the outlets are high, there is less likelihood that the occupants of the house will experience uncomfortable drafts. However, separate duct systems cost more, and require more space. If attic- or roof-mounted equipment is used, the system may be difficult to service.

19.3.2 Chilled water systems

Chilled water systems can be used separately or with the distribution system of a hydronic heating system to provide summer cooling. Water, rather than air, is passed over the evaporator coil where it is cooled and then pumped through the system.

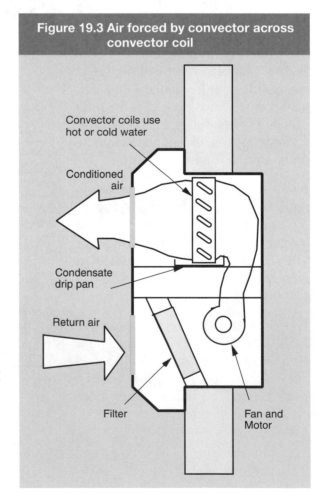

Figure 19.3 Air forced by convector across convector coil

Convector coils use hot or cold water

Conditioned air

Condensate drip pan

Return air

Filter

Fan and Motor

Typically, the piping system for cooling is totally independent of the heating system. This allows both heating and cooling systems to be designed for maximum efficiency. Each convector (Figure 19.3) consists of a coil through which chilled water is circulated, a fan to blow air over the coil, and a filter that removes particulates. Each convector must be fitted with a pan to collect condensate, and a drain, easily visible and accessible for cleaning.

A separate convector is generally located under a window or recessed into a wall to cool the room in which it is located. These convectors are typically designed for individual control, but it is possible to install short ducts to enable the unit to cool more than one room. The units can be designed to heat the house as well.

Hydronic cooling systems are usually more expensive and less effective than ducted air systems. As an alternative, an independent chilled water cooling system may be installed with a ducted air system (Figure 19.4).

19.3.3 Mini-split (ductless) air conditioning

Like central air conditioners, these units have a split design but without an elaborate system of ducts. The split system (also called a mini-split, ductless split, or duct-free system) has at least one unit inside the home (this is the evaporator) and one outdoor unit (the condenser). Small tubes of refrigerant run from the outdoor unit to the indoor units. Indoor units can be wall or ceiling mounted. Ductless splits can be used to cool one zone or multiple zones applying two to four indoor units to one condenser and the indoor units can be used independently of each other.

19.4 Other Approaches

19.4.1 Radiant cooling systems

One innovative approach makes use of the relatively cool temperature of soil surrounding or beneath the house. Water is circulated through a piped subsurface network, where it is cooled to ground temperature. Then it is piped to radiant cooling units. These consist of a metal heat collector into which the cool water circulation system is embedded. The cool water absorbs the heat from the metal plate, thus cooling the interior.

These systems must be carefully designed, otherwise there is potential for condensation on the cool surfaces. This water damage could create other problems, such as supporting mould and fungi growth.

Figure 19.4 Independent chilled water-cooling system connected to a ducted air system

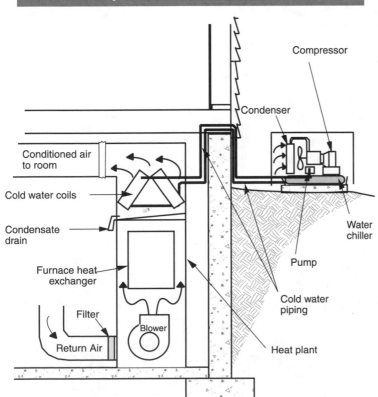

19.4.2 Whole-house fans

Since whole-house fans significantly depressurize a house, they should not be used in houses with gas- or oil-fired hot-water systems that are not direct-vented. They are also not recommended where radon or other soil gasses may be a concern (see Section 18.3.2).

19.5 Cooling and Indoor Air Quality

With a properly designed cooling system, air quality in the home can be maintained while comfort is improved. In fact, the dehumidification aspect of cooling can help substantially in reducing chronic problems with mildew on indoor surfaces and home contents that often occur in hot, humid summer conditions. However, there are two important air quality concerns to consider about cooling systems:

- Cooling can only operate effectively when a home is closed up in hot weather, so the same ventilation needs exist for occupant comfort and health as they do when heating in winter. The ventilation system should always be operated during cooling periods to ensure indoor air quality is maintained.

- All evaporators and chilled components that are in contact with warm, humid air produce condensate. This condensate must be collected by a sloped pan connected to a drain (with a trap, if necessary) that is reliable and easily serviced. Drain pans that become plugged and remain wet can grow mould and bacteria and become a health hazard. Cleaning procedures for cooling equipment should be included in homeowner instruction manuals.

- Builders should ensure that their HVAC contractor carefully commissions the air conditioning system to ensure it is providing optimal dehumidification performance. Our lessons learned to date have shown that this is very important in highly energy efficient homes such as Net Zero. Experience shows that most air conditioning systems are never checked for airflow or refrigerant flow and therefore are rarely providing optimal dehumidification.

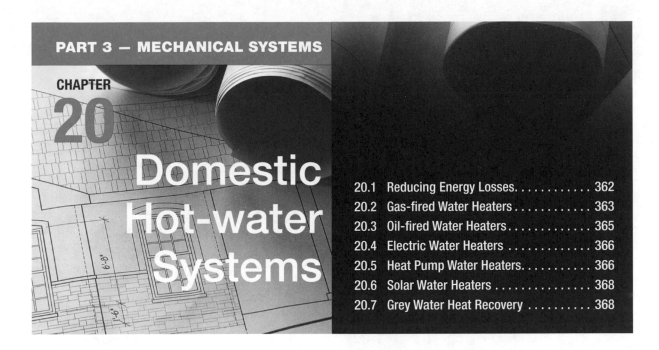

CHAPTER

20

Domestic Hot-water Systems

In energy-efficient houses, some water heaters may consume more energy than space heating or lights and appliances. This chapter examines how to improve the efficiency of the domestic hot-water (DHW) system by selecting and properly installing efficient equipment.

20.1 Reducing Energy Losses

Domestic hot water (DHW) can be heated in several ways by means of:

- Central water heater

- Instantaneous or tankless heater

- Integration with the space heating system using an integrated mechanical system (see Section 16.5)

Heat can be supplied by a fuel burner, an electric resistance element, an earth energy or air-source heat pump, or from solar panels. The operating efficiency of a domestic hot-water system can be significantly improved by designing the system and selecting equipment to reduce standby and line losses, and by installing devices to limit hot-water wastage.

20.1.1 Reducing standby losses

Standby loss is heat lost from the water in a domestic water heater and its distribution system when it is not in use. It is proportional to the temperature difference between the water and the surrounding air, the surface area of the tank and pipes, and the amount of insulation encasing the tank and pipes. There are several measures for reducing standby losses:

- The DHW heater is located close to the area of use to minimize pipe length;

- The DHW heater is placed on protected rigid insulation to reduce heat loss through the bottom of the tank;

- A heat trap is installed above the water heater to stop convection;

- The level of tank insulation is increased (check with the manufacturer to ensure the warranty is not affected); and

- The hot-water pipes are insulated.

20.1.2 Heat traps

As noted in Chapter 2, convective loops will form in a fluid when temperature differences are present. The warmer fluid will rise to the top and the cooler fluid will fall. This loop will continue until all of the fluid is at the same temperature.

This type of convective loop will form in a water heater, especially if it sits on a cold concrete basement floor. A convective loop will also form in the pipe that supplies hot water to the house, where heat will dissipate to the interior air. The water in the pipe will cool quite quickly, because the surface area of the pipe is large relative to the volume of water. As a result, considerable energy can be wasted because of losses from this pipe.

A heat trap is a simple piping arrangement that prevents hot water from rising up the pipe in the first place, thereby reducing heat loss (Figure 20.1).

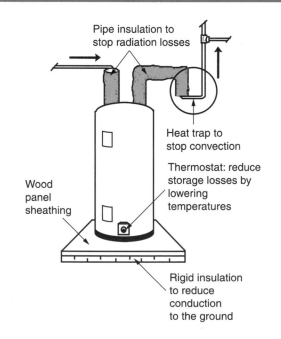

Figure 20.1 Recommended installation of domestic hot-water heating tank

Pipe insulation to stop radiation losses

Heat trap to stop convection

Thermostat: reduce storage losses by lowering temperatures

Wood panel sheathing

Rigid insulation to reduce conduction to the ground

20.1.3 Reducing pipe losses

The best way to reduce heat loss from the piping is to minimize the length of hot-water piping required. Even when this is done, it is a good idea to insulate all hot-water pipes to further reduce heat loss. Pipe insulation is available in a variety of materials and thicknesses, with easy application to most water pipes. For at least the first metre (3 ft.) of pipe from the tank, the pipe insulation should be at least RSI 0.35 (R-2).

Many builders are now using plastic piping instead of copper for reasons of cost and speed. For hot water lines, the most common types are CPVC and PEX. Copper piping has a thermal conductivity which is 850x more than PEX and 2720x more than CPVC. Notwithstanding these significant differences in thermal conductivity, the building codes do not specify a different level of insulation based on pipe material. Therefore, all hot water piping requires insulation, regardless of pipe material.

20.2 Gas-fired Water Heaters

There is a wide range of gas-fired water heating equipment available ranging from natural draft, gas-fired water heaters with a seasonal efficiency in the range of 55%, to high-efficiency condensing units that can have an efficiency of 90%. A measure of seasonal efficiency of water heaters is given by their energy factor. It considers standby losses (affected by the amount of tank insulation) and off-cycle vent losses (affected by the burner and heat exchanger). The higher the energy factor, the more efficient the water heater is. Minimum energy-efficiency levels for water heaters are legislated. Net Zero Energy builders and designers will be using only those in the top efficiency levels.

20.2.1 Natural draft gas-fired water heaters

These units are inexpensive and do not have any fan, either upstream or downstream of the unit, to help move the combustion products.

They have a naturally aspirating burner and a draft hood, as with a conventional gas furnace. They require a vertical chimney vent. The chimney vent creates a natural draft only, and draft losses can be quite significant. As a result, they are more subject to combustion spillage than other gas-fired equipment. Their overall efficiency is fairly low, with an energy factor in the low 50% range. This type of appliance is not a good fit for energy efficient houses. It is advisable to consider water heaters that are direct-vented or have a powered exhaust. These units are not applicable for R-2000, Net Zero Energy and Net Zero Energy Ready.

20.2.2 Induced-draft (fan-assisted) gas-fired water heaters

Induced-draft hot-water heaters (Figure 20.2) use fans downstream of the water heater to move combustion by-products through the venting system rather than relying on dilution air to move gases by natural convection. They can be side-wall vented and thus are more compatible with high-efficiency condensing furnaces. Many of these units still have a pilot light and a draft hood, which tend to lower their overall efficiency.

Figure 20.2 Induced-draft hot-water heater

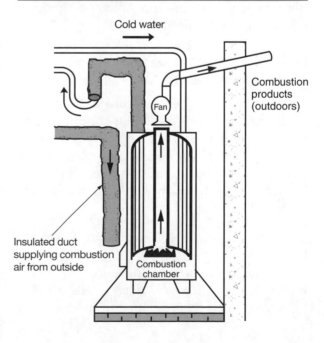

If a water heater is side-wall vented, it is important to install the unit with a vent connector always sloping upward from the water heater to the outside. Care should be taken to use the minimum equivalent length of vent connector possible to minimize the chance of condensation in the venting system.

Most induced-draft (fan-assisted) units require combustion air and dilution air from inside the house. In a poorly sealed building, outside air will leak into the house through cracks and holes in the building envelope to replace the air used for combustion. In an airtight house, a source of combustion air must be provided near the water heater. If a unit is used that does not have a built-in, directly connected combustion air intake, an inlet sized and located according to the Canadian Gas Association (CGA) standard CAN/CGA-B149.1-15 must be provided.

If there is another gas-fired appliance such as a furnace located in close proximity to the water heater, only one combustion air supply is needed. The inlet should be sized to meet the requirements of both appliances, based on the total fuel-burning capacity of the two burners.

This type of water heater is not appropriate for R-2000, Net Zero Energy and Net Zero Energy Ready because of the low efficiency and the concern of backdrafting.

20.2.3 Direct-vent gas-fired water heaters

Direct-vent (sealed combustion) water heaters are designed to bring all of their combustion air in from outdoors through a directly connected inlet, and to vent combustion by-products directly outdoors. There is no interconnection between the burner and the house air (Figure 20.3).

Gas-fired condensing water heaters, similar to the high-efficiency condensing furnaces described in Chapter 16, have lower exhaust temperatures. They only need a small plastic pipe to exhaust the combustion products out

Figure 20.3 Direct-vent gas-fired hot-water heater

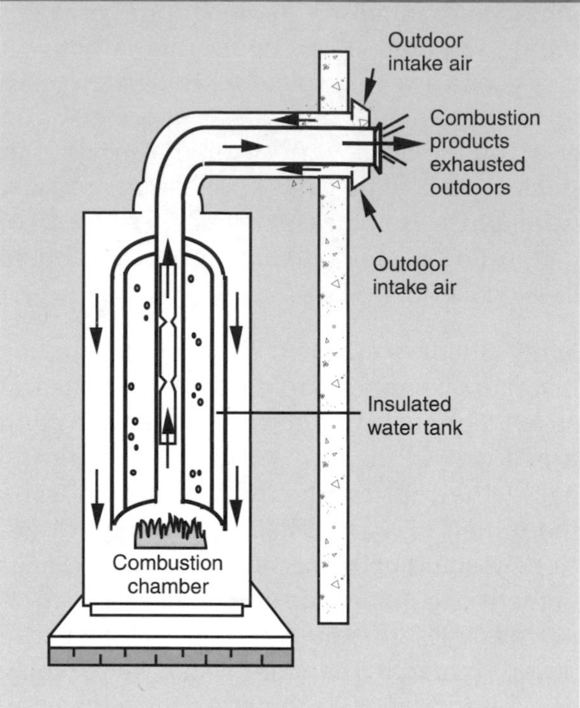

Outdoor intake air

Combustion products exhausted outdoors

Outdoor intake air

Insulated water tank

Combustion chamber

through the side wall of the house. Some of these units can achieve efficiencies as high as 90%. These units are appropriate for use in R-2000, Net Zero Energy and Net Zero Energy Ready homes.

Integrating space and water heating applications in one unit can combine high efficiencies for both applications.

20.2.4 Instantaneous gas-fired water heaters

Instantaneous gas water heaters are common because they provide unlimited hot water, are energy-efficient, conserve space, and are declining in price. They are typically wall-mounted units about the size of a small suitcase. They operate only when hot water is needed – they do not store hot water. They can be used in combination systems to provide both space heating and domestic hot water (see Section 16.4). Typical features are as follows:

- Can be fired by natural gas or propane, and have electronic ignition;

- Require vertical or through-wall venting;

- Require a minimum of about 20 psi. water pressure;

- Have all-stainless, corrosion resistant heat exchangers and fittings;

- Have solid-state automatic controls for regulating flame ignition, flow and temperature;

- Often use a standard flashlight battery for controls and ignition;

- Are available for flow rates of about 4 to 12 L/min (0.75 to 3 gpm) at a standard temperature rise;

- Are available in a range of combustion efficiencies; and

- Have modulating burners.

Tankless water heaters can be cost-effective because, unlike conventional water heaters, they do not have standby losses incurred by continuous use of energy to maintain water in a tank to a set temperature. They also save space and can perform well in a small household with one or two people, or to boost water temperature in cases where a faucet or shower is some distance from the main water heater.

Tankless water heaters that are powered by electricity can be used to provide hot water on demand. For high-flow applications such as soaker or jet bath applications, a larger heater may be required to meet demand. A hot water storage tank should be avoided in a tankless system. Adding storage reintroduces stand-by losses, negating some of the advantages of using a tankless system.

20.2.5 Gas boilers (wall-hung)

Wall-hung gas boilers can be used to provide domestic hot water and space heating with a single, compact unit with dual heat exchangers. Some models have modulation capability so that heating capacity can be matched to demand.

20.3 Oil-fired Water Heaters

20.3.1 Stand-alone oil-fired water heaters

Stand-alone, oil-fired water heaters use a similar form of flame retention head burner as those used in oil-fired furnaces and boilers (Chapter 16), directly heating the water in a storage tank. Efficiency gains have been made by baffling in the flue passage to increase heat transfer and by better insulation of the tank. Equipment with a high static burner provides additional gains due to more efficient energy generation and reduced off-cycle losses up the chimney.

Most oil-fired water heaters can use the same venting system as the oil-fired central furnace/boiler, providing the flue size is adequate to carry all of the combustion products. Some oil-fired water heaters have an additional induced-draft fan mounted on the wall, which allows side-wall venting of the appliance.

20.3.2 Tankless coil water heaters

In some areas, domestic hot water is heated by means of a tankless coil installed inside an oil-fired hot-water boiler. This system can be quite inefficient, requiring the boiler to be hot at all times, even during the summer. Inefficient short-cycling is common, as is the potential for high boiler-casing losses and off-cycle stack losses. Typically, this type of water heater is not appropriate for use in energy efficient homes.

20.3.3 Boiler with indirectly fired water heater

Where a boiler is used to supply a hot-water space-heating system, domestic hot water can be provided by means of a well-insulated storage tank with its own internal heat exchanger heated by the boiler.

The water in an indirectly fired stored water heater provides a thermal mass necessary to allow the boiler to operate for longer cycles and therefore more efficiently. When the tank set-point control is satisfied, the boiler and the hot-water storage tank circulator shut off. They can remain off for some time with hot-water demand met by the hot water stored in the tank.

A thermostatic mixing valve is installed on the storage tank to allow the water in the tank to be heated to a higher temperature than required at the fixtures. When this valve is used in combination with the tank thermostat having a wide differential, the length of the boiler firing cycle and the boiler cycle efficiency can be further increased.

The performance of indirectly fired storage water heaters is expressed in terms of the volume of hot water that can be produced at a specified temperature in a given period of time. The hotter the boiler water supply to the tank heat exchanger and the higher the flow rate to the heat exchanger, the greater the rate of hot water production.

20.4 Electric Water Heaters

20.4.1 Electric resistance water heaters

Electric resistance water heaters (usually 175 L (40 gal.)) are widely used, inexpensive, simple to install and can be used where the venting of gas-fired water heaters could be problematic. They should have a factory-installed insulation level of at least RSI 1.75 (R-10). The seasonal efficiency of these units is about 93%.

In houses where large amounts of hot water are needed, electric DHW tanks may be less effective than fuel-fired units, since they have a slower recovery time. This problem can be overcome by installing a larger volume water tank.

Although the initial cost of an electric water heater is very low, its cost of operation will be significantly higher than an oil- or gas-fired water heater, due to the higher base cost of electricity in many areas of Canada. The only possible exceptions are those areas where

electrical off-peak reduced rates are available, but using these requires a timer storage system. In most areas of Canada, efficient fuel-fired water heaters may be the best option, as they have a much faster recovery time and lower operating costs.

20.5 Heat Pump Water Heaters

Many of the heat pumps used for space heating can also be used to supplement hot water heating needs during parts of the heating and cooling season. In addition, there are heat pumps designed to provide only hot water (Figure 20.4). They extract heat from the inside air or the exhaust airstream of the house to heat the water. These heat pump water heaters self-contained units and follow the same principles as space conditioning heat pumps (Chapter 16).

Figure 20.4 Heat pump water heater

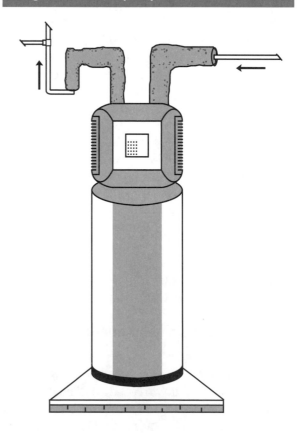

A heat pump will supply more energy than it uses. The ratio of energy supplied to energy used is called the coefficient of performance (COP). Heat pump water heaters generally operate with a COP in the range of 2.5 to 3, and can save up to 60% of the energy used by a typical electric water heating system.

During the summer, a heat pump water heater can reduce air conditioning requirements if it extracts heat from the inside air. However, if it extracts heat instead from the exhaust air stream of the ventilation system, no summer air conditioning effect will be obtained without additional equipment. Conversely, in the winter if the heat is obtained from the heated indoor space, there will be an increased load on the space heating system.

Many of the Net Zero Energy houses have used this equipment because of the high COPs associated with it. With the push to Net Zero Energy Ready by 2030 the government is looking to regulate the efficiency of water heaters. By 2030, the proposal is for efficiencies to be greater than 100%. Practically, this means that heat pump water heaters are the only technology that will meet the requirements in 2030. Research is ongoing with dual-fuel, heat pump units, but electrical units are available and in-use today.

20.5.1 Earth energy systems as water heaters

Most earth energy (geothermal) heat pump systems have the capability to supplement domestic hot water. While in air conditioning mode in the summer, an earth energy system will remove heat from the house and transfer a portion to the hot-water storage tank (Chapter 22). It can provide practically free hot water in the summer, and hot water for approximately one-third of the price of a normal electric water heater during the heating season. Such operation is analogous to the operation of other integrated space and water heating systems (Chapter 16).

Figure 20.5 Solar heater storage system

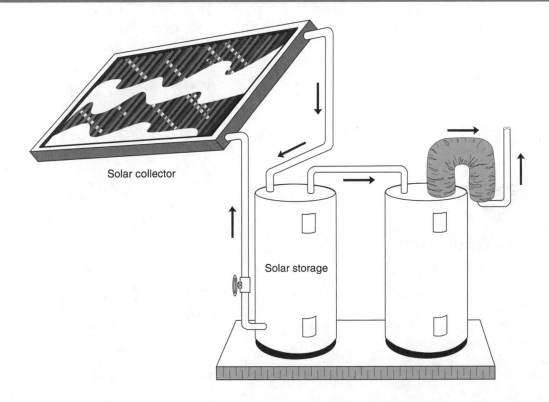

Solar collector

Solar storage

20.6 Solar Water Heaters

Solar DHW systems are common in many areas of the world, and have been in the Canadian market for several years (Figure 20.5). Most commercial systems can provide about 40% to 50% of a home's annual domestic hot water needs, but in some cases, they can provide even more. Solar units are pre-heat systems only, so a storage tank and supplementary heater is required. These systems may be economically advantageous in some locations, especially in areas with high energy costs and considerable available sunshine. However, at current energy prices, they typically have a longer payback period (seven years or more).

The installation of a solar water heater must be carefully considered at the design stage. An area of unshaded southern exposure is needed for installation of the solar collectors. Pre-packaged systems are available that conform to CAN/CSA-F379-09 (R2013) *Packaged solar domestic hot water systems (liquid-to-liquid heat transfer)*. The systems include solar collectors, controls, pumps and water heaters.

'Solar-ready' means providing several elements that allow for the future installation of a solar domestic hot water or an on-site electricity generation system, making a future solar system retrofit less costly and less disruptive.

Solar-ready features usually include design of the roof structure to accept the weight of solar collectors, conduits extending from the attic to the mechanical room to accommodate future pipes and wiring, and space in the mechanical room for future storage tanks, controls and inverters.

20.7 Grey Water Heat Recovery

Because grey water (Chapter 5) is primarily warm or hot water, it contains heat. Some of this energy can be recaptured and used to pre-heat incoming cold water to the domestic water heater using a simple, passive device. To do so, grey water must be separated from toilet water in the home, and it can then be sent through the heat recovery unit. CSA B55.2-15- *Drain water heat recovery units* covers these types of appliances. They are very useful for recovering the heat from shower water. Typically, the warm wastewater is travelling down the drain at the same time that the water heater is providing hot water for the shower. This makes for an ideal time to recover the waste heat and pre-heat the incoming cold water on the way to the water heater.

The grey water heat recovery unit (Figure 20.6) is a length of metal drain pipe, usually about 1.0 to 1.5 m (3 to 5 ft.) long and 100 mm (4 in.) in diameter that is installed in the main plumbing stack. It has a metal water pipe bonded to the outside of it in a spiral loop. Cold water enters the water pipe, picks up heat from the metal wall of the drain pipe, and then flows to the domestic water heater. Depending on hot water use, heating fuel rates and heating equipment type, grey water heat recovery can have a payback of merely a few years through savings in water heating costs.

Figure 20.6 Grey water heat recovery unit

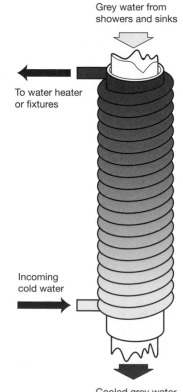

Grey water from showers and sinks

To water heater or fixtures

Incoming cold water

Cooled grey water

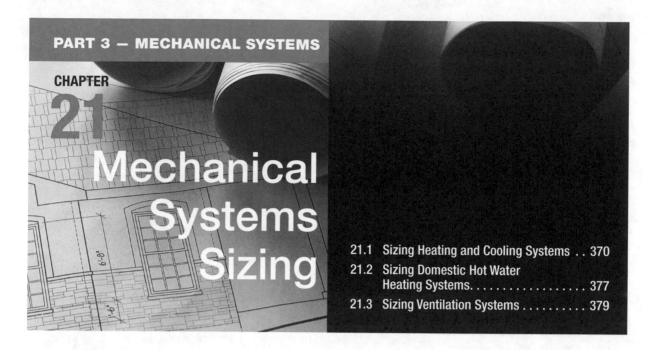

PART 3 — MECHANICAL SYSTEMS

CHAPTER

21

Mechanical Systems Sizing

As the industry moves towards Net Zero, houses have become tighter and more energy efficient, design heating loads have become smaller and smaller while design cooling loads have remained relatively the same or become larger due to more window area and the use of windows with high solar heat gain. These trends can create challenges for builders and their designers which may include:

- Significant differences in airflow requirements for heating and cooling.

- Difficulty in finding forced-air heating equipment with rated capacities low enough to match well with the design heating loads of the energy-efficient homes.

This Chapter discusses sizing of mechanical equipment, and selection of capacity ranges for heating and cooling equipment used in energy-efficient housing. Approaches for selecting appropriate operating capacity staging and modulation ranges are explored to mitigate short cycling issues.

Also discussed are methods for sizing domestic hot water heating and ventilation systems.

21.1 Sizing Heating and Cooling Systems

Detailed heat loss and heat gain calculations are necessary for accurate sizing of heating and cooling equipment and distribution systems.

- If equipment is undersized, the house will not be comfortable and call backs are likely.

- If equipment is significantly oversized, capital cost can be higher and equipment can have short operating cycles which will adversely affect occupant comfort and likely increase call backs due to comfort concerns.

21.1.1 Sizing Heating and Cooling Systems

Heating and Cooling Design Loads

Heating and cooling system capacity requirements should be determined using CSA F280-12 *Determining the Required Capacity of Residential Space Heating and Cooling Appliances*. This standard is referenced in the National Building Code (NBC) and in an increasing number of provincial building codes.

Key points for builders – Design Heating and Cooling Loads:

- Use CSA F280-12 (R2017) heat loss/gain analysis to right size heating and cooling systems, improve homebuyer comfort, and reduce your build cost. Ensure your heat loss/gain professional is accredited, experienced, and using software that conforms to the CSA F280-12 (R2017) standard.

- Provide standardized and comprehensive design details when submitting your house plans for analysis to ensure you get the best results. This includes providing both the U-factor and the solar heat gain coefficient (SHGC) for the windows to allow accurate sizing of heating and cooling equipment. Without these details, designers will have to make conservative assumptions which may result in equipment oversizing and increase your capital costs.

- The CSA F280-12 (R2017) analysis is a fast and cost-effective way of evaluating changes to envelope options (e.g., changes in window parameters) that can further reduce the size and cost of your mechanical systems. HOT2000 however is the program to be used for the EnerGuide analysis required as part of the Net Zero Energy and Net Zero Energy Ready documentation.

- Review the heat loss/gain results to help focus your attention on areas for additional improvement during future builds.

21.1.2 Factors That Most Affect Heating Equipment Sizing

Heating equipment must be sized to have an output that is equal to or greater than 100% of the calculated CSA F280-12 design heat loss (DHL) of the house at the winter design temperature conditions for the house location.

An example of the various heat loss components that make up the DHL for a two-story single detached house are shown in Figure 21.1.

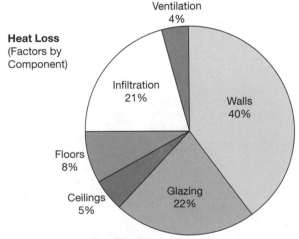

Figure 21.1 Example of heat loss components that impact heating equipment sizing

Design Heat Loss (DHL)
Cold Winter Night

Heat Loss (Factors by Component)

- Ventilation 4%
- Walls 40%
- Glazing 22%
- Ceilings 5%
- Floors 8%
- Infiltration 21%

F280-12: must meet 100% of DHL, or more

CANADIAN HOME BUILDERS' ASSOCIATION

Thermal losses through the walls are the largest component (40%) followed by glazing losses (22%) and infiltration losses (21%). The main window parameter impacting heating equipment sizing is the U-factor of the windows.

21.1.3 Factors That Most Affect Cooling Equipment Sizing

Cooling equipment must be sized with an output that is equal to or greater than 80% of the calculated CSA F280-12 design heat gain (DHG) of the house at the summer design temperature and humidity conditions for the house location.

An example of the various heat gain components that make up the DHG for a two-story single detached house are shown in Figure 21.2. Solar gains through the windows (58%) are the largest component, by a significant margin, of the design heat gain, followed by internal gains (18%) and heat gains through the walls (12%). The main window parameter impacting cooling equipment sizing is the solar heat gain coefficient (SHGC) of the windows.

Figure 21.2 Example of heat gain components that impact heating equipment sizing

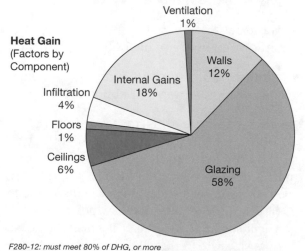

Design Heat Gain (DHG)
Hot Summer Day

Heat Gain
(Factors by Component)

Ventilation 1%
Walls 12%
Internal Gains 18%
Infiltration 4%
Floors 1%
Ceilings 6%
Glazing 58%

F280-12: must meet 80% of DHG, or more

The Impact of Window Solar Heat Gain Coefficient (SHGC) on Cooling Equipment Sizing

In heating dominated climates it is common for builders to specify windows with a high solar heat gain coefficient (SHGC) in order to maximize the amount of passive heating during the heating season. Using windows with a high SHGC will reduce the amount of energy used over the heating season but will have no impact on the size of the heating system needed. The heating system must be sized to provide the heat needed even if there is no sunshine.

In contrast, the window SHGC specified for the house design will have a major impact on the value of the DHG and the size of the cooling equipment needed. This direct correlation between window SHGC and required cooling capacity is illustrated in the example shown in Figure 21.3 for house designs where window specifications are varied and all other envelope parameters remain fixed.

The house used in this analysis was a three-storey, mid-unit townhouse with a basement and an above grade floor area of about 1,600 ft2. The house was constructed using typical building code parameters. The outdoor design conditions used in the analysis were:

- Outdoor temperature of 88°F (31°C),

- Mean daily temperature range of 18°F (10°C) and

- Outdoor humidity ratio of 112 gr/lb (16 g/kg). Humidity Ratio is the mass of water vapour present in the moist air – to the mass of dry air.

Different double and triple-glazed windows were specific, with SHGC values ranging from 0.60 to 0.14, and F280-12 Design Heat Gain (DHG) values for the house were calculated. The chart on the right-hand side of Figure 21.3 plots the DHG for the house versus the SHGC of the windows used. It is clear that

PART 3 — MECHANICAL SYSTEMS | **CHAPTER 21 — MECHANICAL SYSTEMS SIZING**   371

Figure 21.3: Impact of the window Solar Heat Gain Coefficient (SHGC) on cooling equipment sizing

Window Study:

- 3-storey, 1,600ft²
  mid-unit town

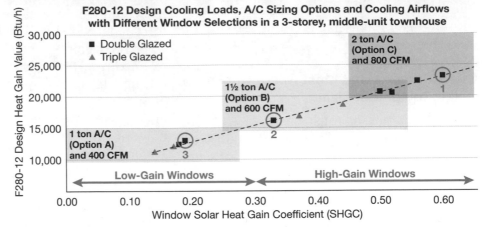

No	Window Description	U-factor (Btu/h/ft²/°F)	SHGC	Energy Rating	Design Heat Gain (Btu/h)
1	Basic, common High-gain Double	0.350	0.60	31	23,248
2	High Performance High-gain Double	0.226	0.33	31	16,112
3	Reference Low-gain Double	0.280	0.19	16	12,909

DHG decreases linearly with the SHGC of the window specified, with similar results for both double and triple-glazed windows.

As an example of how window selection can influence cooling equipment sizing, we will focus on three possible double-glazed window selections with SHGC values of 0.60, 0.33 and 0.19. These windows are identified by the three circles labelled #1, #2 and #3 on the chart and detailed in the small table in Figure 21.3.

Window #1, with a SHGC of 0.60, is typical of the type of window commonly specified for tract-built housing, and results in a DHG value of 23,248 Btu/h. By using Window #2 the DHG can be reduced to 16,112 Btu/h, or even lower by using Window #3 resulting in a DHG of only 12,909 Btu/h or just over half of the original DHG value.

The rectangular coloured areas on the chart in Figure 21.3 indicate the HRAI sizing guidelines

for air conditioning (A/C) units with capacities of 1.0, 1.5 and 2.0 tons of cooling. The A/C sizes and cooling airflow requirements corresponding to these three different window selections are:

- **Window #1:** 2-ton A/C with cooling airflow requirements of about 800 CFM,

- **Window #2:** 1-1/2-ton A/C with cooling airflow requirement of about 600 CFM, and

- **Window #3:** 1-ton A/C unit with cooling airflow requirements of about 400 CFM.

As this example illustrates, selecting an appropriate window SHGC is an effective method for reducing the size of the A/C unit that is needed for a new house. In addition, the reduction in A/C capacity will also reduce cooling airflow requirements, which may allow for the installation of smaller ducts in the home as duct-sizes are frequently based on the design cooling loads and cooling airflow requirements.

Both the smaller the A/C unit and smaller duct sizes will contribute to lower capital costs, and may help to offset any increase in window cost.

Key Points for Builders – Window Specifications and Air- Conditioner Sizing:

- Window SHGC is the most important parameter in determining the cooling equipment size needed for a new house.

- The lowest overall capital cost option for a new build may involve specifying windows with lower SHGC values to enable the use of lower capacity A/C condensing units and smaller forced-air duct systems that are a better match to the duct sizes needed for heating.

- Builders are encouraged to have their window specialists and mechanical designers exchange information to determine if a small change in the window SHGC specification could have a significant impact on the size and cost of the mechanical system.

- This is a more important consideration in regions where air conditioning is commonly used.

21.1.4 How Heating Loads Vary with Climate Regions and Energy Performance Levels

Historically single family homes in Canada typically required heating systems with capacities of 60,000 to 80,000 Btu/h to keep them warm on the coldest days in winter. Modern homes, including Net Zero Energy and Net Zero Energy Ready, being constructed today have evolved and now require smaller heating equipment because of:

- Improved housing designs that are better insulated and air-sealed, have more efficient windows, and the use of heat recovery ventilation;

- Revisions to CSA F280-12 Design Heat Load calculations that reflect the reductions in design loads due to housing technology advances.

As an example of how heating loads have become smaller, Figure 21.4 illustrates the CSA F280-12 design heat loss (DHL) values for a typical 1,400 ft2, two-storey, single detached home located in four different climate regions in Canada with wintertime design temperature ranging from -20°C (-4°F) to -35°C (-31°F).

Figure 21.4: Design Heat Loads for a 2-storey single detached home in four climate regions across Canada

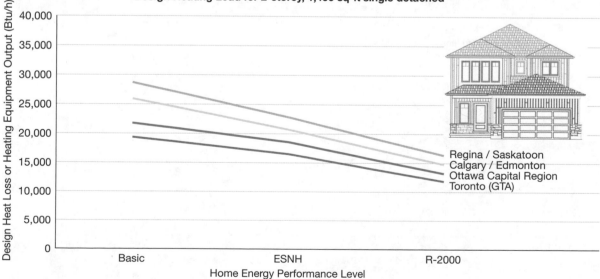

Design Heating Load for 2-storey, 1,400 sq-ft single detached

Regina / Saskatoon
Calgary / Edmonton
Ottawa Capital Region
Toronto (GTA)

The points along each curve represent three different levels of building envelope performance that correspond to:

- "Basic" is a house constructed to either the National or Ontario Building Codes;

- "ESNH" is a house constructed to the ENERGY STAR® for New Homes Standard (version 12.8 and 17.0 Ontario)

- "R-2000" is a home designed to the requirements in the R-2000 Standard.

In all cases, the DHL for this type and size of house constructed to basic code requirements is below 30,000 Btu/h, and could be heated by systems with outputs between about 25,000 and 30,000 Btu/h depending on the location of the home.

As expected, this house model has lower DHL values when constructed to ESNH or R-2000 standards. Depending on location, ESNH models could be heated by systems with outputs in the 20,000 to 25,000 Btu/h range while R-2000 models would require heating systems with outputs of 15,000 to 20,000 Btu/h.

21.1.5 Part-Load Heating Duration Characteristics of Houses in Canada

Building codes require that new homes have heating systems installed with thermal capacities that are equal to or greater than the CSA F280-12 DHL value in order to have the output needed to keep the house warm during the coldest periods of the heating season when the outdoor temperature is at or near the design conditions. Actual heat losses from the house will vary during the heating season with changes in the outdoor temperature and will be lower than the DHL value for most of the time. The distribution of these varying heat losses is shown in the Heat-Loss Duration Curve in Figure 21.5 for a house with a DHL of 20,800 Btu/h. This duration curve predicts the percentage of total heating hours that will be at or above a given heat-loss value during the heating season. For the example house:

- 50% of the hours, heat losses will be greater than 7,100 Btu/h or 34% of DHL,

- 10% of the hours, heat losses will be greater than 14,500 Btu/h or 70% of DHL.

Figure 21.5: Percentage of heating hours above a given heat loss for a house with a Design Heat Loss (DHL) of 20,800 Btu/h

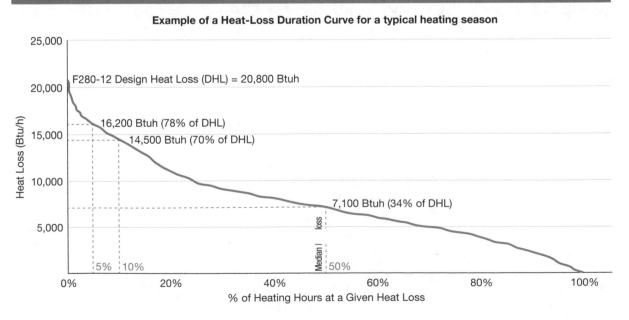

Example of a Heat-Loss Duration Curve for a typical heating season

- 5% of the hours, heat losses will be greater than 16,200 Btu/h or 78% of DHL

Heating equipment compensates for these lower heat losses by cycling ON and OFF during the heating season, under the control of an indoor thermostat.

21.1.6 Heating Equipment Sizing and Equipment Runtimes

At any given period during the heating season the amount of "ON-time" or equipment runtime depends primarily on two factors:

- The outdoor temperature, and

- The thermal capacity of the heating equipment installed relative to the DHL of the house.

Typical heating equipment runtime duration curves are shown in Figure 21.6 for three different single-stage heating systems sized

at 120%, 170% and 250% of DHL of the house. For our example house, with the heat-loss characteristics shown in Figure 21.5, these equipment sizes correspond to thermal outputs of 25,000, 36,000 and 52,000 Btu/h respectively.

The runtime duration curves predict the percentage of total heating hours that will have "ON times" at or above a given number of minutes per hour during the heating season. It is clear from Figure 21.6 that heating system "ON times", or runtimes will become shorter when larger capacity heating equipment is installed in the house.

Longer heating runtimes are preferred and are expected to provide more even temperature distribution throughout the home during the heating season. With single-stage equipment, the longest runtimes require the installation of equipment with rated heating capacities that closely matched the DHL value of the house.

Figure 21.6: Heating System Runtimes for single-stage equipment

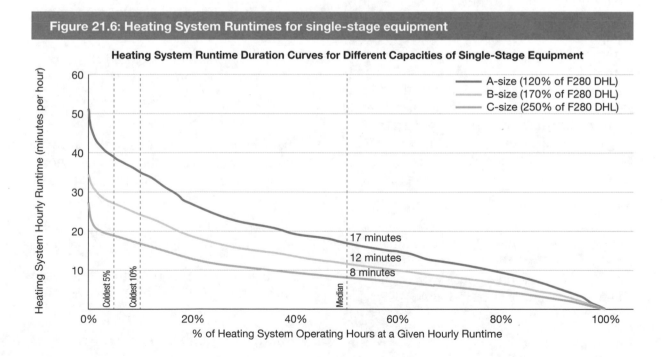

Figure 21.7: Heating System Runtimes for single-stage, two-stage and modulating equipment

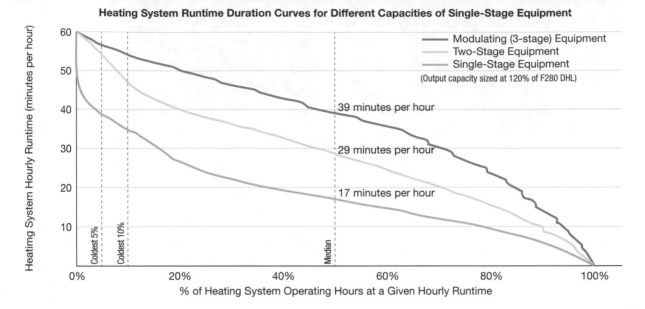

21.1.7 Staged and Modulating Equipment with Variable Capacity

Heating system runtimes can be extended by using either two-stage or modulating equipment. These flexible- output appliances automatically adjust their thermal capacity to better match the changing heat loss demands of a home at different times during the heating season. As a result, variable-capacity heating system runtimes will be longer than with single-stage appliances with similar capacity ratings. This will help maintain more even temperature distribution throughout the home.

Examples of system runtimes are shown in Figure 21.7 for single-stage, two-stage and modulating equipment. Each system has been sized at 120% of the DHL, or 25,000 Btu/h output for our example house with the heating characteristics described in Figure 21.5.

As Figure 21.7 illustrates, heating system runtimes can be extended by using either two-stage or modulating equipment instead of single-stage equipment. The longer runtimes provided by these variable capacity systems are expected to maintain more even temperature distribution throughout the home during the heating season. It is the longer runtimes which is expected to improve occupant comfort compared to single-stage heating equipment.

Key Points for Builders – Heating System Selection and Comfort

These sizing approaches will help provide more even heating comfort:

- Whenever possible, use heating equipment with maximum rated output capacity that closely matches the F280-12 design heat loss (DHL) requirements of the home;

- Consider using variable capacity heating equipment to extend runtimes. Use either:

  ◇ Two-stage equipment with a first-stage firing rate of about 60% of the rated output capacity; or

  ◇ Modulating equipment with three or more stages of heating and a lowest-firing rate of 40% or less of the rated output capacity.

- When available equipment output capacities greatly exceed the F280-12 DHL requirements, the specification and installation of variable capacity heating equipment is desirable (i.e., either 2-stage or modulating equipment), rather than single-stage equipment. The variable capacity equipment will extend heating system runtimes and promote more even temperature distribution and heating comfort throughout the home.

21.2 Sizing Domestic Hot Water Heating Systems

Builders should provide their mechanical designer with the information necessary to size the domestic hot water (DHW) heating equipment. This includes:

- House plans showing all bedrooms and bathrooms,

- List showing both high and low-flow faucet and fixture specifications (e.g., fast-fill tub faucets, shower heads, etc.)

- Maximum fill volume of any large tubs, and

- Any required concurrent shower usage.

Sizing approaches will depend on the type of water heating equipment specified for the home. Two types of equipment are common:

- Tank-based DHW equipment, and

- Whole-house, on-demand DHW equipment.

21.2.1 Sizing of Tank-based DHW Heating Equipment

For tank-based water heating equipment, designers will typically use the house characteristics to size the water heater. For example, ASHRAE had established minimum sizes for storage tank water heater based on the number of bathrooms and bedrooms in a home together with the type of energy input to the water heater (i.e., natural gas/propane, electric or heating oil). Table 21.1 summarizes the minimum sizes for gas storage tank water heaters for one to six bedrooms in one and two family households.

Both the minimum tank storage capacity and burner input sizes are defined by this sizing approach. For example, a house with 3 to 3.5 bathrooms and 4 bedrooms would require a gas water heater with at least 189 L of storage and a burner rated at 38,000 Btu/h or higher. Minimum storage size should also be greater than the fill volume of any large tubs installed in the home.

Table 21.1: Gas Storage-Tank Water Heater Minimum Size Requirements for Residential Houses											
Number of Baths	1-1.5			2-2.5				3-3.5			
Number of Bedrooms	1	2	3	2	3	4	5	3	4	5	6
Storage capacity (L)	76	114	114	114	151	151	189	151	189	189	189
Burner input (kBtu/h)	27	36	36	36	36	38	47	38	38	47	50

Adapted from ASHRAE 2015 Handbook on HVAC Applications

21.2.2 Sizing of Whole-house On-Demand, Tankless Water Heating Equipment

Whole-house on-demand, tankless water heaters are gas heated appliances that are available in a few different sizes with input ratings of around 100,000, 150,000 or 200,000 Btu/h. Low-mass hydronic boilers also commonly provide a separate on-demand domestic hot water heating circuit.

The maximum rated hot water capacity of on-demand water heaters can be specified in different ways:

- On-demand, tankless water heater manufacturers normally rate the capacity of their appliances by specifying a maximum flow rate (i.e., L/min or USGPM) at a specified temperature rise.

- CAN/CSA P.9-11 (R2015) tested combination systems using on-demand water heaters specify DHW capacity by a **One-Hour Delivery Rating (OHR)** (i.e. L/h) at an inlet water temperature of 14.4°C (58°F) and a delivery temperature of 49°C (120°F), which is equivalent to a temperature rise of 34.6°C (62°F).

The delivery capacity of an on-demand water heater will depend on the actual temperature rise needed, which is determined by both the local cold water supply temperature and the hot water temperature delivered to the home.

When selecting an on-demand water heater, designers compare the hot water delivery capacity of various sizes of appliances to the specific needs of the new home. Factors to consider may include:

- Minimum cold water supply temperature to the home,

- Maximum flow rate of any high-flow faucets installed in the home (e.g., large tubs),

- Flow rates of shower heads and the assumed maximum number of simultaneous-use showers in the home, and

- Whether or not drain water heat recovery is installed on the shower drains.

Key Points for Builders – DHW Systems:

- It is important to size and select water heating appliances that are compatible with the faucets and fixtures specified for the new home.

- When using on-demand water heating it is important to consider the minimum cold water supply temperature at the house location when determining the required heating capacity of the water heater needed to satisfy hot water delivery requirements of faucets and fixtures installed in the house.

21.3 Sizing Ventilation Systems

National and Provincial Building Codes in Canada requires mechanical ventilation systems in all residential buildings. Every dwelling unit supplied with electrical power must be provided with a mechanical ventilation system complying with either CAN/CSA F326-M91 (R2014) or a prescriptive approach defined in the applicable building code.

21.3.1 Canadian Standards Association F326

CAN/CSA-F326-M91 (R 2014) Residential Mechanical Ventilation Systems is a guide for effective ventilation systems. The R-2000 Program recognized the importance of ventilation in high-performance houses and has required compliance with CSA-F326 ever since it was developed. CSA-F326 is a performance standard that requires a continuous level of ventilation based on the number and types of rooms in a house.

Net Zero Energy and Net Zero Energy Ready housing require designers to provide adequate ventilation as well and use this standard (F326) as a base.

21.3.2 Building Code Prescriptive Approach to Ventilation Sizing

Prescriptive design and sizing requirements for ventilation systems are described in the National or applicable Provincial Building Codes that are loosely based on the F326 standard. These prescriptive approaches deal with various design details including:

- Ventilating rates based on the number of bedrooms,

- Exhaust from all bathrooms and kitchens,

- Protection against depressurization and air pollutants,

- Provision of make-up air for exhaust devices if fuel-burning appliances are not direct vented,

- Provision of carbon monoxide detectors in dwellings with fuel-burning appliances or attached garages, and

- Specifications for sone (noise) ratings of fans used in the ventilation system.

Key Points for Builders – Ventilation Systems:

- Mechanical ventilation is required in all new dwellings.

- Building Codes provide prescriptive design and sizing approaches for code-compliant and ENERGY STAR for New Home (ESNH) house designs.

- CAN/CSA F326 Standard provides a performance approach for ventilation system design, and is the required design and sizing method for R-2000, Net Zero Energy and Net Zero Energy Ready house designs.

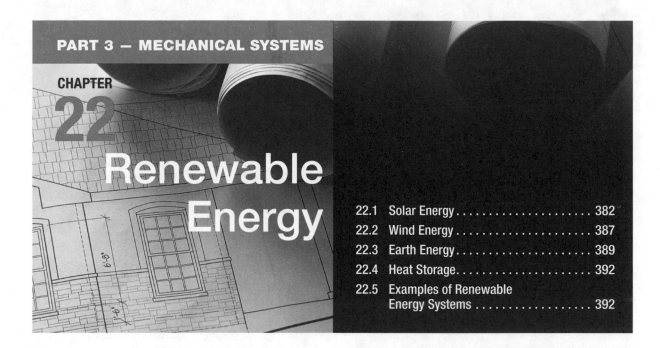

PART 3 — MECHANICAL SYSTEMS

CHAPTER

22

Renewable Energy

As the cost of fossil fuels and grid electricity rises, there is increasing incentive to consider renewable energy sources, which are non-polluting and immune to rising energy prices. The houses described later in this chapter all employ some type of renewable energy; these examples serve to heighten awareness of technologies currently available and becoming more cost-competitive.

Utilities are revising policies to enable the purchase of excess electricity from small producers, and governments are offering incentive programs to encourage the use of renewable energy technologies. This chapter describes renewable energy technologies currently available.

22.1 Solar Energy

Solar energy can be used to provide electricity and heat. Electricity is produced using photovoltaic cells, while heat can be produced using liquid- or air-based collectors. Heat can be used for space heating or water heating, or both.

Table 22.1 shows solar radiation potential for Canadian locations based on horizontal surfaces. A horizontal surface is not the ideal angle for the collection of solar energy but is provided here for comparison. The annual radiation will generally be higher on an inclined surface, such as a sloped roof, because solar insolation is most productive when the collector is perpendicular to the sun's rays.

Table 22.1 Solar radiation potential	
Location	**Annual solar radiation (gigajoules/m^2) on a horizontal surface**
St. John's	4.11
Halifax	4.60
Quebec	4.46
Montreal	4.59
Ottawa	4.65
Toronto	4.69
Winnipeg	4.61
Calgary	4.53
Edmonton	4.17
Vancouver	4.52

22.1.1 Electricity from photovoltaic cells

Sunlight is converted to electricity by means of photovoltaic (PV) cells. Photovoltaic cells are semiconductor devices, usually made of silicon and containing no liquids, corrosive chemicals or moving parts. The cells produce electricity whenever visible light shines on them.

Each PV cell is made from two thin silicon wafers with different electrical properties. When sunlight strikes the solar cell, electrons naturally travel from one layer to the other, and an electrical current is created. Currently available PV cells convert about 12 % to 15 % of the sun's light into electricity, but laboratory prototypes are now reaching 30 % efficiency.

Photovoltaic arrays

To capture and convert more energy from the sun, photovoltaic cells are linked to form photovoltaic modules (also called panels), and modules are assembled together to make arrays (Figure 22.1). An array is simply a large number of modules connected to produce higher voltages and increased power. An array producing 50 watts of power measures approximately 40 x 100 cm (16 x 40 in.). Photovoltaic arrays are a familiar sight along roadsides for powering construction signs and emergency telephones. If an array is properly sized, it can produce enough electricity to power buildings.

For residential applications, photovoltaic arrays would normally be placed on roofs facing southeast to southwest and inclined at 20° to 60° from the horizontal. Solar electricity can power any electric device, but it is not considered cost-effective for space or water heating since photovoltaic arrays are still relatively expensive and a Code-built house still uses considerable amounts of heat. As the price of photovoltaic equipment declines and houses continue to reduce their heating requirements, solar electricity will be used more for heating. (See Chapter 5 for loads in Net Zero Energy Homes.) Net Zero Energy and Net Zero Energy Ready builders have gotten the loads down low enough that photovoltaic power is a viable option.

Converting DC to AC current

Photovoltaic (PV) modules generate direct current (DC) electricity when their cells are exposed to sunlight. Therefore, some additional electrical equipment is required to make the electricity compatible with house systems which use alternating current (AC) or to store electricity for use when the sun is not shining (Figure 22.2).

Figure 22.1 Photovoltaic array

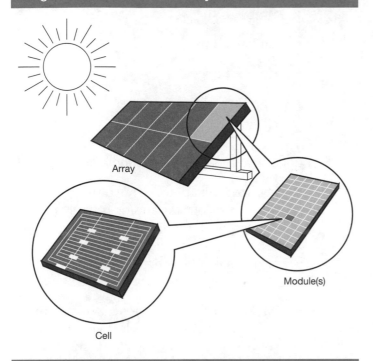

Array

Module(s)

Cell

Figure 22.2 Solar power conversion

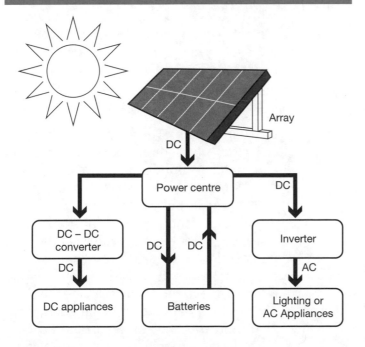

To provide the 120-volt alternating current (AC), an inverter is required to convert the DC current to AC current. Inverters vary in both size and quality of electricity they supply. Less expensive inverters are suitable for simple loads, such as lights and water pumps, but models with good quality waveform output are

needed to power electronic devices such as TVs, stereos, microwave ovens and computers.

Storing electricity

Photovoltaic panels produce electricity in both cloudy conditions and full sunlight. To make electricity available after sundown or for times when demand exceeds supply, the energy must have been stored. Rechargeable batteries are used to store energy (Figure 22.2) and must be able to discharge and recharge repeatedly.

PV systems are usually equipped with some type of electronic charge controller to feed electricity from the PV panel to the battery in the most efficient manner, to prevent the solar panel from overcharging the battery, and to protect the solar panels from electrical damage. Some charge controllers include a built-in power inverter.

Grid-connected photovoltaic systems

Rather than storing the electricity in batteries, an option available in many regions is to connect a home PV system to the electricity grid. This allows for electricity to be added to the grid when the PV system is producing more than the house requires, and for the house to use electricity from the grid when needed. In addition, the cost of the photovoltaic system can be reduced because storage batteries are not required. Grid-connected solar PV systems consist of four main components:

• Array of solar PV modules on the roof (or other suitable location);

• DC disconnect switch;

• DC to AC inverter and an AC disconnect switch; and

- Wiring and sometimes a combiner box (a combiner box consolidates several sources of electricity into one main feed – they are used when there are a number of panels) and metering.

Excess electricity is exported into the electrical grid and credited to the homeowner's account (where provincial electrical regulations permit). Electricity from the electrical grid is used at night and during high house loads.

PV inverters incorporate several fail-safe technologies. For safety reasons, they shut down during power outages to ensure the safety of utility personnel possibly working on distribution lines. They are becoming increasingly sophisticated, often including integrated DC and AC disconnects and web-enabled features that allow for easy remote retrieval and viewing of real-time and historic operational data.

The market for grid connected solar PV is growing at a rate of 50% per year around the world, and the ability to sell surplus electricity to the electrical grid certainly enhances that market. Photovoltaic technology is well proven, and the cells have an expected service life of 30 years. Photovoltaic systems are modular-additional capacity can easily be added to meet increasing energy demands.

22.1.2 Solar heating

A solar heating system uses the sun to heat air or liquid. The heat can be used for a number of purposes including:

- Swimming pool heating;

- Domestic water heating;

- Space heating; and,

- Ventilation air heating.

A liquid-based solar heating system typically consists of six major components:

- Solar collectors;

- Pump;

- Storage tank;

- Heat exchanger;

- Controller; and,

- Heat transfer fluid (liquid or air).

Solar heating collector technologies include:

- Unglazed flat plate: These are generally made from plastic and/or rubber and are used for low-temperature applications such as heating for swimming pools. They are inexpensive, and are the most efficient type for low-temperature applications.

- Glazed flat plate: These are medium-temperature collectors used year-round for typical residential applications. The collector consists of an insulated metal box, a black-coated metal absorber plate and a glass top (Figure 22.3). The absorber converts the solar energy into heat, and tubes on the back of the absorber allow circulating heat transfer fluid to be heated. Typical dimensions are 1200 x 2400 mm (4 x 8 ft.), but some smaller sizes are available.

- Evacuated tube: These high-temperature collectors are used for both residential and commercial applications. The evacuated tube is much like a fluorescent light bulb, with an absorber surface and heat pipe inside and a manifold on the top. These collectors raise the temperature of the heat transfer fluid to higher levels than flat plate collectors, since heat loss is significantly reduced due to the vacuum inside the tube. The absorber converts the solar energy into heat, and the heat pipe carries the heat from the absorber into heat transfer fluid circulating through the manifold. These collectors are generally more expensive than glazed flat plate collectors, but can be more efficient on an annual basis.

Heat transfer fluids for solar heaters include a propylene glycol/water mix, and distilled or municipal water, depending on the type of collector, the system configuration, and heating application.

Closed-loop systems always contain a freeze-protected mix of propylene glycol and water. The glycol/water mix needs to be checked annually to ensure that it has not become acidic due to summer-time stagnation and that the freeze protection is still adequate.

Figure 22.3 Solar hot-water collector

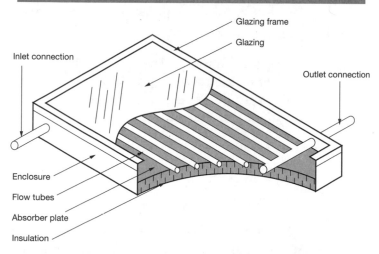

Figure 22.4 Typical solar domestic hot-water system

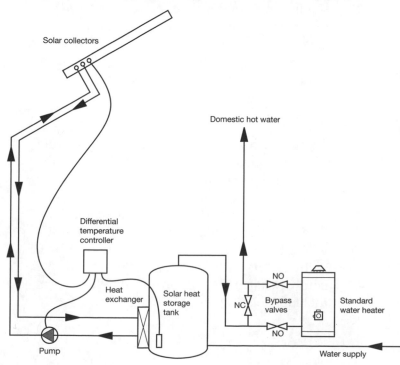

Drain back systems use water for the heat transfer fluid, and allow it to drain out of the collectors and the piping whenever the pump turns off. This prevents the water in the collectors from being exposed to freezing conditions in the winter or stagnation conditions in the summer.

22.1.3 Solar domestic hot-water heating

The least expensive and most common type of residential solar heating is active solar domestic water heating using glazed flat-plate collectors (Figure 22.4) and a storage tank that resembles a conventional water heating tank. A pair of small, insulated pipes and temperature sensor wiring connects the two. The collectors are situated on the roof, wall or other solar-accessible location with good solar exposure, and the rest of the equipment is in the basement. If flat-plate solar collectors are integrated into the house roof or are finished with bevelled flashing, they can appear similar to a large skylight when viewed from the street.

Whenever the collectors are warmer than the tank, a differential temperature controller turns on the pump to circulate the heat transfer fluid between the collectors and the heat exchanger. Some systems use a solar photovoltaic module to directly energize and control the pump. Typically, the system can operate on any day of the year.

Most installations use one, two or three collectors. A typical family will get two-thirds of its domestic water heating energy from a two-collector system, thereby reducing greenhouse gas emissions by up to 2 tonnes per year, depending on the heating fuel displaced and the amount of water used.

Solar domestic water heating systems are plumbed in a pre-heat configuration between the cold water supply and the conventional water heater. They can be easily installed in new or retrofit applications and used with both tank-based and tankless water heaters. If the solar-heated water is not at the required set temperature, then the conventional water heater provides the balance of the heat needed to reach the set temperature. Since the solar domestic water heater also includes a storage tank, the combined system reduces the likelihood that the household will run out of hot water.

Other solar domestic water heating technologies include three-season passive, thermosyphon and batch water heaters that are suitable for anytime when there is not a risk of frost.

The planning and installation of a solar domestic hot-water system has several considerations:

- Design: A system needs to be either CSA listed or designed by a professional engineer. This will help eliminate unproven systems, as well as poor sizing, selection, or location of components.

- Components: Solar collectors should be certified to applicable standards and tests from the CSA, the American Solar Rating and Certification Corporation, or the Florida Solar Energy Center. Three CSA standards explicitly relate to solar water heating products: CAN/CSA-F378-87 for solar collectors, CAN/CSA F379.1-09 (R2013) for packaged solar domestic hot-water systems, and CAN/CSA-F383-08 (R2013) for installing packaged solar domestic hot-water systems. The Canadian Solar Industries Association (CanSIA) provides a list of standards applicable to all solar DHW system components, plus a list of collectors and systems that meet these standards.

- Controllers: Controllers should be selected that use the temperature difference between the collector and the tank to start and stop the pump (not just a single system temperature).

- Piping: Solar collectors can produce temperatures as high as 200°C. Copper piping needs to be used in the solar loop between the solar collectors and the heat exchanger to withstand the hot fluids. Drain back systems also need solar loop piping to be properly sloped to ensure that the water drains out of the collectors and piping when the pump stops.

- Roof penetrations: These are critical to the building's integrity and must be properly flashed and sealed to avoid air, water and vapour leakage.

- Installation: Installers should have a CSA F383-08-based Solar Hot-Water System Installer certificate from CanSIA or equivalent.

Liquid-based solar space heating systems

Active solar space heating uses the same collectors as solar domestic hot water systems. Depending on the house location, winter shading, house heat requirements and amount of solar heating desired, the number of collectors might range from 7 to 50. Heat storage is sized for the required heating loads, number of collectors and duration of autonomy from any back-up heating sources.

Experience has shown that system design and installation need to be kept very simple to avoid problems. High tilt angles or wall mounting are optimal for space heating collectors to maximize wintertime solar gain, eliminate snow coverage and enhance reflection from snow-covered yards. A due south orientation typically provides the maximum solar heat gain, but deviations of up to 30° from due south result in less than 10% reduction in incident solar radiation.

Air-based solar space heating systems

Air-based solar heating systems do exist, but have not performed up to expectations when used for whole house heating, and are not common.

Some new air-based systems are available that utilize simple and inexpensive solar air collectors with integral fans that mount onto a south-facing wall and duct solar heat straight into a room during sunny winter days. These can also be adapted for pre-heating ventilation air.

22.2 Wind Energy

Energy from wind is becoming more common in North America for large-capacity generation, and is a practical energy alternative for some residential applications. Wind energy systems require a fairly constant wind. Wind mapping has been completed for most regions of Canada, and gives an indication of the viability of wind energy for a certain area.

Systems are usually designed to begin operating at wind speeds greater than 15 km/h and shut down at very high wind speeds to protect them from damage. Wind is not always available with enough velocity to power a wind energy system. This is why many systems are used in combination with another energy source such as solar panels, gas generators or grid electricity.

Small wind turbines (10 kW to 50 kW) should be installed on large lots (at least a half-acre or more) that have unobstructed access to wind. The amount of power generation increases with height, but so does tower cost, so the tradeoff needs to be evaluated.

The turbine needs to be located at a distance of at least one tower height from current and proposed property lines and structures to prevent damage or injury from a potential tower collapse or cable fault, and to allow room for guy wires (if required). Local by-laws must be consulted to verify the required property set-back. In addition, the tower needs to be located 100 metres horizontally from any obstacles that are at approximately the same height (Figure 22.5).

Figure 22.5 Wind turbine siting

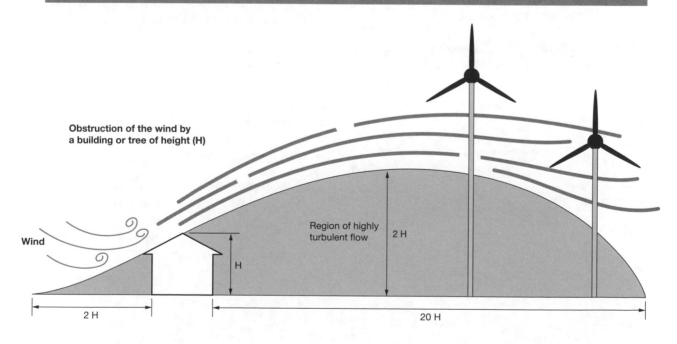

Small wind turbines usually consist of the following components (Figure 22.6):

- Rotor blades and shaft: The blades are usually fibreglass, metal, or reinforced plastic or wood. The energy generation capability is a factor of the diameter of the circle formed by the blades.

- Generator/alternator: Electricity is produced from the rotation of the turbine rotor either as direct current (DC) power (produced by a generator) or alternating current (AC) power (produced by an alternator), depending on the application for the turbine.

- Tail vane: The tail vane aligns the turbine blades into the wind.

- Tower: The tower holds the turbine in the path of the wind, and must be designed to survive extreme winds and icing.

In the far north, turbine blades are also susceptible to rime ice. In addition, most small turbines include a control and protection system to guard against over-speeding. The sophistication of the system varies depending on the application of the wind turbine and the energy system it supports. Most turbines above 10 kW use a gearbox to match the rotor speed to that of the generator/alternator.

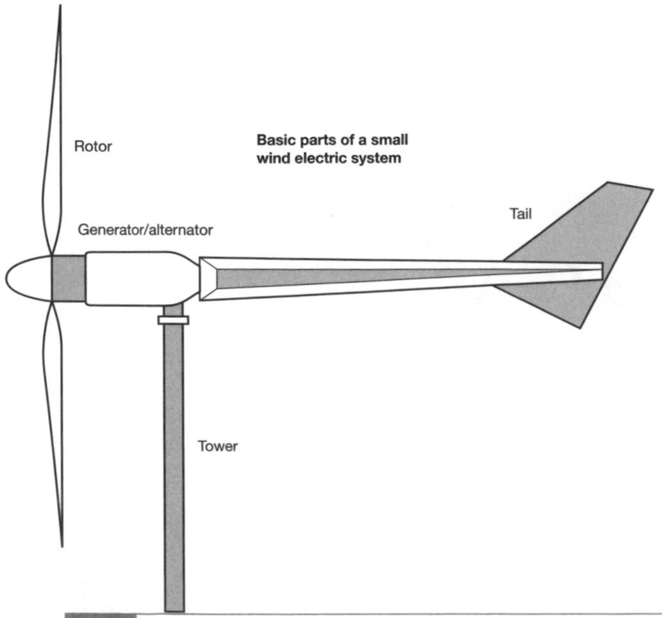

Consideration of wind energy requires a site assessment to determine potential energy output.

For most open spaces, wind speed increases 12% each time the height is doubled. A small increase in wind speed leads to a large increase in energy output, as the energy available in the wind is proportional to the cube of the wind speed.

For household electricity generation, other components may be required:

- An inverter may be required (if the turbine is not equipped with an alternator) to convert from DC to AC power. Light-duty inverters (100-1,000 W) are typically 12 V DC and suitable for lights and small appliances such as televisions, radios and small hand tools. Heavy-duty inverters (400-10,000 W) can be 12, 24 or 48 V DC, and can be used to run appliances.

- Batteries are needed to store electricity if the turbine is not connected to the electrical grid. The best batteries for renewable energy systems are deep discharge batteries that can be safely discharged a significant amount (50-80% of the battery storage) daily and charged back up the next day. They typically last three to five years.

Disconnect switches, circuit breakers, fuses and other protective equipment (as recommended by the manufacturer and required by electrical code) are important for the safe operation of the system. They electrically isolate the wind turbine from the batteries and the batteries from the inverter and load.

A monitoring system comprised of a voltmeter (for measuring battery voltage and depth of discharge) and an ammeter (to monitor energy production or use) provides protection against low- or high-voltage conditions.

Figure 22.6 Small wind turbine

Basic parts of a small wind electric system

Rotor

Generator/alternator

Tail

Tower

22.3 Earth Energy

Earth energy uses heat in the ground or in groundwater to cool or heat air and water for buildings. For example, a heat pump can extract heat from beneath the ground to heat a building. In the summer, the heat pump can be reversed to provide air conditioning-removing heat from building air and rejecting it to the ground.

Direct exchange (DX) geothermal heat pump systems are also available in which a refrigerant exchanges heat directly with the soil through copper tubing. This eliminates the plastic water pipe and water pump to circulate water found in a water-source geothermal heat pump.

Earth energy is more efficient than a combustion furnace because less energy is required to move heat from one place to another than to convert energy from one form into another. However, the capital cost to install a complete earth energy system is higher than the cost to install a furnace and an air conditioning unit. Once installed, an earth energy system can reduce heating and cooling energy costs. There are more than 30,000 applications of residential, commercial, institutional and industrial earth energy systems in Canada.

All homes have heat pumps in the form of refrigerators or freezers, which pump heat from the interior box to the fins on the back. A ground-source heat pump operates on the same basis-it pumps heat from the ground to inside the house. A typical arrangement is shown in Figure 22.7.

Figure 22.7 Typical arrangement for a ground source heating system

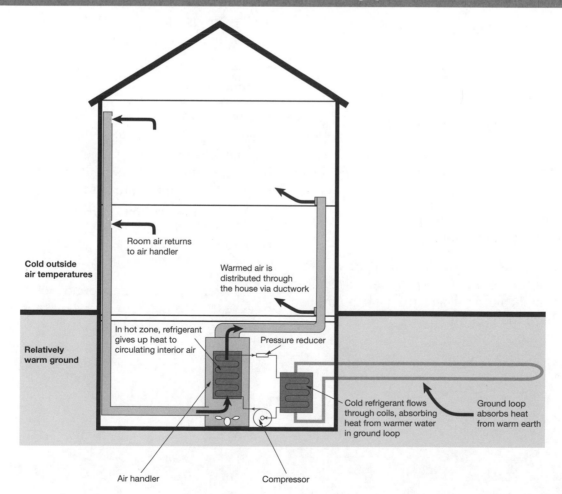

The Canadian Standards Association International (CSA) and the geothermal heat pump industry have developed the CAN/CSA 448-02 (R2012) *Design and Installation of Earth Energy Systems* standard for earth energy heat pump installation. In addition, several provinces have developed certification and apprenticeship training courses to ensure that systems are designed and installed correctly. Most manufacturers also provide training for equipment installers, as well as technical support for their dealers.

A complete geothermal heat pump system consists of three components:

- Ground-coupled heat exchanger;

- Heat pump; and,

- Heat distribution system (air handler, hydronic, or a combination thereof).

A ground-coupled heat exchanger consists of:

- Vertical borehole, horizontal trench, pond, or lake to act as a heat source and sink;

- High-density polyethylene piping running through the source/sink (called loops);

- Grouting (in the case of vertical boreholes);

- Underground manifold connecting the loops to the heat pump (if multiple loops are required);

- Fluid-circulating pump (normally located inside the house); and,

- Fluid consisting of either straight water or an antifreeze mixture. Antifreeze is required in applications where the heat pump can freeze the ground.

A good approach for designing heat pumps is to size them for about 75% of the design heating load. For those few days when a home's heating load exceeds system capacity, a supplemental heat source is provided. Options for supplemental capacity include electric resistance duct heaters, extra elements or burners in a hot-water tank, or a supplemental boiler.

The ground loop is designed to meet the flow requirements of the heat pump. Some factors that affect loop design include:

- The amount of heating and cooling energy that the heat pump is required to supply (this is a primary factor determining overall loop length);

- The moisture content and type of ground (loops perform better in solid rock or moist, dense soil because heat is conducted to the loop more quickly than in light, dry soil);

- The footprint available for drilling and trenching; and,

- The distance between the boreholes or trenches.

System operation

Fluid is circulated through the ground loop and its manifold and back into the heat pump. The heat pump first extracts heat from the fluid, reducing its temperature before it is circulated back to the ground loop to pick up more heat. While in the ground loop, the temperature of the fluid is again heated up to the ground temperature. The roles of the heat pump are to:

- Transfer heat from the ground loop through a heat exchanger to an evaporating and condensing fluid (refrigerant);

- Upgrade the temperature of the refrigerant through the thermodynamic heat pump cycle; and,

- Transfer the refrigerant's heat through a second heat exchanger to the house heat distribution system.

For forced-air heat distribution systems, the refrigerant's heat is transferred to the house forced-air heating loop through a refrigerant-to-air heat exchanger (coil). House air is heated by the coil and then distributed throughout the house in the same manner as a regular forced-air heating system. This type of heat pump is called a water to air heat pump; it raises the temperature of the air by between 10° and 15°C (50° to 59°F), feeding the house with air up to 35°C (95°F) (as compared to gas furnaces that raise it by 20° to 30 C° (68° to 86°F) to supply the house with 50°C (122°F) air). These lower supply-air temperatures will not create comfort problems, provided warm air outlets are strategically located. The heat pump must deliver more air through the house to distribute the heat.

For hydronic heat distribution systems, the refrigerant's heat is transferred to the heating water, which is circulated to room radiators, convectors, radiant floors, or a combination of these devices. This type of heat pump is called a water to water heat pump; it raises the temperature of the house loop fluid to no more than about 50°C (122°F), which limits the choices for equipment to distribute the heat. Baseboard radiators typically operate with water heated to 65°C (149°F) and are less effective when the water is not as warm. As a result, larger radiators or more of them are needed to distribute an equivalent amount of heat. A radiant floor system must be designed to operate within heat pump temperatures, and therefore may require closer spacing of the in-floor pipes.

Newer and more environmentally safe hydrochlorofluorocarbon (HCFC) refrigerants such as R 22 have replaced most chlorofluorocarbons (CFCs). HCFCs, in turn, are being phased out under the Montreal Protocol and have been replaced by hydrofluorocarbons (HFCs), such as R-410A, that have no ozone depletion potential.

Most heat pumps can provide domestic water heating by one of two methods: on demand or through a "de-superheater". A de-superheater is a small auxiliary heat exchanger that transfers heat to water from superheated refrigerant produced by the heat pump's compressor. Whenever the heat pump's compressor is operating, regardless of whether the house is being heated or cooled, domestic water from a conventional water heater circulates through the de-superheater to extract heat from the refrigerant.

When the heat pump is not running, hot water is heated in a conventional manner. During periods of air conditioning, since the de-superheater's heat is an unwanted by-product, the water heating is free. Depending on hot-water consumption, a de-superheater can provide from 30% to 60% of the hot water needed by an average household.

Two very important performance ratings for heat pumps are the coefficient of performance (COP) and the seasonal energy efficiency ratio (SEER). The COP rating evaluates heating performance, and the SEER rating evaluates cooling performance. In heating dominated climates, the COP rating is more important. COP is like an efficiency rating-it indicates how much energy the unit delivers compared to how much it uses to operate. Ground source heat pump COPs range from 3 to 5. This means that for every one unit of electrical energy used to operate the heat pump's compressor, fan, and pump, it extracts another 2 to 4 units of heat from the ground, to provide the house with a total of 3 to 5 units of heat. The operating costs of homes with ground source heat pump systems can be substantially less than with other types of heating systems, depending on the source fuel typically used.

Most heat pumps have two-stage compressors and multi-speed fans that more closely match their heat supply with the house heating and cooling loads. In spring and autumn, when full-system heating capacity is not needed, the compressor and fan will operate at low speed and lower power levels. During cold winters and very hot summers, the system will operate at high speed. Most earth energy heat pumps are installed with thermostats that switch from heating to cooling automatically.

22.4 Heat Storage

All materials in a house store heat when house temperatures increase, and release it when temperatures decrease. This is known as thermal mass, and it typically includes such items as drywall, and concrete (or masonry) walls, floors and countertops. Heavier materials store more heat per unit volume than lighter materials.

House design needs to ensure that the mass is not isolated from the heat sources and loads when needed. Generally, thermal mass is used to store heat for both short and long term. On a short-term basis (daily), it has been found that the passive heat from the sun penetrates approximately 12 mm (½ in.) into a material. Drywall, therefore, is an excellent material for absorbing heat during the day and releasing it after the sun goes down at night.

Water in insulated tanks or insulated rock bed storage can be used for larger or longer-term storage needs, but the storage unit needs to be properly sized and designed in order to provide maximum benefit. Some new systems that store and release heat through the change of the liquid/solid phase of materials are being developed. Storage of heat in the ground from summer to winter is of increasing interest among a number of builders, especially when coupled with active solar heating systems and geothermal heat pumps.

22.5 Examples of Renewable Energy Systems

The examples that follow are intended to demonstrate the feasibility of building housing that uses renewable energy systems.

22.5.1 Riverdale EQuilibrium house

The Riverdale EQuilibrium house in Edmonton uses a combination of high insulation levels, solar heating and solar photovoltaic energy to reach its goal of net zero annual purchased energy and net zero annual emissions. The house has heat transfer loops for solar heat collection; domestic water heating supply; space heating supply; forced air heating and ventilation air, as follows:

- Solar heat collection: A pump circulates water to seven solar collectors (total array area of 21 square metres) and then to a heat exchanger in a 300 L (66 gal.) daily heat storage tank. This tank takes the place of a conventional domestic hot-water heater. If the daily storage tank is already charged with heat, then solar-heated water is diverted to a heat exchanger in a 17,000 L (3,700 gal.) seasonal heat storage tank. A 30 L (6.5 gal.) drain back tank stores the water from the collectors when the pump is not operating so that the collectors are dry when not in use and therefore protected from freezing and stagnating.

- Domestic water heating: This system is only slightly different from that in a conventional house. Cold water from the city mains goes through a drain water heat exchanger to be pre heated whenever drain water is available from showers. This tempered water then feeds showers, laundry and the daily heat storage tank. While in the tank, water is heated by the solar heat exchanger. If the water temperature is less than a certain value, an electric heating element provides the balance required. Heated water is then fed to three destinations: the clothes washer, a super-hot tap in the kitchen, and a tempering valve, where it is mixed with incoming cold water for the balance of the domestic hot-water loads. System controls minimize the use of the electric heater.

- Space heating: A pump circulates hot water to a fan coil in the house's air distribution system. The setting of bypass valves allows heat to be drawn from the seasonal storage tank or from the daily storage tank. Heat can also be transferred between the two storage tanks if required.

- Forced-air heating: As with any forced-air heating system, a fan circulates house air from return air ducts through a fan coil, where it is heated and fed to the house through supply ducts. The supply ducts are located at the centre of the house rather than at the walls, because the very high performance walls and windows do not require bathing with hot air, as would normally be the case.

- Ventilation air: The house ventilation system uses a conventional heat recovery ventilator (HRV). An exhaust fan draws air from bathrooms and the kitchen, and sends it through the HRV core to the outdoors. A supply fan draws outdoor air through the HRV core for pre-heating by the exhaust air. This tempered outdoor air is fed into the forced air heating system to supply adequate ventilation.

- Optional ground loops

- 41 m (135 ft.) of plastic piping were buried under the garage floor and 55 m (180 ft.) were buried around the foundation. If required, these loops can provide small amounts of space cooling by circulating water through the buried piping to the fan coil.

- Optional heat pump: A very small heat pump (¾ tonne capacity-the size of a large refrigerator) can be added to the system as an option.

For occupants of the Riverdale Equilibrium house, the solar space/water heating system will function identically to a normal furnace and water heater, with a thermostat in the daily tank and a thermostat on the main floor house wall. No significant maintenance is expected.

This heating system is expected to provide 8.1 GJ (2,200 kWh) of heat yearly for space heating (67% of net required), and 6.9 GJ (1,900 kWh) for domestic water heating (92% of net required). Solar photovoltaic provides the balance of the heating needs via the electric resistance heating element-there is no natural gas supply to the house. The annual energy bill consists of the conventional connection charges to the electric utility grid and energy charges that are slightly in surplus.

The house has no annual energy-related greenhouse gas emissions, which is 16 tonnes per year less than if it were built with conventional construction. The house envelope alone has an EnerGuide for Homes rating of 86. Passive solar energy increases the EG rating to 93; active solar energy increases it to 96, and the solar photovoltaic system increases it to just over 100.

22.5.2 The Drake Landing Solar Community

The Drake Landing Solar Community in Okotoks, south of Calgary, is a solar district heating system with seasonal heat storage that will provide 90% of the heat to 52 homes built to R-2000 energy efficiency standards. It is a good example of community-scale solar heating, the first such system outside of several in Europe, and the first in the world with more than 90% of its space heating supplied by solar energy. The project reduces each home's GHG emissions by five tonnes per year.

Figure 22.8 is a schematic of the project's five main heat transfer systems described as follows:

- Solar collectors: The project incorporates 800 solar heating collectors mounted on the roofs of several banks of detached garages. Pumps circulate a 50% propylene glycol and water solution through the collectors to absorb the heat and move it to short-term storage tanks.

- Short-term storage tanks: Two 125,000 L tanks in an Energy Centre building store the solar heat for up to a few days. A control system decides whether heat should be moved from the tanks via a district heating system to the houses for immediate use, held for a few days in case the houses will need it later, moved to a borehole field for seasonal heat storage, or moved from the borehole field to the tanks.

- Borehole storage field: A borehole thermal energy storage (BTES) field is used to save heat collected in the spring, summer and fall for use the following winter. A field consisting of 144 wells drilled 35 m deep under a park stores heat from summer to winter. Each borehole has a U-tube in it, in which water is circulated from the short-term tanks to transfer heat to and from the surrounding ground. Although this is an earth energy system, it only uses circulating water to transfer heat-not a refrigerant based heat pump.

- District heating system: Heat is transferred from the short-term tanks to the houses via a district heating system that supplies all the houses in parallel. It consists of an insulated supply and a return line buried 1 m (3.3 ft.) deep in its own trench between the houses and the public sidewalk. Each house has a branch line from the district heating system. Natural gas boilers in the Energy Centre supply the 10% remaining balance of the community's space heat. Management, operation and maintenance of the solar, Energy Centre and district heating systems are provided by a solar utility specialist contractor.

- House air handlers: Each house has an air handler in the basement that combines a heat recovery ventilator with a forced-air heating system. Heated water drawn from the district heating system's branch line feeds a heating coil in the air handler. The HRV also supplies the coil with its pre warmed fresh air. The air handler operates exactly like a warm-air furnace using a conventional thermostat.

Figure 22.8 Schematic of the Drake Landing energy system

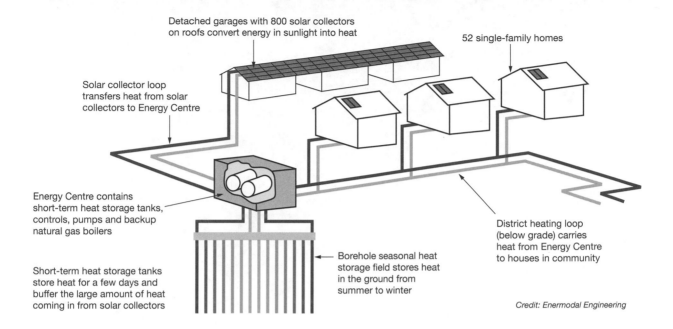

Detached garages with 800 solar collectors on roofs convert energy in sunlight into heat

52 single-family homes

Solar collector loop transfers heat from solar collectors to Energy Centre

Energy Centre contains short-term heat storage tanks, controls, pumps and backup natural gas boilers

District heating loop (below grade) carries heat from Energy Centre to houses in community

Short-term heat storage tanks store heat for a few days and buffer the large amount of heat coming in from solar collectors

Borehole seasonal heat storage field stores heat in the ground from summer to winter

Credit: Enermodal Engineering

The individual Drake Landing houses also have their own two-collector, roof-mounted solar domestic water heating systems, which are expected to provide about two-thirds of their domestic water heating needs. A conventional natural gas water heater provides the balance.

The system has undergone detailed monitoring since it was brought into service in July 2007. As of the beginning of 2012, the system was performing very close to expectations based on modelling. In its fourth year of operation the solar fraction (the ratio of the amount of input energy contributed by a solar energy system to the total input energy required for a specific application) was 86%, indicating that the system should achieve the design target of more than 90% in year five. For years 2012–2016 the solar fraction was consistently above 90% with an average of 96%. In 2015–2016 the solar fraction was 100%.

Drake Landing is demonstrating that high solar fraction systems are technically feasible in a cold Canadian location with 5200 heating degree-days and a design temperature of -31°C.

The success of the project has led to the possibility of implementing a similar but much larger system, serving twenty times the number of living units. The feasibility study for this second project is underway.

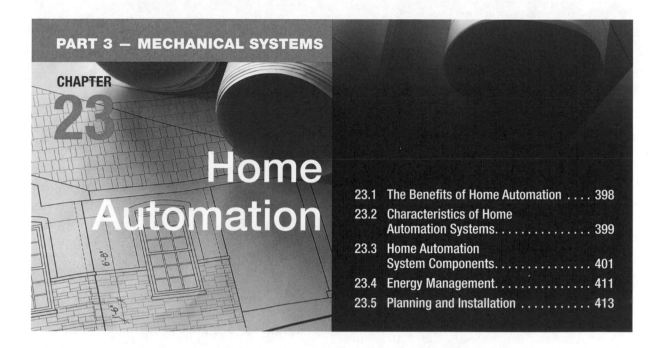

PART 3 — MECHANICAL SYSTEMS

CHAPTER

23

Home Automation

Home automation is a class of technologies that can be used to make a home more secure, more comfortable, or to enhance entertainment capability. It can also be used to reduce energy consumption. To date, home automation has mostly been reserved for new construction due to the planning and wiring infrastructure required, and it has been relatively costly. However, recent advances have substantially simplified home automation systems and reduced the need for wiring infrastructure. Costs have dropped to an affordable level, and sophisticated home automation can now be retrofitted in existing homes with little, if any, need for wiring infrastructure.

This Chapter outlines the benefits of home automation, identifies the key components and characteristics, and provides examples. It also indicates how home automation can be used to manage and reduce energy consumption, and provides steps for planning and installation.

This Chapter uses terms that may be new to readers as follows:

A/V controller a specialized piece of audio and/or video equipment meant to manage distribution of audio and video to different rooms.

Cat5e Ethernet cable used for most wired local area networks (LANs) and capable of supporting high data transfer speeds.

Ethernet a family of computer networking technologies for local area networks (LANs) that support high data transfer speeds.

IP (Internet protocol) camera a digital video camera commonly employed for surveillance that can send and receive data via a computer network and the Internet.

LAN (local area network) a computer network that interconnects computers in a limited area such as a home.

Mesh networking a type of networking where each node must not only capture and disseminate its own data, but also serve as a relay for other nodes (see Figure 23.5).

POE (power over Ethernet) a system that conducts electrical power safely, along with data, on Ethernet cabling.

PLC (PowerLine carrier) transferring data on a conductor that is also used simultaneously for AC electric power transmission.

UPB™ (universal powerline bus) a protocol for communication among devices used for home automation that uses power line wiring for signalling and control.

WSN (wireless sensor network) a network of sensors for monitoring and controlling physical or environmental conditions, such as temperature, sound, pressure, etc. through a network to a central location.

X-10 home automation protocol that uses house electrical systems to transmit control signals between transmitters and receivers. It is an earlier version of UPB™ (universal powerline bus).

Z-wave™ a wireless communications protocol designed for home automation, specifically to remotely control applications in residential and light commercial environments.

Zigbee™ a specification for a suite of high level communication protocols using small, low-power digital radios local area networks.

23.1 The Benefits of Home Automation

There are four major benefits of automating a home:

- **Energy Management:** Home automation can be used to manage and minimize energy consumption. Homeowners can better manage their overall energy consumption by monitoring costs and usage, and in some cases, automatically control consumption based on pricing information supplied by smart electrical meters. Lighting levels and temperature can be automatically adjusted based on occupancy, preset scenes, or the cost of energy. In terms of Net Zero houses, heating and cooling loads are substantially reduced which makes plug loads one of the largest energy consumers. Plug loads are largely life-style dependant and as

such, feed-back can go a long way to helping homeowners manage their energy consumption. Knowing the consumption will allow occupants to make changes to reduce energy.

- **Safety and Security:** An automated home delivers safety and security capabilities that go well beyond traditional alarm systems. For example, automatic lighting that turns on during a burglary means the intruder will be far more likely to leave the premises sooner. Automatic lighting can make it faster and easier to exit the home in the event of a night-time fire emergency. Or, occupants can be warned in the event of a gas leak, water leak or heating/cooling failure.

- **Comfort and Convenience:** This is the traditional "core" of home automation and includes features such as controlling lighting from a single location. Room lights, as well as the level of light throughout the home, can be easily controlled with preset "scenes." Entire household systems can be controlled at the touch of a single button. For example, a press of a button "Arrive Home" can disarm security, turn lights on, adjust temperature, and play favourite music. The home can be controlled from a remote location via telephone or Internet. And the home can automatically notify the homeowners when something needs attention, such as a wine cellar temperature rise, or a child arriving home past curfew.

- **Entertainment:** There is a growing convergence of entertainment and home automation technology. Many traditional home automation vendors offer basic entertainment capabilities, and newer entertainment technology provides home automation capabilities. "Entertainment" generally refers to home theatre and multi-room audio distribution. Music selections can be automatically played as part of preset lighting scenes. When a button "Play Movie" is pressed, lights can be dimmed, video equipment can be powered up, and a projection screen can be lowered.

Figure 23.1 Examples of home automation

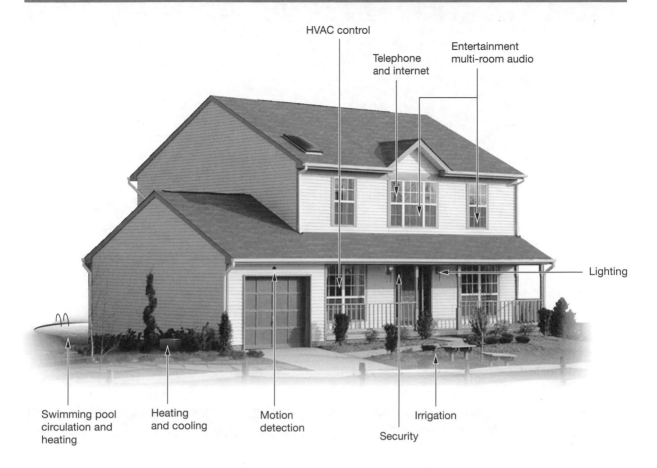

HVAC control

Telephone and internet

Entertainment multi-room audio

Lighting

Swimming pool circulation and heating

Heating and cooling

Motion detection

Security

Irrigation

Examples of where home automation can be used in and around a home are shown in Figure 23.1.

23.2 Characteristics of Home Automation Systems

There are a variety of automation technologies offering a wide range of capabilities. A home automation "system" is merely a combination of technologies (products and devices) that work together to deliver the capabilities needed.

The core home automation technologies range from simple, low-cost, do-it-yourself products available via the Internet, to sophisticated, expensive, specialized products that require professional installation and programming. Typically, a home automation manufacturer makes sensing devices, some form of keypad to control the system, and a "controller" to run the entire system.

Each system delivers a different range of capabilities from the very basic (lights or devices ON/OFF), to the very advanced (automatic adjustment of all home systems). They all support different types, styles, and brands of devices such as sensors (motion, water, gas), and input devices (keypads, keyfobs, and touch screens), and they have different means of interconnection (wired, wireless, powerline carrier, etc.). Some provide security, some provide entertainment, and some merely offer control of the things and systems already in a home. Some require the installation of dedicated control devices (controllers) while others merely utilize an existing home computer.

The array of technologies can seem overwhelming. However, all home automation systems have the following core characteristics:

- Inclusion of technology products specifically developed for home automation including core "controller" technology.

- Integration with existing HVAC, lighting, security systems. Some product lines actually deliver a full-function security system.

- Integration of disparate but compatible devices and products.

- Interconnection of all components via wired or wireless connection.

- Connection to phone and/or Internet for external communication.

- Utilization of customer-supplied smart devices such as smart phones (i.e., Apple© and Android©), and tablet computers.

Essentially, a home automation system is really an integration of new technologies, devices, interconnection, and existing systems within the home. Good automation contractors will carefully select core systems and devices that are proven to work well together. They need to fully understand interconnection technology (wired and wireless), as well as how to interface with lighting and HVAC systems. Further, they must have a solid understanding of residential construction principles to safely install wires and devices. If for example, the automation system controls HVAC, there will be no heating or cooling in the event of an automation system failure.

Home automation technology can control just about any electrical/electronic device in the home and is limited only by device capabilities and the homeowner's imagination. Table 23.1 shows some examples of typical "scenarios" that just about any home automation system can easily implement.

Table 23.1 Examples of typical home automation scenarios

Energy Management

Scenario → Clothes washer and dishwasher loaded, homeowner leaves
Time-of-use monitor delays start to off-peak electrical hours

Scenario → Smart meter detects electricity cost increase
Home automation dims lights and reduces electrical demand

Scenario → Temporary spike in electricity costs
Automatically instruct devices to consume less electricity

Scenario → Arrive home
Entrance lights ON. Adjust temperature to comfort levels. Disarm security. Open garage door.
Turn on TV. Start music playlist.

Scenario → Leave home
Interior Lights OFF. Fireplace OFF. Outside lights ON when dark. Kitchen lights 10% ON. Lower temperature. Arm security. Close garage door. TV OFF. Music OFF. After midnight – turn on interior lighting randomly (simulated occupancy).

Table 23.1 Examples of typical home automation scenarios (continued)

Emergencies

Scenario → Home unoccupied, night-time burglary intrusion
All lights ON 100%. Sound siren. Flash outside lights to alert neighbours and emergency responders. Automatically dial out to a pre-determined call list. Notify monitoring company.

Scenario → Home occupied, fire detected
All lights ON 100% to aid evacuation. Sound evacuation siren to wake occupants. Turn HVAC OFF to reduce spread of smoke/flame. Flash outside lights to alert neighbours and emergency responders. Automatically dial out to a pre-determined call list. Notify monitoring company.

Scenario → Elderly/infirm homeowner, water detected on bathroom floor
Shut off water. Flash outside lights to alert neighbours and emergency responders. Automatically dial out to a pre-determined call list. Notify monitoring company and emergency personnel.

Alerts

Scenario → Basement temperature drops to 10°C
Shut off water automatically. Send notification calls and text messages to homeowner's cell phone, HVAC contractor, and neighbour.

Scenario → Child arrives home past curfew
Send notification call to parent's cell phone and office telephone. Send email to parents recording the details.

Scenario → Garage door open, home unoccupied
Close door if outside temperature < 5°C. Notify homeowner via text message or cell phone.

Scenario → Home unoccupied, courier arrives at front door
Doorbell triggers 3-minute video recording of courier. Email and text message sent to homeowner. Homeowner watches video via Internet.

Lifestyle Support

Scenario → Watch a movie
Dim room lights. Power ON TV/Projector. Display movies for selection. Drop projection screen. Flash lights if phone rings.

Scenario → Enforce children's gaming play time

23.3 Home Automation System Components

Home automation usually consists of the following six elements:

- Controller: The controller is the "brain" of the system-it contains the program that determines system operation.

- Interconnection: Interconnection links all the devices and equipment and enables them to communicate.

- User interface: The interface is the means by which the user interacts with the system to control it, (give it commands) and interrogate the system for information about the home.

- Devices: These are the various sensors and equipment needed to measure things such as temperature, and to control lighting, HVAC, etc.

- Communication and control: These components determine how the system will communicate with the outside world (via telephone, email, text messages) and how the homeowner can remotely control the home from outside (via telephone, Internet).

- Entertainment: If entertainment is part of a home automation system, it may be comprised of a home theatre and multi-room audio distribution.

23.3.1 Controller

Every home automation system has a "brain", known typically as a controller. The functions of the controller are:

- Stores the program (software) that monitors and makes adjustments to house conditions based on predetermined criteria.

- Communicates with all devices/equipment and the home's internal systems (lighting, HVAC, computer network, entertainment systems).

- Connects to the home's Internet service and telephone system for external communications and remote control.

There are three primary forms of automation controller:

- A utility controller (Figure 23.2) consists of a circuit board permanently mounted in a locked enclosure in the home's utility room, typically next to the electrical panel. It often features a full-function security system. All wired devices are connected to this board, and it is often linked to the electrical panel for PowerLine carrier (PLC) communication with light switches (see Section 23.3.2 Interconnection).

- A software controller is home automation application software for a personal computer (Figure 23.3) that allows the computer to function as the controller. Connections to systems and devices are made via interface boards plugged into the computer. Voice recognition is a popular feature of this type of software, so the user can speak a command such as "Turn on kitchen lights".

- An A/V controller is a specialized piece of audio and/or video equipment meant to manage distribution of audio and video to different rooms (Figure 23.4). It is usually situated alongside the rest of the audio/video equipment such as the DVD player and stereo, either on a shelf or in an A/V rack. It typically connects to the Ethernet

via Cat5e cables, and/or the Wi-Fi network and features WSN mesh networking to control WSN-enabled wireless devices such as light switches, thermostats, and various sensors. This is by far the most common type of controller.

Figure 23.2 Utility controller

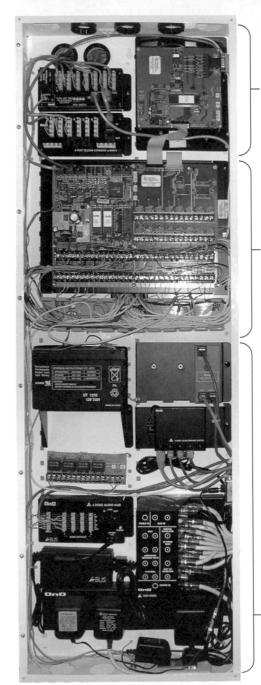

Telephone interconnect, expansion

Controller

Power, Ethernet/Internet, device relays

Figure 23.3 Sample home automation software screen

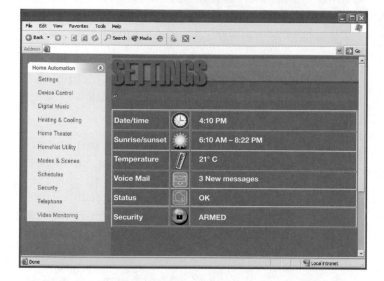

Figure 23.4 A/V controller

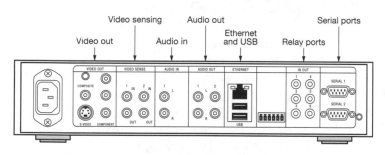

There are many things to consider in choosing a home automation controller. For new construction, a utility controller might be best because the wiring and the controller are concealed. The A/V controller is ideal for retrofits because it can be installed by plugging it into the home's Ethernet and communicate with devices via mesh networking. A software controller is best suited to a homeowner who is most comfortable using the personal computer as the central point of control for the home.

23.3.2 Interconnection

Interconnection refers to the means by which all the various devices, the main system controller(s), and the home's internal systems (HVAC, Lighting, Security,

LAN) will be connected so that they can communicate. For example, the controller needs to issue commands to the thermostat to reduce heat, or to the kitchen lights to dim to 50%.

There are three broad categories of interconnection: Hardwired (physical copper wires of some form); PowerLine Carrier (PLC); and Wireless. All three are vastly different, but can be mixed and matched. This provides maximum flexibility as the system is expanded in the future. For example, if cables are hardwired in wall and floor assemblies during construction, additional devices can be added to the system later by using wireless interconnection.

Hardwired

Hardwiring means a physical wire must connect devices. The type of wire will be determined by the particular device. Most home automation devices today can be connected by Cat5e (Ethernet) cabling. For example, a video camera might require a coaxial cable and an additional 120V power line, whereas an IP camera will often operate on a cat5e cable connection (including in some cases power over the same cable, known as power over Ethernet (POE).

Hardwire cables should be run whenever possible (for instance, during new construction), for the following reasons:

• Cables are less susceptible to interference than wireless;

• Cables generally support higher transmission speeds than wireless; and

• Some cables can be used for multiple purposes.

In particular, multi-room audio and video distribution should be pre-wired with cable, if possible. The wireless technologies used for audio and video streaming present severe loads on today's wireless network technologies, and until this improves, cabling presents a reliable, high-speed solution for minimal cost during new construction.

PowerLine carrier

PowerLine carrier (PLC) technologies send commands and control data over existing electrical lines. For example, automated light switches can replace an existing light switch, and the controller talks to the switch via a signal on the existing power lines. A neutral wire is usually required for PLC devices to work properly and reliably. There are several types of PLC technology on the market. Older PLC technologies such as X-10 have been greatly improved and several manufacturers offer modern variations on X-10 technology. An example of newer, high-end PLC technology is UPB™ (universal powerline bus), which has extremely high reliability and transmission speeds-and speed is important. For example, if an automated home has 30 automated lights (not uncommon in a larger home), it might take 30 seconds or more for the ALL OFF command to finish turning off all 30 lights, which can be disconcerting for the homeowner.

PLC technologies have the advantages of wireless (they do not require that any new wires be run), but without the drawbacks of wireless (radio frequency interference, and battery replacement). PLC devices have to be connected to the home's electrical system. For this reason, the most common form of PLC device is the dimmable light switch. The switch replaces the existing switch, and the controller talks to the switch via existing electrical lines.

Wireless

More and more home automation devices are supporting wireless interconnection. This is essential for retrofits, where it is not possible to run wires behind existing drywall.

Wireless devices include sensors (door/window contacts, motion sensors, water sensors), home automation controllers, user interface devices such as touch screens and wall-mounted keypads, and even audio components such as wireless "speaker points."

There are two types of wireless technologies in common use in home automation systems and devices:

- Wi-Fi is wireless technology for home and office computer networks, or Local Area Networks (LANs). Adhering to the IEEE 802.11 standard, it is a general-purpose wireless technology for computers and Internet. Wi-Fi is commonly found in laptop computers and LAN devices such as routers.

- WSN (Wireless Sensor Network) is wireless monitoring and control for home automation and light commercial applications. WSN is a new wireless technology designed specifically for home automation and has a range of 10-30 meters. Many future home automation devices will have this wireless capability built in. Devices with WSN capability are physically smaller and lighter than Wi-Fi devices. WSN devices form a mesh network (Figure 23.5), which allows for continuous connections and reconfiguration around broken or blocked paths by "hopping" from device to device until the destination is reached. Mesh networks are self-healing-the network can still operate even when a device breaks down or a connection goes bad.

There are two competing WSN technologies:

- Z-Wave™ is a proprietary technology and the Z-Wave alliance consists of a consortium of 160 companies offering home automation devices that use Z-Wave.

- Zigbee™ is a technology based on industry standard IEE 802.15.4 and over 200 companies make devices that utilize Zigbee technology.

Figure 23.5 Mesh network

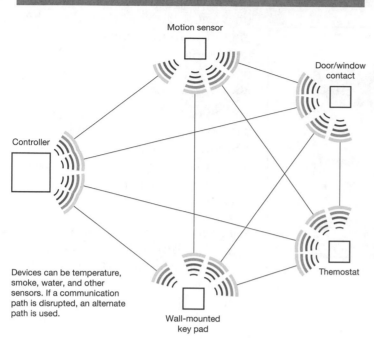

Motion sensor

Door/window contact

Controller

Themostat

Devices can be temperature, smoke, water, and other sensors. If a communication path is disrupted, an alternate path is used.

Wall-mounted key pad

Wi-Fi is used for computer network usage, as well as audio and music distribution (known as "streaming"), whereas WSN is designed exclusively for home automation device communication. Z-Wave and Zigbee are not compatible with each other, so a single automation system cannot contain devices that use both WSN formats.

Important considerations for using wireless interconnection are as follows:

1. Each device requires that batteries be replaced periodically. This can add up to many batteries in a larger home with many devices (30-50 would not be uncommon).

2. The devices are physically larger than a wired device.

3. The system may be susceptible to some potential radio-frequency interference.

4. Adjacent wireless systems (in the same condominium building for instance) must be carefully configured to avoid potential interference with each other.

23.3.3 User interface

There are many different ways for the home automation users to interact with the system to give commands ("Turn on living room lights 75%", "Increase heat to 21°C", "Run playlist romantic music in living room", etc.). All systems display a menu of some form or another that allows the user to select any feature of the system by selecting a top-level menu item, then "drilling down" to more specific choices.

The various means of user interface are as follows:

• Wall-mounted keypad: A dedicated keypad with buttons or a touch-sensitive screen that displays the menu options (Figure 23.6).

• Wireless touchscreen: A table-top Wi-Fi touch screen, typically 10 inches or so in size, that can be hand-carried around the home.

• Handheld remote: A specialized universal remote control that replaces all other remotes in the home, and allows full control of the home automation via a small LCD screen on the remote.

• Television: Automation menu is displayed on the household TV set, and the specialized remote is used to control the system (Figure 23.7).

• Smart device (Smart phone or touchscreen tablet): Used to display the main menu and select options.

Figure 23.6 Key pad

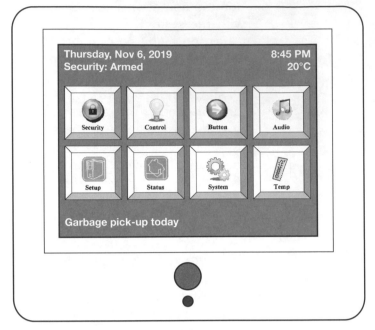

Figure 23.7 Home automation television menu

A typical automated home might have at least one wall-mounted touchscreen in the primary living area. Manufacturers are increasingly utilizing smart phones (Apple and Android) and portable touchpads as the primary means of controlling the home. Smart Home Apps (application programs) are available on these portable smart devices, so the homeowner does not need to purchase dedicated touchscreens and have them installed on a wall – they can simply use their existing smart phone or portable touchpad.

23.3.4 Devices

There is a wide array of devices that can be used in an automated home, and more devices are coming on the market every year. The following highlights some of the more common devices:

- Light switches: Replacement wall mounted light switches typically using UPB™ or WSN (Wireless Sensor Network) control technology. Often dimmable to up to 1000 watts or more (Figure 23.8).

- Door/window contacts: Wired magnetic contacts (for new construction), or WSN for retrofits.

- Motion sensors: Wired or WSN sensors used for security or to turn room lights on/off based on occupancy. For instance, all basement lights can be turned OFF if no motion is sensed for 20 minutes.

- Water sensors: Used to detect spills in bathrooms, or leaks under water heaters, etc.

- Gas detectors: Sense presence of hazardous gases in the home.

- Thermostats: "Smart" thermostats that are controlled by the home automation, so heating/cooling can be adjusted according to the program (for example, to adjust to comfort settings upon arrival home).

- Wall-mounted keypad: A dedicated keypad with buttons or a touch-sensitive screen that displays the menu options.

- Remote door locks: A special keyless passage device with wireless communication that can be controlled (locked and unlocked) remotely.

- Scene switches: Switches with 3, 6, or 8 buttons for various preset scenes such as "Dining", "Party", "Entertain", etc. (Figure 23.9).

- Cameras: IP (Internet Protocol) type cameras that connect to the home's Ethernet, or traditional cameras that require coaxial connection and dedicated power. A typical automated home will have multiple surveillance cameras (for instance, one over the front door and one over the back door), and will feed into a digital video recorder (DVR) to record the images.

These devices are typically installed specifically for the purpose of home automation. In addition to these devices, a home automation system usually needs to interface with existing systems such as:

- Furnace (to control heating/cooling)

- Smoke detectors (for fire alarm alerts)

- Electrical system (for PLC communication)

- Telephone system (for homeowner notification)

- Ethernet (for access to Internet)

An advanced home automation system could also connect to and control other household systems such as the swimming pool (circulation and temperature), hot tub (temperature), lawn sprinkler systems (scheduled watering based on weather), basement sump pump (alarm if pump fails), wine cellar (alert upon temperature variation), home theatre (one-button control), or motorized shades (raise/lower shades based

on daylight), and more. This is often achieved through the use of general-purpose contact points. The system can be programmed to turn external devices on or off through a contact relay, even if it is not explicitly aware of the device or system it is controlling.

Figure 23.8 Regular switch (left) and "smart" automated switch (right)

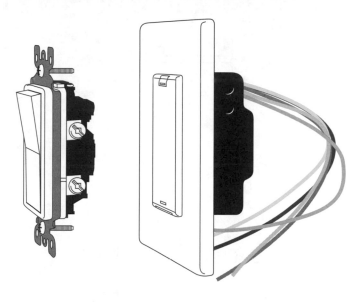

Figure 23.9 Scene switch

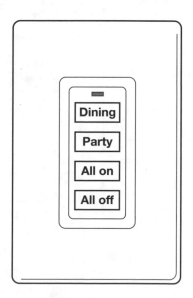

Figure 23.10 Typical system arrangement

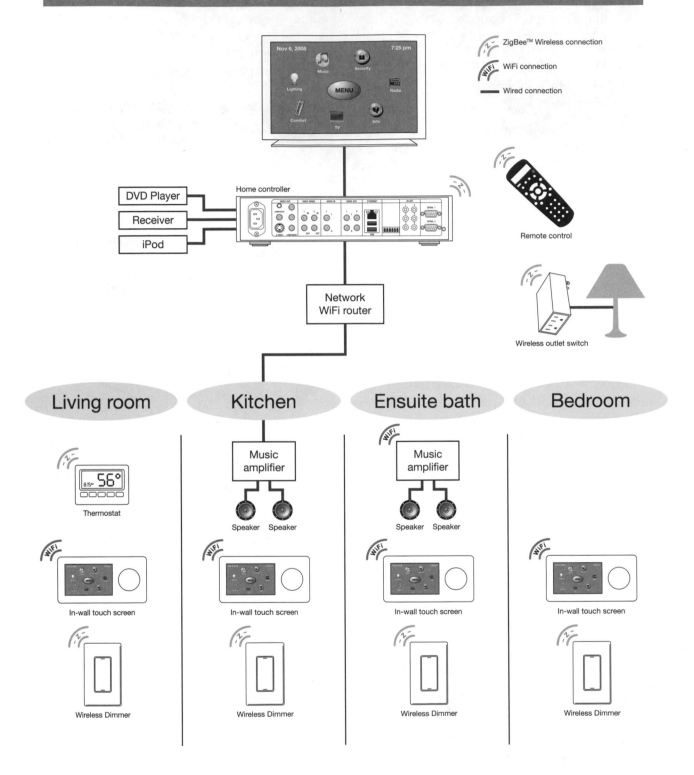

23.3.5 Sample system layout

Figure 23.10 shows a sample home automation and entertainment system that combines the components described in the preceding sections. In this example, both wired and wireless interconnection is used. Ethernet cable (Cat5e) is used to connect the controller to the bedroom and bathroom. In addition, two types of wireless interconnection are used-Wi-Fi is used for the touch screens in the family room and kitchen and ZigBee wireless is used to communicate with the remaining devices, including light switches, thermostat, and the outlet switch with the tabletop lamp. Note that in the bathroom, an Ethernet cable is used to connect to the speaker point (audio requires more robust interconnection), but the wall-mounted keypad used for in-room control, utilizes ZigBee wireless. This is typical of an installation in new houses whereby Ethernet cabling is utilized for the heavy work of audio distribution, but lighter duty applications and future additions to the system can be wireless.

23.3.6 Communication and control

An automated home can be controlled from outside the home (remote control), and it can communicate with the outside world to provide notification or to receive instructions.

Remote control

Most systems can be controlled from outside the home in the following ways:

- Telephone: The homeowner can call into the system, enter a security code, then operate a voice menu system. All the commands/ controls that can be used on the wall-mounted keypad can be entered via phone by pressing buttons corresponding to menu options. For instance, the homeowner could call on a cell phone to arm the house and turn the lights off.

- Internet: Most systems offer a means of accessing and controlling the system from the Internet (Figure 23.11). For instance, the homeowner could go online to raise the home's temperature in advance of arrival. Some systems require that a computer be left running inside the home and others do not. Some manufacturers offer a monthly "subscription service" for Internet access capability. Generally, all the menu items and control capability available on the user interface devices within the home are presented via the Internet application.

Figure 23.11 Remote control via the Internet

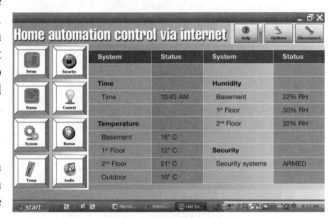

Notification

One of the most powerful and highest-value capabilities of home automation is the ability to provide external notification via telephone or Internet when attention is needed. The system can be programmed with a series of alerts or situations requiring outside notification (water on floor, power failure, burglary, furnace failure, child arriving home after curfew, etc.). Then, the notification method can be specified for each situation. The type of notification is typically determined by the urgency of the situation, as shown in the sample notifications in Table 23.2.

Table 23.2 Sample notifications

Situation	Notification
Child not home by curfew	Text message to child, parent(s)
Fire / burglary	Notify authorities, neighbours. Cell phone call to owner(s)
Power failure	Cell phone call to owner(s)
Water on floor	Cell phone call to owner(s), plumber
Wine cellar temperature fluctuation	Text message to cellphone
Window left open, air conditioning ON	Cell phone call to owner(s)
Cleaner left 2 hours early	Email message

Some manufacturers allow notification by both telephone and Internet, but most offer only one of the two methods. The manner of notification varies somewhat among manufacturers, but the methods below are typical:

- Telephone: The homeowner can pre-record the home's address into the system. The system then annunciates a message when calling out, adding pre-recorded words from an internal vocabulary of words to the address to form a complete message, such as "Water on basement floor of 123 Maple Street". Many systems will call a list of pre-defined numbers until a recipient answers and stops the process with an authorized code. Some systems will send only a text message to the phone number.

- Internet: Most systems will send an email or text message notification, for instance, "Elizabeth has not arrived home for 10:00 PM curfew."

Entertainment

Entertainment is a growing component of home automation. Many homeowners have invested heavily in audio and video entertainment systems, and this investment can often exceed the total investment in home automation. Therefore, there is a rapidly growing convergence of home automation and entertainment technologies. There are entertainment systems that offer home automation capabilities, and home automation systems that offer entertainment capabilities.

Entertainment options consist primarily of home theatre control, content streaming, and multi-room audio distribution.

- Home theatre control: All the home theatre devices (DVD player, TV/Projector, Cable box, etc.) are connected to a device called a Home Theatre Controller. The controller displays a menu on the TV of movies in the player/changer, and the user selects a movie from the remote. When Play is pressed, the lights are dimmed, the needed equipment is powered up, and the screen is lowered (in the case of a projection screen). Such controllers often use WSN networking to deliver home automation capability.

- Content Streaming: Music, TV programs, and even Hollywood movies can be streamed live over the internet and presented on various displays (TV, computers, smart phones, etc.) throughout the home. Specialized steaming devices manage the content by presenting a menu for the homeowner to select their desired content, managing the billing and payment, and sending the content to the selected devices. Most video content requires high-bandwidth cable runs for high-quality High-Definition transmission (e.g. HDMI cable), but wireless transmission is beginning to emerge.

- Multi-room audio distribution: The homeowner's music is stored on a high-capacity hard drive (250 GB or more) device called a Music Server. The device then distributes the music throughout the home to various rooms (Figure 23.10). Different music can be played in different rooms. For instance, jazz can be playing in the family room while rock is playing in the recreation room. In each room, a wall-mounted keypad and/or remote control can be used to select the music, play/pause, and control the volume. Music is typically distributed via Ethernet or Wi-Fi.

For new construction, music control devices in the rooms consist of control devices installed in the walls that connect directly to the speakers, which are typically embedded in the ceiling. For retrofits, a stereo-like box called a Speaker Point is placed on a shelf, and external cabinet speakers are plugged into the box. The Speaker Point is typically connected to the music server via Ethernet or Wi-Fi (if Ethernet is not available in the room). Hard-wire interconnection for distributed audio/video generally performs somewhat more reliably than Wi-Fi, although Wi-Fi reliability is very good.

23.4 Energy Management

A well-planned home automation system can reduce the total energy consumption of the home. This is not to say a system will reduce energy consumption-the system has to be appropriately implemented and used in a manner that will reduce energy. The capability exists for substantial savings, depending on a number of factors including:

- The total energy consumption of the home: Larger homes, in areas of greater temperature extremes, will consume more heating/cooling energy and therefore offer a greater opportunity for savings through home automation.

- The type of heating/cooling system in use: An older, less efficient HVAC system will use more energy. A modern geothermal or similar system may use very little energy to deliver the same comfort levels.

- The number of electrical devices/systems: If the home has more electricity-consuming systems, there is a greater opportunity to reduce consumption via home automation. For instance, a home with many incandescent lights, a swimming pool, a hot tub/Jacuzzi, electric radiant floor heating, electric baseboard heating, roof de-icing coils, etc. will consume far more electricity, presenting a greater opportunity for savings via home automation.

- Lifestyle: A retired couple living alone and not leaving home very often has a fairly constant energy use pattern with little opportunity to reduce consumption. On the other hand, a younger family with many occupants constantly coming and going, children leaving lights on and the temperature constantly being adjusted, provides far greater opportunity for savings via home automation.

A home automation system can reduce total energy consumption in the following ways:

- Reducing wastage: The normal day-to-day wastage that typically goes unnoticed can be reduced with home automation. Lighting, HVAC, and other systems can be turned off when not needed. When occupants leave the home, the system can force all lights off. When a room or level of the home is not being used, the lights can be turned off. Similarly, the heating for pool or garage can be turned off when not being used or otherwise needed.

- Reduced lighting levels (dimming): A light can be operated at less than 100% when full light is not needed. This reduces energy consumption and prolongs light bulb life. Dimming a light by 50% consumes 40% less energy. Note that most CFLs (compact fluorescent lights) cannot be dimmed, but this may change with new designs. Automated scenes allow for light levels to be dimmed less than 100% as required.

- Power-sensing: A power-sensing outlet switch can eliminate power-hungry standby modes by cutting power to A/V devices when not in use.

Savings can only be realized if the homeowner takes full advantage of the capabilities of the automation system, and programs it accordingly as in the following examples:

- Basement motion sensor detects no motion in the basement for 20 minutes. Turn lights and home entertainment equipment OFF.

- Outside lighting ON only when sun sets.

- Shut off power to large A/V devices when occupants are away to eliminate standby

- power consumption.

- Rain detected by a rain sensor keeps the lawn irrigation cycle from activation.

- Set back heating/cooling to below comfort levels when the home

- is unoccupied.

- Turn driveway lights ON only if a vehicle pulls up.

- Activate floor heating ON only if outside temperature < 10°C.

- Lower garage door if outside temperature < 10°C.

- Reduce pool circulation and temperature when home is not occupied.

Smart Meters

Some provinces like Ontario have converted residential power meters to so-called Smart Meters, which measure electrical consumption according to the time-of-use (TOU) billing (Figure 23.12).

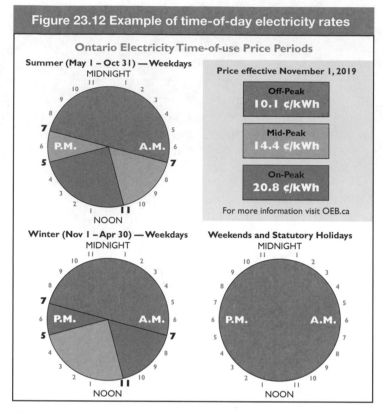

Figure 23.12 Example of time-of-day electricity rates

Source – Ontario Energy Board

An automated home has further opportunities to reduce overall energy bills:

- Monitored consumption: The system can alert the homeowner, via on-screen notification, that consumption levels have exceeded a pre-determined threshold.

- Time-of-use adjustment: The system can automatically reduce consumption during more costly on-peak periods. Lights can be reduced to 75% brightness, pool heating can be shut off, and heating/cooling can be reduced during on-peak periods.

- Consumer behaviour changes when energy monitors are used. CHBA's Net Zero Energy Program requires energy monitors to be installed.

Smart meter manufacturers are building WNS networking capability into next-generation smart meters. This means that a home equipped with WNS-enabled home automation can "read" the meter and take action according to the electricity rates. Suppose for instance that the electrical authority encountered excess peak demand and had to temporarily purchase power at 5 times normal price. A home automation system would be able to read this warning, issue an onscreen notification "warning – electrical rates are now 5 times higher", and automatically adjust consumption downward through reduced lighting, etc.

Some leading home automation suppliers deliver controllers dedicated to the task of managing energy. Figure 23.13 shows a schematic of such a system. These controllers exchange up-to-the minute consumption data between customer and utility and provide intelligent automation and control of smart devices throughout the house. These systems are generally designed, built, and delivered in conjunction with the electrical utility company. They are commonplace in the USA and will inevitably be deployed in Canada.

These controllers communicate with the utility company to allow consumers to participate in demand response (DR) or automated load management programs. Homeowners can also opt in to various conservation programs offered by the utility companies.

A device called the energy management controller transforms metered data into useful insight for consumers, such as electricity use by device category, pricing information, energy cost comparisons, and relevant energy-saving tips (Figure 23.14).

23.5 Planning and Installation

The following are the essential steps for designing and installing a reliable home automation system:

- Step 1 – Design: Decide what the system will be primarily used for. Is it mainly for entertainment (emphasis on audio/video distribution), energy management (emphasis on lighting, smart meter, and HVAC), life safety (emphasis on safety and security)? Plan the type and style of devices. Select one primary home automation technology (product line) to provide the basic "smarts" of the system. The brand selected will be primarily driven by whether this is a new construction, or a retrofit project. Decide on the type of interconnection (hard-wire for new construction, wireless for retrofit). Select a security system, and decide where to place sensors on door and windows. Use motion sensors for occupancy-based control. Decide on the physical location of devices. Select the user interface devices and their

Figure 23.13 Schematic of an energy management system

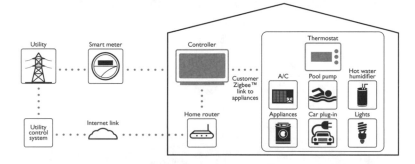

Figure 23.14 Sample energy management controller display

physical location. Decide on the quality and location of home entertainment equipment. Choose locations for in-wall devices on the home theatre, such has projectors, speakers, screens, and TV. Select ancillary devices and equipment not provided by the home automation manufacturer, such as motion sensors, audio equipment, cameras, etc.

- Step 2 – Pre-Wire (for new construction): Run CAT5e (computer data cable) to all devices in all locations, where possible. Run coaxial cable for non-IP cameras. Bring power to powered devices such as in-wall touch screens. Run A/V cables between devices in the home theatre, such as component video and HDMI (high-definition multimedia interface). Terminate all cables with appropriate wall jacks and face plates. In the case of a retrofit, install a Wi-Fi LAN or other wireless network.

- Step 3 – Install devices/Equipment: In the case of new construction, this is usually done after painting is completed. Connect devices to the wiring according to manufacturers' instructions and be careful not to power up the system at this stage. In the case of Ethernet or Wi-Fi interconnection, it is important to install and configure an Ethernet that is fast, reliable, and robust. Test the underlying Ethernet or Wi-Fi network for proper operation and speed. Interconnect to the home's internal systems (HVAC, security, lighting, computer network, telephone).

- Step 4 – Test all Devices/Equipment: Test individual devices/equipment for proper operation, independent of the overall system. Make sure they operate correctly and that they are communicating to the remainder of the system properly. Then, test devices/equipment for overall system operation. For instance, validate that the ALL LIGHTS OFF does not miss any lights, and that it happens at an acceptable speed. Confirm that all commands are properly executed by all devices.

- Step 5 – Program. Program the system based on the homeowner's needs. Define the scenes and behaviour of all devices and systems exactly the way the homeowner intended. Enter telephone dial-out lists. Test and validate that the programs runs as it is supposed to. Simulate and test all scenes and all scenarios, and validate that the home reacts as it should

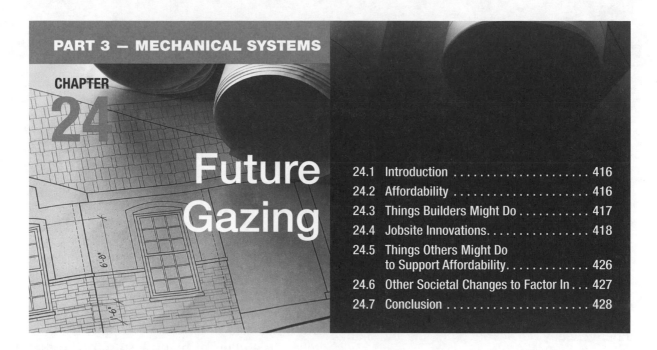

Previous editions of CHBA's Builders' Manual have included a final chapter that looked to the future to provide readers with some insight as to where the industry may be moving. The Builders' Manual has always tried to provide the reader with the building science that supports how we build today and with the tools to evaluate potential new materials, new products and new designs which may emerge in the future.

24.1 Introduction

A solid basis in building science will help builders decide what materials and techniques to use to construct the best houses possible and to support those decisions using the latest testing and research done by Government Agencies and academics across Canada. Over the years the future vision has been R-2000 and beyond. Prior to 2000 the focus was primarily energy. Following that, indoor air quality and environmental responsibility, including water conservation, became important considerations for builders but all the while, with energy being in the forefront. Most recently Net Zero Energy Houses and Net Zero Energy Ready Houses are emerging and taking the building science even further.

Net Zero Energy Ready is expected to be mandated by Building Code as of 2030 in most parts of Canada. This keeps energy at the top of the list. This Manual has focused on what we know about building at the Net Zero Energy level. The CHBA's Net Zero Energy Homes Technical Requirements for constructing a Net Zero Energy house can be summed up as, "build an R-2000 house with an EnerGuide Rating of 0".

In the next pages we try to answer the age-old question, what does the future hold? While no one knows for sure, the products and ideas presented in this Chapter are being used today, even if only experimentally. It is often a long process to get from working in a laboratory to working in the field so readers should make up their own minds about which of the technologies presented in this Chapter will be of value to them.

24.2 Affordability

Canadian Home Builders have demonstrated that the construction of high performance houses, while challenging is well withing their skill level. They have demonstrated that they can construct Net Zero Energy houses with the building materials and trades available today. The challenge for the future however is believed to be affordability.

Owning a home has long been a dream of Canadians. In fact, 69% of Canadian own a home. Studies show that 4 out of 5 Millennials want to buy a home. And the home has not simply been a place to live for Canadians, but it has also been a key component in the retirement plans of many – so much so that the value of the Canadian housing stock is estimated at $4 Trillion.

The challenge facing Canadian builders will be to keep housing affordable so that more Canadians can achieve their dream of home ownership in the years ahead. With any great challenge comes great opportunities and the Canadian housing industry has responded to every challenge that has been placed before it and provided solutions. This one is not expected to be any different.

While there are efforts underway to develop better (and less expensive) building materials, experience has shown us that there is simply not enough time between now and 2030 to undergo several product cycles. Practically, this means that the products we are going to build with in 2030 are, for the most part, already here. Not that this is a problem, CHBA builder members have been demonstrating that Net Zero Energy and Net Zero Energy Ready homes can successfully be built today with the materials we have available for several years now.

It is recognized that Net Zero Energy and Net Zero Energy Ready houses are "better" houses and as such they command a higher price. Once these houses become Code in 2030, we want to ensure that all those who want to buy a house, will be able to afford a house.

This Chapter looks at some of the things builders might do with the house design, on the job site with new tools and techniques and what others might do to support the Canadian dream of owning a home.

It is recognized that some of the technologies presented here may require approvals or the adoption of the technologies will require the involvement of other groups (including government), and they may require training for skills we don't currently train for. These are presented as suggestions for consideration, to stimulate discussion and get encourage the innovative spirit that has always been a part of the Canadian Home Building Industry.

24.3 Things Builders Might Do

There are many costs associated with the building of a new house that builders have no control over. This section describes some of the opportunities builders may consider to make the cost of home ownership more affordable for their clients.

24.3.1 Make the House a Money Generator

Net-Positive Energy Housing: With Net Zero Energy housing scheduled to be Code in 2030, houses that produce more energy than they consume are likely to be close behind. Areas where the electrical utility will pay for the energy put onto the grid will be the first areas to see these houses. The monthly payment for energy delivered to the grid will be a welcome contribution to homeowners to support the mortgage payments. Currently, in many areas the electrical utility limits the amount of energy that a homeowner can supply to the grid, but this may not always be the case.

Legal Secondary Suites and Sharing-Economy Accommodations: The need for rental accommodation will always be a part of the Canadian housing mix. Giving Canadians more options in rental housing, and providing Canadian home owners with an opportunity to rent out part of their home to supplement their income may help those homeowners to plan for a home. Including a legal secondary suite will provide needed rental accommodation and the rent paid to the homeowner will help to improve the affordability of the home.

Canada's seniors are already showing how the future might look as well. In some cities, single seniors with houses are being paired with university students needing accommodation. This arrangement has been receiving good reviews and it addresses, both the needs of seniors (loneliness, help around the house, supplemental income) and students (temporary housing they can afford, convenient locations, and quiet environments to study).

Our seniors are also demonstrating alternative housing arrangements can work. In one particular case, 4 single seniors have had a home renovated for them wherein each has a private bedroom with ensuite bathroom, and they have a communal kitchen, living, and dining rooms. While the first of these units was a renovation project, there is no technical reason these types of homes could not be built to Net Zero Energy levels. Ownership and municipal zoning may present challenges in some areas, but innovation doesn't only need to happen on the technical front.

24.3.2 Change Materials or Build Smaller

Change Materials: This is an area in the control of the builder which they can use to respond to the needs of the home buyer. Once Net Zero level building becomes Code this necessitates a high-performance building envelope, attention to air sealing details, continuous insulation, high-performance mechanical equipment and sub-slab insulation. While the builder has many options for how to achieve the goal, the goal is pre-defined by the decision to mandate Net Zero Ready, thereby committing the builder to a level of performance, and the cost associated with achieving it.

Places where the builder may be able to reduce costs to make the house more affordable are the features where the builder has some discretion. These include the finishes (inside and out); the exterior cladding and roofing, but also the interior kitchen and bath cabinets and fixtures. The builder also decides on the flooring, inclusion of a fireplace (or not), quality of appliances (if builder supplied), stair materials, as well as stair finishes and paints. While it seems the customer of today believes that all the finest finishes are a necessity in a home, that was not always the case. It was not uncommon in the past for homeowners to move into a house which was not completely finished, and then finish it as they had money and/or do some jobs themselves. The building requirement is for the house to be safe and structurally sound, not necessarily finished. For some home buyers who have building skills, this approach may allow them to purchase their dream home, even if it does require them to complete some aspects of the home after they move in, and over time.

Build Smaller/Build Differently: Another solution in the hands of the builder. Typically, it is more expensive to build in the ground than it is to build above ground so in those cases we may see a third storey instead of a basement.

Originally, basements were built for very practical reasons – to protect the footings from the frost. Basements were treated as a place to put the mechanical systems and as additional storage. But over the years the basement was transformed in to "liveable" space. This was done by using appropriate insulation levels, adding more natural light, making ceilings higher, all in an attempt to make the customer feel that they were not living below ground. We can build high performance houses without digging a basement. Houses on piles or slab-on-grade construction can provide the structural support necessary. The question is whether customers will be drawn to this type of home even if it is less expensive to purchase? We know that some builders are already specializing in this type of home (single storey, slab-on-grade) and targeting their marketing directly at seniors who simply do not want to climb stairs any more.

Build Multi-Unit: Building multi-unit townhouses helps to keep costs down when it comes to exterior finishing. Townhouse units by nature of the design have significantly less exterior surface area, meaning less cladding and less insulation relative to the same number of detached units. As affordability becomes more important it is expected that more multi-unit buildings will be offered to purchasers.

24.4 Jobsite Innovations

The shortage of skilled trades is a recurring message in the building industry. As older workers leave the industry CHBA is working hard to encourage young people to go into the trades, but even with that, a shortfall of people is still being predicted. Those in the industry will be challenged to "do more with less" and this is expected to lead to jobsite innovations being adopted to speed up, or automate the work load. Some of the promising innovations follow.

3D Design: Many of the jobsite innovations in this section will require our houses to be designed using 3D software. Currently, most plans are completed in 2D (a flat piece of paper) to be interpreted by the builder and the trades. Typically these don't show where the ducts will run, or where the plumbing and wiring will be. As a result, the trade that gets to the jobsite first gets the pick of the joist and stud cavities to run their wires, pipes or ducts. As the move to 3D design becomes the norm, the 3D design software will act as the platform which many other technologies will use to do their jobs. It will all start with a designer inputting the building as a 3D model. This is known as **BIM – Building Information Modeling**. Once this occurs it will allow architecture, engineering and construction professionals the insight and tools to more efficiently plan, design and manage buildings and infrastructure. This planning will include where each component will be located in the structure, including which joist cavity will have the ductwork, the wires, and the pipes. This level of detail at the planning stage can provide the builder with more flexibility in choosing how to do the structure. For example, knowing where the mechanical systems will be allows for those sections to be pre-installed in walls and floor systems which are prefabricated off site.

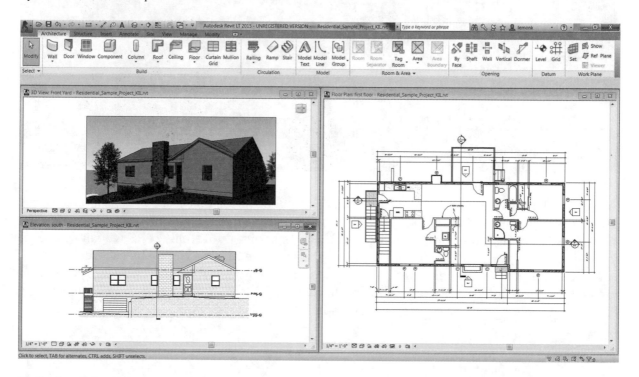

Credit: Autodesk.ca

Aerial Topography

Once the plans are in 3D, adding topography will be straight-forward using a satellite or a survey drone fly over. The software will be able to determine quantities for cut and fill for lot grading. The topographical information combined with the building design can then be provided to all other trades working on the job site and needing this data.

Credit: Natnan Srisuwan/Shutterstock

Surveying: Finding the corners of the lot or positioning the house on the lot with proper setbacks from property lines and easements will become quicker using instruments that are tracked by satellite GPS. Using data from the plans and the lot surveys, the satellite GPS will allow the lot to be quickly and accurately identified and staked-out. Then, using the plans and the GPS, the house can be quickly and accurately positioned on the property for the excavator. Once the excavation is complete, the corners of the footings can be identified and the corners of the foundation. This should save time, money and eliminate errors.

Credit: Adzem/Shutterstock

Robotic Excavators: Bulldozers on road building sites have been using an automated blade positioning technology guided by a laser on the site. In development, and undergoing in-field trials are robotic excavators. Early versions will have human operators and be computer assisted, but the goal is to achieve completely autonomous excavators which create perfectly sized and level excavations every time, including trenches for sub-slab piping, sumps or other sub-slab components. This will be based on the BIM data and the excavator essentially removes all of the material that is not supposed to be there. This will prove to be a reduction in time and person-power (the excavator doesn't need to "see" so excavating at night is an option), with no waste due to over/under excavation. The excavation will be exact, and the bottom will be perfectly level, meaning that the job of installing footings will be much easier and all soil under the footings will be undisturbed (as is required by Code).

Credit: bogdanhoda/Shutterstock

But the benefits don't stop there. Knowing that an excavation will be level prior to digging it creates new opportunities for builders in choosing foundation systems. Footings must be placed on undisturbed soil. In traditional excavations, irregularities resulting from digging errors are addressed by the footings. The final footings provide a level surface upon which the foundation walls can be placed. The footings also provide the loading area to distribute the weight of the building to the soil. With a level excavation to start with, new foundation options exist.

Precast Concrete Foundations: While this technology has been used successfully for several years, it still needs footings to support it. With a level excavation base, the potential to use precast foundation walls with built in footings becomes a possibility – this would save one step in the building process. The 3D plans complete with BIM data, emailed to the precast facility, can allow for the creation of basement walls complete with insulation, wiring, nailing boards, connections with gaskets and external drainage layer. Using a boom truck to move these pieces into position and bolting the pieces together will increase the speed of construction of the foundation, improve the energy efficiency, improve the water tightness and make the foundation more accurate. Precast components can be built in a climate controlled factory, using stronger concrete, and improved quality control than onsite work. The resulting product should be stronger, more durable, more energy efficient and installed faster.

Photo Credit: Superior Walls by: Magnis

3D Printing: Although this technology has been talked about for a while, practical applications in the housing sector are just starting to be undertaken. Using the 3D models of the house plans, the 3D printing simply "fills in" the areas that need to be completed. This approach has the potential to reduce labour and time. The printer can run day and night.

Credit: Apis Cor

The advantages do not stop there. The foundation wall of poured concrete has almost always been soild concrete. This is primarily for practical reasons related to how it is constructed.

With a 3D printer, the outer wall and the inner wall can be linked with a "truss-like" design, thereby leaving cavities that can be filled with insulation. Spray foam insulation installed in these cavities would add to the structural strength of the wall by creating a "sandwich" design, but other insulation products could also be used. The wall can be made any thickness, depending on the level of insulation required, and the insulation would be fully protected to the full height of the wall.

Credit: Apis Cor

Automated Brick Laying: Several versions of these robots are here now and the next generation of them is on the way. SAM, short for Semi-Automated Mason can reportedly lay 3000 bricks per day and works 500% faster than humans. The Australian, Hadrian X brick laying robot is reported to lay 1000 bricks per hour using an industrial glue. The industrial adhesive is used to replace traditional mortar. The Hadrian X is truck mounted and lays bricks to within 1mm of accuracy even at the full extension of its' 28 m boom. There are also brick laying machines which use conventional bricks and traditional mortar.

Credit: Copyright © 2021 FBR Limited

Credit: Roman Korotkov/Shutterstock

Personal Exoskeletons: These are in use now, with improvements on the horizon. They are human-wearable robotics which provide the user with more strength, thereby boosting efficiency and reducing injuries. In some cases users can comfortably control and move 1000 lb. objects (453 kg). Use of this equipment should open the possibility of more panelization in construction; as long a the panel weight is kept to under the capacity of the suit, no cranes are necessary. One employee with a suit can move and position a panel into place and hold it while others fasten it into position. This is expected to be just the beginning with the ability to move heavy materials into position such as steel beams, water tanks, trusses and air conditioners.

Credit: © 2020 Copyright Sarcos Corp

Increased Use of Factory-Built Components: Many site builders are already taking advantage of the many benefits that factory built components have to offer. With the advances in robotics and the incorporation of these robotics in factories there should be an improvement in efficiency of production leading to reduced costs of some components. In addition to trusses, stairs and cabinets, look for floors, walls, and partitions to be supplied from factories and craned into position. Not far behind will be complete kitchens and bathrooms as modules, fully assembled (plumbed, fixtures installed, wiring, lights and finishes) and ready to move into position.

A New Breed of Builder

Changes in the Supply Chain: Other economic sectors, when faced with the same issues of affordability, skill shortages, and materials limitations, changed the way they did business. Many builders today are vertically integrated, meaning that they employ all trades so they do everything in-house. This approach assists with scheduling. Factory builders are an example of this vertical integration. However, when site builders work with factory-built components, there is an opportunity to specialize, and optimize, the construction of wall panels, roof and floor cassettes, kitchens and bathrooms sold as pre-plumbed and pre-wired modules that are simply craned into place on the job site. Such specialization requires consolidation within the industry.

Lifelong Learning: With changes in technology, new knowledge must be integrated into the way builders do business. Technology is not going to stop, new ways of doing things will be found and, as we are seeing, the technology curve will accelerate. The coming years will be the most exciting time in history to be in the construction industry, but it means builders will have to be lifelong learners to not only stay ahead of the curve, but simply to keep up.

24.5 Things Others Might Do to Support Affordability

Governments
Modifications could be made to the mortgage rules to allow for longer (30 + year) mortgages.

Legal and zoning changes could be made to encourage secondary suites and co-housing projects.

Development fees could be spread out over several years by becoming an addition to the house taxes. This would reduce the initial price of the house but increase the carrying costs.

Financial Institutions
Recognize the value of energy savings when evaluating customers for a mortgage. The total carrying cost for a home owner is Principal, Interest, Taxes and Energy (PITE). The additional costs added to the principal to build to the Net Zero Energy level reduces the energy carrying cost – leaving more money in the wallet of the homeowner. However, most financial institutions and appraisers do not recognize energy savings as a valid feature. The money saved on energy can be used somewhere else. It increases the amount of disposable income of the family once the PITE bills have been paid. This savings means the mortgage payer is more likely to be able to meet and make all payments; i.e. there is less risk to the lending institution.

Housing Product Manufacturers
Better performing insulation, that being insulation with a higher R-value per unit thickness could offer a savings by allowing builder to return to smaller dimensioned lumber.

Better performing windows. In the building envelope, windows, doors and skylights are the envelope components with the lowest R-values. A typical Net Zero Energy wall may be R-40, but the window in that wall may be R-3. There is room for better performing windows & doors and there are manufacturers working on them. R-values of up to R-20 are reportedly being achieved on some windows today.

Look for cost reductions by manufacturers making products do double duty. One place we are seeing this happening is manufacturers incorporating solar panels (PV) into roofing "shingles" and exterior siding.

Conceptually this makes good sense, because 2 materials are incorporated into one, thereby saving money and time. It is especially attractive for builders who were intending to supply PV panels to meet the energy production requirements of Net Zero Energy Housing. PV combined with roofing and siding are not the only areas where this is happening; motion sensors are being used to direct ventilation air as well as for security, fireplaces are now so efficient and house loads are so low that the ambiance of the fire is coupled with the ability to heat the home, thereby preventing the heating source from needing to be run. As an example of more than double duty, home automation systems are being used to save energy, provide security, provide back ground music and to set off an alarm if the if the door to the pool opens when small children are home.

Utilities

Electrical companies could agree to buy excess energy from "net positive energy homes" at a rate which gives home owners an incentive to do so if the house and the site make it a possibility.

Rainwater harvesting and/or greywater for irrigation have the potential to offset the use of municipally treated, fresh water currently being used for the same purpose. The on-site use of greywater also reduces the load on the municipal treatment plant.

24.6 Other Societal Changes to Factor In

Aging Population: For the first time in history Canada has more people over the age of 65 than we have under the age of 14. This is expected to put a strain on publicly funded services such as health care. Research shows that Canadians want to live in their homes as long as possible. It is expected that more healthcare will be administered at home and as such, homes will need to be modified to make life easier for our seniors and people with disabilities. As noted, some people will be aging in their homes, including those with medical conditions requiring continuous monitoring and health support. In some cases the house will require access to continuous, uninterrupted power to support the medical equipment. This means a generator or possibly battery storage.

DC Equipment: Achieving Net Zero Energy will mean very low loads for the building. It also means that energy is being produced and, if not being used immediately, will likely be stored in batteries as the costs come down. Currently where houses are using energy storage, the energy is collected as DC energy, stored as DC energy in the batteries and then converted to AC to use in equipment. Every time energy changes from DC to AC, losses occur. These can be reduced by using the energy in the same form it was collected; with the use of DC motors, lights, fans and other equipment. In many cases, DC equipment, because of its low voltage, can be installed less expensively that the higher voltage products.

Integrated Design Process: Pioneers of Net Zero Energy building used an integrated design process to achieve their results. This process brought together specialists in energy, energy modelling, water quality and waste disposal as well as the traditional team of architects, engineers, designers and builders. As new, as-yet unapproved materials and techniques become available, the design process may become more inclusive, possibly involving zoning officials, certification agencies, specialists in materials technology and other specialists. In this manner, everyone who will have contact with the house in some form will be part of the design team.

Autonomous (Driverless) Vehicles: The widespread use of automobiles by the early 20th Century dictated how our cities were designed. New, autonomous cars will have just as much of an impact in the 21st Century. Initially, autonomous cars are expected to reduce traffic congestion, improve commute times and increase the value of land farther from the downtown cores of cities. Autonomous cars will also make the most valuable land – parking lots in the cores of cities – suddenly available. These cars will be programmed to park more efficiently, not to mention more closely together (since the driver does not have to get out of the car). Studies done at the University of Toronto estimate our current parking lots are 80 percent bigger than autonomous cars will require. Furthermore, as we increasingly buy rides instead of cars, cars will be in transit, not parked.

Today's cars are parked and not in use for over 90 percent of the time. This may free up land currently used for parking, and change lot layouts since driveways and garages may not be necessary.

24.7 Conclusion

Thank you for your interest to purchase and read the CHBA's Builders' Manual. We hope you find it to be a useful reference for your work in the building industry.

Over the years, some of the best minds in Canadian housing have provided research, wisdom and lived experience to make this book what it has become today. This document has been created from the efforts of those who came before us, and those who gave of their time and knowledge to make it so.

Please keep in mind that besides the Appendices in this book there are additional Appendices available online. The online Appendices consist of documents that you may reference occasionally or documents which may change before the next edition of this Manual is published. An example of the latter is the Net Zero / Net Zero Ready Technical Requirements, which are available on-line now.

Also, please note that as new reference material becomes available, it will be added to the Appendices online. Expected editions include; Net Zero Energy Renovations Technical Requirements.

Appendix 1 – Insulation Values

Insulation Values

The following pages show the thermal resistance values of various building materials, and a discussion of how to calculate the thermal resistance of building assemblies.

Building Material	RSI/mm (R/in.) (average)	RSI (R) for thickness listed
Building Material		
Polyurethane boardstock	0.041 (6.0)	
Polyurethane (foamed in place)	0.041 (6.0)	
Extruded polystyrene boardstock	0.034 (5.0)	
Isocyanurate, sprayed	0.034 (5.0)	
High density glass fibre boardstock	0.029 (4.2) to 0.031 (4.5)	
Expanded polystyrene boardstock	0.026 (3.8) to 0.030 (4.4)	
Glass fibre roof board	0.028 (4.0)	
Cork	0.026 (3.8)	
Cellulose fibre, blown(settled thickness)	0.025 (3.6)	
Cellulose fibre, sprayed (settled thickness)	0.024 (3.5)	
Mineral fibre, batt	0.024 (3.5)	
Wood fibre	0.023 (3.3)	
Mineral fibre, loose-fill	0.023 (3.3)	
Glass fibre, batt	0.022 (3.2)	
Glass fibre loose-fill (poured in)	0.021 (3.0)	
Glass fibre loose-fill (blown in)	0.020 (2.9)	
Fibreboard	0.019 (2.7)	
Mineral aggregate board	0.018 (2.6)	
Wood shavings	0.017 (2.5)	
Expanded mica (vermiculite, zonolite, etc.)	0.016 (2.3)	
Compressed straw board	0.014 (2.0)	
Structural Materials		
Cedar logs and lumber	0.0092 (1.3)	
Softwood lumber (except cedar)	0.0087 (1.3)	
Concrete 480–2400 kg/m³ (30–150 lb./ft.³)	0.0069–0.00045 (1.0–0.06)	

Building Material (continued)	RSI/mm (R/in.) (average)	RSI (R) for thickness listed
Structural Materials (continued)		
Concrete block (3 oval core)		
Sand and gravel aggregate 100–300 mm (4–12 in.)		0.12–0.22 (0.68–1.25)
Cinder aggregate 100–300 mm (4–12 in.)		0.20–0.33 (1.14–1.9)
Lightweight aggregate 100–300 mm (4–12 in.)		0.26–0.40 (1.5–2.3)
Common brick		
Clay or shale, 100 mm (4 in.)		0.07 (0.4)
Concrete mix, 100 mm (4 in.)		0.05 (0.3)
Stone (lime or sand)	0.00060 (0.087)	
Steel	0.000022 (0.003)	
Aluminum	0.0000049 (0.0007)	
Glass (no air films), 3–6 mm (1/8–1/4 in.)		0.01 (0.06)
Air		
Enclosed air space (non-reflective)		
Heat flow down, 20–100 mm (1–4 in.)		0.18 (1.0)
Heat flow horizontal, 20–100 mm (1–4 in.)		0.17 (l.0)
Heat flow up, 20–100 mm (1–4 in.)		0.15 (0.9)
Air surface films		
Outside air film (moving air)		0.03 (0.2)
Inside air film (still air)		
Horizontal, heat flow down		0.16 (0.9)
Vertical, heat flow horizontal		0.12 (0.7)
Horizontal, heat flow up		0.11 (0.6)
Sloping 45°, heat flow up		0.11 (0.6)
Attic air film		0.08 (0.5)
Roofing		
Asphalt roll roofing		0.03 (0.2)
Asphalt shingles		0.08 (0.5)
Wood shingles (cedar shakes)		0.17 (l.0)
Built-up membrane (hot mopped)		0.06 (0.3)
Sheathing Materials		
Softwood plywood	0.0087 (1.3)	
Mat-formed particleboard	0.0087 (1.3)	
Insulating fibreboard sheathing	0.017 (2.5)	
Gypsum sheathing	0.0062 (0.9)	
Asphalt-coated kraft paper vapour diffusion retarder (VDR)	negligible	
Polyethylene	negligible	

Building Material (continued)	RSI/mm (R/in.) (average)	RSI (R) for thickness listed
Cladding Materials		
Fibreboard siding		
Medium-density hardboard, 9.5 mm (3/8 in.)		0.10 (0.6)
High-density hardboard,9.5 mm (3/8 in.)		0.08 (0.5)
Softwood siding (lapped)		
Drop, 18 x 184 mm (1 x 8 in.)		0.14 (0.8)
Bevel, 12 x 184 mm (1/2 x 8 in.)		0.14 (0.8)
Bevel, 19 x 235 mm (1 x 10 in.)		0.18 (1.0)
Wood shingles		0.17 (1.0)
Brick (clay or shale),100 mm (4 in.)		0.08 (0.5)
Brick (concrete and sand (lime)),100 mm (4 in.)		0.05 (0.3)
Stucco, 25 mm (1 in.)	0.0014 (0.20)	0.03 (0.2)
Metal siding		
Horizontal clapboard profile		0.12 (0.7)
Horizontal clapboard profile with backing		0.25 (l.4)
Vertical V-groove profile		0.12 (0.7)
Vertical board and batten profile		negligible
Interior Finish		
Gypsumboard, gypsum lath,12.7 mm (1/2 in.)	0.0062 (0.89)	0.08 (0.5)
Gypsum plaster Sand aggregate, 12.7 mm (1/2 in.)	0.0014 (0.20)	0.02 (0.1)
Lightweight aggregate,12.7 mm (1/2 in.)	0.0044 (0.63)	0.06 (0.3)
Plywood, 7.5 mm (5/16 in.)	0.0093 (1.34)	0.07 (0.4)
Hardboard (standard), 6 mm (1/4 in.)	0.0053 (0.76)	0.03 (0.2)
Insulating fibreboard, 25 mm (1 in.)	0.017 (2.45)	0.42 (2.4)
Drywall, gypsumboard, 12.7 mm (1/2 in.)	0.0061 (0.88)	0.08 (0.5)
Flooring		
Maple or Oak (hardwood), 19 mm (3/4 in.)	0.0063 (0.91)	0.12 (0.7)
Pine or Fir (softwood), 19 mm (3/4 in.)	0.0089 (1.28)	0.17 (l.0)
Plywood, 16 mm (5/8 in.)	0.0088 (1.27)	0.14 (0.8)
Mat-formed particleboard, 16 mm (5/8 in.)	0.0088 (1.27)	0.14 (0.8)
Wood fibre tiles, 12.7 mm (1/2 in.)	0.016 (2.31)	0.21 (l.2)
Linoleum or tile (resilient), 3 mm (1/8 in.)	0.01 (0.06)	
Terrazzo, 25 mm (1 in.)	0.00056 (0.08)	0.01 (0.06)
Carpet, typical thickness		
Fibrous underlay		0.37 (2.1)
Rubber underlay		0.23 (l.3)

Calculating the Thermal Resistance of Building Assemblies

Calculate the effective insulating value of a windowless wall comprised of 38 x 140 mm (2 x 6 in.) wood studs at 600 mm (24 in.) o.c. with batt insulation and 25mm (1 in.) of extruded polystyrene boardstock. The wall has a 19 mm (3/4 in.) drainage cavity (rainscreen) and stucco siding.

Wood framing typically accounts for 10% of a wall area for 600mm (24 in.) spacing. This means that 90% of the wall does not have thermal bridging. Effective insulating value takes into account the nominal values of the insulating materials and any reducing factors due to thermal bridges such as wood studs.

Construction	RSI (R) between framing	RSI (R) at framing or strapping
1. Outside surface (24 kmh/15 mph wind)	0.03 (0.20)	0.03 (0.20)
2. Siding, 25 mm (1 in.) stucco	0.03 (0.20)	0.03 (0.20)
3. 25 mm (1 in.) air space	0.17 (1.0)	–
4. 19x64 mm (1x3) vertical wood strapping (3/4 in. nominal)	–	0.017 (0.98)
5. 25mm (1 in) extruded polysterene board stock (continuous)	0.86 (5.0)	0.86 (5.0)
6. RSI 3.5 (R-20) batt-type insulation	3.5 (20)	–
7. Nominal 38 x 140 mm (2 x 6 in.) wood stud	–	1.26 (7.15)
8. Gypsum wallboard, 12.7 mm (1/2 in.)	0.08 (0.50)	0.08 (0.50)
9. Inside surface (still air)	0.12 (0.70)	0.12 (0.70)
Total Thermal Resistance—RSI(R)	**4.79 (27.6)**	**2.40 (14.73)**

$$\frac{1}{RSI\ (R)av.} = (\text{fraction of wall surface between framing}) \times \frac{1}{(\text{insulating value between framing})}$$
$$+ (\text{fraction of wall surface at framing}) \times \frac{1}{(\text{insulating value at framing})}$$

$$\frac{1}{RSI\ eff.} = (0.90) \times \frac{1}{(4.79)} + (0.10) \times \frac{1}{(2.40)} = 0.23 \qquad RSI\ eff. = \frac{1}{0.23} = 4.4$$

$$\frac{1}{R\ eff.} = (0.90) \times \frac{1}{(27.6)} + (0.10) \times \frac{1}{(14.73)} = 0.039 \qquad R\ eff. = \frac{1}{0.04} = 25.0$$

The insulation values for materials can be used to calculate the effective insulating value of any assembly. In addition, published information can be used to determine the effective insulating value.

Appendix 2 – Vapour and Air Permeance

Vapour Permeance

Materials considered sufficiently resistant to the flow of water vapour to be used as vapour barriers (also known as vapour diffusion retarders) are rated in terms of their permeance (perm). The lower the perm rating of a material, the more effectively it will retard diffusion.

In SI (metric) units, a perm represents a transfer of one nanogram of water per square metre of material per second under a pressure difference of one pascal. In imperial units, this corresponds to one grain (0.002285 oz.) of water per square foot of material per hour under a pressure difference of one inch of mercury (1.134 ft. of water).

A vapour barrier must have a water vapour permeance no greater than 60 ng/(Pa.s.m^2), but is subject to the climatic location of the building and the anticipated indoor relative humidity.

Air Permeance

Air leakage is a very important building consideration. It is responsible for major transfers of heat, water vapour, and air-borne pollutants. Many materials have the characteristics required of air barriers. The air permeance of a building material is defined as the rate of airflow (L/s) per unit area (m^2) and, per unit static pressure differential (Pa).

The following table provides water vapour and air permeance for some common residential construction materials and general comments on their use as a vapour barrier (VB) and air barrier (AB).

Material	Water Vapour Permeance,(Dry Cup) ng/ (Pa•s•m²)[1] Shaded values indicate materials that are good *vapour* barriers based permeance less than 60	Air Leakage Characteristic, L/ (s•m²) at 75 Pa (Air Permeance)[1] Shaded values indicate materials that are good *air* barriers based on negligible or low air permeance	Comments[2]
Sheet and panel-type materials			
Gypsum board, 12.7 mm	2600	0.02	Suitable AB (ADA)
Painted (1 coat primer)	1300	negligible	Suitable AB (ADA)
Painted (1 coat primer + 2 coats latex paint)	180	negligible	Suitable AB (ADA)
Painted with VDR (vapor diffusion retarder) paint (1 coat)	26	negligible	Suitable AB (ADA) and VB
Gypsum board, 12.7-mm, foil-backed	negligible	negligible	Suitable AB (ADA) and VB
Gypsum board sheathing, 12.7 mm	1373	0.0091	Suitable AB
Oriented strandboard, 11 mm	44 (range)	0.0108	Suitable AB, vapour permeable up to 12.5-mm thick
Cement board, 12.5 mm	590	0.147	Suitable AB
Plywood (from 9.5 to 18 mm)	40 – 57	negligible – 0.01	Suitable AB, vapour permeable up to 12.5-mm thick
Fibreboard sheathing	100 – 2900	0.012 – 1.91	Suitable AB above certain thickness, vapour permeable
Wood sheathing, 17 mm	982	high – depends on no. of joints	Suitable for neither AB nor VB
Insulation			
Polyisocyanurate, 27 mm, foil-faced	4.3	negligible	Suitable AB (EIA) or for VB use on warm side
Polyisocyanurate, 27 mm, paper-faced	61.1	negligible	Suitable exterior AB (EIA)
Polystyrene, extruded, 25 mm	23 – 92	negligible	Suitable exterior AB (EIA)
Polystyrene, expanded (Type 2), 25 mm	86 – 160	0.0214	Suitable exterior AB (EIA)
Fibrous insulations	very high	high	Requires separate AB and VB
Polyurethane spray foam – low density, 25 mm	894 – 3791	0.011	Requires VB
Polyurethane spray foam – medium density, 25 mm	96 (resin layer lowers the value)	negligible	Requires VB

Membrane-type materials			
Asphalt-impregnated paper (10 min paper)	370	0.0673	Suitable weather barrier
Asphalt-impregnated paper (30 min paper)	650	0.4	Suitable weather barrier
Asphalt-impregnated paper (60 min paper)	1800	0.44	Suitable weather barrier
Polyethylene, 0.15 mm (6 mil)	1.6 – 5.8	negligible	Suitable AB (SPA) and VB when located on warm side
Building paper	170 – 1400	0.2706	Suitable weather barrier
Spun-bonded polyolefin film (expanded)	3646	0.9593	Suitable exterior AB (HWA) Suitable weather barrier

Other materials			
50-mm reinforced concrete (density: 2330 kg/m^3)	23	Negligible	Suitable AB, needs to be sealed to other AB system components; separate VB recommended

1. Adapted from NBC Table A-25.5.1.(1).

2. All panel and membrane materials used for air barriers must have sealed joints and have an airtight connection to other components of the air barrier system.

3. Air barrier terms (see Chapter 8): SPA – sealed polyethylene approach; ADA – airtight drywall approach; EIA – exterior insulation approach; and, HWA – house wrap approach.

Appendix 3 – Sample heat load calculations using F280-12

There are a number of calculation tools that have been used by HVAC contractors in the past to calculate the proper size of heating and cooling equipment required to provide adequate comfort in a home. None of these tools have proven adequate for modern housing, with its increased air tightness, advanced windows, higher thermal performance and mechanical ventilation systems with heat recovery. The result has been a chronic over-sizing of mechanical equipment, leading to inefficiency, ineffective operation and comfort issues. It has also led to duct sizes that are too large, and overall inefficiency of space conditioning systems.

Increasingly, local codes are recognizing the CSA F280-12 as the most accurate mechanical equipment sizing tool.

CHBA's Net Zero Labelling Program mandates F280-12 as the only acceptable method of calculating heat loss/gain in a house and determining the proper equipment size.

F280-12 takes into account a number of things not accurately reflected by other methods:

- Recognizes the heat recovery provided by HRV and ERVs

- Reflects advances in window and wall technologies

- Reflects an overall increase of home air tightness and provides a new air tightness metric

- Accounts for system losses through duct leakage

- Provides room-by room heat gain/loss calculations which take into account:

  ◇ room size and R-value of walls

  ◇ window size, orientation and specs (including frame, U-value, glazing treatments (i.e. low-e) and SHGC

  ◇ ducts, ventilation

  ◇ air leakage

This appendix provides a sample of a F280-12 worksheet showing details of these calculations, for a Code built house and for the same house built to Net Zero requirements.

It is usually not expected the builder have knowledge of F280-12, it is the responsibility of the HVAC system designer.

Ontario Code Package A1

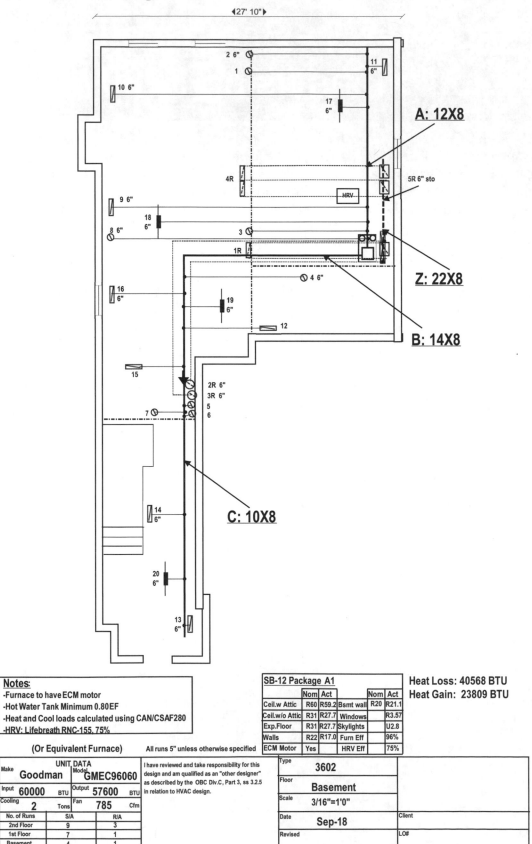

◀ 27' 10" ▶

A: 12X8

5R 6" sto

HRV

Z: 22X8

B: 14X8

C: 10X8

Notes:
- Furnace to have ECM motor
- Hot Water Tank Minimum 0.80EF
- Heat and Cool loads calculated using CAN/CSAF280
- HRV: Lifebreath RNC-155, 75%

(Or Equivalent Furnace)   All runs 5" unless otherwise specified

SB-12 Package A1					
	Nom	Act		Nom	Act
Ceil.w Attic	R60	R59.2	Bsmt wall	R20	R21.1
Ceil.w/o Attic	R31	R27.7	Windows		R3.57
Exp.Floor	R31	R27.7	Skylights		U2.8
Walls	R22	R17.0	Furn Eff		96%
ECM Motor	Yes		HRV Eff		75%

Heat Loss: 40568 BTU
Heat Gain: 23809 BTU

UNIT DATA			
Make **Goodman**	Model **GMEC96060**		
Input **60000** BTU	Output **57600** BTU		
Cooling **2** Tons	Fan **785** Cfm		
No. of Runs	S/A	R/A	
2nd Floor	9	3	
1st Floor	7	1	
Basement	4	1	

I have reviewed and take responsibility for this design and am qualified as an "other designer" as described by the OBC Div.C, Part 3, ss 3.2.5 in relation to HVAC design.

Type	**3602**	
Floor	**Basement**	
Scale	**3/16"=1'0"**	
Date	**Sep-18**	Client
Revised		LO#

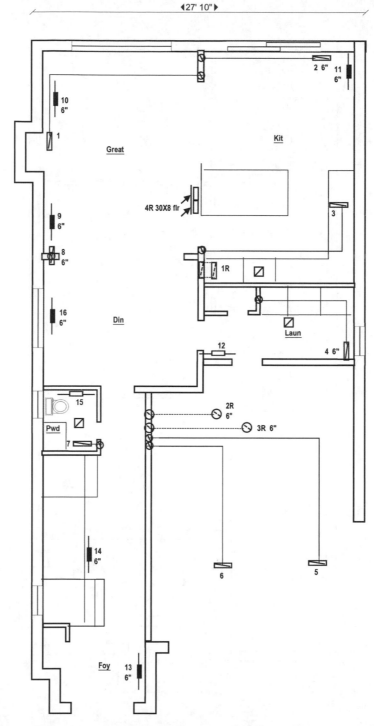

All runs 5" unless otherwise specified

UNIT DATA			I have reviewed and take responsibility for this design and am qualified as an "other designer" as described by the OBC Div.C, Part 3, ss 3.2.5 in relation to HVAC design.	Type	3602	
Make	Model			Floor	First	
Input	BTU	Output	BTU	Scale	3/16"=1'0"	
Cooling	Tons	Fan	Cfm	Date	Sep-18	Client
No. of Runs	S/A	R/A		Revised		LO#
2nd Floor						
1st Floor						
Basement						

CANADIAN HOME BUILDERS' ASSOCIATION

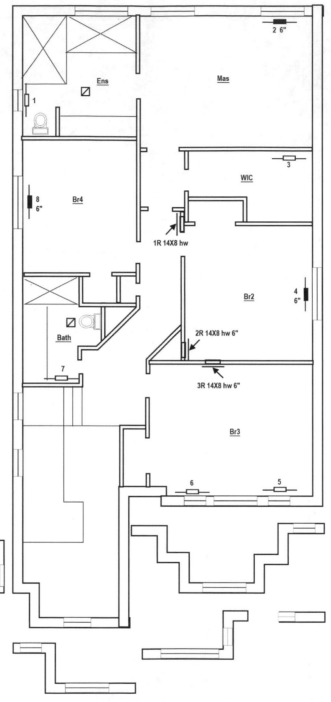

All runs 5" unless otherwise specified

Make	UNIT DATA		I have reviewed and take responsibility for this design and am qualified as an "other designer" as described by the OBC Div.C, Part 3, ss 3.2.5 in relation to HVAC design.	Type	3602	
	Model			Floor	Second	
Input	BTU	Output BTU		Scale	3/16"=1'0"	
Cooling	Tons	Fan Cfm		Date	Sep-18	Client
No. of Runs	S/A	R/A		Revised		LO#
2nd Floor						
1st Floor						
Basement						

MECHANICAL VENTILATION DESIGN SUMMARY RESIDENTIAL

Housetype	3602

File #	0

Builder	0
Address	
City	
Phone	

Heat Loss Due to Mechanical Ventilation

PVC X DTDh X 1.08 X (1-E)=	1923	BTU

Heat Gain Due to Mechanical Ventilation

PVC X DTDc X 1. 08=	950	BTU

Combustion Appliances

- [✓] a) Direct Vent (sealed combust) including fireplaces
- [ ] b) Positive venting induced draft (exclude fireplace)
- [ ] c) Natural Draft,B vent or induced draft fireplaces
- [ ] d) Solid Fuel
- [ ] e) No Combustion Appliances

Total Ventilation Capacity

Bsmt & Master	2	21.2 cfm	42.4
Other Bed	3	10.6 cfm	31.8
Bath & Kitchen	4	10.6 cfm	42.4
Other Rooms	3	10.6 cfm	31.8
		Room Count cfm	148.4

Heating System

- [✓] Forced Air
- [ ] Non Forced Air
- [ ] Electric Space Heat

Housetype

- [✓] I - Type a or b appliances only, no solid fuel
- [ ] II - Type I with solid fuel (including fireplace)
- [ ] III - Type C appliance
- [ ] IV - Type I or II with electric space heat
- [ ] Other - Type I,II,or IV no forced air

Supplemental Ventilation Capacity

TVC room or air change (which larger)	148
Less Principal Exhaust Capacity (HRV)	80
Required Supp.Vent Capacity CFM	68

System Design Option

- [✓] Exhaust Only/Forced air system
- [✓] HRV Simplified Connection to Forced Air System
- [ ] HRV with ducting to forced air system
- [ ] HRV fully ducted/ not coupled with forced air sys.
- [ ] Part 6 design CSA F326-M91
- [✓] Part 9 9.32.3.1

Supplemental Fans

Location	cfm	Model	Pipe
Ens	50	Broan ZB80M	5"
Pwd	50	Broan ZB80M	5"
Bath	50	Broan ZB80M	5"
all fans HVI listed			

HRV-Principal Ventilation

Model		
RNC Lifebreath 155		
	37.5 L/S	80 cfm
ASE		84

Designer Certification

I have reviewed and take reponsibility for this design
and am qualified as an "other designer" as required
by the OBC 3.2.5 as it relates to residential HVAC design

Heat Loss Calculation

Customer
Housetype 3602
File #
Date Sep-18
Township Woodstock

I have reviewed and take responsibility for this design & am qualified as an "other designer" as required by the OBC 3.2.5 as it relates to residential HVAC design.

Heat loss ^T 74 f   Heat Gain ^T 74 f   11 f   Bsmt ^T 62 f

Eff / Fac	Row	Ens Act	Ens Loss	Mas Act	Mas Loss	WIC Act	WIC Loss	Br2 Act	Br2 Loss	Br3 Act	Br3 Loss	Bath Act	Bath Loss	Br4 Act	Br4 Loss	Great Act	Great Loss	Kit Act	Kit Loss	Laun Act	Laun Loss	Foy Act	Foy Loss	Pwd Act	Pwd Loss	Din Act	Din Loss	Bsmt Act	Bsmt Loss
	Width	11		16		16		14		15		10		10		14		13		13		9		9		14		32	
	Length	10		12		6		12		13		9		12		18		20		6		24		5		12		33	
	Area	110		192		96		168		195		90		120		252		260		78		216		45		168		1056	
	Height	8		9		8		8		10		8		8		9		9		9		16		9		9		8	
	LinFtWall	21		28		6		12		28		9		12		34		33		19		57		10		16		164	
	Gr.Wall	168		252		48		96		280		72		96		306		297		171		912		90		144			
17.0	Net Wall	144	627	216	941	48	209	80	349	214	932	72	314	80	349	258	1124	233	1015	163	710	863	3760	82	357	124	540		
	Windows																												
	E,W	16	333	36	748					66	1372					48	998	64	1330			28	582					4	83
	S	8	166											16	333							21	436	8	166	20	416	4	83
	N							16	333											8	166							4	83
3.57	Skylight																												
4	Door									12	223									21	390	22	408						
59.2	Ceiling	110	138	192	241	96	120	168	210	195	244	90	113	120	150														
29.8	Cold Flr							50	124	195	486									216	271	216	271						
17.0	Header															34	136	33	132	19	76			10	40	16	64	164	658
	HL bgcr																												5551
	SlabHLbgcr																												
	People/App			1				1		1				1		1		3		2									
	HL agcr		1264		1930		329		1016		3257		426		831		2258		2478		1342		5457		564		1020		
	HL airr	2	266	2	407	2	69	2	214	2	686	2	90	2	175	1	492	1	540	1	293	1	1150	1	123	1	222		4768
	HL dr							50	123	195	394																		
	Tot.Rm.Loss BTU		1530		2336		399		1353		4337		516		1007		2751		3018		1635		6607		687		1243		11227

HL airb= 27999 X 0.018 X 74 = (Br3 x 0.2550)

Hlairr Multipliers

	BTU	Factor
2nd BTU (0.2)	9054	0.21
1st BTU (0.3)	13119	0.22
Bsmt BTU (0.5)	6459	0.74

BasementHLR 2795 W | 1627 W | 9536 W x 3.41 | BTU 5551 BTU

All Calculations based on CAN/CSAF280 and HRAI Digest Standards

Total Structure Heat Loss	38645
Mech.Vent Loss	1923
TOTAL HEAT LOSS BTU	**40568**

Heat Gain Calculation

I have reviewed and take responsibility for this design & am qualified as an "other designer" as required by the OBC 3.2.5 as it relates to residential HVAC design.

Customer
Housetype 3602
File #
Date Sep-18
Township Woodstock

Heat loss ^T 74 f   Heat Gain ^T 11 f   Bsmt ^T 62 f

Fac	Ens Act	Ens Gain	Mas Act	Mas Gain	WIC Act	WIC Gain	Br2 Act	Br2 Gain	Br3 Act	Br3 Gain	Bath Act	Bath Gain	Br4 Act	Br4 Gain	Great Act	Great Gain	Kit Act	Kit Gain	Laun Act	Laun Gain	Foy Act	Foy Gain	Pwd Act	Pwd Gain	Din Act	Din Gain	Bsmt Act	Bsmt Gain
Width	11		16		16		14		15		10		10		14		13		13		9		9		14		32	
Length	10		12		6		12		13		9		12		18		20		6		24		5		12		33	
Area	110		192		96		168		195		90		120		252		260		78		216		45		168		1056	
Height	8		9		8		8		10		8		8		9		9		9		16		9		9		8	
LinFtWall	21		28		6		12		28		9		12		34		33		19		57		10		16		164	
Gr.Wall	168		252		48		96		280		72		96		306		297		171		912		90		144			
Net Wall (17.03)	144	51	216	76	48	17	80	28	214	75	72	25	80	28	258	91	233	82	163	57	863	304	82	29	124	44		
Windows																												
E,W (27)	16	437	36	984					66	1804					48	1312	64	1750			28	765					4	109
S (18)	8	145											16	291							21	382	8	145	20	363	4	73
N (11)							16	174											8	87							4	44
Skylight (49)																												
Door (4)									12	18									21	32	22	33						
Ceiling (59.22)	110	150	192	261	96	131	168	229	195	265	90	122	120	163							216	294						
Cold Flr (29.8)							50	2		7																		
Header (17.03)		64		109		12		36		178		12		40	11	116	11	151	19	15		146	10	3	16	5		
HG svr																								15		34	164	53
HG dr								330																				23
Total Cond		783		1322		148		433		2170		148		482		1414		1842		182		1778		178		412		279
Air Leak.		21		35		4		11		57		4		13		37		49		5		47		5		11		7
Peop/App	1	240	1	240	1	240	1	240	1	240	1	240	1	240	1	750	3	1650	2	1200						750		
HG sr		868		1705		164		1050		2645		164		775		2317		3541		1402		1971		197		1207		309

HG salb= 27999 X 0.018 X 11 = 11570 BTU

Mech. Vent Gain 950 BTU   HG cb

X 0.055 X = 305 BTU   89 W

Total Structure Heat Gain   18315
Latent Load Multiplier   1.3
Total Heat Gain BTU   23809

All Calculations based on CAN/CSAF280 and HRAI Digest Standards

Customer	3602
Housetype	
File #	
Date	Sep-18
Township	Woodstock

I have reviewed and take responsibility for this design & am qualified as an "other designer" as required by the OBC 3.2.5 as it relates to residential HVAC design.

Duct Calculation

Trunk	C					B							A							
Outlet #	13	20	14	6	5	15	12	19	16	4	2	11	1	10	17	9	18	3	8	
Outlet Loc	Foy	Bsmt	Foy	Br3	Br3	Pwd	Laun	Bsmt	Din	Br2	Mas	Kit	Ens	Great	Bsmt	Great	Bsmt	WIC	Br4	
BTU/RM	6607	11227	6607	4337	4337	687	1635	11227	1243	1353	2336	3018	1530	2751	11227	2751	11227	399	1007	
# Out/Rm	2	4	2	2	2	1	1	4	1	1	1	1	1	2	4	2	4	1	1	
CFM/Outlet	67	57	67	44	44	14	33	57	25	27	47	61	31	28	57	28	57	8	20	
Act&Eff Len	145	160	170	180	195	145	160	170	180	185	155	160	170	180	190	195	200	205	210	
Adj.Press	0.09	0.08	0.08	0.07	0.07	0.09	0.08	0.08	0.07	0.07	0.08	0.08	0.08	0.07	0.07	0.07	0.07	0.06	0.06	
Pipe Size	6	5	6	5	5	5	5	5	5	5	5	6	5	5	5	5	5	5	5	
Tr.Fl.Rate					290					447									338	
TrunkWidth					10					14									12	
Tr.Height					8					8									8	
Velocity					522					574									507	

Trunk	Z				
Inlet #	4R	5R	3R	1R	2R
CFM	375	90	90	140	90
Inlet Size	30X8	6"	6"	14X8	6"
Act&Eff Len	245	225	200	185	170
Adj.Press.	0.04	0.05	0.06	0.06	0.06
Tr.Fl.Rate					785
Tr.Width					22
Tr.Height					8
Velocity					642

Equipment	
Manufacturer	Goodman
Furnace	GMEC96060
Output	57600
AirFlow	785
AC Size	2

Supply Air Pres	0.15
S.Air Plenum Pres	0.14
Diffuser Loss	0.01
System Static	0.5

Return Air Pres	0.15
R.Air Plenum Pres	0.11
Diffuser Loss	0.04

Required equipment capacity based on CAN/CSA-F280 standards

All Calculations based on CAN/CSAF280 and HRAI Digest Standards

Duct Calculation by Heat Gain

Customer
Housetype   3602
File #
Date   Sep-18
Township   Woodstock

I have reviewed and take responsibility for this design & am qualified as an "other designer" as required by the OBC 3.2.5 as it relates to residential HVAC design.

Trunk	C					B						A								
Outlet #	13	20	14	6	7	5	15	12	19	16	4	2	11	1	10	17	9	18	3	8
Outlet Loc	Foy	Bsmt	Foy	Br3	Bath	Br3	Pwd	Laun	Bsmt	Din	Br2	Mas	Kit	Ens	Great	Bsmt	Great	Bsmt	WIC	Br4
BTU/RM	1971	309	1971	2645	164	2645	197	1402	309	1207	1050	1705	3541	868	2317	309	2317	309	164	775
# Out/Rm	2	4	2	2	1	2	1	1	4	1	1	1	1	1	2	4	2	4	1	1
CFM/Out	42	3	42	57	7	57	8	60	3	52	45	73	90	37	81	3	80	3	7	33
Act&Eff Len	145	160	170	180	185	195	145	160	170	180	185	155	160	170	180	190	195	200	205	210
Adj.Press	0.09	0.08	0.08	0.07	0.07	0.07	0.09	0.08	0.08	0.07	0.07	0.08	0.08	0.08	0.07	0.07	0.07	0.07	0.06	0.06
Pipe Size	5	5	5	5	5	5	5	6	5	5	5	6	6	5	6	5	6	5	5	5
Tr.Fl.Rate						208					377									408
Tr.Width						8					12									12
Tr.Height						8					8									8
Velocity						468					565									612

Heat Loss & Gain Calculation Summary Sheet — CSA-F280-M12

These documents issued for the use of	Project #
and may not be used by any other person without authorization. Documents for permit and/or construction are signed in red	

Building Location

Model:	Unit 3602	Site:	
Address:		Lot:	
City:	Woodstock	Postal Code:	

Calculations Based On

Dimensional Info. Based on:

Attachment:	Detached		Front Face:	East	Assumed?	Yes
# of Stories:	2+Bsmt		Air Tight:	Very Tight	Assumed?	Yes
Weath Loc:	Woodstock	Ventilated? Yes	Wind Exp:	Partial Shade		
HRV?	Yes		Int.Shade:	Yes	Occupants:	5
Recovery %	75		Unit:	Imperial		

Heating Design Conditions | Cooling Design Conditions

Out Temp:	-19	Ind.Temp:22	Soil Temp:	10	Out Temp:30	Ind.Temp:	24	Lat:43.13	ST ran:12

Above Grade Walls | Below Grade Walls

Style A:	R22 Nominal	Style A:	R20ci Nominal
Style B:	(R 17.03 Actual)	Style B:	(R21.12 Actual)
Style C:		Style C:	
Style D:		Style D:	

Floors on Soil | Ceilings

Style A:		Style A:	R60 Nominal
Style B:		Style B:	(R59.22 Actual)
		Style C:	(R27.65 Actual Ceiling with no attic)

Exposed Floors | Doors

Style A:	R31 Nominal		
Style B:	(R29.8 Actual)	Style A:	Assumed Insulated

Windows

		Style B:	
Style A:	U 0.28	Style C:	
Style B:	(R 3.57 Actual)		

Skylights

Style C:		Style A:	U 0.49
Style D:		Style B:	(R 2.04 Actual)

Att.Docs:	
Notes:	96% Furnace; Min 0.8EF HWT

Calculations Performed By

I have reviewed and take responsibility for this design & am qualified as an "other designer" as required by the OBC 3.2.5 as it relates to residential HVAC design.

Name:	
Company:	
Address:	
City:	
Postal Code:	
Phone:	
Email:	

Envelope Air Leakage Calculator

Supplemental tool for CAN/CSA-F280

Weather Station Description	
Province:	Ontario ▼
Region:	Woodstock ▼
Weather Station Location:	Open flat terrain, grass ▼
Anemometer height (m):	10

Local Shielding	
Building Site:	Suburban forest ▼
Walls:	Very heavy ▼
Flue:	Heavy ▼
Highest Ceiling Height (m):	7.31

Building Configuration	
Type:	Detached ▼
Number of Stories:	Two ▼
Foundation:	Full ▼
House Volume (m³):	792

Air Leakage/Ventilation		
Air Tightness Type:	Custom - BDT values ▼	
Custom BDT Data:	ELA @ 10 Pa. ▼	56 cm²
	2.5	ACH @ 50 Pa
Mechanical Ventilation (L/s):	Total Supply: 37.5	Total Exhaust: 37.5

Flue Size				
Flue #:	#1	#2	#3	#4
Diameter (mm):	0	0	0	0

Envelope Air Leakage Rate	
Heating Air Leakage Rate (ACH/H):	**0.255**
Cooling Air Leakage Rate (ACH/H):	**0.055**

Residential Foundation Thermal Load Calculator

Supplemental tool for CAN/CSA-F280

Weather Station Description	
Province:	Ontario ▼
Region:	Woodstock ▼
Site Description	
Soil Conductivity:	Normal conductivity: dry sand, loam, clay ▼
Water Table:	Normal (7-10 m, 23-33 Ft) ▼

Foundation Dimensions		
Floor Length (m):	8.2	
Floor Width (m):	16.7	
Exposed Perimeter (m):	49.8	
Wall Height (m):	2.5	**Insulation Configuration**
Depth Below Grade (m):	1.9	
Window Area (m^2):	1.1	
Door Area (m^2):	0	

Radiant Slab		
Heated Fraction of the Slab:	0	
Fluid Temperature (°C):	33	

Design Months	
Heating Month	1

Foundation Loads	
Heating Load (Watts):	**1627**

Net Zero Ready House

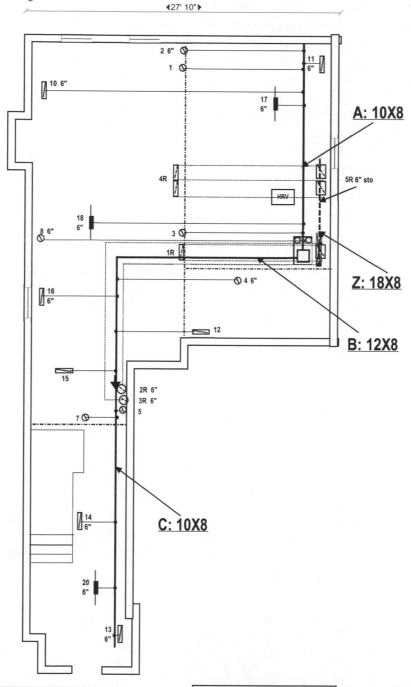

A: 10X8

Z: 18X8

B: 12X8

C: 10X8

5R 6" sto

HRV

Notes:
-Furnace to have ECM motor
-Cooling to be provided with an ASHP
-Heat and Cool loads calculated using CAN/CSAF280
-ERV: Venmar Vanee 85% apparent sensible

(Or Equivalent Furnace)

All runs 5" unless otherwise specified

Heat Loss: 27475 BTU
Heat Gain: 18434 BTU

SB-12 Performance					
	Nom	Act		Nom	Act
Ceil.w Attic	R70	69.2	Bsmt wall		R30
Ceil.w/o Attic	R31	R27.7	Windows		R5.55
Exp.Floor	R31	R27.7	Skylights		U2.8
Walls	R30	25.03	Furn Eff		96%
ECM Motor	Yes		ERV Eff		85%

UNIT DATA				
Make	Goodman	Model	GMEC96040	
Input	40000	BTU	Output 38400	BTU
Cooling	1.5	Tons	Fan 625	Cfm
No. of Runs	S/A		R/A	
2nd Floor	7		3	
1st Floor	6		1	
Basement	3		1	

I have reviewed and take responsibility for this design and am qualified as an "other designer" as described by the OBC Div.C, Part 3, ss 3.2.5 in relation to HVAC design.

Type	3602
Floor	Basement
Scale	3/16"=1'0"
Date	Sep-18
Revised	
Client	
LO#	

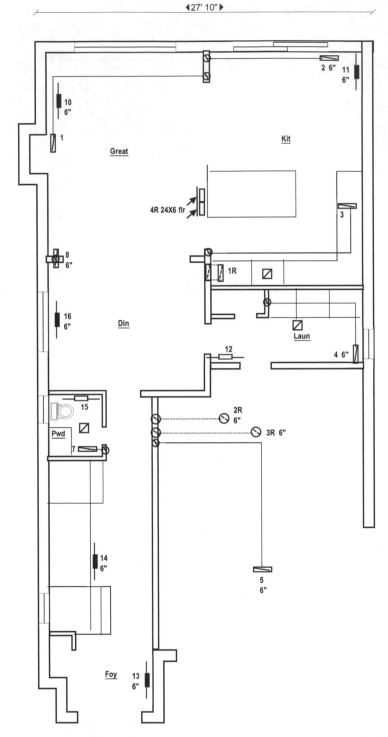

27' 10"

Great

Kit

10 6"

1

4R 24X6 flr

8 6"

3

1R

16 6"

Din

Laun

12

2 6"

11 6"

4 6"

15

Pwd

7

2R 6"

3R 6"

14 6"

5 6"

Foy

13 6"

All runs 5" unless otherwise specified

Make	UNIT DATA	Model		I have reviewed and take responsibility for this design and am qualified as an "other designer" as described by the OBC Div.C, Part 3, ss 3.2.5 in relation to HVAC design.	Type	3602	
Input	BTU	Output	BTU		Floor	First	
Cooling	Tons	Fan	Cfm		Scale	3/16"=1'0"	
No. of Runs	S/A	R/A			Date	Sep-18	Client
2nd Floor							
1st Floor					Revised		LO#
Basement							

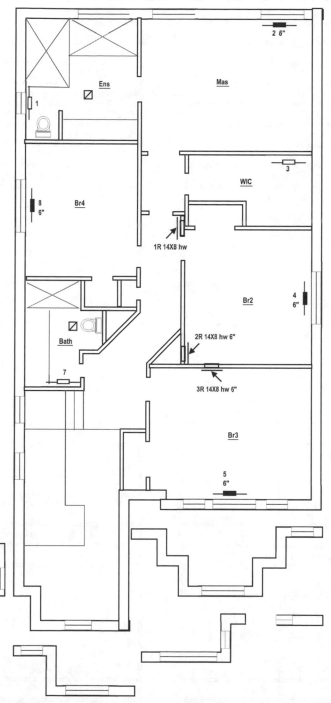

◄27' 10"►

2 6"

Ens

Mas

1

3

WIC

8
6"

Br4

1R 14X8 hw

4
6"

Br2

2R 14X8 hw 6"

Bath

3R 14X8 hw 6"

7

Br3

5
6"

All runs 5" unless otherwise specified

UNIT DATA				I have reviewed and take responsibility for this design and am qualified as an "other designer" as described by the OBC Div.C, Part 3, ss 3.2.5 in relation to HVAC design.	Type	3602	
Make	Model				Floor	Second	
Input	BTU	Output	BTU		Scale	3/16"=1'0"	
Cooling	Tons	Fan	Cfm		Date	Sep-18	Client
No. of Runs	S/A	R/A			Revised		LO#
2nd Floor							
1st Floor							
Basement							

MECHANICAL VENTILATION DESIGN SUMMARY RESIDENTIAL

Housetype	3602

File #	0

Builder	0
Address	
City	
Phone	

Heat Loss Due to Mechanical Ventilation

PVC X DTDh X 1.08 X (1-E)=	962	BTU

Heat Gain Due to Mechanical Ventilation

PVC X DTDc X 1. 08=	950	BTU

Combustion Appliances

- ☑ a) Direct Vent (sealed combust) including fireplaces
- ☐ b) Positive venting induced draft (exclude fireplace)
- ☐ c) Natural Draft,B vent or induced draft fireplaces
- ☐ d) Solid Fuel
- ☐ e) No Combustion Appliances

Total Ventilation Capacity

Bsmt & Master	2	21.2 cfm	42.4
Other Bed	3	10.6 cfm	31.8
Bath & Kitchen	4	10.6 cfm	42.4
Other Rooms	3	10.6 cfm	31.8
		Room Count cfm	148.4

Heating System

- ☑ Forced Air
- ☐ Non Forced Air
- ☐ Electric Space Heat

Housetype

- ☑ I - Type a or b appliances only, no solid fuel
- ☐ II - Type I with solid fuel (including fireplace)
- ☐ III - Type C appliance
- ☐ IV - Type I or II with electric space heat
- ☐ Other - Type I,II,or IV no forced air

Supplemental Ventilation Capacity

TVC room or air change (which larger)	148
Less Principal Exhaust Capacity (HRV)	80
Required Supp.Vent Capacity CFM	68

System Design Option

- ☑ Exhaust Only/Forced air system
- ☑ HRV Simplified Connection to Forced Air System
- ☐ HRV with ducting to forced air system
- ☐ HRV fully ducted/ not coupled with forced air sys.
- ☐ Part 6 design CSA F326-M91
- ☑ Part 9 9.32.3.1

Supplemental Fans

Location	cfm	Model	Pipe
Ens	50	Broan ZB80M	5"
Pwd	50	Broan ZB80M	5"
Bath	50	Broan ZB80M	5"

all fans HVI listed

HRV-Principal Ventilation

Model
Venmar Vanee ERV

37.5 L/S	80 cfm
ASE	85

Designer Certification

I have reviewed and take reponsibility for this design
and am qualified as an "other designer" as required
by the OBC 3.2.5 as it relates to residential HVAC design

			Customer	
			Housetype	3602
			File #	
			Date	Sep-18
			Township	Woodstock

I have reviewed and take responsibility for this design & am qualified as an "other designer" as required by the OBC 3.2.5 as it relates to residential HVAC design.

Duct Calculation

Trunk	C					B				A							
Outlet #	13	20	14	7	5	15	12	16	4	2	11	1	10	17	18	3	8
Outlet Loc	Foy	Bsmt	Foy	Bath	Br3	Pwd	Laun	Din	Br2	Mas	Kit	Ens	Great	Bsmt	Bsmt	WIC	Br4
BTU/RM	4450	8037	4450	358	3092	444	1210	797	960	1533	1920	1000	1760	8037	8037	283	670
# Out/Rm	2	3	2	1	1	1	1	1	1	1	1	1	1	3	3	1	1
CFM/Outlet	52	63	52	8	73	10	29	19	23	36	45	24	41	63	63	7	16
Act&Eff Len	145	160	170	185	195	145	160	180	185	155	160	170	180	190	200	205	210
Adj.Press	0.09	0.08	0.08	0.07	0.07	0.09	0.08	0.07	0.07	0.08	0.08	0.08	0.07	0.07	0.07	0.06	0.06
Pipe Size	5	6	5	5	6	5	5	5	5	5	5	5	5	6	6	5	5
Tr.Fl.Rate					249				330								295
TrunkWidth					10				12								10
Tr.Height					8				8								8
Velocity					449				495								531

Trunk	Z				
Inlet #	4R	5R	3R	1R	2R
CFM	235	90	90	120	90
Inlet Size	24X6	6"	6"	14X8	6"
Act&Eff Len	245	225	200	185	170
Adj.Press.	0.04	0.05	0.06	0.06	0.06
Tr.Fl.Rate					625
Tr.Width					18
Tr.Height					8
Velocity					625

Equipment	
Manufacturer	Goodman
Furnace	GMEC96040
Output	38400
AirFlow	625
AC Size	1.5

Supply Air Pres	0.15
S.Air Plenum Pres	0.14
Diffuser Loss	0.01
System Static	0.5

Return Air Pres	0.15
R.Air Plenum Pres	0.11
Diffuser Loss	0.04

Required equipment capacity based on CAN/CSA-F280 standards

All Calculations based on CAN/CSAF280 and HRAI Digest Standards

Heat Gain Calculation

I have reviewed and take responsibility for this design & am qualified as an "other designer" as required by the OBC 3.2.5 as it relates to residential HVAC design.986

	Customer	
	Housetype	3602
	File #	
	Date	Sep-18
	Township	Woodstock

Heat loss ^T 74 f Heat Gain ^T 11 f Bsmt ^T 62 f

Row	Fac	Ens (Act/Gain)	Mas	WIC	Br2	Br3	Bath	Br4	Great	Kit	Laun	Foy	Pwd	Din	Bsmt
Width		11	16	16	14	15	10	10	14	13	13	9	9	14	32
Length		10	12	6	12	13	9	12	18	20	6	24	5	12	33
Area		110	192	96	168	195	90	120	252	260	78	216	45	168	1056
Height		8	9	8	8	10	8	8	9	9	9	16	9	9	8
LinFtWall		21	28	6	12	28	9	12	34	33	19	57	10	16	164
Gr.Wall		168	252	48	96	280	72	96	306	297	171	912	90	144	
Net Wall	25.03	144/35	216/52	48/12	80/19	214/51	72/17	80/19	258/62	233/56	163/39	863/207	82/20	124/30	
Windows															
E,W	17	16/269	36/606			66/1111			48/808	64/1077		28/471			4/67
S	11	8/90						16/180				21/236	8/90	20/224	4/45
N	7				16/108						8/54				4/27
Skylight	30														
Door	4	4				12/18					21/32	22/33			
Ceiling	69.2	110/128	192/224	96/112	168/196	195/227	90/105	120/140				216/252			
Cold Flr	29.8				50	195/7									
Header	25.03								34/8	33/8	19/5	10/2	/2	16/4	164/40
HG svr		65	110	15	40	176	15	42	109	142	16	149	14	32	22
HG dr					318										
Total Cond		522	881	123	325	1414	122	338	878	1141	129	1198	112	258	179
Air Leak.		8/14	14	2	5	23	2	5	14	18	2	19	2	4	3
Peop/App		1/240	1/240	1/240	1/240	1/240	1/240	1/240	1/750	3/1650	2/1200			1/750	
HG sr		595	1245	141	929	1853	139	626	1752	2809	1348	1367	128	1044	205

HG salb= 27999 X 0.018 X 11 | HG cb | 7622 BTU

Mech. Vent Gain 950 BTU

36 W X 0.022 122 BTU

All Calculations based on CAN/CSAF280 and HRAI Digest Standards

Total Structure Heat Gain	14180
Latent Load Multiplier	1.3
Total Heat Gain BTU	18434

Duct Calculation

Customer	
Housetype	3602
File #	
Date	Sep-18
Township	Woodstock

I have reviewed and take responsibility for this design & am qualified as an "other designer" as required by the OBC 3.2.5 as it relates to residential HVAC design.

Trunk		C					B			A							
Outlet #	13	20	14	7	15	5	12	16	4	2	11	1	10	17	18	3	8
Outlet Loc	Foy	Bsmt	Foy	Bath	Pwd	Br3	Laun	Din	Br2	Mas	Kit	Ens	Great	Bsmt	Bsmt	WIC	Br4
BTU/RM	4450	8037	4450	358	444	3092	1210	797	960	1533	1920	1000	1760	8037	3037	283	670
# Out/Rm	2	3	2	1	1	1	1	1	1	1	1	1	1	3	3	1	1
CFM/Outlet	52	63	52	8	10	73	29	19	23	36	45	24	41	63	63	7	16
Act&Eff Len	145	160	170	185	145	195	160	180	185	155	160	170	180	190	200	205	210
Adj.Press	0.09	0.08	0.08	0.07	0.09	0.07	0.08	0.07	0.07	0.08	0.08	0.08	0.07	0.07	0.07	0.06	0.06
Pipe Size	5	6	5	5	5	6	5	5	5	5	5	5	5	6	6	5	5
Tr.Fl.Rate						249			330								295
TrunkWidth						10			12								10
Tr.Height						8			8								8
Velocity						449			495								531

Trunk	Z				
Inlet #	4R	5R	3R	1R	2R
CFM	235	90	90	120	90
Inlet Size	24X6	6"	6"	14X8	6"
Act&Eff Len	245	225	200	185	170
Adj.Press.	0.04	0.05	0.06	0.06	0.06
Tr.Fl.Rate		625			
Tr.Width		18			
Tr.Height		8			
Velocity		625			

Equipment	
Manufacturer	Goodman
Furnace	GMEC96040
Output	38400
AirFlow	625
AC Size	1.5

Supply Air Pres	0.15
S.Air Plenum Pres	0.14
Diffuser Loss	0.01
System Static	0.5

Return Air Pres	0.15
R.Air Plenum Pres	0.11
Diffuser Loss	0.04

Required equipment capacity based on CAN/CSA-F280 standards

All Calculations based on CAN/CSAF280 and HRAI Digest Standards

Duct Calculation by Heat Gain

Customer	
Housetype	3602
File #	
Date	Sep-18
Township	Woodstock

I have reviewed and take responsibility for this design & am qualified as an "other designer" as required by the OBC 3.2.5 as it relates to residential HVAC design.

Trunk	C					B				A							
Outlet #	13	20	14	7	5	15	12	16	4	2	11	1	10	17	18	3	8
Outlet Loc	Foy	Bsmt	Foy	Bath	Br3	Pwd	Laun	Din	Br2	Mas	Kit	Ens	Great	Bsmt	Bsmt	WIC	Br4
BTU/RM	1367	205	1367	139	1853	128	1348	1044	929	1245	2809	595	1752	205	205	141	626
# Out/Rm	2	3	2	1	1	1	1	1	1	1	1	1	1	3	3	1	1
CFM/Out	30	3	30	6	82	6	59	46	41	55	124	26	77	3	3	6	28
Act&Eff Len	145	160	170	185	195	145	160	180	185	155	160	170	180	190	200	205	210
Adj.Press	0.09	0.08	0.08	0.07	0.07	0.09	0.08	0.07	0.07	0.08	0.08	0.08	0.07	0.07	0.07	0.06	0.06
Pipe Size	5	5	5	5	6	5	5	5	5	5	6	5	6	5	5	5	5
Tr.Fl.Rate					151				303								322
Tr.Width					8				10								10
Tr.Height					8				8								8
Velocity					340				546								580

Heat Loss & Gain Calculation Summary Sheet — CSA-F280-M12

These documents issued for the use of	Project #
and may not be used by any other person without authorization. Documents for permit and/or construction are signed in red	

Building Location

Model:	Unit 3602	Site:	
Address:		Lot:	
City:	Woodstock	Postal Code:	

Calculations Based On

Dimensional Info. Based on:

Attachment:	Detached	Front Face:	East	Assumed?	Yes
# of Stories:	2+Bsmt	Air Tight:	Very Tight	Assumed?	Yes
Weath Loc:	Woodstock Ventilated? Yes	Wind Exp:	Partial Shade		
HRV?	Yes	Int.Shade:	Yes	Occupants:	5
Recovery %	85	Unit:	Imperial		

Heating Design Conditions

Out Temp:	-19	Ind.Temp:22	Soil Temp:	10

Cooling Design Conditions

Out Temp:30	Ind.Temp:	24 Lat:43.13	ST ran:12

Above Grade Walls

Style A:	R30
Style B:	(R 25.03 Actual)
Style C:	
Style D:	

Below Grade Walls

Style A:	R30
Style B:	
Style C:	
Style D:	

Floors on Soil

Style A:	
Style B:	

Ceilings

Style A:	R70 Nominal
Style B:	(R69.22 Actual)
Style C:	(R27.65 Actual Ceiling with no attic)

Exposed Floors

Style A:	R31 Nominal
Style B:	(R29.8 Actual)

Doors

Style A:	Assumed Insulated
Style B:	
Style C:	

Windows

Style A:	U 0.18
Style B:	(R 5.55 Actual)
Style C:	
Style D:	

Skylights

Style A:	
Style B:	

Att.Docs:	
Notes:	96% Furnace; ASHP used for cooling

Calculations Performed By

I have reviewed and take responsibility for this design & am
qualified as an "other designer" as required by the OBC 3.2.5
as it relates to residential HVAC design.

Name:	
Company:	
Address:	
City:	
Postal Code:	
Phone:	
Email:	

Envelope Air Leakage Calculator

Supplemental tool for CAN/CSA-F280

Weather Station Description	
Province:	Ontario ▼
Region:	Woodstock ▼
Weather Station Location:	Open flat terrain, grass ▼
Anemometer height (m):	10

Local Shielding	
Building Site:	Suburban forest ▼
Walls:	Very heavy ▼
Flue:	Heavy ▼
Highest Ceiling Height (m):	7.31

Building Configuration	
Type:	Detached ▼
Number of Stories:	Two ▼
Foundation:	Full ▼
House Volume (m^3):	792

Air Leakage/Ventilation		
Air Tightness Type:	Custom - BDT values ▼	
Custom BDT Data:	ELA @ 10 Pa. ▼	56 cm^2
	1	ACH @ 50 Pa
Mechanical Ventilation (L/s):	Total Supply:	Total Exhaust:
	37.5	37.5

Flue Size				
Flue #:	#1	#2	#3	#4
Diameter (mm):	0	0	0	0

Envelope Air Leakage Rate	
Heating Air Leakage Rate (ACH/H):	0.135
Cooling Air Leakage Rate (ACH/H):	0.022

Residential Foundation Thermal Load Calculator

Supplemental tool for CAN/CSA-F280

Weather Station Description	
Province:	Ontario ▼
Region:	Woodstock ▼
Site Description	
Soil Conductivity:	Normal conductivity: dry sand, loam, clay ▼
Water Table:	Normal (7-10 m, 23-33 Ft) ▼

Foundation Dimensions

Floor Length (m):	8.2	
Floor Width (m):	16.7	
Exposed Perimeter (m):	49.8	
Wall Height (m):	2.5	Insulation Configuration
Depth Below Grade (m):	1.9	
Window Area (m^2):	1.1	
Door Area (m^2):	0	

Radiant Slab

Heated Fraction of the Slab:	0
Fluid Temperature (°C):	33

Design Months

Heating Month	1

Foundation Loads

Heating Load (Watts):	**1423**

Summary Sheet

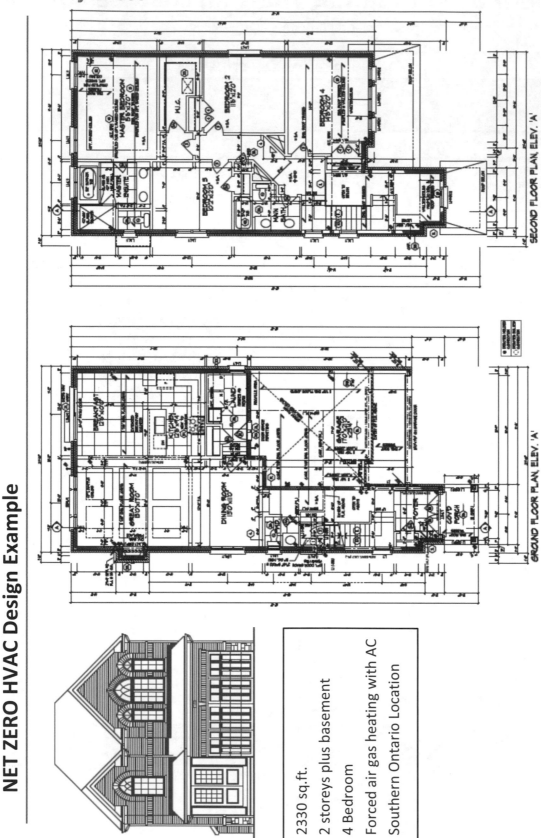

NET ZERO HVAC Design Example

SECOND FLOOR PLAN, ELEV. 'A'

GROUND FLOOR PLAN, ELEV. 'A'

2330 sq.ft.

2 storeys plus basement

4 Bedroom

Forced air gas heating with AC

Southern Ontario Location

NET ZERO HVAC Design Example – House Built to "Code" Specifications

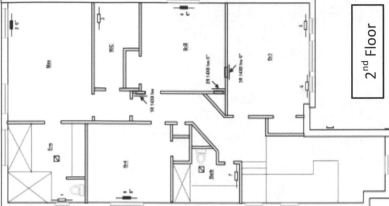

2nd Floor

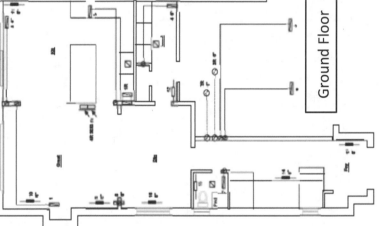

Ground Floor

Basement

A-12X8

Z-22X8

B-14X8

C-10X8

HVAC Specifications	
Heat Loss	40,500 BTUs/hr
Heat Gain	23,800 BTUs/hr
Furnace Size	60,000 BTUs/hr
System Airflow	760 CFM
System Static Pressure	0.5 in. W.C.

Enclosure	Specifications
Ceiling	R60
Walls	R22
Windows	U=1.6 (0.28)
Basement	R22
Air Leakage	2.5 ACH50
Ventilation	75%

NET ZERO HVAC Design Example – House Built to "Net Zero" Specifications

2nd Floor

Ground Floor

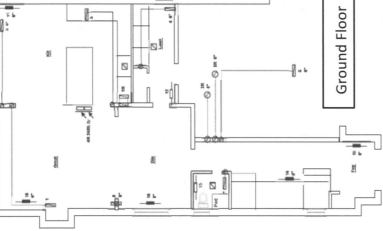

Basement

HVAC Specifications	
Heat Loss	27,500 BTUs/hr
Heat Gain	18,500 BTUs/hr
Furnace Size	40,000 BTUs/hr
System Airflow	650 CFM
System Static Pressure	0.5 in. W.C.

Enclosure	Specifications
Ceiling	R70
Walls	R30
Windows	U=1.1 (0.18)
Basement	R30
Air Leakage	1.0 ACH50
Ventilation	85%

Appendix 4 – Selecting the Building Envelope

This section provides one strategy for conceptualizing the type of building envelope to use. The thermal insulation values (Appendix 1) and the vapour and air permeance values (Appendix 2) are a major part of the decision-making.

Step 1: Establish the desired standard that a given house is intended to achieve.
Possibilities include:

- The local Building Code as a minimum;

- Energy Star;

- LEED;

- R-2000;

- Net Zero Energy or Net Zero Energy Ready or

- Some target based on the EnerGuide Rating System for Houses.

This decision will determine the effective insulating value required for the various building envelope components (i.e., ceiling, above-grade walls, below-grade walls, sub-slab insulation, cantilevered fl oors, rooms over unheated spaces, etc.) and the air leakage target.

Step 2: Conceptualize the type of envelope system to be used: Considerations include wood-framing, steel-framing, ICF, single or double walls, sheathing, rainscreen, cladding, windows, doors, etc. Some useful questions to ask at this time include:

- What effective insulating value is required and where (above-ground, windows and doors, and areas in contact with the ground)?

- What insulation product(s) will I use to achieve the required effective insulating value?

- Do I need to limit thermal bridging by using advanced framing techniques or an exterior insulation?

- Do I need to have a deeper floor assembly over unheated spaces to achieve the required effective insulating value?

Step 3: Design to meet the desired air leakage target: Consider whether any of the insulation, structural components or interior wall finish can also serve as the air barrier. Consider how the designated air barrier will interface with other components of the air barrier system such as windows and other openings. Some useful questions at this stage include:

- What will be the air barrier for the ceiling?

- What will be the air barrier for above-grade walls?

- What will be the air barrier for below-grade walls?

- How will I ensure continuity of the air barrier across window and door openings?

- How will I seal any floors over unheated spaces?

- How will I seal structural transitions such as concrete-to-wood framing, walls-to-ceilings, and floor/wall intersections?

- Is the air barrier system simple to construct and test and do the installers have proper training?

- How will penetrations through the air barrier be limited and properly sealed? Which trade will have responsibility for installing the air barrier and ensuring that penetrations are sealed and damages are repaired?

- Should the air barrier be tested before completion to ensure air tightness?

Step 4: Design to limit the movement of moisture: Identify the vapour barrier method such as foil, foil-backed drywall, polyethylene, VDR (vapor diffusion retarder) painted drywall, or rigid or spray foam. Check that it is located on the warm side of the wall (for heating climates).

Step 5: Special considerations: Think through the insulation, air sealing and vapour protection of areas such as rooms over unheated spaces, walls and ceilings separating living spaces from garages, bay and bow windows, etc.

Step 6: Is it practical? Check the selected envelope system for cost and buildability. Some useful questions at this point include:

- How expensive will this be to build?

- How complicated will it be to build?

- Do I need to be on site to supervise or can I explain what I want well enough to my team or trades?

- Can I get all of the materials and services that I need in my area?

- What are the critical points/times in the construction process that I need to be aware of?

If these questions raise any concerns or doubts, repeat Steps 1 to 5 until an envelope design is conceived that meets code, cost and energy target requirements.

Appendix 5 – Ventilation System Checklist

This checklist has been specifically developed for an HRV installation, but it can be applied generally to any type of ventilating system.

General

The installer should:

- Be trained and registered by the Heating, Refrigeration and Air Conditioning Institute of Canada (HRAI).

- Perform the installation in accordance with CAN/CSA-F326-M91 *Residential Mechanical Ventilation Systems* (if an HRV is being installed).

- Provide the builder (or homeowner) with all system documentation and maintenance and operation manuals.

Ventilating equipment should be:

- Located inside the heated interior of the house.

- Located away from noise-sensitive living areas (dining room, living room, bedroom, etc.).

- Located close to an outside wall to minimize insulated duct runs.

- Positioned close to a drain (for condensate) and to an electrical supply.

- Made easily accessible for maintenance purposes.

- Situated away from hot chimneys, electrical panels, and other possible fire sources.

- Sealed with duct sealer or aluminium tape (not duct tape) at all joints, seams and splices in the ducts.

Ventilator Installation

The ventilator should be installed with:

Vibration isolators such as rubber hangers and a short, straight section of flexible acoustic duct between the unit and the main ductwork.

- A control system capable of providing continuous low-speed operation plus humidity-controlled and manually controlled high speed override.

- Airflow measuring stations built into the HRV/ERV.

Cold-Side Ducts

Cold-side ducts should connect the HRV to the outside, with one bringing in fresh air and the other exhausting stale air. The ducts should:

- Be as short and straight as possible.

- Contain no kinks or depressions where condensate water might accumulate.

- Be insulated with a minimum of RSI 0.4 (R-2) insulation.

- Be sealed from end to end (outside the insulation) with a vapour barrier.

- Have their vapour barriers sealed to the vapour barrier of the house envelope.

- Be clearly marked as to which is for fresh air and which is for exhaust air.

- Terminate in two accessible rain hoods, each equipped with a 6 mm (1/4 in.) or coarser wire mesh bird screen. If finer insect screens are used, they must be accessible for regular cleaning.

The cold-side fresh air inlet should be:

- Located at least 450 mm (18 in.) above ground (more if exposed to blockage by snow, etc.) and at least 1800 mm (72 in.) away from the exhaust outlet.

- Located away from sources of contamination such as carports, driveways, garages, bushes, tall grass, garbage, dryer vents, central vacuum exhausts, other vents, oil fill pipes, gas regulators, etc.

- Equipped with a filter in the duct or at the inlet, if the HRV does not have a filter.

The cold-side exhaust outlet should be:

- Located away from walkways and other areas where ice accumulation could be a problem (since moisture in the exhaust air may condense and freeze).

- Terminated outdoors (*not* in a garage or attic), at least 100 mm (4 in.) above ground (more if practical).

Warm-Side Ducts

Warm-side ducts should connect the HRV to the house, with one duct system distributing fresh air while a second collects exhaust air.

- Either an exhaust or a fresh air duct should be provided to every room.

- Duct systems should be designed to minimize their length and complexity (turns, right angles, etc.).

- Rigid ducts should be used wherever possible in preference to flexible ducts, since the ribbing in flexible ducts doubles the resistance to airflow.

- Duct runs in unheated spaces and in exterior walls should be avoided.

- Duct joints should be securely fastened and sealed.

Warm-Side Exhaust Ducts

Warm-side exhaust ducts should:

- Run from such areas as bathrooms and kitchens, and other areas where contaminants are generated.

- Contain a filter in the duct or at the grilles, if the HRV does not have a filter.

In the kitchen:

- The range hood must not be connected to the HRV.

- Good practice is for the general kitchen exhaust (connected to the HRV) to be located at least 1500 mm (60 in.) horizontally removed from the cooking surface.

- The kitchen exhaust must be ducted in sheet metal.

In the laundry room:

- Clothes dryers should be vented directly to the outside (unless heat pump dryers are used).

Warm-Side Fresh Air Ducts

Fresh air can be distributed throughout the house by a separate system of ducts or by a forced-air furnace. If a separate system of ducts is used, grilles should be located to minimize discomfort from cold drafts by placing them near the ceiling.

If a forced-air furnace is used to distribute fresh air, the HRV supply air ducting should be directly connected to the return air duct of the heating system, not less than 3 m (10 ft.) upstream of the plenum connection to the furnace, as measured along the length of the duct.

Verification of Operation

Once the unit is operational, the installer should take the following steps:

- Where the HRV has its own distribution ductwork, check and adjust flows in all ducts to ensure that sufficient airflow is provided to all rooms when the doors are closed.

- Adjust the total airflow to provide the continuous ventilation rate as specified.

- Balance the flow, where appropriate, to equalize the flow rates of the fresh air and the exhaust air.

- Ensure that the controls work as designed. This includes the (de)humidistat and an interval timer and/or manual override.

- Mark the minimum ventilation settings on all dampers and speed controls so that they may be readjusted after installation, if necessary.

Appendix 6 – Glossary

Adfreezing The process whereby wet soils freeze to below-grade materials such as foundation walls or insulation, forcing movement of the material.

Air Barrier A material carefully installed within a building envelope assembly to minimize the uncontrolled passage of air into and out of a dwelling. Air barriers may be made of either membrane materials such as polyethylene or rigid materials such as drywall. In either case, they are carefully sealed to ensure continuity.

Air Change per Hour (ach) A unit that denotes the number of times per hour that the entire volume of air in a house is exchanged with outside air. This is generally used in two ways: 1) under natural conditions; and 2) under a pressure difference of 50 pascals. A well-built house should have no more than 1.5 ach at 50 pascals.

Air Leakage The uncontrolled flow of air through a component of the building envelope, or the building envelope itself, that takes place when a pressure difference is applied across the component. Infiltration refers to air leakage into the house, and exfiltration refers to the outward leakage of air.

Air Permeability A measurement of the degree to which a building component allows air to pass through it when it is subjected to a differential pressure.

Air Pressure The pressure exerted by the air. This may refer to static (atmospheric) pressure, or dynamic components of pressure arising from airflow, or both acting together.

Air Sealing The practice of sealing (from the interior) unintentional gaps in the building envelope in order to reduce uncontrolled air leakage. All joints, holes and cracks in the air barrier should be carefully sealed with compatible caulking materials or gaskets.

Airtightness The degree to which unintentional openings have been avoided in a building's structure.

Ambient Temperature The temperature of the air, (1) outside the building, or (2) within a room.

Automatic Flue Damper A damper added to the flue pipe downstream of a furnace or boiler and connected with automatic controls to the burner. Its function is to reduce heat loss up the chimney when the unit is not operating. Consequently, it provides the greatest savings during relatively mild weather when the furnace is operating only infrequently.

Backdrafting (flow reversal) The reverse flow of chimney gases into a building through the barometric damper, draft hood or burner unit. Backdrafting can be caused by chimney blockage, or it can occur when the pressure differential is too high for the chimney to draw.

Braced wall panel A portion of a wood-frame wall where bracing, sheathing, cladding or interior finish is installed to provide the required resistance to wind and earthquake loads. Braced wall panels lie along a braced wall *bands*.

Building Orientation The siting of a building on a lot. The term is generally used when discussing solar orientation, which is the siting of a building with respect to access to solar radiation.

Combination heating appliance A gas, oil, hydronic or heat pump unit that provides both space heating and domestic hot water heating.

Combustion Air The air required to provide adequate oxygen for fuel-burning appliances in a building.

Condensation The beads or drops of water (and frequently frost or ice in extremely cold weather) that accumulate on the inside of the exterior covering of a building (most easily observed on windows). Condensation occurs when warm, moisture-laden air from the interior contacts a colder surface; the air cools and can no longer hold as much moisture.

Convection The transfer of heat from one point to another in a fluid (e.g., air, water), by the mixing of one portion of the fluid with another.

Controlled Ventilation Ventilation brought about by mechanical means through pressure differentials induced by the operation of a fan.

Dampproofing The process of coating the exterior of a foundation wall with bituminous emulsions or plastic cements. The purpose of dampproofing is to restrict the movement of soil vapour through basement walls and floor slabs to the interior of the basement.

(De)humidistat An electronic sensing and control device used to regulate mechanical ventilation according to the relative humidity in the building. When the relative humidity surpasses a preset limit, the dehumidistat activates the ventilation system in order to exhaust house air.

Design Heat Losses The total predicted envelope heat losses over the heating season for a particular house design in a particular climate.

Dewpoint The temperature at which a given air/water vapour mixture is saturated with water vapour (i.e., 100% relative humidity). If air is in contact with a surface below this temperature, condensation will form on the surface.

Dilution Air The air required by some combustion heating systems in order to isolate the furnace from outside pressure fluctuations and to maintain a constant chimney draft.

Direct Gain A type of solar heating system where the solar collection area is an integral part of the building's usable space; for example, windows.

Earth Energy Heating or cooling energy (geothermal or ground-source) extracted from the ground.

Envelope The exterior surface of a building including all external additions, e.g., chimneys, bay windows, etc.

Equivalent Leakage Area (ELA) An estimate of the total area of all the unintentional openings in a building's envelope, generally expressed in square centimetres or square inches.

Exfiltration The uncontrolled leakage of air out of a building.

Expansive Soils Fine-grained soils such as clay, silt and fine sand that are frost-susceptible and are therefore more subject to frost heaving.

Fan Depressurization A process by which a large fan exhausts air from a building and creates a pressure difference across the building envelope. An analysis of the flow rate through the fan at different pressure points provides a measurement of airtightness.

Flanking Sound Airborne or impact sound that finds an indirect path through junctions of assemblies and bypasses the parts of the floors and walls constructed to limit sound transmission.

Frost Heaving The movement of soils caused by the phenomenon known as ice lensing or ice segregation. Water is drawn from the unfrozen soil to the freezing zone, where it attaches to form layers of ice, forcing soil particles apart and causing the soil surface to heave.

Heating Degree Day The number of degrees of temperature difference on any one day between a given base temperature and the mean daytime outside temperature. The base is usually 18°C (64°F). The total number of degree days over the heating season indicates the relative severity of the winter for a specific location.

Heat Recovery The process of extracting heat (usually from a fluid such as air or water) that would otherwise be wasted. Heat recovery in housing usually refers to the extraction of heat from exhaust air.

Humidistat *See* Dehumidistat.

Ice Lensing *See* Frost Heaving.

Impact Isolation Class (IIC) A rating used to compare and evaluate the performance of floor-ceiling constructions in isolating impact noise.

Impermeable Not permitting water vapour or other fluid to pass through.

Induced-Draft Flue System A type of heating system equipped with a fan downstream of the furnace. The fan pulls gases from the furnace and propels them to the outside, thereby eliminating the requirement for dilution air.

Infiltration The uncontrolled leakage of air into a building.

Integrated Mechanical System A package appliance meeting CSA P-10 unit that combines space heating, domestic water and ventilation.

Intrinsic Heat Heat from human bodies, electric light bulbs, cooking stoves, and other objects not intended specifically for space heating.

Latent Heat Heat added or removed during a change of state (for example, from water vapour to liquid water) while the temperature remains constant.

Mechanical Systems All the mechanical components of the building, i.e., plumbing, heating, ventilation, air conditioning and heat recovery.

Moisture Barrier A material, membrane or coating designed to keep moisture coming through the foundation wall from penetrating the interior foundation insulation or the wood members supporting the insulation and interior finishes.

Negative Pressure A pressure below atmospheric pressure. A negative pressure exists when the pressure inside the house envelope is less than the air pressure outside. Negative pressure will encourage infiltration.

Net-zero energy housing (NZEH) Highly energy-conserving and energy-efficient housing that produces, on an annual basis, as much energy from integrated on-site renewable energy systems as it uses.

Normalized Leakage Area (NLA) The NLA is calculated by dividing the Equivalent Leakage Area (ELA) from a fan test by the area of the exterior envelope of the house.

Orientation The direction (with respect to the points of a compass) that a building faces.

Pascal A unit measurement of pressure in the SI (metric) system. House airtightness tests are typically conducted with a pressure difference of 50 pascals between the inside and outside. 50 pascals is equal to 5.008 mm (0.2 in.) of water at 12.9°C (55°F).

Permeance Water vapour permeance is the rate at which water vapour diffuses through a sheet of any thickness of material (or assembly between parallel surfaces). It is the ratio of water vapour flow to the differences of the vapour pressures on the opposite surfaces. Permeance is measured in perms (ng/Pa.m2s, or grain/ft2hr (in. Hg)).

Positive Pressure A pressure above atmospheric pressure. A positive pressure exists when the pressure inside the house envelope is greater than the air pressure outside. A positive pressure difference will encourage exfiltration.

Pressure Difference The difference in pressure of the volume of air enclosed by the house envelope and the air surrounding the envelope.

Radiant Heat Transfer The transfer of heat energy from a location of higher temperature to a location of lower temperature by means of electromagnetic radiation.

Relative Humidity The amount of moisture in the air compared to the maximum amount of moisture that the air could retain at the same temperature. This ratio is expressed as a percentage.

Renewable Energy Energy originating from resources that are unlimited, rapidly replenished or naturally renewable such as wind, water, sun, wave and wood, and not from the combustion of fossil fuels.

Resistance Value (RSI) Thermal resistance value. This is a measurement of the ability of a material to resist heat transfer.

Sealants Flexible materials used on the inside of a building to seal gaps in the building envelope in order to prevent uncontrolled air infiltration and exfiltration.

Solar Heat Gain A term used in the passive solar heating field to describe the amount of heat gained through windows during the heating season. Net solar gain refers to the solar heat gain less the heat losses through the windows.

Sound Transmission Class (STC) A rating for evaluating the effectiveness of construction in isolating airborne sound transmission.

Stack Effect Pressure differential across a building caused by differences in the density of the air due to a difference of temperature between indoors and outdoors.

Thermal Break A material of low conductivity used in a building assembly to reduce the flow of heat by conduction from one side of the assembly to the other. The term is often used to refer to materials used for this purpose in the frame of metal windows.

Vapour Barrier Any material of low water vapour permeability used to restrict the movement of water vapour due to vapour diffusion. There are two classes of vapour barriers. A *Type I* vapour barrier has a permeance of 15 metric perms (0.25 perms in imperial units) or less; a *Type II* vapour barrier has a permeance of 45 (0.75) perms or less before aging, and 57.5 (1.0) perms or less after aging. Any material with a perm rating higher than 57.5 (1.0) perms is *not* a vapour barrier.

Vapour Diffusion The movement of water vapour between two areas caused by a difference in vapour pressure, independent of air movement. The rate of diffusion is determined by (1) the difference in vapour pressure; (2) the distance the vapour must travel; and (3) the permeability of the material to water vapour (hence the selection of materials of low permeability for use as vapour diffusion retarders in buildings).

Vapour Diffusion Retarder See vapour barrier.

Water Vapour Pressure The pressure exerted by water vapour in the air. Water vapour moves from an area of high pressure to an area of low pressure.

Appendix 7 – Conversion Factors

Imperial	Metric
Lumber sizes	
2 x 2	38 x 38 mm
2 x 3	38 x 64 mm
2 x 4	38 x 89 mm
2 x 6	38 x 140 mm
2 x 8	38 x 190 mm
2 x 10	38 x 235 mm
2 x 12	38 x 286 mm
Other	
2' x 8'	600 x 2400 mm
4' x 8'	1200 x 2400 mm
16" O.C.	400 mm
24" O.C.	600 mm
1"	25.4 mm
1-1/2"	38 mm
2"	51 mm

Basic Metric Conversions	to get	multiply	by
length	mm	inches	25.4
	m	feet	0.3048
area	m^2	ft^2	0.0929
		yd^2	0.836127
volume	m^3	ft^3	0.028317
		yd^3	0.764555
flow	1/s	cfm	0.471947
energy	W	Btu/h	0.293072
energy	kWh	Btu	3409.52
energy	mJ	kWh	3,600
energy	kW	tons of refrigeration	3.5169
insulation R-value	RSI	R	0.1761
insulation R/unit thickness	RSI/mm	R/in.	0.00693
mass	kg	lb.	0.454
permeance (water vapour)	$Ng/Pa.m^2s$	$grain/ft^2hr$ (in. Hg)	57.5
resistance to moisture flow	$Pa. m^2s/ng$	ft^2h (in.Hg)/grain	0.0174

Appendix 8 – Index

M

Make-up air. *167, 294–296, 338–339, 352, 379*

Manufactured housing. *CH. 14*

Marketing environmental features. *96*

Mechanical systems. *Ch. 15–Ch. 22*

Membrane air barrier. *99–101, 115, 146–150, 186–193, 219, 237–239*

Moisture barrier. *105, 123–124, 160, 168, 170–171, 474*

Mould. *27, 29, 32, 34, 40, 64–69, 290, 297, 299, 333, 359–360*

Multi-unit buildings. *55–62, 193–194, 232–237*

N

Net zero energy housing. *8, 10, 23, 76–77, 271*

Neutral pressure plane. *28*

Northern foundations. *178–184*

O

Off-gassing. *See Emissions from building materials*

Oil heating systems. *315–317, 365–366*

P

Permeance. *99–103, 111, 113–115, 141, 146, 170, 201, 209, 225, 435*

Polyethylene air and/or vapour barrier. *130–135*

Polyisocyanurates insulation. *112*

Polystyrene insulation. *100, 111–112, 115, 130, 135, 140–141, 163, 165, 170, 172–174, 190, 201, 225, 227, 279, 285, 430*

Polyurethane insulation. *110, 112–113, 115, 117, 130, 146, 163, 165, 171, 227, 279, 430*

R

Radiant barrier insulation. *110, 111, 113*

Radiant cooling systems. *22, 41, 359*

Radiant heating systems. *23, 310, 313, 330–331*

Radon. *67–69, 74, 163–164, 341–342*

Rain screen. *230*

Recycling. *75, 92–95*

Renewable energy. *Ch. 24*

Rim joists. *135, 166, 170, 186–189, 197, 216, 231*

Roofs. *Ch. 12*

S

Sealants. *71, 73, 98–99, 115–118*

Sealed polyethylene approach (SPA) air barrier *130–134*

Sheathing membrane. *29, 97–99, 101, 103–104, 106, 120, 127, 132, 147–150, 168–169, 187–188, 190, 221, 274*

Site orientation. *44–45*

Soil gas. *See Radon*

Solar gains. *51, 261, 262–265, 269*

Solar energy. *20, 44–45, 50, 52, 75, 262–263, 266, 382–386*

Solar heat gain coefficient. *16–17, 49, 263–265, 269, 356, 370–372*

Solar ready. *75, 369*

Sound transmission. *37–39, 56–60, 193–194, 217, 232*

Space conditioning. *Ch. 15*

Stack effect. *26–28, 52, 245–246, 292, 475*

Steel framing. *186, 199–201*

T

Tankless (instantaneous) water heater. *312*

Termite barrier. *107–108*

Thermal mass. *16, 49, 165, 269, 323, 330, 365, 392*

Treated wood. *71, 124, 183*

Truss uplift. *246–247, 254*

Trusses. *195, 222, 224, 236–237, 248–250*

U

Unvented gas appliances. *297*

V

Vapour barrier. *31–32, 99–103, 113–115, 118, 130–131, 135, 141, 146, 156*

Ventilation systems. *Ch. 18, 379–380*

Vibration. *186*

W

Walls. *Ch. 11*

Water conservation. *86–87*

Water filtration. *90–91*

Water heating. *Ch. 20, 377–378*

Weather barriers. *103–104, 120–123, 190, 203*

Wind energy. *387–389*

Windows. *Ch. 13*

Wood burning heating systems. *319–324*